Turn to page 108
if you want my
number!

Science Insights
Exploring Earth and Space

Authors

Michael DiSpezio, M.A.
Science Consultant
North Falmouth, Massachusetts

Marilyn Linner-Luebe, M.S.
Former Science Teacher
Fulton High School
Fulton, Illinois

Marylin Lisowski, Ph.D.
Professor of Education
Eastern Illinois University
Charleston, Illinois

Bobbie Sparks, M.A.
K–12 Science Consultant
Harris County Department
  of Education
Houston, Texas

Gerald Skoog, Ed.D.
Professor and Chairperson
Curriculum and Instruction
Texas Tech University
Lubbock, Texas

Content Reviewers

Steve Blume
Science Teacher
St. Tammay Parish Schools
Slidell, Louisiana

James Cole, Jr.
Science Teacher
Clemente High School
Chicago, Illinois

Kenneth Eiseman
Supervisor of Science
West Chester Area School District
West Chester, Pennsylvania

Jean Lake
Eighth Grade Science Teacher
John Marshall Middle School
Wichita, Kansas

Michele McCarthy
Science Teacher
Fleming Junior High School
Los Angeles, California

Kathie Poff
Science Teacher
Parkhill Junior High School
Dallas, Texas

Dr. Tim Cooney
Professor of Earth Science
University of Northern Iowa
Cedar Falls, Iowa

Donna Stull
Science Teacher
Western High School
Ft. Lauderdale, Florida

Clive Tucceri
Eighth Grade Science Teacher
East Hampton Middle School
East Hampton, Connecticut

Dr. James Walters
Professor of Earth Science
University of Northern Iowa
Cedar Falls, Iowa

Dr. Thomas Hockey
Associate Professor of Astronomy
University of Northern Iowa
Cedar Falls, Iowa

Multicultural Reviewers

Gloriane Hirata
San Jose Unified School District
San Jose, California

Joseph A. Jefferson
Ronald McNair School
East Palo Alto, California

Peggy P. Moore
Garnet Robertson Intermediate
Daly City, California

Modesto Tamez
Exploratorium
San Francisco, California

About the Cover: One of the most interesting sights that an astronaut sees from space is the earth. As you explore the earth, you will discover why it is such a unique planet. You will learn about the earth's many different processes, including the formation of beautiful gemstones.

Front cover photographs: Telegraph/FPG International (earth); Gareth Hopson for Addison-Wesley Longman (geode); NASA/Dan McCoy/Rainbow (astronaut); Jeff Foott/Bruce Coleman Inc. (honeycomb); Telegraph/FPG International (integrated chip wafer).

Back cover photographs: Gareth Hopson for Addison-Wesley Longman (geode); NASA/Dan McCoy/Rainbow (astronaut).

Printed in the United States of America.

ISBN 0-201-33283-3

10 11 12 13 14 15 DO 07 06 05 04 03

Contents

Unit 1
Exploring the Sciences

page 1

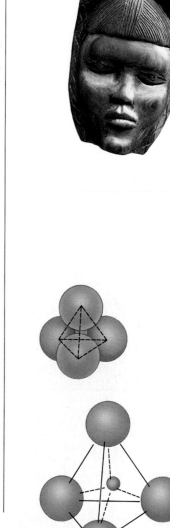

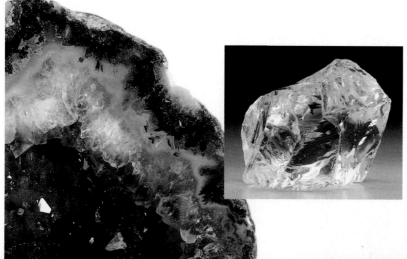

v

Unit 4
Changes on the Earth's Surface

page 236

Unit 5
Earth's Waters

page 314

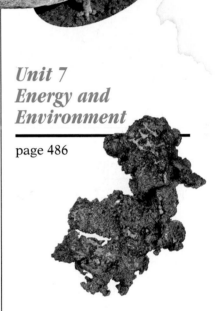

Unit 7
Energy and
Environment

page 486

Unit 8
Astronomy

page 534

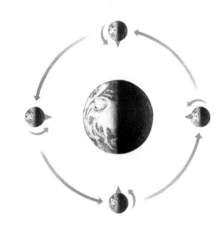

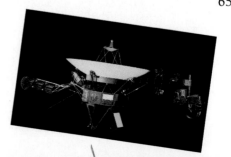

Features

Hands-On Science

Activities

SkillBuilder Activities

Problem Solving/Process Skills

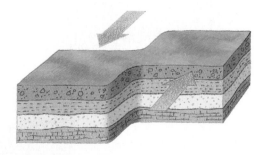

Skills WarmUp Activities

Skills WorkOut Activities

Integrated Science Activities Links

Concept Mapping...

Reading a science textbook is not like reading a magazine or a story. You usually don't have to work hard to understand a story. You probably won't remember it for a long time, either. But when you read science, you are reading to learn something new. You will need to think about what you read. You will also need to remember as much as you can. You may just *read* a story, but you will need to *study* your textbook.

Build a Concept Map

One way to help you study and remember what you have learned is to organize the information in the chapter visually. You can do this by making concept maps. In a concept map, the main ideas are identified by a word or phrase enclosed in a box. When these boxes are linked together, you can better understand the meanings of the ideas by seeing how the concepts are connected to one another. To build a concept map, follow the steps below.

Identify

1. Identify the concepts to be mapped. They may come from a short section of your book, directions from an activity, or a vocabulary list. List the concepts on a separate sheet of paper or on small cards.

Decide

2. Decide which concept is the main idea. Look for ways to classify the remaining concepts. You may want to list or rank the concepts from the most general to the most specific. For example, look at the concept map shown above. Notice that "solar system" is general, and then "meteoroids," "planets," "asteroids," and "comets" are more specific concepts.

Organize

3. Place the most general concept at the top of your map. Link that concept to the other concepts. Draw a circle or square around each concept.

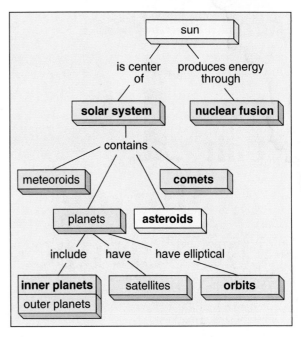

Choose

4. Pick linking words for your map that identify relationships between the concepts. Linking words should not be the concepts themselves. Label all lines with linking words that explain how each pair of concepts relate to each other.

Create

5. Start making your map by branching one or two general concepts from your main concept. Add other, more specific, concepts to the general ones as you progress. Try to branch out. Add two or more concepts to each concept already on the map.

Connect

6. Make cross-links between two concepts that are already on the map. Label all cross-links with words that explain how the concepts are related. Use arrows to show the direction of the relationship.

As you build a concept map, you are doing two things. First, you are automatically reviewing what you already know. Second, you are learning more. Once you have a completed map, you can use it to study and test yourself. You will often find that several different maps can be made from the same group of concepts.

Unit 1

Exploring the Sciences

Data Bank

Use the information on pages 620 to 621 to answer the following questions about topics explored in this unit.

Measuring

Approximately how many kilometers long is the Rio Grande River?

Interpreting a Map

What areas of the United States have the highest elevation? What areas have the lowest elevation?

Reading a Map

What state is located between 25° and 30°N latitude and 80° and 85°W longitude?

The photograph to the left is of a 50-meter dome that covers a United States base in the South Pole, Antarctica. Why do you think research is being conducted in Antarctica?

1

Chapter 1

Studying Science

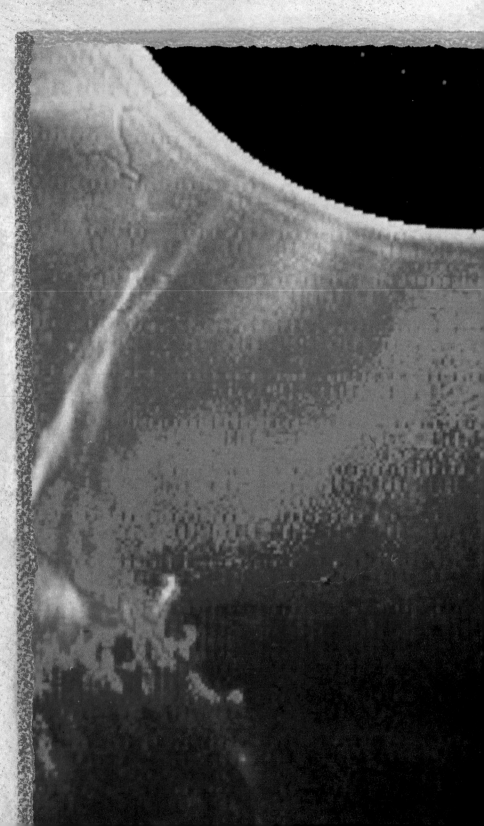

What do you see?

"I see a picture of the sun and the fire around it. I think it is very large. I really can't estimate how large, because it's probably bigger than I think. The picture was made by a satellite up in space— many miles up. Scientists could use this to learn what the sun is made of. They could also learn what temperatures the sun has in the core and the outer surfaces of the sun."

Frank Dahlquist
Snohomish Junior High
Snohomish, Washington

To find out more about the photograph, look on page 28. As you read this chapter, you will discover some of the methods scientists use to learn about your world.

1.1 Science Skills and Methods

Objectives

▶ **Identify** and **use** science skills.

▶ **Explain** what an experiment is.

▶ **Describe** the scientific method.

▶ **Distinguish** between fact and theory.

▶ **Apply** science and safety skills to everyday life.

How do you gain knowledge about the world around you? Much of your knowledge comes from personal experiences, books, television, and other sources. You also learn a lot from people. Which kind of knowledge do you trust the most?

The desire to gain the most trustworthy, accurate knowledge is the main motivation behind science. Science is a particular way of gathering and organizing information about the natural world. Science involves observing, experimenting, and studying information in an orderly and objective way.

Science Skills

When scientists study, observe, and experiment, they gather information, or **data**. While they work, scientists use many skills. Sometimes these skills are called science process skills. As you read about these skills, you will discover a kind of secret. These skills are not some mysterious or hard way to do something. You may not realize it, but you use many of these skills every day.

Observe The most direct way of gaining knowledge about something in nature is to observe it. When you observe, you use one or more of your senses to get information about your surroundings. Your senses are sight, touch, taste, smell, and hearing. Your ability to observe can be extended through the use of tools, such as telescopes, thermometers, and rulers. Look at the object in Figure 1.1. Write as many observations as you can about it. Which sense did you use?

Figure 1.1 ▲
You can make observations about the color, shape, and size of this crystal.

Figure 1.2 ▲
What can you infer about where the chunks of ice came from?

Infer When you infer, or make an inference, you make a logical deduction from something you know or observe. You can often make more than one inference from an observation. Look at Figure 1.2. Where do you think the big pieces of floating ice came from? If you notice that the white wall in the background is a huge wall of ice, or glacier, you might infer that the floating pieces broke off of the glacier. Closer observation of the glacier and the ice chunks may support this inference.

Estimate When you estimate, you make careful guesses. Estimating skills are used to gather information when exact measurements are not needed or when they would be impossible or too time-consuming to get. You learn to make estimates about many things. You estimate speed, distance, size, time, and so on.

Measure When you need exact and careful information about an observation, you measure. Measurements describe the amount of something. Measurements include both a number and a unit. The volume of water in a lake, the number of fish living in the lake, and the temperature at the lake's surface—all these are forms of measurement.

Predict When you predict, you state what you think might happen in the future. Predictions are based on past experiences and observations. With this knowledge, you can state both how something might occur and why it might occur. One way to check a prediction is by doing an experiment.

Figure 1.3 ▶
How will the weather change? What is your prediction?

◀ **Figure 1.4**
What are some different ways in which you could classify these rocks?

Classify When you classify, you group things based on how they are alike. You may be able to group things in many different ways. Some ways to group things are by size, color, shape, texture, or any other characteristic. For example, an area of land may be classified by its location, climate, vegetation, height, type of soil, or even by the number of people living on it.

Hypothesize When you state a hypothesis (hy PAHTH uh sihs), you state one possible explanation for some event that happened. Your hypothesis is based on the information you already know. Think of a hypothesis as an explanation or an idea that states why something may always occur. Once you state a hypothesis, you can test your hypothesis by observing, studying, or experimenting. Your observations, research, or the results of experiments should support your hypothesis. If not, you need to think about your hypothesis again and then state a new one.

Record and Organize Scientists must keep careful records of their observations. During activities and investigations, you, too, will record observations, measurements, predictions, and so on. Often you will want to organize the data you collect in some way. There are a number of ways you can record and organize data. Some ways are tables or charts, graphs, and diagrams.

Analyze Once data have been recorded and organized, you need to analyze the data. When you analyze data, you study the data to look for trends or patterns. You are looking to see if your data support your hypothesis, prediction, or inference.

▼ **ACTIVITY**

Interpreting Data

Cover to Cover

Look through the index in the back of this book. How is the information in the index organized? How is the organization related to the use of the index?

SKILLS WORKOUT

Safety Skills

Just as safety is important in everyday life, safety is important in your science classroom. When working in a laboratory, you should always follow these general safety guidelines:

▶ Do not chew gum, eat, or drink in the laboratory.

▶ Read through the activity before you start. Reread each procedure before you follow it.

▶ Clean up your laboratory work area after you complete each activity.

Study the safety symbols and guidelines in Table 1.1. By following these guidelines, you can help make the science laboratory a safe place.

Table 1.1   Laboratory Safety

 Plant Safety
▶ Use caution when collecting or handling plants.
▶ Do not eat or taste any unfamiliar plant or plant parts.
▶ If you are allergic to pollen, do not work with plants or plant parts without a gauze face mask.

 Eye Safety
▶ Wear your laboratory safety goggles when you are working with chemicals, open flame, or any substances that may be harmful to your eyes.
▶ Know how to use the emergency eyewash system. If chemicals get into your eyes, flush them out with plenty of water. Inform your teacher.

 Heating Safety
▶ Turn off heat sources when they are not in use.
▶ Point test tubes away from yourself and others when heating substances in them.
▶ Use the proper procedures when lighting a Bunsen burner.
▶ To avoid burns, do not handle heated glassware or materials directly. Use tongs, test-tube holders, or heat-resistant gloves or mitts.

 Clothing Protection
▶ Wear your laboratory apron. It will help protect your clothing from stains or damage.

 Poison
▶ Do not mix any chemicals unless directed to do so in a procedure or by your teacher.
▶ Inform your teacher immediately if you spill chemicals or get any chemicals on your skin or in your eyes.
▶ Never taste any chemicals or substances unless directed to do so by your teacher.
▶ Keep your hands away from your face when working with chemicals.

 Animal Safety
▶ Handle live animals with care. If you are bitten or scratched by an animal, inform your teacher.
▶ Do not bring wild animals into the classroom.
▶ Do not cause pain, discomfort, or injury to an animal. Be sure any animals kept for observation are given the proper food, water, and living space.
▶ Wear gloves when handling live animals. Always wash your hands with soap and water after handling live animals.

 Fire Safety
▶ Tie back long hair when working near an open flame. Tuck in loose clothing.
▶ Do not reach across an open flame.
▶ Know the location and proper use of fire blankets and fire extinguishers.

 Glassware Safety
▶ Check glassware for chips or cracks. Broken, cracked, or chipped glassware should be disposed of properly.
▶ Do not force glass tubing into rubber stoppers. Follow your teacher's instructions.
▶ Clean all glassware and air dry each piece.

 Electrical Safety
▶ Use care when using electrical equipment.
▶ Check all electrical equipment for worn cords or loose plugs before use.
▶ Keep your work area dry.
▶ Do not overload electric circuits.

 Sharp Objects
▶ Be careful when using knives, scalpels, or scissors.
▶ Always cut in the direction away from your body.
▶ Inform your teacher immediately if you or someone else is cut.

Experiments

What's the best way to find out about something? If you said, ask questions, you're on the right track. In your everyday life, you ask many questions to find out information. Science inspires you to ask questions, then find the answers to your questions. One of the best ways to find answers in science is to experiment.

An experiment is a way of testing a hypothesis. It is designed to provide evidence about whether a hypothesis is true or false. The setup of an experiment, therefore, is determined by the hypothesis to be tested.

When a hypothesis is stated as precisely as possible, it makes a claim about how two separate factors are related. Look at Figure 1.5. The hypothesis in this experiment relates one factor, the temperature of water, to another factor, its rate of evaporation. These two factors are both called variables.

The hypothesis states that changes in one variable, water temperature, *cause* changes in the other variable. A variable that causes a change in another is an **independent variable**. The variable that changes *in response to* the independent variable is the **dependent variable**.

In an experiment, a scientist changes the independent variable and observes the changes that occur in the dependent variable. But how can a scientist be sure that *other* factors aren't causing the changes? There are always many other factors that could affect the dependent variable. These other factors are variables, too. To be sure they don't affect the outcome, the scientist sets up a **control**.

In a control, all variables are identical to those in the experimental setup except for the independent variable. When a factor is identical in both the control setup and experimental setup, it is a controlled variable.

Figure 1.5   An Experiment ▼

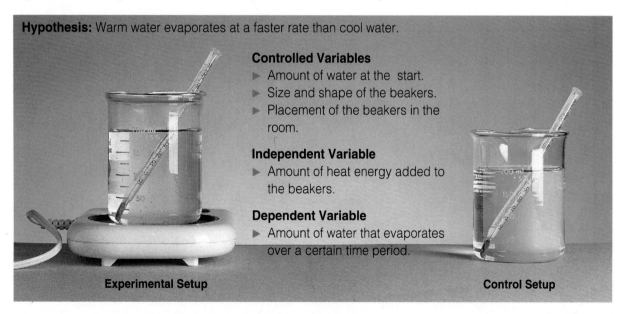

Hypothesis: Warm water evaporates at a faster rate than cool water.

Controlled Variables
▶ Amount of water at the start.
▶ Size and shape of the beakers.
▶ Placement of the beakers in the room.

Independent Variable
▶ Amount of heat energy added to the beakers.

Dependent Variable
▶ Amount of water that evaporates over a certain time period.

Experimental Setup   **Control Setup**

After 6 days, the beaker in the experimental setup contains 60 mL of water and the beaker in the control setup contains 150 mL of water. Do these results support the hypothesis? Write a conclusion.

Methods of Science

Is there one method of approaching a problem, an experiment, or an issue? The answer is yes and no. You may have heard the phrase *scientific method* used to describe the way scientists find out about the natural world. Modern scientific method is the systemized testing of ideas, hypotheses, predictions, and inferences about the natural world. The scientific method also involves a lot of communication. Scientists constantly exchange ideas and information.

The scientific method is not a set of steps to follow like those in a cookbook recipe. Instead, there are many different ways to study, investigate, and think about scientific problems.

Read Figures 1.6 and 1.7. They show a model for designing and planning an experiment and a model for decision making. They will help you as you do the activities in this book—and in daily life.

Figure 1.6   Designing and Planning an Experiment ▼

State the Problem
What do you want to find out? State the problem as a question. Make the question as specific as possible.

Hypothesize
What do you think is the cause of the problem you are studying? State a logical answer to your question. This answer, your hypothesis, should give one explanation for the cause.

Plan Your Experiment
The goal of an experiment is to test your hypothesis. What is the variable? What will be the control? Write a clear step-by-step procedure so that another person can repeat the same process exactly.

Make a Prediction
From your hypothesis, make and record a prediction about the outcome of your experiment.

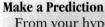

Gather and Organize Data
What kinds of data will you collect: measurements, observations, or estimates? Will you use graphs, tables, and drawings to organize the data?

Analyze Data
Do you see any trends or patterns in the data? Do the data support your hypothesis or prediction? Do you need more information?

Conclude
State your conclusion based on your data. Your data should either support your conclusion or lead you to another hypothesis. Have any new questions or problems come up?

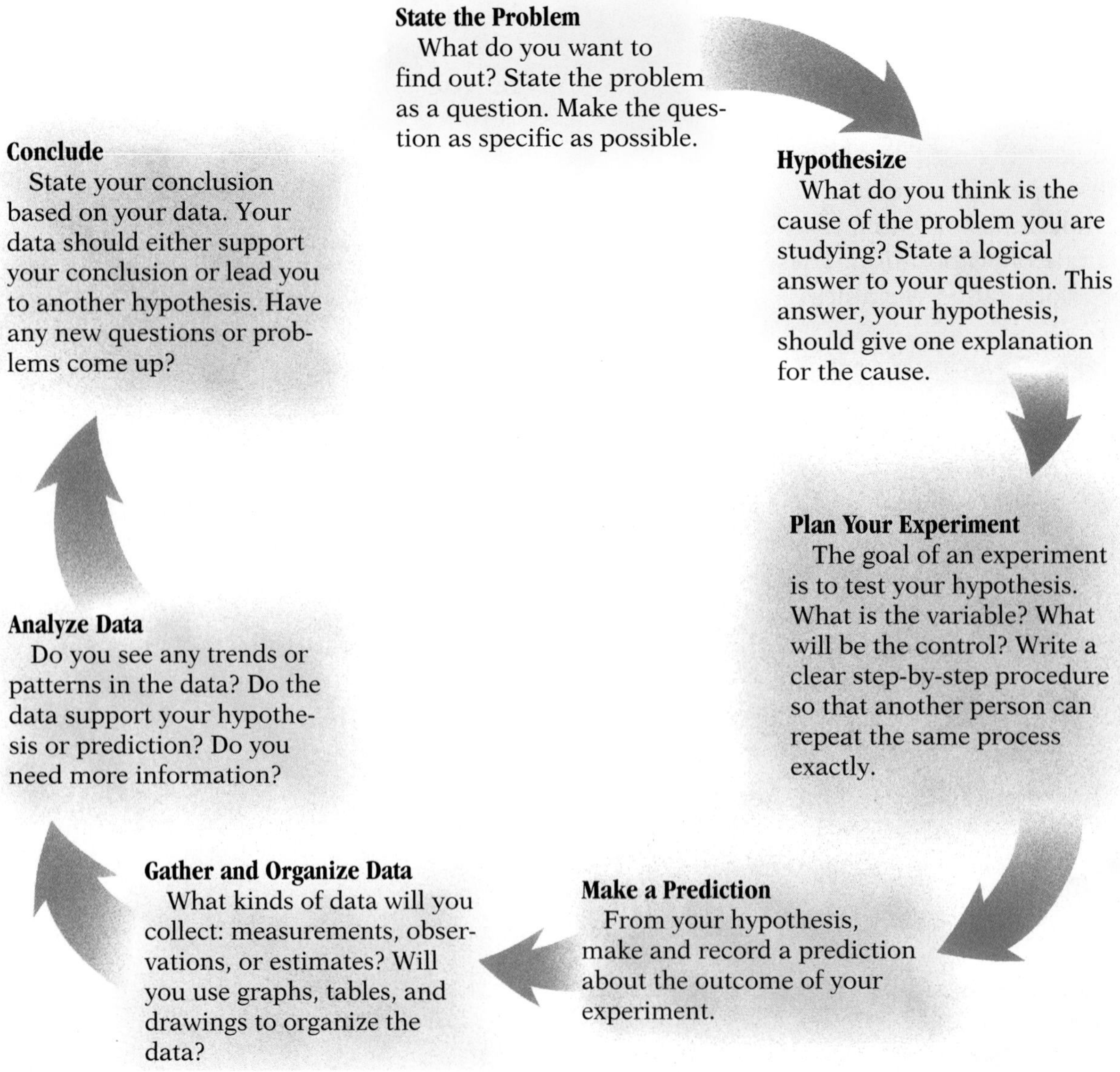

Figure 1.7 Decision Making ▼

Think About It
  Do you clearly understand the issue? State the issue in your own words. What are the different points of view about the issue?

Write About It
  Research information about the issue. Find information about each point of view. Remember that most issues have at least two points of view.

Organize It
  Organize the information so that you can see what information supports the different points of view.

Analyze and Evaluate It
  Evaluate the points of view. What solutions and reasons are given for each point of view? What are the possible results of each point of view?

Decide About It
  Do you need more information? If so, complete more research.

Conclude
  Write a conclusion that expresses your opinion. Be sure that you support your conclusion with data.

Facts, Laws, and Theories

In science, facts and statements are always backed by observations, studies, tests, and experiments. Facts are the things that are true or real. Anything that scientists accept as a fact is based on many observations. Facts do not change, but scientists often discover new facts that add to their knowledge.

Although facts never change, two scientists may interpret the same set of facts in different ways. Also, scientists may agree about one interpretation, then change their minds after making new observations or gathering new data.

Based on their observations, scientists make certain statements called *laws*. A law is a description of the rela-

tionship between events that occur together repeatedly. For example, Newton's first law of motion states that a body at rest will not move unless a force acts on it. This law has been verified over and over.

Scientists always try to explain what they observe. When scientists try to explain a complex event in nature, they state a theory. A theory is an explanation that has been partly verified. Before a scientific theory is accepted, the facts and ideas that support it are tested many times by observations and experiments.

Scientific theories may change. As new hypotheses are tested, theories are often redefined. If an existing theory cannot explain new facts and discoveries, a completely new theory may replace it.

The Model Classroom

On a sheet of paper, draw a model of your classroom. What kind of model is it? What information does it contain? How can it be used?

SKILLS WORKOUT

Models in Science

Have you ever seen a model train set? A model is a way to represent something. It is a small copy that is built to scale. There is a mathematical ratio between the dimensions of the model and the real object. For example, the scale for the model of a building may be 1 centimeter to 2 meters, meaning each centimeter on the model will equal 2 meters on the real building.

There are many types of models. Some models are drawn on paper, such as building blueprints. Maps are also models. Maps do not look like the objects they represent. The map of a city, for example, is just a sheet of paper. Yet it is very useful because it shows the same relationships among streets that exist in the real city.

Some models are mental models. In a mental model, you imagine what something would look like if you could observe it. Mental models can often be written down as diagrams, charts, tables, or mathematical equations. Many theories are based on a mental model.

Many people besides scientists, such as architects and engineers, use models in their work. A model can be a plan from which they build a real object. Models are also used to help people understand things that may not or could not be observed directly.

Figure 1.8 ▶
You will use many kinds of models to learn about science. This model represents overflow rainwater on a hillside. The overflow is collected and measured. Why do you think scientists want to know how much rainwater overflows on a hillside? What can be learned from this model?

Science and You *Everyday Scientific Method*

Scientists are not the only people who use the scientific method. You probably use it to solve everyday problems without even knowing it. For example, you might use the scientific method to solve a problem like finding your science textbook after you have misplaced it.

Imagine you arrive home and realize that you don't have your science textbook. You state the problem: "Where is my science textbook?" You make a hypothesis about where your book might be found. You hypothesize that it might be somewhere between your science classroom and home. You plan a careful, step-by-step procedure for testing your hypothesis, similar to an experiment. You think carefully about the best order of steps to follow.

First, you write down every place where the book may have been left. Second, you gather data by returning to each place on your list. Third, you record and organize your data by excluding the places that don't contain your science book. You finally reach the end of your list, but your book is still not found!

You analyze your data by searching for any patterns in the information you collected. You decide that your original hypothesis was incorrect. You conclude that you need to add to your original information.

You try another approach. You make a new hypothesis and plan. You decide to call your friends to find out if one of them accidentally took home your book, thinking it was theirs. This time your investigation succeeds. You find that your book is at a friend's house.

▼ ACTIVITY

Predicting

What's for Dinner?

 What will you have for dinner tomorrow night? On what observations, inferences, or past experiences do you base your prediction?

SKILLS WORKOUT

Check and Explain

1. In an experiment, what is the purpose of a control?

2. Give an example of a fact. How is a fact different from a theory?

3. **Apply** What observations do you use to help you predict what the weather will be like?

4. **Classify** Think of all the clothes you have. Classify them into groups according to characteristics that make sense to you.

Activity 1 *How do you perform a simple experiment?*

Skills Measure; Collect Data; Control Variables

Task 1 Prelab Prep

1. Collect the following items: scissors; metric ruler; one sheet each of white, black, blue, and red construction paper; sheet of graph paper; Celsius thermometer; timer.
2. Carefully cut each sheet of construction paper to measure 30 cm long and 10 cm wide.

Task 2 Data Record

1. On a separate sheet of paper, draw the data table below.

Table 1.2   Highest Temperature Reached

	Black Paper	White Paper	Red Paper	Blue Paper
Paper Temp (°C)				

2. On the graph paper label a *y*-axis *Maximum Temperature*. Label an *x*-axis *Color*. Title the graph *Highest Temperature Reached*.
3. Record your temperature measurements in the data table. After all of the data are collected, make a bar graph to show and compare the data.

Task 3 Procedure

1. Find a location in the sun. If there is no sun available, use a bright lamp for your heat source.
2. Choose one color of construction paper. Position the sheet of paper so the light falls uniformly on the paper. Place the thermometer in the center of the paper.
3. Wait exactly 5 minutes. Read the temperature on the thermometer. Record the temperature in the data table.

4. Allow 1 minute for the thermometer to return to normal room temperature.
5. Repeat steps 2, 3, and 4 for each color of construction paper.
6. On the graph paper, graph the results for each color.

Task 4 Analysis

1. Identify the independent variable and the dependent variable in this experiment.
2. List other factors or variables that could affect the dependent variable. How did you control for these other variables during the experiment?
3. Which color produced the highest temperature? The lowest?
4. Give a reason why light was chosen as a heat source.
5. **Hypothesize**   Form a hypothesis to explain the results of your experiment.
6. **Predict**   What will happen if you repeat the experiment using brown, green, purple, and yellow paper? On what do you base your predictions?

Task 5 Conclusion

Based on what you have learned, write a short paragraph explaining how color affects the absorption of energy from sunlight.

Everyday Application

Do you wear different colors on hot days and cold days? Based on your results in this experiment, what color clothes would be best on a very hot day? What color do you think is best on a cold but sunny day?

Extension

Think about the different colors of the earth as seen from space. Based on the colors only, where would you expect the temperature on the earth to be the warmest? The coolest? Explain.

1.2 Measuring with Scientific Units

Objectives

▶ **Identify** the SI base units and prefixes.

▶ **Compare** mass and weight.

▶ **Measure** common objects using SI units.

How old are you? How tall are you? The answers to these questions are measurements. Measurements are important in both science and everyday life. Hardly a day passes without the need for you to measure amounts of money or the passage of time. When was the last time you measured something?

When something is measured, you describe it in terms of numbers and units. The system of measurement used throughout most of the world today is the *Systéme Internationale d'Unités,* or SI. This system was developed in France in 1791 and was revised and modernized in 1960. You may have heard it called the metric system. The name comes from its base unit of length, the meter.

Some SI base units are shown in Table 1.3. You are most likely to use the units for length, mass, time, and temperature. SI units are easy to use. Unlike other system of measurement, SI units are based on multiples of ten. SI uses prefixes, such as *kilo-,* to indicate how many times a unit should be multiplied or divided by ten. These prefixes are shown in Table 1.4.

Table 1.3   Some SI Units

Measure	Unit/Symbol
Length	Meter/m
Mass	Kilogram/kg
Volume	Liter/L
Temperature	Degrees Kelvin/°K
Time	Seconds/s

Table 1.4 Prefixes Used with SI

Measurement	Unit	Symbol
kilo	1,000	k
hecto-	100	h
deca-	10	da
deci-	1/10	d
centi-	1/100	c
milli-	1/1,000	m
micro-	1/1 000 000	μ

A Matter of Meters

Arrange the following lengths in the correct order from shortest to longest.

a. 5,000 mm

b. 9 km

c. 7.3 dm

d. 72 cm

e. 1.1 m

Figure 1.9 ▲

You will measure many distances that are less than 1 meter. The numbers on this ruler's metric scale represent centimeters.

Multiples of ten make conversion between units very simple. You simply move the decimal point. For instance, 130 centimeters equals 1.3 meters. Think of it in terms of U.S. money: $1.00 = 100 pennies or 10 dimes. These are base = 10 measurements. A centimeter is 1/100 of a meter, and a kilogram is 1,000 grams.

Length

The basic SI unit of length is the **meter.** A meter is about the distance from the floor to the knob of a door. Chances are that the SI measuring tool that you'll be using in class is a metric ruler, which shows centimeters.

A metric ruler, a tape measure, or any other measuring device with a scale marked in equal divisions makes it possible for you to make exact measurements. A scale helps you find out how many units there are as you measure, without having to count them one by one.

Commonly used SI units of length are the kilometer (km), the meter (m), the centimeter (cm), and the millimeter (mm). Use whichever unit is most appropriate for the length you are measuring. The metric ruler is marked in units called centimeters. A centimeter is 1/100 of a meter. Your little finger is about 1 centimeter across. Each centimeter is divided into ten smaller units called millimeters. A dime is about 1 millimeter thick. How long is the rock in Figure 1.9?

Figure 1.10 ▶

A tape measure works best for larger measurements outdoors.

Volume

Take a deep breath. As your lungs fill with air, you can feel your chest expand. The change in lung size can be measured in terms of **volume**. Volume is the amount of space that something occupies. As your lungs expand, they occupy more space. A greater amount of air will fit inside them.

Because the SI base unit of length is the meter, the unit of volume is the cubic meter, or m^3. A cubic meter is the space occupied by a cube that is 1 m × 1 m × 1 m. This unit of volume is used to measure large quantities, such as the volume of concrete in a building.

In your science activities, you are more likely to use the cubic centimeter (cm^3). How big is a cubic centimeter? How many cubic centimeters do you think will fit in a teaspoon?

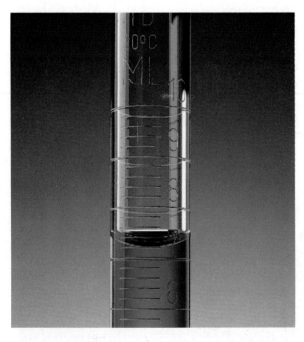

Figure 1.11 ▲
To read the volume of liquid in a graduated cylinder, keep your line of sight level with the liquid, and read the bottom of the meniscus.

You are probably most familiar with the basic SI unit of volume, the **liter** (L). Soft drinks often come in 1-liter or 2-liter containers. A smaller unit of volume is the milliliter (mL). There are about 20 drops of water in each milliliter.

In your science class, you will probably use a graduated cylinder to measure liquid volumes. As you can see in Figure 1.11, the cylinder is marked in milliliters. Notice that liquids in a graduated cylinder have a curved surface. The liquid rises slightly up the sides of the container and dips slightly in the center. That dip in the surface of the liquid is called the *meniscus* (meh NIHS kuhs). To measure the volume of liquid accurately, you read the level of the liquid at the *lowest point* of the meniscus. The best way to do this is to look at the surface of the liquid at eye level.

Mass and Weight

Did you know that things are slightly lighter when weighed at the equator than at the poles? The reason is because an object's weight depends on the force of gravity. At the equator, gravity is measurably less, so things are lighter.

Because weight measurements depend on where they are taken, weight can be unreliable for scientific use. That is why scientists use a measurement called **mass**. Mass depends on the number and kinds of atoms that make up an object. Because it does not depend on gravity, an object's mass always remains the same, no matter where the measurement is taken.

The basic SI unit of mass is the **kilogram** (kg). Your mass is probably between 35 and 75 kg. In the laboratory, however, scientists often use a much smaller unit called the gram (g). A paper clip has a mass of about 1 gram. For even smaller measurements, scientists use a milligram (mg).

You will use a balance to determine an object's mass. A balance lets you compare an unknown mass with a known mass. Look at the triple-beam balance in Figure 1.12. The known masses are the riders on the three beams. You move the riders to make the pointer of the balance read zero. Then you add together the numbers under each rider to determine the object's mass.

Density

Imagine you have a plastic spoon in one hand and a metal spoon in the other. They are both the same size. Which feels heavier? The metal spoon has a greater mass because metal has a greater **density**

than plastic. Density is the measure of how much matter is packed into a given volume. In mathematical terms:

$$\text{density} = \frac{\text{mass}}{\text{volume}}$$

Every substance has its own characteristic density. Scientists often measure density in grams of matter per cubic centimeter (g/cm^3). Pure water has a density of 1 g/cm^3. This means that for every cubic centimeter of water, there is 1 gram of matter. In contrast, lead has a density of about 11 g/cm^3. On the less-dense side, balsa wood has a density of only about 0.1 g/cm^3. What is a substance that is even less dense than balsa wood?

In addition to helping identify a substance, an object's density determines whether the material will float or sink. The density of everything is compared to the density of pure water. Materials with densities greater than that of pure water (1 g/cm^3) always sink. Materials with densities less than that of water always float. How will an object with the same density as water behave? If you put some balsa wood in water, will it float or sink? What happens to you in water? What's your density compared to water?

Figure 1.12

What is the mass of the rock? ▼

clip has a mass of about 1 gram. For even smaller measurements, scientists use a milligram (mg).

You will use a balance to determine an object's mass. A balance lets you compare an unknown mass with a known mass. Look at the triple-beam balance in Figure 1.12. The known masses are the riders on the three beams. You move the riders to make the pointer of the balance read zero. Then you add together the numbers under each rider to determine the object's mass.

Density

Imagine you have a plastic spoon in one hand and a metal spoon in the other. They are both the same size. Which feels heavier? The metal spoon has a greater mass because metal has a greater **density**

Figure 1.12
What is the mass of the rock? ▼

than plastic. Density is the measure of how much matter is packed into a given volume. In mathematical terms:

$$\text{density} = \frac{\text{mass}}{\text{volume}}$$

Every substance has its own characteristic density. Scientists often measure density in grams of matter per cubic centimeter (g/cm^3). Pure water has a density of 1 g/cm^3. This means that for every cubic centimeter of water, there is 1 gram of matter. In contrast, lead has a density of about 11 g/cm^3. On the less-dense side, balsa wood has a density of only about 0.1 g/cm^3. What is a substance that is even less dense than balsa wood?

In addition to helping identify a substance, an object's density determines whether the material will float or sink. The density of everything is compared to the density of pure water. Materials with densities greater than that of pure water (1 g/cm^3) always sink. Materials with densities less than that of water always float. How will an object with the same density as water behave? If you put some balsa wood in water, will it float or sink? What happens to you in water? What's your density compared to water?

1.2 Measuring with Scientific Units

Objectives

▶ **Identify** the SI base units and prefixes.

▶ **Compare** mass and weight.

▶ **Measure** common objects using SI units.

How old are you? How tall are you? The answers to these questions are measurements. Measurements are important in both science and everyday life. Hardly a day passes without the need for you to measure amounts of money or the passage of time. When was the last time you measured something?

When something is measured, you describe it in terms of numbers and units. The system of measurement used throughout most of the world today is the *Systéme Internationale d'Unités*, or **SI**. This system was developed in France in 1791 and was revised and modernized in 1960. You may have heard it called the metric system. The name comes from its base unit of length, the meter.

Some SI base units are shown in Table 1.3. You are most likely to use the units for length, mass, time, and temperature. SI units are easy to use. Unlike other system of measurement, SI units are based on multiples of ten. SI uses prefixes, such as *kilo-*, to indicate how many times a unit should be multiplied or divided by ten. These prefixes are shown in Table 1.4.

Table 1.3   Some SI Units

Measure	Unit/Symbol
Length	Meter/m
Mass	Kilogram/kg
Volume	Liter/L
Temperature	Degrees Kelvin/°K
Time	Seconds/s

Table 1.4 Prefixes Used with SI

Measurement	Unit	Symbol
kilo	1,000	k
hecto-	100	h
deca-	10	da
deci-	1/10	d
centi-	1/100	c
milli-	1/1,000	m
micro-	1/1 000 000	µ

ACTIVITY

A Matter of Meters

Arrange the following lengths in the correct order from shortest to longest.

a. 5,000 mm
b. 9 km
c. 7.3 dm
d. 72 cm
e. 1.1 m

SKILLS WORKOUT

Figure 1.9 ▲
You will measure many distances that are less than 1 meter. The numbers on this ruler's metric scale represent centimeters.

Figure 1.10 ▶
A tape measure works best for larger measurements outdoors.

Multiples of ten make conversion between units very simple. You simply move the decimal point. For instance, 130 centimeters equals 1.3 meters. Think of it in terms of U.S. money: $1.00 = 100 pennies or 10 dimes. These are base = 10 measurements. A centimeter is 1/100 of a meter, and a kilogram is 1,000 grams.

Length

The basic SI unit of length is the **meter.** A meter is about the distance from the floor to the knob of a door. Chances are that the SI measuring tool that you'll be using in class is a metric ruler, which shows centimeters.

A metric ruler, a tape measure, or any other measuring device with a scale marked in equal divisions makes it possible for you to make exact measurements. A scale helps you find out how many units there are as you measure, without having to count them one by one.

Commonly used SI units of length are the kilometer (km), the meter (m), the centimeter (cm), and the millimeter (mm). Use whichever unit is most appropriate for the length you are measuring. The metric ruler is marked in units called centimeters. A centimeter is 1/100 of a meter. Your little finger is about 1 centimeter across. Each centimeter is divided into ten smaller units called millimeters. A dime is about 1 millimeter thick. How long is the rock in Figure 1.9?

Volume

Take a deep breath. As your lungs fill with air, you can feel your chest expand. The change in lung size can be measured in terms of **volume**. Volume is the amount of space that something occupies. As your lungs expand, they occupy more space. A greater amount of air will fit inside them.

Because the SI base unit of length is the meter, the unit of volume is the cubic meter, or m^3. A cubic meter is the space occupied by a cube that is 1 m × 1 m × 1 m. This unit of volume is used to measure large quantities, such as the volume of concrete in a building.

In your science activities, you are more likely to use the cubic centimeter (cm^3). How big is a cubic centimeter? How many cubic centimeters do you think will fit in a teaspoon?

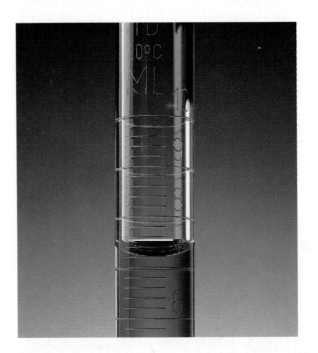

Figure 1.11 ▲
To read the volume of liquid in a graduated cylinder, keep your line of sight level with the liquid, and read the bottom of the meniscus.

You are probably most familiar with the basic SI unit of volume, the **liter** (L). Soft drinks often come in 1-liter or 2-liter containers. A smaller unit of volume is the milliliter (mL). There are about 20 drops of water in each milliliter.

In your science class, you will probably use a graduated cylinder to measure liquid volumes. As you can see in Figure 1.11, the cylinder is marked in milliliters. Notice that liquids in a graduated cylinder have a curved surface. The liquid rises slightly up the sides of the container and dips slightly in the center. That dip in the surface of the liquid is called the *meniscus* (meh NIHS kuhs). To measure the volume of liquid accurately, you read the level of the liquid at the *lowest point* of the meniscus. The best way to do this is to look at the surface of the liquid at eye level.

Mass and Weight

Did you know that things are slightly lighter when weighed at the equator than at the poles? The reason is because an object's weight depends on the force of gravity. At the equator, gravity is measurably less, so things are lighter.

Because weight measurements depend on where they are taken, weight can be unreliable for scientific use. That is why scientists use a measurement called **mass**. Mass depends on the number and kinds of atoms that make up an object. Because it does not depend on gravity, an object's mass always remains the same, no matter where the measurement is taken.

The basic SI unit of mass is the **kilogram** (kg). Your mass is probably between 35 and 75 kg. In the laboratory, however, scientists often use a much smaller unit called the gram (g). A paper

Temperature

You've probably had your temperature taken when you were sick. Unless you had a fever, your body temperature was probably about 98.6 degrees Fahrenheit (F), which is the average human body temperature. Scientists, however, do not use Fahrenheit temperature readings. Instead, they measure temperature using the Celsius scale. In fact, most of the countries of the world use Celsius as their temperature scale. On this scale, your body temperature is about 37 degrees Celsius, or 37°C.

In your classroom, you probably will use a Celsius thermometer to measure temperature. A thermometer is a thin glass tube filled with a colored liquid. As the liquid heats up, it expands and moves up the tube. As the liquid cools, it moves down the tube. The sides of this tube are marked in degrees Celsius. Two important reference marks on the Celsius scale are the freezing point (0°C) and the boiling point (100°C) of water.

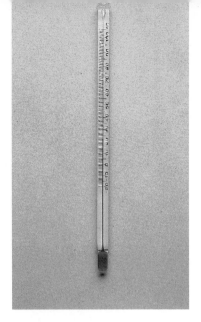

Figure 1.13 ▲
On the Celsius scale, water freezes at 0°C and boils at 100°C.

SkillBuilder   *Measuring*

Average Mass

You want to compare the soil in two different places. You dig a hole at each place and find that one of the main differences is the size of the rocks in the soil. What is the best way to describe this difference with numbers? You would probably want to determine the *average* mass of the rocks in both places.

Earth scientists often want to find the average mass of a group of similar objects. Practice this skill by finding the average mass of a group of rocks.

1. Collect 20 small rocks or pebbles of similar size.

2. On a separate sheet of paper, copy the data table shown.

3. From your group of rocks, choose one that seems average. Measure its mass and record it in the table.

Number of Rocks	Mass	Average Mass
1		
5		
10		
20		

4. Count out 5 rocks and measure their mass together. Divide this number by 5. Record this measurement in your table as the average mass of 5 rocks.

5. Repeat step 4 using 10 rocks, then 20 rocks.

How "average" was the first rock you chose? Did the average masses vary as your sampling size increased? Does a larger sample of rocks give you a more accurate average? Explain.

Time

The basic SI unit of time is the second. In your classroom, you will use a watch with a second hand to measure time. As you know, other units such as the minute, hour, day, and year are not based on the number ten. There are 60 seconds in a minute, 60 minutes in an hour, 24 hours in a day, and 365.25 days in a year. This system of measuring time is used everywhere in the world. In science, the prefix *milli-* is used with the unit second for some short time measurements.

Science and Society
Measurement Standards

You've just bought a tape deck made in Japan. The box says it is 30 cm long, so you trust it will be 30 cm according to your metric ruler. Centimeters, like other SI units, are the same throughout the world. They are standard units. However, a standard, universal system of measurement did not always exist.

You may be surprised to know that early systems of measurement were often based on the human body. The Egyptians defined a cubit as the distance between the elbow and the tip of the middle finger, a distance that varied for each person. In order to be more useful, units such as this one had to be defined according to an unchanging standard.

In SI, each unit is precisely defined. A meter is equal to 1 650 763.73 wavelengths of red-orange light given off by the element krypton. A kilogram is the mass of the cylinder stored at the National Institute of Standards and Technology in Maryland.

Figure 1.14 ▲
This photograph shows the cylinder that defines a kilogram of mass in the United States. The cylinder is at the far right of the turntable.

Check and Explain

1. List the SI units for mass, length, and volume.

2. Why do scientists use mass instead of weight?

3. **Predict**   A certain material has a density of 0.95 g/cm³. Will a block of it sink or float?

4. **Measure**   In your classroom, find objects with the following measurements: less than 1 cm long, about 20 g in mass, more than 1 L in volume.

1.3 Graphing

Objectives

▶ **Identify** the types of graphs.

▶ **Explain** how data are plotted on a line graph.

▶ **Make a graph** showing the number of people in a group with blue, brown, and green eyes.

▼ **ACTIVITY**

Gathering Data

Hands on the Table

Count and record the number of left-handed and right-handed people in your class.

Display this information in a table, a bar graph, and a circle graph. Which organizer seems best for showing the information?

SKILLS WARMUP

How would you present the data from an experiment in which you measured changes in temperature over time? You might choose to make a graph. A graph is a picture or diagram of data. You've probably seen many different graphs in newspapers and magazines, and on television news reports. Graphs are useful tools for presenting lots of information in a small space.

Kinds of Graphs

There are three kinds of graphs: circle, bar, and line graphs. No matter which kind of graph you look at, all graphs let you compare numerical data. Each kind of graph, however, shows the data in a different way.

Circle Graphs Think about a pie cut into pieces, and you have a mental model of a circle graph. A circle graph is a divided circle. It shows how a part or share of something relates to the whole. You can see what fraction, percentage, or share each part represents.

Look at the circle graph in Figure 1.15. The circle represents the amount of water used during one year in the United States. Each "slice" of the circle shows the percentage of that amount used for a particular kind of purpose.

Bar Graphs Just as its name describes, a bar graph has bars. The bars help you compare things. You can compare measurements, amounts, and changes.

Look at the bar graph in Figure 1.16 on page 20. It shows the lengths of the four longest rivers on the earth. You can see very easily which river is the longest and how its length compares to the others.

**Use of Water
in the United States**

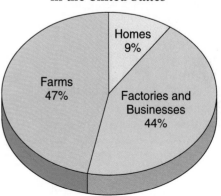

Figure 1.15 ▲
What type of water use is the largest?

Figure 1.16
Which river is the longest? ▼

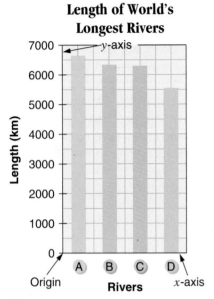

Length of World's Longest Rivers

Key

Ⓐ Nile
Ⓑ Amazon
Ⓒ Mississippi/Missouri
Ⓓ Ob/Irtysh

Notice that on the left side of the bar graph is a scale showing length in kilometers. The data on river length are plotted according to this vertical line, called the *y*-axis. Each bar is labeled on the horizontal line, called the *x*-axis. On this graph, the labels are letters keyed to the names of the rivers.

When you make a bar graph, you need to choose the scale by looking at the highest and lowest numbers in your data. On this graph, the scale ranges from 0 to 7,000 km. Notice that the scale is higher than the longest river. Also, the scale is divided into 1,000-km segments. All bar graphs have a scale and equal divisions.

Line Graphs   Line graphs are made from pairs of numbers. Each pair expresses a relationship between two factors, or variables. For this reason, line graphs are useful for showing changes that occur in related variables. Line graphs can help you answer if-then questions. They also help you see patterns or trends in data. Unlike bar graphs and circle graphs, line graphs let you plot several different sets of data on one graph. In this way, you can make comparisons between the sets of data.

Look at the line graph in Figure 1.17. Do the data look familiar? The data it shows are from the evaporation experiment on page 7. Notice that the graph includes two sets of data, one from the control setup and one from the experimental setup. For each day of the experiment, the volume of each beaker is plotted as a dot according to the scale on the *y*-axis. For example, above day 1 on the *x*-axis is a dot showing 180 mL for the experimental setup. What is the volume of the beaker in the control setup on day 4?

Figure 1.17 ▶
What kind of data can be shown on a line graph?

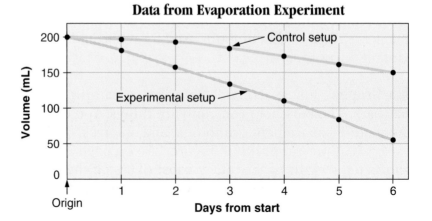

Data from Evaporation Experiment

The dots for each beaker are connected with a line. The lines, as you can see, vary in steepness. This difference indicates that the water in the experimental setup evaporated at a faster rate than the water in the control setup. You can see that line graphs are very useful for both showing and analyzing data from experiments. Line graphs are also good for showing any kind of change over time.

Science and Technology *Graph Uses*

You will see many graphs in this book. All of these graphs were produced by computers. As you may know, graphs are not just used in textbooks. In the business world, graphs are often used for important presentations. For example, a manager may need to present statistics that show his or her department's financial gains for the year. The manager may use a bar, circle, or line graph to show the information.

In the field of medicine, graphs are used to interpret information in a number of ways. An electrocardiograph, or EKG, is an instrument that picks up and records electrical currents produced by the human heart. The currents are picked up by metal strips, or electrodes, attached to the patient's body. The EKG records the currents on paper as wavy lines. The graph that is produced is used by physicians to diagnose heart damage. The damage may have been caused by blood pressure or other factors. The EKG also helps determine irregular heartbeats and the amount of injury caused by heart attacks.

▼ **ACTIVITY**

Making a Graph

Figure It Out

1. Find the correct numbers for one of the following:
a. the distances between the sun and the four nearest planets
b. the ten longest rivers in the world
c. the populations of the five largest countries
2. Choose which kind of graph—bar, circle, or line— would best represent the information.
3. Draw your graph and present it to the class.

SKILLS WORKOUT

Check and Explain

1. What are three kinds of graphs?

2. What does a dot or point represent on a line graph?

3. **Analyze** The average rainfall in five cities is given in centimeters: 25, 35, 43, 45, and 68. What scale would you use to show these data on a bar graph? What would be the equal divisions?

4. **Make a Graph** Count the number of students in your class with blue eyes, brown eyes, and green eyes. Display these data in a graph.

Classifying

What on Earth?

List the different materials that make up the following:
- the earth
- the earth's surface
- the earth's atmosphere

How many different kinds of materials can you find?

Classify the materials into a few groups. What basis do you use for your classification?

SKILLS WARMUP

Figure 1.18
Parts of the Earth ▼

1.4 Studying the Earth

Objectives

▶ **Identify** six parts of the earth studied by earth scientists.

▶ **Explain** what the biosphere is.

▶ **Infer** how living things are dependent on the nonliving parts of the earth.

▶ **Communicate** what it might be like to be an earth scientist.

Imagine you have the power to go anywhere on the earth. You can sail across the ocean or dive to the ocean floor. You can climb the highest mountains, trek across deserts, or tromp through tropical jungles. You can explore caverns deep in the earth or climb down into a volcano. You can even fly high above the clouds.

This power to go anywhere in the world may only take place in your imagination, but in a way, the pages of this book can also give you that power. Within this book, you will take many different journeys of exploration. You will discover that your home planet is amazingly varied and very beautiful.

Ocean
Most of the earth's surface is covered by huge bodies of salt water called oceans. The oceans are home to a great variety of living things.

There are many places to go on Earth if you want to understand it as a whole planet. Earth is a massive, rocky sphere moving in space. On its surface are oceans and landmasses. Above the surface is an envelope of air. The air and water on the earth are always moving and changing, affecting the landmasses in different ways.

All over the earth's surface are living things, or *organisms*. They depend on nonliving substances such as air and water to stay alive. Organisms, in turn, affect the nonliving parts of the earth. Look at Figure 1.18 to learn about the parts of the earth you will be studying.

Atmosphere
Between the earth's surface and outer space is an envelope of air and water vapor called the atmosphere. In the atmosphere, certain changes occur that produce wind, rain, snow, and changes in temperature.

Rocks
Much of the earth is made of different kinds of rocky material. The upper layer of the rocky earth moves and changes, forming mountains and other features.

Fresh Water
Water flows on the earth's surface in rivers and streams. It fills lakes and ponds. Fresh water is also found under the surface and in frozen masses called glaciers.

Organisms
The earth's atmosphere, fresh water, oceans, and soil are homes for the billions of organisms that live on earth. Scientists classify the organisms into five large kingdoms: plants, animals, fungi (FUHN jeye), monerans, and protists.

Soil
The breakdown of rocks and the decay of dead organisms produce soil. Soil nourishes plants. It also contains many living things.

Biosphere

Where do organisms live on the earth? Most organisms you're familiar with live right at the surface, just as you do. You know that many organisms also live in the ocean. Crabs, clams, and other organisms even live on the ocean floor.

On land, some organisms live below the surface. Insects and worms live in the soil. Some organisms live in caves. Others live in the tiny, water-filled spaces between rocks that lie underneath riverbeds.

Organisms also live well above the earth's surface. Birds and insects make their homes in trees. Some birds soar so high you can't see them from the ground. Some spiders have been found floating on webs several kilometers above the surface. All the places where life exists make up the biosphere (BY uhs feer). The **biosphere** is a zone of life that extends from the ocean floor to high in the atmosphere.

Career Corner

What Careers Use Scientific Skills and Knowledge?

Careers that use scientific skills or knowledge are many and varied. In some of these careers, you mostly do scientific research. However, there are many careers that require some science study, but involve nonscientific work, including underwater photographer, weather forecaster, or air traffic controller.

Each branch of earth science is different from the others. Each prepares you for certain opportunities. Look at the table to the right to get an idea of what kinds of careers are related to each branch of science.

Careers in Science

Branch	Study	Careers
Geology	The structure and makeup of the earth	Geologist, land use planner, geophysicist
Biology	All living things	Park ranger, public health educator, medical illustrator
Oceanography	The earth's oceans and the organisms living in them	Oceanographer, fisheries biologist, underwater photographer
Chemistry	Makeup of substances and the changes that substances undergo	Environmental technician, chef, food scientist
Meteorology	Weather and the earth's atmosphere	Air pollution technician, air traffic controller, weather forecaster
Space Science	The solar system, galaxy, and universe	Planetarium technician, astronomer, astronaut
Geography	Earth's surface features, both natural and human-made	Cartographer, surveyor, urban planner

Geography

How much of the earth's surface does the town or city you live in cover? What is the name of the tallest mountain in Africa? How deep is the Grand Canyon? What's the average summer temperature in Mexico City? To answer these questions and others like them, you would look up information provided by geographers. Geographers study the earth. They look at the size, shape, and features of the earth. They also study what is beneath the earth's surface. Geography is often considered an earth science.

In addition to the earth's natural features, geographers look at features made by humans. They study what humans do to the earth's surface, what they build, and where they live. Geographers collect data on human populations and their growth and movement over time. They look for patterns in how humans use the earth's surface and relate these patterns to factors such as rainfall. They also study how humans interact with their environments. Geographers want to know how humans use the earth and how they change it as they use it.

Geographers provide much of the information used to make maps. In fact, maps are often a geographer's most important tools. Because maps can represent large parts of the earth's surface, they are useful for providing a variety of information. In this book, you will see many kinds of maps. As you study these maps, remember that many would probably not even exist for you if it weren't for the important work of geographers.

Science and Technology *Telescopes*

Earth is one of nine planets in the solar system. The nearby star called the sun is one of many billions of stars in the Milky Way. The Milky Way is a huge collection of stars called a galaxy. It is one of many galaxies in the universe. What is Earth's place in the vast space of the universe? This, too, is a concern of earth scientists. The study of planets, stars, and other bodies in space is called astronomy (uh STRAHN uh mee).

Astronomers depend on special tools for studying distant objects in space. The most important of these tools are several kinds of telescopes. Telescopes that focus light from stars and planets to form a magnified image are *optical telescopes*. A *reflecting telescope*, shown

Figure 1.19 ▲
How does geography help you learn more about the earth?

Figure 1.20 ▲
A reflecting telescope at Mt. Hamilton in California (left). The radio telescopes (right) are located in New Mexico.

in Figure 1.20, is a kind of optical telescope that uses both mirrors and lenses to focus light. A *refracting telescope* focuses light using only lenses.

Visible light is only one of the many forms of energy given off by stars and other objects in space. Other forms of energy include invisible radiation called radio waves. Radio waves can be collected and focused just like visible light. The telescope that collects radio waves is called a *radio telescope*. You can see an example of a radio telescope in Figure 1.20. This telescope is a large dish that collects the radio waves and focuses them on an antenna. The antenna transmits the waves to a computer that converts the electrical signals into an image.

Check and Explain

1. What is the envelope of air above the earth's surface? What does it contain?

2. Describe the biosphere. What are the boundaries of the biosphere?

3. **Infer** Name at least five ways that organisms are dependent on the nonliving parts of the world. Explain.

4. **Communicate** Choose a part of the earth you would like to study. Write a short story about an adventure you have as an earth scientist studying that part of the earth.

Chapter 1 Review

Concept Summary

1.1 Science Skills and Methods
▶ In their study of nature, scientists observe, infer, estimate, measure, predict, classify, hypothesize, record, organize, and analyze.
▶ Scientists perform experiments to gather data and test hypotheses.
▶ Scientific theories may change to explain new facts and discoveries.
▶ Scientists use models to represent the parts of nature they study.

1.2 Measuring with Scientific Units
▶ Scientists measure length, volume, mass, density, temperature, and time with standard SI units.
▶ Mass is the amount of matter an object contains; it is not the same as weight.

▶ Density is the measure of how much mass is in a certain volume of matter.

1.3 Graphing
▶ Circle graphs show percentages of the different parts that make up a whole.
▶ Bar graphs compare one characteristic of several different things.
▶ Line graphs show data defined by two variables.

1.4 Studying the Earth
▶ The earth is made up of oceans, an atmosphere, and a rocky crust. Its landmasses contain soil, bodies of fresh water, and fossils.
▶ The biosphere extends from the ocean bottoms into the atmosphere.

Chapter Vocabulary

data (1.1)	control (1.1)	liter (1.2)	density (1.2)
independent variable (1.1)	meter (1.2)	mass (1.2)	biosphere (1.4)
dependent variable (1.1)	volume (1.2)	kilogram (1.2)	

Check Your Vocabulary

Use the vocabulary words above to complete the following sentences correctly.

1. When you measure _____ , you determine how much matter an object contains.
2. You use the SI unit called the _____ to measure length.
3. When you study nature, you gather information called _____ .
4. The variable in an experiment that causes a change in another variable is the _____ .
5. The liter is a unit of _____ .
6. The zone of the earth in which organisms live is the _____ .

7. Matter's _____ is measured in g/cm³.
8. The variable in an experiment that changes in response to changes in the independent variable is the _____ .
9. Experiments often have an experimental setup and a _____ setup.
10. The mass of your body is best measured in _____ .
11. In the science laboratory, you will measure volumes using the unit called the _____ .

Write Your Vocabulary

Write sentences using the vocabulary words above. Show that you know what each word means.

Chapter 1 *Review*

Check Your Knowledge

Answer the following in complete sentences.

1. All measurements must include what two parts?

2. When you work in the laboratory, what should you wear?

3. How are experiments related to hypotheses?

4. How are organisms related to non-living substances such as air and water?

5. Give two examples of a scientific model.

6. What are two SI units used to measure volume?

7. What is the difference between mass and weight?

8. What is an inference? How does an inference differ from a prediction?

9. What should you do if you get a chemical in your eyes during a laboratory activity?

Determine whether each statement is true or false. Write *true* if it is true. If it is false, change the underlined word(s) to make the statement true.

10. Scientific theories <u>never</u> change.

11. SI units are based on multiples of <u>1,000.</u>

12. You read the level of the <u>lowest point</u> of the meniscus to measure the volume in a graduated cylinder.

13. Density is measured in <u>kilograms</u>.

14. <u>Circle</u> graphs have an *x*-axis and a *y*-axis.

15. <u>Optical</u> telescopes capture and focus radio waves.

Check Your Understanding

Apply the concepts you have learned to answer each question.

1. **Application** What kind of graph—circle, bar, or line—would you use to show each of the following kinds of data?

    a. The heights of four different mountains.

    b. The amount of time you spend each day sleeping, eating, working, studying, being with friends, and watching television.

    c. The increase in the number of sit-ups you can do through a six-week exercise program.

    d. The world population from 1800 to the present.

2. **Critical Thinking** How does a prediction differ from a hypothesis?

3. **Mystery Photo** The photograph on page 2 is a false-color image of solar flares coming off the surface of the sun. What is the importance of the sun to the earth and its life?

4. Which is the greater length, 0.5 km or 50 m? Which is the larger volume, 2 m^3 or 2 L?

5. **Application** Measure and record your height in meters. If possible, also measure your mass in kilograms.

6. **Compare and Contrast** What is the difference between a reflecting telescope and a refracting telescope?

7. What SI unit or units would you use to measure each of the following?

    a. The volume of water in a swimming pool.

    b. The density of pure gold.

    c. The temperature of a pond.

Develop Your Skills

Use the skills you have developed in this chapter to complete each activity.

1. **Interpret Data** The line graph below shows the highest temperature reached each day for four days in two different cities.

   a. What was the highest temperature in Pineville on October 15?

   b. Describe the change in temperature in Pineville over the four-day period.

   c. On which day did Pineville have a higher maximum temperature than Central City?

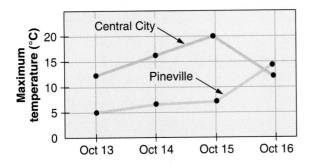

2. **Data Bank** Use the information on page 612 to answer the following questions.

   a. What is the diameter of Jupiter? How much larger than Earth is Jupiter?

   b. Which three planets have the greatest average density?

3. **Graph** Use the following data about a pet snake to construct a line graph: 1990, 1.4 m long; 1991, 1.7 m long; 1992, 2.1 m long; 1993, 2.3 m long.

4. **Calculate** Make the following conversions.

   a. 100 cm = ＿＿ m

   b. 0.5 kg = ＿＿ g

   c. 1,000 mL = ＿＿ L

Make Connections

1. **Link the Concepts** Below is a concept map showing how some of the main concepts in this chapter link together. Only parts of the map are filled in. Copy the map. Using words and ideas from the chapter, complete the map.

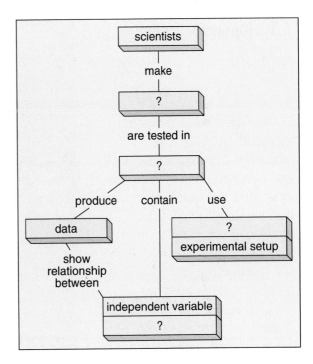

2. **Science and Society** Throughout history, most scientists have been men. What is it like to be a woman scientist? Research the life and work of a well-known female scientist. Choices include Marie Curie, Rachel Carson, Barbara McClintock, and Mary Leakey. Write a report about the person you choose. Describe the obstacles she faced and how she overcame them.

3. **Science and Living** Choose one of the science process skills. Describe how improving that skill could benefit your daily life. Give several examples.

Topography and Geography

What do you see?

❝I see patches of farmland with streams in the foreground and background. If I was making a map of this area, I would include the individual patches and what's growing in each one. I would also include the streams. The roads in between the patches and the buildings will also be put into my map. I would show the road with a black line and the buildings with boxes. The streams would be big blue lines.❞

Frank Sturniolo
McTigue Junior High
   School
Toledo, Ohio

To find out more about the photograph, look on page 52. As you read this chapter, you will learn about the surface of the earth and different methods of mapping it.

2.1 Earth's Surface

Objectives

▶ **Locate** the seven continents and the four oceans.

▶ **Name** and **describe** four major landforms.

▶ **Explain** how biomes can be used to describe the distribution of living things on the earth's surface.

▶ **Map** a route through all four oceans.

▼ **ACTIVITY**

Locating

Where Am I?

Using a globe or a world map, locate your city or town. Was it easy for you to find your location? How could you locate it more easily next time?

SKILLS WARMUP

A thousand years ago, most people lived in small villages. Almost everything they knew about the world around them was based on what they could see with their own eyes. Imagine you're one of those ancient people. Your village is near a river, below a tall, forested mountain. In the other direction stretches a wide, grassy plain.

To find out what lies beyond this familiar landscape, you climb to the top of the mountain. You see more mountains in the distance. The plain goes on as far as you can see. The world is much bigger than you thought!

Now imagine you're suddenly transported into the future. You're a passenger on a spaceship blasting off the surface of the earth. What do you see as you look out the window? As you climb higher, you realize that what you see below is all part of a huge sphere.

Earth from Space

The sphere is the planet Earth. Viewed from space, Earth is a watery globe partly hidden by clouds. It rotates slowly around an axis, like a spinning top. How is this view from space different from the view of a person standing on the surface?

People have viewed the earth from space, and they have studied and explored its surface features. Both ways of looking at the earth have contributed to their knowledge of it. As a result, people have a very complete picture of their planet.

Figure 2.1 ▲
What can you observe about the earth's surface from this point of view?

**Table 2.1
Area of the Continents**

Continent	Area (thousands of km²)
Africa	30,340
Antarctica	14,000
Asia	45,120
Australia	8,550
Europe	9,850
North America	24,370
South America	17,890

Continents

From space, the earth's land appears as large green and brown shapes surrounded by the blue of the oceans. These large landmasses are the earth's **continents**. Most people say there are seven continents, but others think there should be six. Look at Figure 2.2. How many continents do you count?

The largest landmass you see is usually divided into two continents, Europe and Asia. When this landmass is counted as one continent, it is named Eurasia. Directly below Europe, find the continent of Africa. Now look to the right of Africa and find Australia.

On this page you can see North America and South America. Below South America you can see another continent, Antarctica. Antarctica lies over the South Pole, so parts of it are also visible below Africa and Australia.

Figure 2.2   Earth's Continents and Oceans ▶

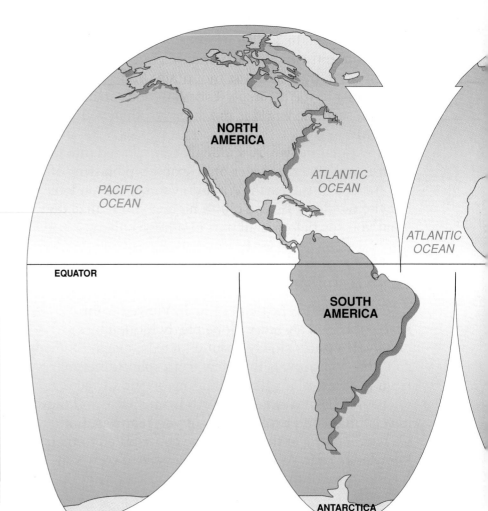

▼ **ACTIVITY**

Estimating

Ocean Size
   What percentage of the earth's surface is covered by the Pacific Ocean? How can you check your estimate using the data in Tables 2.1 and 2.2?

SKILLS WORKOUT

The World Ocean

The continents are only about 28 percent of the earth's surface. The other 72 percent is one large body of water. This body of water is the world ocean.

The world ocean is usually divided into four oceans with different names. Look at Figure 2.2 and find the Arctic Ocean, which surrounds the North Pole. Most of the Arctic Ocean is permanently covered by an ice cap. Now find the Indian Ocean, located south of Asia between Africa and Australia. Where is the Atlantic Ocean? Where is the Pacific Ocean?

You may notice that small parts of the oceans are mostly surrounded by land. These bodies of salt water, much smaller than a whole ocean, are called seas. One of the largest seas on the earth is the Caribbean Sea, located between North and South America.

Table 2.2
Area of the Oceans

Ocean	Area (thousands of km^2)
Arctic Ocean	13,240
Atlantic Ocean	86,660
Indian Ocean	73,500
Pacific Ocean	166,440

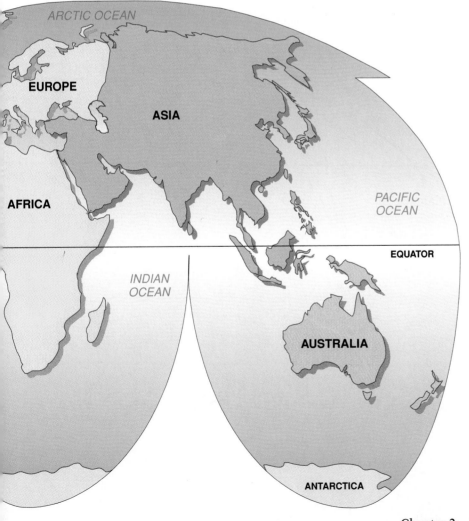

Landforms

Features of the earth's surface smaller than continents and oceans are best seen from a closer, bird's-eye view. Have you ever climbed a mountain or crossed a valley? Mountains and valleys are landforms, the main features of the earth's varied landscape. Landforms are defined by their shape, size, and elevation. Elevation is the distance above sea level. Look below to see examples of the earth's major landforms.

Figure 2.3 Features of the Earth's Surface ▼

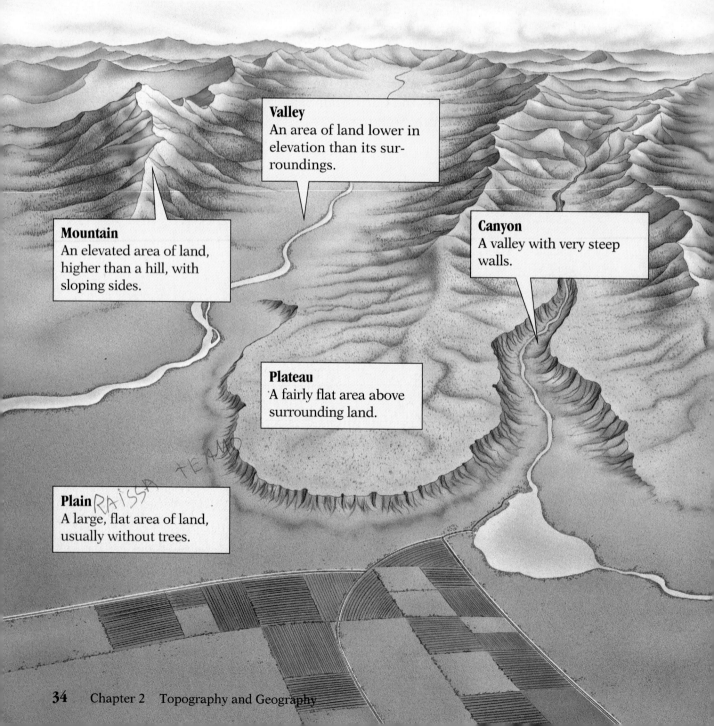

Valley
An area of land lower in elevation than its surroundings.

Mountain
An elevated area of land, higher than a hill, with sloping sides.

Canyon
A valley with very steep walls.

Plateau
A fairly flat area above surrounding land.

Plain
A large, flat area of land, usually without trees.

Ocean and Coastal Features

Where land and water meet, pieces of land and bodies of water take on a variety of sizes and shapes. The land defines bodies of water such as bays and straits. Areas of land such as islands and peninsulas are defined by the water around them. Have you ever been on an island? What makes an island different from a peninsula? Look below to see examples of these and other coastal features.

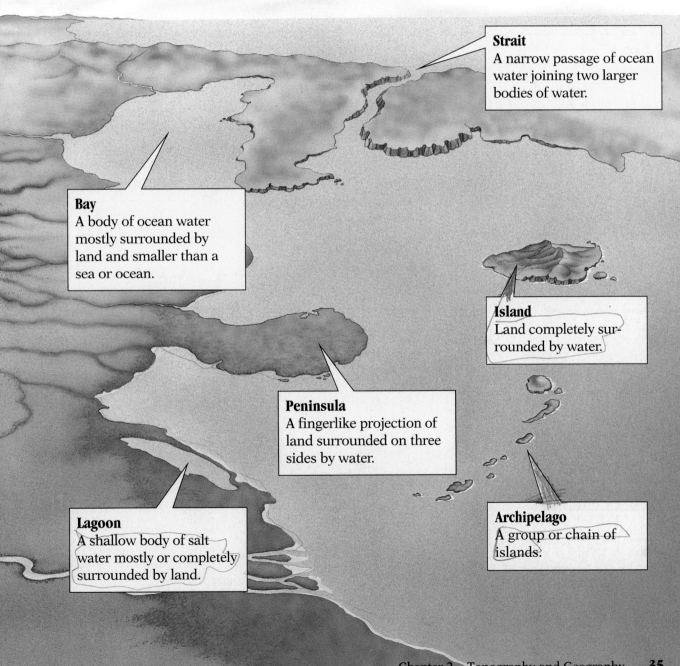

Strait
A narrow passage of ocean water joining two larger bodies of water.

Bay
A body of ocean water mostly surrounded by land and smaller than a sea or ocean.

Island
Land completely surrounded by water.

Peninsula
A fingerlike projection of land surrounded on three sides by water.

Lagoon
A shallow body of salt water mostly or completely surrounded by land.

Archipelago
A group or chain of islands.

Table 2.3
Characteristics of the Major Land Biomes ▼

Biome	Characteristics
Rain forest	Thick forest; high rainfall
Grassland	Tall grasses and few or no trees
Desert	Sparse vegetation; very low rainfall
Tundra	Low plants covered by ice and snow most of the year
Coniferous forest	Cone-bearing needle-leafed trees
Deciduous forest	Broadleaf trees that lose leaves in winter

Life on Earth's Surface

Do you have polar bears in your backyard? Does cactus grow around your school? Can you visit a nearby forest? Will you see monkeys in the trees? You probably can't answer yes to more than one of these questions. That's because different parts of the earth's land surface have different organisms living on them.

The major factors that determine where an organism can live are temperature and rainfall. These factors vary depending on location. Average temperature is highest near the earth's middle and lowest near its two ends, or poles. Rainfall depends on many factors, such as surrounding landforms and nearness to an ocean.

Variations in rainfall and temperature across the land surface can be seen in the differences in vegetation, the kinds of plants that grow on the landscape. Based on vegetation patterns, scientists have defined six different major life zones, or **biomes**. Each biome is described in Table 2.3. The map in Figure 2.4 shows where each biome is located on the earth. Where is the tundra biome? Where on the earth are rain forests located? What biome do you live in?

Figure 2.4 Earth's Major Land Biomes ▼

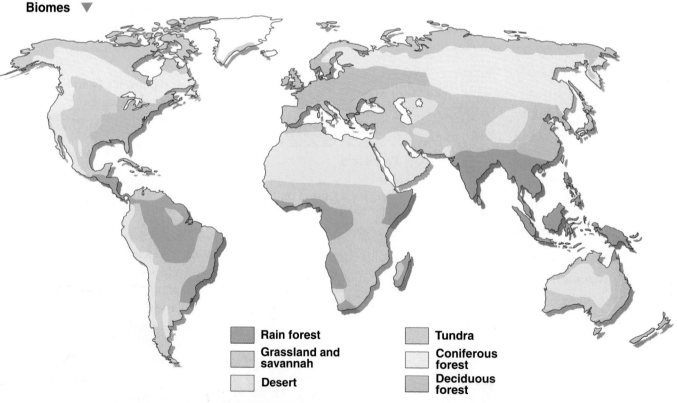

- Rain forest
- Grassland and savannah
- Desert
- Tundra
- Coniferous forest
- Deciduous forest

Science and Society *Sharing the Oceans*

For every person on the earth, the oceans are an important resource. For centuries, the oceans have connected the nations of the world like a watery highway. Ocean trade routes have allowed the people of the world to share goods and to experience each other's cultures.

The oceans also provide much of the world's food. Over 70 million metric tons of fish are harvested by fishing nations every year. Other sea animals such as crabs, shrimps, lobsters, and oysters are also caught. Ocean plants are harvested as well. Seaweed is eaten as food, and it is used to make ice cream and salad dressing. Some ocean plants are collected for use in medicines and vitamins.

Even countries without an ocean coastline depend on the oceans. Tiny algae floating near the ocean's surface, among the plankton organisms, produce some of the oxygen that land animals and humans breathe. The clouds that drop life-giving rain on land develop mainly from water that evaporates from the oceans.

The ocean is such an important resource that the nations of the world have had to agree on how it is used. Under an agreement called the Law of the Sea, each nation has rights to ocean waters near its coast. The rest of the ocean, however, is free for all to use. Under this and other agreements, nations try to keep any one nation from damaging the shared parts of the ocean and its limited resources.

Figure 2.5 ▲
People from many nations harvest food from the oceans.

Check and Explain

1. List the seven continents, and tell which oceans border each one.

2. What's the difference between a mountain, a plateau, and a plain?

3. **Generalize** Where is the rain forest biome located? Where is the deciduous forest located?

4. **Make a Map** Copy the map of the world on pages 32–33. Select a starting point on the coast of one continent, and draw a sailing route that would take you through all four oceans and back to your starting point.

Life Science
L I N K

Study the map on page 36 to determine which biome you live in. Research your biome's characteristic vegetation. Outside your home or school, collect a few samples of vegetation that represent your biome. Display and label these samples on a sheet of posterboard.

A C T I V I T Y

Degree of Accuracy

Collect a piece of paper, a protractor, and a pencil.

1. Draw a half circle on the piece of paper by tracing around the protractor.

2. Make marks on the half circle at 10° intervals. Label the marks.

3. Complete the circle by turning the protractor over and tracing around it.

Study the circle. How might degree measurements be used in mapping the earth?

2.2 Mapping the Earth

Objectives

▶ **Explain** how longitude and latitude are used to map the earth's surface.

▶ **Compare** two different map projections.

▶ **Interpret** the symbols on a map legend.

▶ **Locate** a position on a map.

You want to invite people to your birthday party who don't know where you live. How do you help them find your house? You might draw them a map. They can use the map to see where your house is located in relation to landmarks they know, such as streets and buildings.

You've probably used maps many times in your life. They show, on a piece of paper, the space relationships among real objects. Maps can represent any size area, from your classroom to the entire surface of the earth.

Earth's Reference Points

If you had to draw a map of your room, you could do it without having to learn how. But what about making a map of the whole earth? Mapping the earth poses special problems because it is a huge sphere.

The first step in mapping the earth is to set up reference points on the earth itself. Recall that the earth's rotation gives it two fixed points through which an imaginary line called an axis passes. These fixed points are the North Pole and the South Pole. Locations on the earth can be described in terms of their distance from one of these poles.

An imaginary line can be drawn around the center of the earth that is equidistant from the two poles. This imaginary line is the **equator**. Look at Figure 2.6. Notice that the earth can be divided into two equal halves. The equator is the dividing line between the halves. Each half is called a **hemisphere**. These reference points and lines on the earth are the basis for all maps made of the earth's surface.

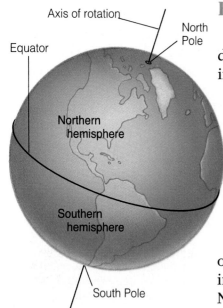

Figure 2.6 ▲
Do you live closer to the equator, the North Pole, or the South Pole?

Latitude and Longitude

When you place a point on a line graph, you need to know two numbers. One is for the *x*-axis and one for the *y*-axis. Locating a point on the earth also requires two measurements.

The first measurement of location on the earth is provided by imaginary lines telling the distance away from the equator. These are lines of **latitude**. Look at Figure 2.7. It shows lines of latitude drawn around the earth. Notice that all the lines are parallel and that each forms a circle of a different size.

Each line of latitude is numbered in units called degrees. They range from 0° for the equator to 90° for each of the poles. Latitude lines in the Northern Hemisphere are labeled with an N for north. In the Southern Hemisphere they are labeled S for south. A point halfway between the equator and the North Pole, therefore, is at 45°N latitude.

The other measure of location on the earth is provided by lines of **longitude**

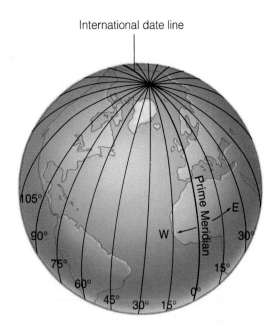

International date line

Figure 2.8 ▲
At what points do all longitude lines meet?

(LAHN jih tood). Longitude lines run from pole to pole and are also called meridians. They are shown in Figure 2.8.

Unlike lines of latitude, longitude lines have no natural reference points from which to measure distance. Therefore, people have defined a line of reference—the meridian passing through Greenwich, England. This longitude line is called the prime meridian and is labeled 0°. Locations west of the **prime meridian** are measured in degrees west. Locations east of the prime meridian are measured in degrees east.

Lines of longitude range from 0° to 180° in both directions. The line of longitude that measures 180° is directly opposite the prime meridian. The **international date line** closely follows the 180° longitude but does not cross any land mass.

Together, latitude and longitude locate any place on the earth. For example, Mexico City is located near 20°N latitude and 100°W longitude. What is the latitude and longitude of your hometown?

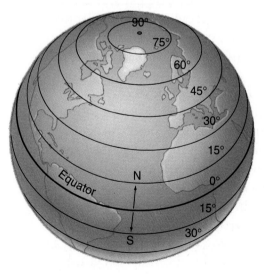

Figure 2.7 ▲
Latitude lines form concentric circles around the earth. What is another name for 90°N latitude?

Map Projections

A globe represents the spherical earth very accurately. But a globe is difficult to carry around and can't show much detail. To solve these problems, the curved surface of the earth must be shown on a flat map. How is this done?

Look at Figure 2.9 below. Imagine a light at the very center of the globe. The globe is marked with latitude and longitude lines and the continents. The light will cause an image of the latitude lines, longitude lines, and continents to appear on the cylinder wrapped around the globe. If the images are traced and the cylinder unrolled, a map results! This map is an example of a *projection*. A projection is a way of transferring the features of the earth onto a flat surface.

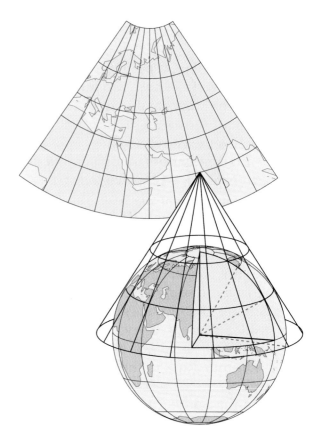

Figure 2.10 ▲
What advantage does a conic projection have over a cylindrical projection?

There are many different kinds of map projections. The projection in Figure 2.9 is a cylindrical projection. It shows the shapes of continents accurately, but it distorts their size. Landmasses away from the equator look much larger than they really are.

The conic projection in Figure 2.10 is another common type of projection, produced by projecting the globe's features onto a cone. A conic projection does not distort the sizes of the continents very much. However, it can only show one hemisphere.

Each type of map projection is best for a certain kind of use. A cylindrical projection, for example, is ideal for navigating on the ocean. All distances can be calculated as straight lines.

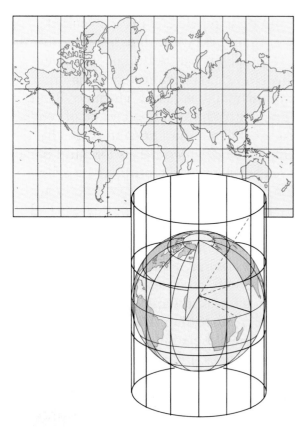

Figure 2.9 ▲
Most maps of the world are cylindrical projections.

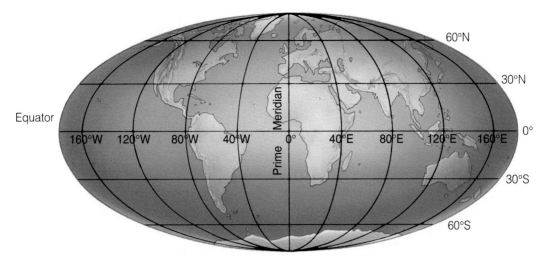

Figure 2.11 ▲

This equal-area projection shows the sizes of the continents accurately. In what way are the continents distorted?

You are probably used to seeing the countries of the world shown on maps made by cylindrical projection. Therefore, you probably think of countries away from the equator, such as the United States, as being large compared to others. But the United States is not really as large as it appears on a cylindrical projection map.

Maps made by cylindrical projection may cause people to have a false view of the size of some land areas. For instance, on a cylindrical projection, Greenland appears to be as large as Africa. Actually Africa is about 14 times larger than Greenland. To avoid this problem, mapmakers have learned how to make maps in which the areas of the continents are very accurate and the edges are only slightly distorted. These maps are called equal-area projections.

An equal-area projection of the world is shown in Figure 2.11. Compare the sizes of its continents to those on the cylindrical projection in Figure 2.9. Where is the difference in size greatest?

Types of Maps

Maps are made for many purposes. A world map, for example, can show the earth's physical features, or it can show the borders of different countries. A map showing national borders is called a political map. Road maps show people how to travel from place to place. Transit maps help you find the shortest bus route. Mall maps locate your favorite stores.

Many maps show a particular kind of information. A weather map, for example, shows weather patterns for a certain area. A population map can use color-coding to show the number of people per square kilometer. A geologic map shows rock types.

In a similar way, maps can show rainfall, temperature, vegetation, land use, minerals, average income of people, or many other things. Maps can even be used to record history by showing the locations of old cities or important events such as battles.

Mapping Methods

Maps are made by cartographers. For thousands of years, cartographers or surveyors went to the area to be mapped. They used relatively simple instruments to measure the land and then draw it on maps. This mapping method is called field mapping. Much of the earth's land was accurately mapped this way.

With advances in technology, map-making has changed. Satellites with remote-sensing devices pass high over the earth's surface gathering information useful for mapping. The satellites take photographs that show differences in the amount of heat given off by the surface. Because different kinds of objects give off different amounts of heat, these photographs can be used to distinguish among forests, cities, and water. A computer interprets this photographic data and makes accurate, detailed maps.

Figure 2.12 ▲
Photographs like this one are valuable for making maps. The red color indicates land, which is warmer than the dark blue water.

Reading a Map

Through lines, shapes, colors, numbers, and symbols, maps carry a great deal of information. To get the most out of a map, you need to be able to interpret and read it. Just like reading a book, reading a map requires certain skills.

Symbols   Every map uses a certain set of symbols to represent different features. Freeways, highways, and streets, for example, may be shown by lines of different thickness. The sizes of cities can be indicated by dots and circles of varying size. Important buildings, such as schools and hospitals, may each have their own symbol.

The symbols used in a map are collected together in a legend. The legend explains the meaning of each symbol. Look at the legend of the map in Figure 2.13. What is the symbol for an airport? What is the symbol for a railroad?

Direction   Where on a map is north? If you answer that north is up, you're correct for most maps, but not all. Most maps of small areas of the earth are drawn so that the sides are parallel to lines of longitude and the top and bottom are parallel to lines of latitude. On these maps, an arrow labeled *North* may point straight up. West is then to the left, and east is to the right.

Longitude lines, however, are not exactly parallel to each other on the earth's surface. This begins to make a difference on maps of larger areas. On these maps, longitude lines are not shown parallel, except for maps with certain projections. When longitude lines aren't parallel, north-south direction will vary depending on which part of the map you're looking at!

Scale Every map is drawn so that a certain distance on the map represents a certain distance on land. The relationship between these two distances is called a map's **scale**. For example, a centimeter on a map may be equal to one kilometer on the earth's surface.

Scale can be expressed in different ways. Some maps have a graphic scale. On a graphic scale, a line divided into equal parts is labeled with the actual distances each segment on the line represents. Scale can also be expressed as a ratio. The scale 1:25,000, for example, means that 1 unit on the map equals 25,000 of the same units on the ground. A third way to state a map's scale is shown in Figure 2.13.

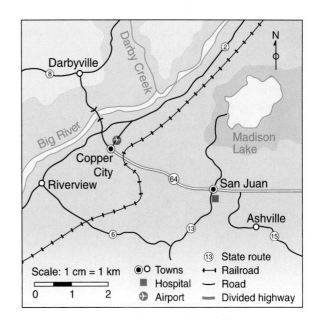

Figure 2.13 ▲

This map shows roads, towns, and bodies of water.

SkillBuilder *Reading a Map*

Find Your Way

How good are your map-reading skills? Study the map in Figure 2.13 above. Then answer the following questions.

1. What is the scale of the map? State the scale as a ratio. Remember that both parts of the ratio must be the same unit.

2. What is the approximate distance between the hospital and the airport? Between the hospital and Big River?

3. What is the driving distance between Riverview and Copper City? What is the straight-line distance between the two cities?

4. Which city has a larger population, San Juan or Ashville? How do you know?

5. Which direction do you travel when you ride a bicycle from San Juan to Copper City?

6. What highways do you travel on to get from Riverview to Ashville?

7. Which city is most likely to have a railroad station?

8. What physical feature lies between Copper City and Darbyville?

9. Using a separate sheet of paper, trace the roads and cities that appear on the map. With a different color pen or pencil, show a route you can take between Riverview and Madison Lake that does not involve traveling on Highway 64. How far will you travel if you take this route?

Choose a place on the map where you'd like to live. In a paragraph or two, describe the natural and human-made features around that place.

Figure 2.14 ▲
You often need maps to find your way around a big city.

Science and You   *A Map or More a Day*

You may not even realize it, but you may encounter many different maps in the course of a day. Imagine the following sequence of events. Could this be a typical day in your life?

You go into the kitchen for breakfast and find your mother looking at a road map. "The radio reported a big accident on the freeway," she says. "I need to find another route to work." Then your father comes in. He says to you, "I left the transit map on the table, so you can figure out which bus to take to the library after school. Be sure to take your umbrella. The weather map in the paper shows a storm heading our way."

You eat, grab the transit map, and catch the bus to school. In social studies class, you study a map of Africa as your teacher talks about the people of Nigeria. In science class, you read this chapter about maps. Finally, when school's over for the day, you check your transit map and see that you need to catch a bus on Route 53 to get to the library.

When you get to the library, you use the map on the wall to locate the reference section. You copy information you need for your report on maps, and then leaf through an atlas, a big book full of maps of everywhere in the world.

You decide to head for the mall to get a present for your mother's birthday. The mall map tells you the location of the store that will have what you want. When you get home, you finish your report on maps. You've had a day full of maps!

Check and Explain

1. What does a latitude measurement tell you about a location? What does a longitude measurement tell you about the same place?

2. What is one important way cartographers obtain data for making maps?

3. **Evaluate**   What advantages does an equal-area projection have over a cylindrical projection?

4. **Locate**   Which continent is located at 15°S latitude and 50°W longitude? Use the map on page 41.

2.3 Topographic Maps

Objectives

▶ **Describe** what topographic maps show about the earth's surface.

▶ **Explain** how contour lines show topography.

▶ **Interpret** contour lines on a topographic map.

▶ **Calculate** average slope.

You and a group of friends are going to hike to the top of a mountain in a local park. When you meet, you find there are three different trails leading to the summit. Which one should you take? "I have a topographic map," says one of your friends. "That will help us decide."

Why will the topographic map help? Unlike regular maps, a topographic map shows **topography**, the variations in elevation over the landscape. By looking at the trails on the topographic map, you can tell the steepness of each trail. Topographic maps are useful not just for hikers, but for earth scientists and other people, too.

Contour Lines

How can a flat map show the very uneven surface of the earth? Some maps give an impression of topography with shading. Topographic maps, however, show topography very precisely with **contour lines**. A contour line connects points that have the same elevation. If you've ever walked along a trail on the side of a mountain that went neither down nor up, you have followed a contour line.

A topographic map shows contour lines for only certain elevations. Lines may be drawn, for example, at 50 m, 100 m, 150 m, and so on. The elevation of any location can be estimated by finding the elevation of the nearest contour line. Contour lines show topography with their shape and spacing. A set of contour lines forming smaller and smaller loops, for example, indicates a mountain or hill. The closer the spacing of the lines, the steeper the slope of the mountain.

Figure 2.15 ▲
As long as this trail stays horizontal, it follows a contour line.

Figure 2.16 Topographic Map of an Island ▼

Look at Figure 2.16. In the upper left, it shows how the topography of a three-dimensional structure such as a mountainous island can be projected onto a two-dimensional map.

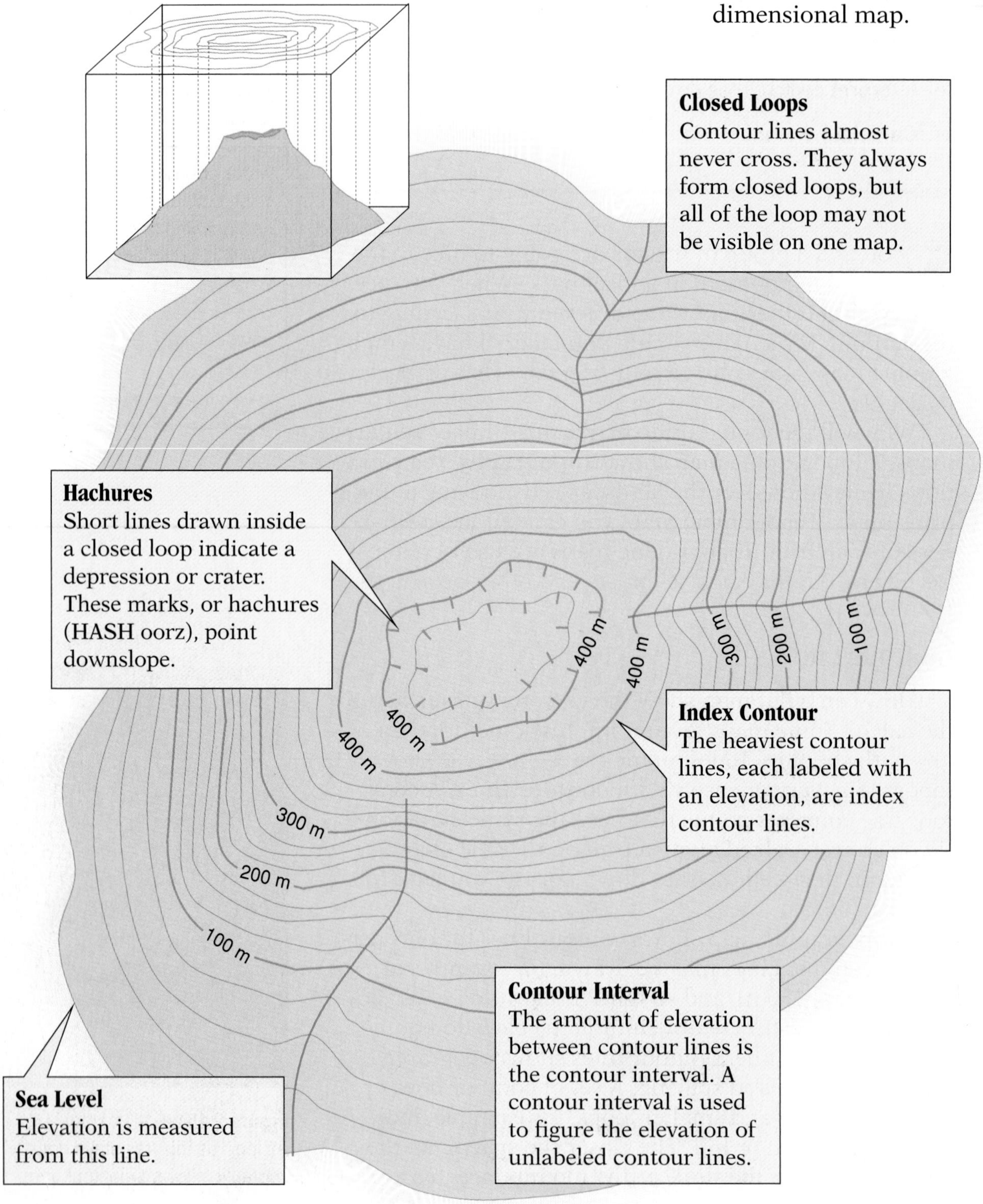

Closed Loops
Contour lines almost never cross. They always form closed loops, but all of the loop may not be visible on one map.

Hachures
Short lines drawn inside a closed loop indicate a depression or crater. These marks, or hachures (HASH oorz), point downslope.

400 m

400 m

400 m

400 m

300 m

200 m

100 m

Index Contour
The heaviest contour lines, each labeled with an elevation, are index contour lines.

300 m

200 m

100 m

Contour Interval
The amount of elevation between contour lines is the contour interval. A contour interval is used to figure the elevation of unlabeled contour lines.

Sea Level
Elevation is measured from this line.

Slope

The slope, or steepness, of the land is important to hikers, skiers, geologists, and builders. Topographic maps provide the information needed to create an accurate picture of any slope. Look at Figure 2.17. It shows a cross section, or profile, of the slope represented by the contour lines above it. The cross section is like a graph, with elevations plotted by horizontal distance. The cross section is made along a profile line drawn between two points on a topographic map, usually at right angles to contour lines.

You can also use a topographic map to figure the average slope of any hill or mountainside. Average slope is calculated as the change in elevation divided by the horizontal distance in which this change occurs. If the elevation rises from 10 m to 60 m in a distance of 100 m, for example, the average slope is

$$\frac{60-10}{100} = \frac{1}{2} = 50 \text{ percent.}$$

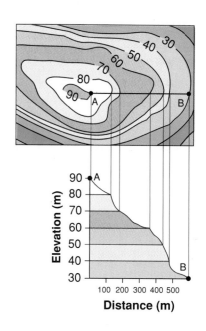

Figure 2.17 Profile of a Slope ▲

Career Corner *Cartographer*

Who Designs and Makes Maps?

Cartographers have been making maps for thousands of years. The ancient Greeks had road maps. The Romans used maps for military purposes.

Today cartographers are still in demand. Maps are constantly revised. New maps are always being made to show information to scientists, governments, employees, business owners, motorists, and many others.

Mapmaking is more than just drawing maps. Cartographers plan and design maps, and they collect information. Some cartographers work mainly indoors drawing maps. Others work in the field. They collect information from airplanes, helicopters, trucks, or on foot.

A cartographer must have mathematical ability, as well as knowledge of drafting and computer science. Experience in photography and an eye for detail are also important.

A college degree in cartography, geography, or civil engineering is often desirable. However, a college degree is

not required for all jobs in cartography. If you are interested in mapping the land, you can prepare by taking math, art, and computer science classes in high school.

Topographic Map Symbols

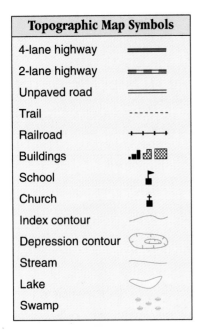

4-lane highway	
2-lane highway	
Unpaved road	
Trail	
Railroad	
Buildings	
School	
Church	
Index contour	
Depression contour	
Stream	
Lake	
Swamp	

Figure 2.18

Most topographic maps use the same symbols (above). Can you read the topographic map below? ▼

Using Topographic Maps

Using a topographic map requires all the skills you use in reading any map, plus some others. The main skill to learn is how to interpret contour lines. This means learning to see in your mind three-dimensional landforms when you look at contour lines. The guidelines below will help you interpret contour lines:

1. The closer the spacing of the contour lines, the steeper the slope. Flat places have widely spaced lines, and cliffs have very closely spaced lines.

2. Contour lines that cross a valley are V-shaped. If a stream or river flows in the valley, the Vs point upstream.

3. A series of increasingly smaller closed loops indicates a hill or mountain.

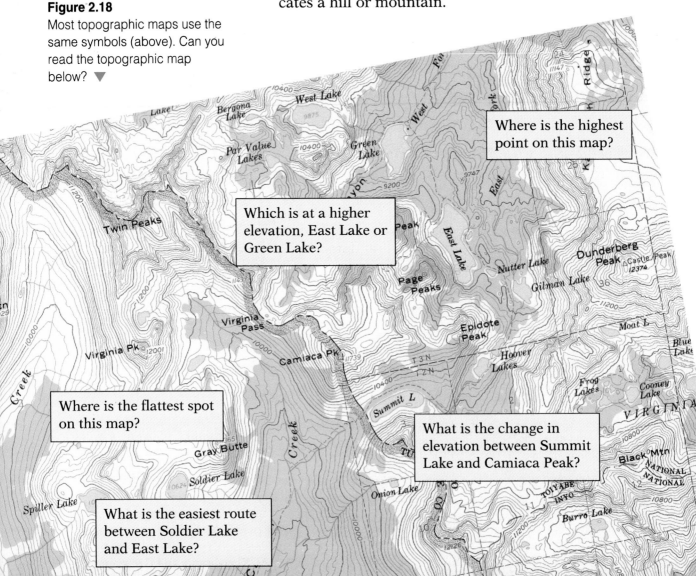

Science and Technology
Topographic Mapping by Satellite

The date is 1882. A group of men and horses are working their way up a steep, rocky slope. Each horse carries a load of heavy equipment. The men walk beside them, coaxing the animals up the slope. The party sets up camp at a small flat spot. Before the sun sets, several men take out long chains and place them across the land, making measurements. Others peer at compasses and make marks on paper. Another uses an altimeter to take a reading that will help to determine elevation.

The group was part of the United States Geological Survey (USGS), established in 1879. Its goal was to map the topography, geology, mineralogy, and biology of the western territories. The instruments were crude, but the results were relatively accurate.

Topographic maps produced by the USGS today look much the same as they did in the 1880s. However, the detail, accuracy, and amount of information has greatly changed. The USGS now uses data from Landsat satellites traveling almost 1,000 km above the earth's surface. Through Landsat technology, every spot on the earth's surface is photographed every 16 days. More than 90 percent of the United States has been mapped using information from Landsat satellites.

It may sound like the new technology for mapping will soon put itself out of a job. Once a place is mapped, does it have to be mapped again? Very often it does, because the land is always changing. Roads are built, forests cut down, slopes eroded. Landsat data are always needed for updating of maps.

Figure 2.19 ▲
Map makers need computers to process the information provided by satellites.

Check and Explain

1. How are topographic maps different from other maps?

2. Describe how a mountain looks on a topographic map. Make a drawing to go with your answer.

3. **Reason and Conclude** Why do contour lines almost never cross?

4. **Calculate** What is the average slope of a hillside that rises 25 m over a horizontal distance of 75 m?

Activity 2 *How can you make a topographic map?*

Skills Measure; Interpret Data; Model

Task 1 Prelab Prep

1. Collect the following items: block of modeling clay, piece of wax paper, rubber band, pencil, metric ruler, paper, brown and blue colored pencils, butter knife.
2. Using the modeling clay, mold a small mountain a little over 10 cm high. Include gullies or valleys where streams would be. Place the mountain on the wax paper.
3. Use the rubber band to attach the pencil 2 cm from the end of the ruler, as shown in Figure 2.20.

Task 2 Procedure

1. Hold the ruler upright, with the pencil point touching the clay model.
2. Mark a line completely around the mountain by moving the ruler assembly.
3. Move the pencil to the 4-cm mark on the ruler. Repeat step 2.
4. Mark a contour line every 2 cm until you reach the top.
5. Peel the wax paper off, and place the mountain on a sheet of blank paper. Trace around the outside edge with the brown pencil. Take the mountain off the paper, and put it back on the wax paper.
6. Using the butter knife, carefully cut your mountain at the 2-cm elevation contour line. Move the knife all around the mountain, and make the cut as flat as possible. Be careful not to change the shape of the mountain.
7. Remove the wax paper and the bottom slice. Set the slice aside. Place the remainder of the mountain in the center of the contour line loop you drew on the paper. Trace the edge as before, and put the mountain back on the wax paper.

8. Repeat the procedure for all the remaining contour lines to complete the topographic map of your mountain.
9. Label the first contour line 0 cm, the next 2 cm, and so on, to the top of the mountain. Using the blue pencil, draw streams in the gullies or valleys.

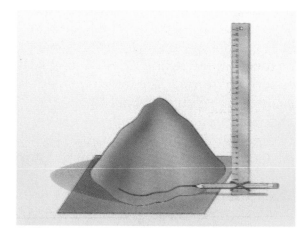

Figure 2.20 ▲

Task 3 Analysis

1. Look at your mountain and your topographic map. Is the topographic map an accurate representation of the mountain?
2. What is your mountain's elevation?
3. Draw a straight line down one side from the top of your mountain to the bottom. Calculate the average slope along this line.

Task 4 Conclusion

Imagine your mountain is real. Describe what you would see during a hike to the top.

Extension

Trade topographic maps with a classmate. Don't look at each other's mountains. Get more modeling clay, and mold a mountain to look like the one in the topographic map you borrowed. When you are done, compare your mountain to the original mountain. How close did you come to making the mountains look the same?

Chapter 2 Review

Concept Summary

2.1 Earth's Surface

▶ The surface of the earth has landmasses called continents and bodies of salt water called seas and oceans.

▶ Types of landforms include mountains, plateaus, valleys, canyons, and plains.

▶ Ocean and coastal features include bays, straits, lagoons, islands, peninsulas, and archipelagos.

▶ Major life zones, or biomes, differ in their temperature and rainfall patterns.

2.2 Mapping the Earth

▶ The equator, an imaginary line drawn exactly between the two poles, divides the earth into two halves called hemispheres.

▶ Latitude lines and longitude lines locate points on the earth.

▶ A map projection is a way of showing the surface of the earth on a flat map.

▶ Features such as roads and buildings are shown on a map with different symbols. A map scale tells the relationship between the distance on the map and the distance on the land.

2.3 Topographic Maps

▶ Topographic maps show variations in elevation over a landscape.

▶ A contour line on a topographic map connects points with the same elevation. Contour lines form closed loops and never cross.

▶ Contour lines show slope, or steepness. Contour lines can be used together with the map scale to calculate average slope.

Chapter Vocabulary

continent (2.1)	hemisphere (2.2)	prime meridian (2.2)	topography (2.3)
biome (2.1)	latitude (2.2)	international date line (2.2)	contour line (2.3)
equator (2.2)	longitude (2.2)	scale (2.2)	

Check Your Vocabulary

Use the vocabulary words above to complete the following sentences correctly.

1. The lines that show land elevations on a topographic map are called ____ .

2. The Northern and Southern Hemispheres are divided by the ____ .

3. The earth's land surface can be divided into six major life zones, or ____ .

4. The variation in elevation over a landscape is called ____ .

5. The large landmasses on the surface of the earth are ____ .

6. Lines on a map that tell the distance in degrees from the equator are called lines of ____ .

7. On a map the relationship between distances on the map and distances on land is shown by the ____ .

8. The longitude line that passes through Greenwich, England, is the ____ .

9. The earth can be divided into two ____ .

10. The lines on a map drawn from pole to pole are meridians, or lines of ____ .

11. The meridian that measures 180° is called the ____ .

Write Your Vocabulary

Write sentences using the vocabulary words above. Show that you know what each word means.

Chapter 2 Review

Check Your Knowledge

Answer the following in complete sentences.

1. What is elevation? How is elevation related to topography?

2. Describe four major coastal features.

3. What is the purpose of latitude and longitude lines?

4. List two types of map projections and describe how they differ.

5. Why do maps contain symbols? Give examples of two map symbols.

6. What is an index contour?

7. How do you calculate the average slope of a hill? Give an example.

8. Name the four oceans of the earth.

9. List the earth's six biomes.

Choose the answer that best completes each sentence.

10. A flat, raised area of land is a (mountain, plateau, plain, valley).

11. The two fixed points through which the axis of the earth pass are (the North and South Poles, the equator and the poles, the equator and the prime meridian, the poles and the prime meridian).

12. The short lines that indicate depressions on a topographic map are called (slopes, contour intervals, meridians, hachures).

13. When contour lines form V-shapes, the Vs always point (upstream, downstream, north, toward a mountain).

14. Land completely surrounded by water is a(n) (archipelago, peninsula, strait, island).

Check Your Understanding

Apply the concepts you have learned to answer each question.

1. Compare cylindrical map projections to conical map projections.

2. **Critical Thinking** Decide whether you think the earth has six or seven continents. Explain why.

3. What are the differences between lines of latitude and lines of longitude? How are they similar?

4. Describe the methods cartographers use for mapping the earth.

5. Describe where on the earth's surface each of the six major biomes is located.

6. Name a use for topographic maps.

7. Determine the average slope of a hill if the elevation rises from 5 to 25 m in a distance of 80 m.

8. List the continents that have land in the northern hemisphere. List the continents that have land in the southern hemisphere. Which continents appear on both lists?

9. **Extension** Using graph paper divided into squares, make a map of your classroom. Label the x-axis and y-axis of your map as you would a line graph. Name the points on your grid that would identify where you sit. What points correspond to the door?

10. **Application** Discuss the different types of maps you have used. Tell why you used each type of map.

11. **Mystery Photo** The photograph on page 30 shows the view of a rural area taken from an airplane. Make a map of the area shown in the photograph. Write a legend for the symbols used in your map.

Develop Your Skills

Use the skills you have developed in this chapter to complete each activity.

1. Interpret Data The graph below shows a slope profile for a hill.

a. What is the average slope from point A to point B?

b. Name a section of the hill where the slope is steeper than the average slope.

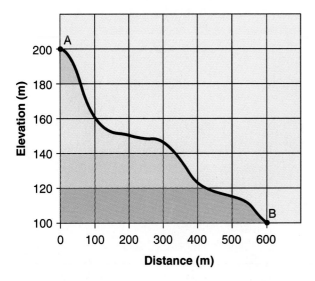

2. Data Bank Use the information on pages 620–621 to answer the following questions.

a. What mountain range is located in northern Alaska?

b. What is the elevation of most of the Central Plains?

c. What are the locations of two major swamps in the United States?

3. Read a Map Using a map of the United States, find and name each location.

a. 41°N, 74°W

b. 30°N, 90°W

c. 45°N, 109°W

Make Connections

1. Link the Concepts Below is a concept map showing how some of the major concepts in this chapter link together. Only part of the map is filled in. Finish the map, using words and ideas from the chapter.

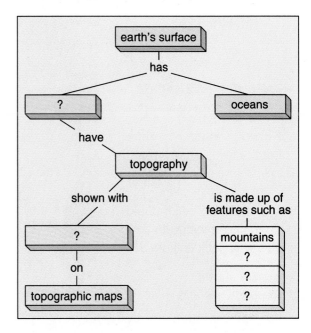

2. Science and You Write down directions from your home to school. Now draw a map from your home to school. Which is easier to understand, the written directions or the map? Explain.

3. Science and Social Studies Find a copy of a map of North or South America made by early European explorers. Compare this map to a modern map of the same place. How accurate were the early explorers?

4. Science and Art Drawing to scale is not limited to mapmaking. Artists often draw objects to scale to create a realistic picture. Draw a piece of fruit using a 1:10 scale.

Chapter 3

Structure of the Earth

What do you see?

"I think it is a body of very hot liquid or water. I think it is hotter than we can imagine. The white matter could be clouds or foam from the water. I think the water could be from inside the earth and shows how hot it is there."

Colleen Kenna
Neshaminy Junior High School
Langhorne, Pennsylvania

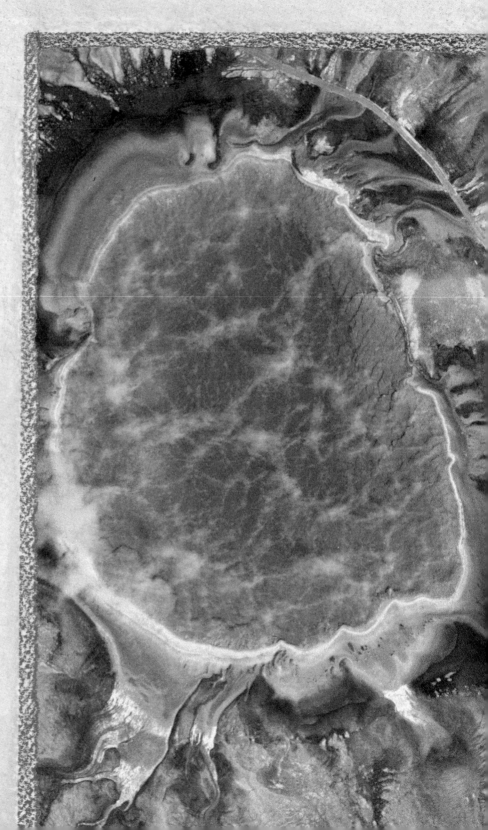

To find out more about the photograph, look on page 68. As you read this chapter, you will learn about the composition of the earth.

3.1 Layers of the Earth

Objectives

▶ **Describe** and **compare** the crust, mantle, and core.

▶ **Describe** the structure of the lithosphere.

▶ **Explain** why matter within the asthenosphere moves.

▶ **Make a model** of the earth and its layers.

The rocks, soil, and water you can see on the earth's surface make up only a tiny fraction of the total mass and volume of the earth. What is the earth like below its surface? What makes up the interior of our planet?

At one time, some people thought the earth might be hollow. They imagined a person could find cracks in the surface that would lead them into enormous underground caverns. In 1864, French writer Jules Verne wrote about just such an adventure in *Journey to the Center of the Earth*. In this book, three explorers go deep into the earth and encounter a huge sea, prehistoric animals, and monster mushrooms. Today, scientists know there are no open, hollow spaces deep in the earth. But they also know that it is not all solid rock.

Earth's Interior

What would you find if you could bore a hole down deeper and deeper into the earth until you reached its center? First, you would find that the chemical makeup of the materials changes as you go deeper. Second, you would discover that the materials increase in density. Third, you would observe that temperature and pressure increase with depth, but at different rates.

Because of the way these factors interact, the materials of the earth's interior form *layers*. The layers contain different chemical substances and have quite different physical properties. Earth scientists classify three main layers according to their location from the outside to the center of the earth. You will read more about those layers on the next pages.

Figure 3.1 ▲
Even the deepest caverns are nowhere near the earth's interior.

Chemical Makeup of Layers

From Earth's outside to its center, the three main layers are the crust, mantle, and core. The **crust** is the outermost layer of the earth. The **mantle** is the middle layer of Earth. The center layer of the earth is the **core**.

The three layers are made of different chemicals. Rocky materials called silicates are the main substances of the crust and the mantle. Silicates are compounds of silicon and oxygen combined with other elements. The silicates of the crust are rich in aluminum, iron, and magnesium. In contrast, the silicates of the mantle contain mostly iron and magnesium. Unlike the other layers, the core is made up primarily of two metals: iron and nickel.

Figure 3.2
Layers of the Earth ▼

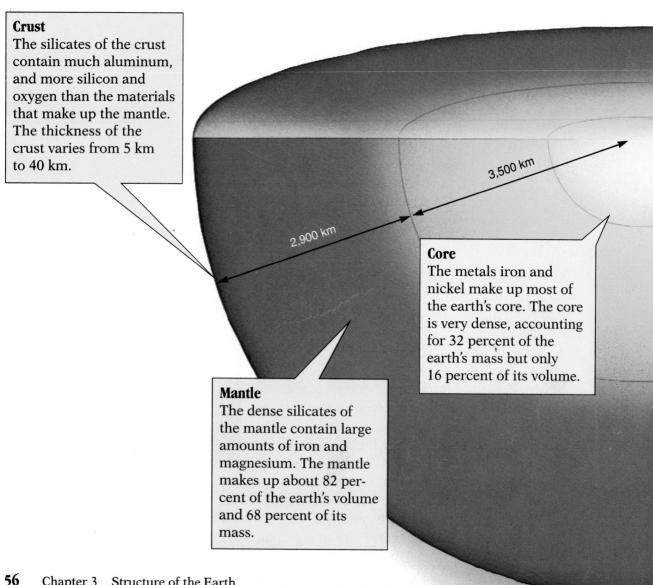

Crust
The silicates of the crust contain much aluminum, and more silicon and oxygen than the materials that make up the mantle. The thickness of the crust varies from 5 km to 40 km.

2,900 km

3,500 km

Core
The metals iron and nickel make up most of the earth's core. The core is very dense, accounting for 32 percent of the earth's mass but only 16 percent of its volume.

Mantle
The dense silicates of the mantle contain large amounts of iron and magnesium. The mantle makes up about 82 percent of the earth's volume and 68 percent of its mass.

Physical Properties of Layers

The temperatures deep inside the earth are high enough to melt the silicates and other substances that make it up. Yet most of the earth's interior is not liquid. Why? The enormous pressures inside the earth offset the high temperatures. In much of the earth's interior, high pressures will not allow the matter to melt.

The balance between temperature and pressure in the earth varies with depth. Depending on this balance, the matter can be solid, liquid, or in-between. Note the differences among the zones in the diagram below. The outer zone, the **lithosphere** (LITH uhs FEER), is cool and rigid. Below it, the **asthenosphere** (as THEHN uhs FEER), is hot and semiliquid. The lithosphere includes the crust and upper mantle. The asthenosphere is in the mantle.

4,000°C-4,500°C   3,200°C-4,000°C   1,600C°-3,200°C   1,300C°-1,600°C

Lithosphere
The cool, solid lithosphere "floats" on top of the asthenosphere. The lithosphere includes the crust and the uppermost part of the mantle.

Inner Core
The very high pressure in the inner core is a more important factor than the very high temperature. As a result, the inner core is solid.

Mantle
This layer is solid and rigid compared to the asthenosphere because the temperature is not high enough to overcome the high pressure.

Outer Core
Temperature is the controlling factor in the outer core, which is liquid. Circulation of its molten iron is thought to be the source of the earth's magnetic field.

Asthenosphere
The right balance of pressure and temperature in the asthenosphere makes its rocky material soft and flowing but not completely liquid. This condition is called *plasticity*.

Structure of the Lithosphere

The crust is the only layer of the earth that people have direct contact with. Together with the upper mantle, it forms a cool, rigid layer, the lithosphere, which undergoes slow but important changes. These changes, which you will learn about in later chapters, affect the earth's surface and its living things.

The lithosphere, like the rest of the earth, has a layered structure. You already know that it includes the crust and upper mantle. But the crust itself is made up of two distinct parts called continental crust and oceanic crust. Look at Figure 3.3 below. It is a cross section of the lithosphere showing these two kinds of crust. Notice that continental crust lies underneath continents and oceanic crust is underneath the oceans. Both kinds of crust are on the top of the lithosphere.

How are these two kinds of crust different? Continental crust is less dense than oceanic crust. Compared to oceanic crust, it is made up of a higher percentage of silicon and oxygen, and contains more aluminum. The rocks that make up continental crust are mostly granite and rhyolite. Denser, darker rocks called basalt and gabbro make up oceanic crust.

Continental crust, as you can see in Figure 3.3, varies in thickness. Tall mountains have deep "roots." You can stand on top of a tall mountain and have over 40 km of continental crust below you. At a continent's edge, in contrast, the thickness of continental crust thins to zero.

Figure 3.3 ▶

Two kinds of crust float on top of the lithosphere. Where do these two kinds of crust touch each other?

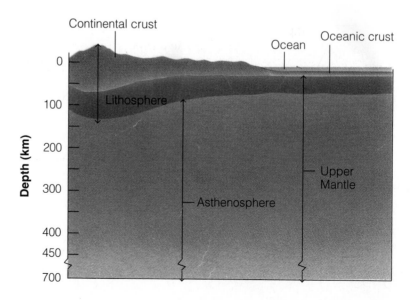

Movement in the Asthenosphere

The material of the asthenosphere is like thick liquid or hot tar. As intense heat from the earth's core moves toward the surface through the mantle, it causes the material of the asthenosphere to circulate. Matter rises through certain parts of the asthenosphere. Then it cools and slowly sinks in other places. The result is a circular flow of matter called **convection** (kuhn VEHKT shuhn).

Convection in the asthenosphere is shown in Figure 3.4. This circulation is so slow that a piece of rock may take millions of years to rise through the asthenosphere. Yet this movement has a very important effect on the lithosphere above, as you will find out in Chapter 5.

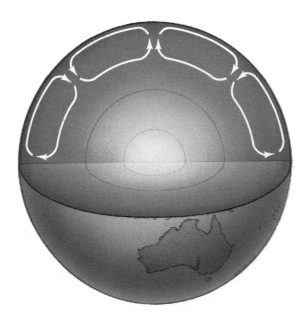

Figure 3.4 ▲
Matter in the asthenosphere moves slowly by convection.

SkillBuilder Graphing

Temperature Changes in the Earth

Most of the earth's surface and its underlying crust are cool. Below the crust, however, the temperature begins to increase. At the earth's center, the temperature is estimated to be over 4,000°C!

How does the temperature of the earth's interior increase with depth? This is an important question, because the temperature and pressure at a particular depth determine whether the material there will be solid, liquid, or plastic.

Use the table of data at the right to make a graph showing how temperature increases with depth. Then answer the questions below.

1. On which axis did you put depth? Why? What would your graph look like if you put depth on the other axis?

2. What is the shape of the curve on your graph?

Depth	Estimated Temperature
25 km	20°C
50 km	500°C
100 km	900°C
150 km	1,350°C
200 km	1,550°C
300 km	1,600°C
400 km	1,800°C

3. Where on the curve does temperature increase at the fastest rate? The slowest?

4. Your graph goes to 400 km in depth. Where in the earth is this? Through which layers do you pass to get there?

In a short paragraph, describe what the graph tells you about the earth's interior.

Science and You *Living on Oceanic Crust*

Most oceanic crust is covered with ocean water. Yet it is possible that oceanic crust lies right under your feet. Many islands are made of oceanic crust. In addition, at the surface of some parts of continents there are thick sheets of basalt, the same rock that makes up oceanic crust.

Regions with oceanic crust at the surface include the Hawaiian Islands and parts of Alaska. Iceland is another region of the world made up of oceanic crust. It is part of an area in the Atlantic Ocean where the ocean floor rises above the ocean's surface. The Columbia Plateau is a sheet of basalt almost 2 km thick covering parts of Idaho, Washington, and Oregon. Formed by a volcanic flow, the Plateau is very similar to oceanic crust but was never under water.

Living on land made of oceanic crust or basalt can be different from living on continental crust. For example, the soils formed from basalt and similar rocks are different from those formed from the granitic rock of continental crust. Soil formed from basalt contains large amounts of the elements iron and magnesium. It contains relatively small amounts of many of the elements plants need to grow. As a result, this type of soil is usually not very fertile. It is often used to grow crops such as wheat, barley, and sugarcane, or for grazing animals such as sheep and cattle.

Figure 3.5 ▲

People living in Iceland build their houses directly on rocks of the oceanic crust.

Check and Explain

1. How does the mantle differ from the core?

2. What makes up the earth's lithosphere?

3. **Reason and Conclude** Why do earth scientists use two different ways of classifying the earth's layers?

4. **Make a Model** Choose a way to make a model of the earth and its layers. After the model is complete, answer these questions: What does your model show about the earth? What doesn't it show? What kind of model would you need to make it show these other characteristics?

3.2 Studying the Earth's Interior

Objectives

▶ **Identify** two types of seismic waves.

▶ **Describe** the movement of seismic waves.

▶ **Explain** how earth scientists make inferences about the earth's core.

▶ **Infer** the characteristics of an object through indirect observation.

▼ **ACTIVITY**

Inferring

What's in the Balloons?

Collect three dark-colored balloons and ten dried beans.

1. Put ten dried beans into one balloon. Put a tablespoon of water into the second balloon. Put a shredded piece of paper into the third.

2. Inflate and tie each balloon.

3. Have a partner infer what is inside each balloon. What types of observations did your partner use?

SKILLS WARMUP

How have earth scientists found out about the structure and composition of the earth's interior? The interior cannot be observed directly. The deepest mine is less than 4 km deep. On land, the deepest hole ever bored into the crust went down only 15 km—still far from the mantle.

The earth's surface does provide some clues to what lies below. For example, the molten rock, or magma, that flows from volcanoes is evidence for high temperatures inside the earth. However, to gain most of their knowledge of the earth's interior, earth scientists have relied on one kind of indirect observation. They have made inferences based on how shock waves from earthquakes travel through the earth.

Seismic Waves

When you hit a softball with a bat, you feel vibrations from the impact in your hands. The vibrations, or shock waves, travel through the bat to your hands. In a similar way, shock waves travel through the earth.

Earthquakes—sudden movements of the crust—are a cause of shock waves in the earth. Shock waves from an earthquake are called **seismic** (SYZ mihk) **waves**. Seismic waves can pass all the way from one side of the earth to the other. Earth scientists use tools called seismographs to detect seismic waves. Seismographs are located all over the earth's surface. By comparing the strength and arrival time of waves at different locations, scientists gain valuable information about the earth's interior.

Figure 3.6 ▲
The same earthquake that caused these cracks in the surface sent seismic waves throughout the earth.

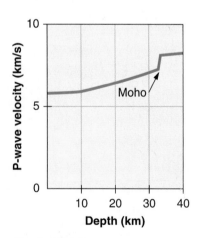

Figure 3.7 ▲

What happens at the Moho to change the velocity of P waves?

Types of Seismic Waves An earthquake produces several kinds of seismic waves. The two types most useful for studying the earth's interior are called P waves and S waves. P waves travel by a back-and-forth movement of rock particles. The particles are squeezed together and pulled apart as the wave passes through. S waves, in contrast, travel by an up-and-down movement of rock particles. P waves and S waves behave differently as they pass through the earth. S waves, for example, cannot travel through liquids.

Bending of Waves The speed at which both kinds of seismic waves travel is determined in part by the density of rock; the higher the density, the faster the speed. As a seismic wave passes through the earth, it encounters rock of different densities. Its speed changes. If it passes through rock layers at even a slight angle, its change in speed results in a change of direction, too. Most seismic waves travel in curved lines through the earth. This curving of direction is called *refraction*. When a wave passes from rock of one density into rock of very different density, its path may bend sharply.

Inferring From Seismic Waves

With knowledge of how seismic waves travel, scientists have developed a good picture of the earth's interior. They have determined the location of boundaries between layers. They have also inferred the composition and physical properties of the layers.

The Moho In 1909, the Croatian scientist Andrija Mohorovičić (MOH huh ROH vuh chihch) discovered the boundary between the crust and the mantle. He found that at a depth of between 30 and 35 km below the surface, seismic waves suddenly speeded up. He inferred that at this depth the rocks became much more dense and were therefore probably different in chemical makeup.

Figure 3.7 shows how the speed, or velocity, of P waves varies with depth. Notice that the velocity rises gradually until 30 km deep, where a sudden increase in velocity marks the Moho. In honor of Mohorovičić, the boundary between the crust and mantle was named the Mohorovičić discontinuity, or **Moho**, for short.

The Core When an earthquake occurs in the crust, it sends seismic waves in all directions. Over a large part of the earth's surface, both S and P waves from the quake can be detected by seismographs. At a certain distance away from the earthquake, however, a zone in which no waves can be detected at all begins. Earth scientists have inferred that this **shadow zone** is caused by the earth's core. Look at Figure 3.8 below to see why the core creates a shadow zone. Directly across the earth from the earthquake, only P waves are detected. What does this suggest about the core?

Figure 3.8
The Core's Effect on Seismic Waves ▼

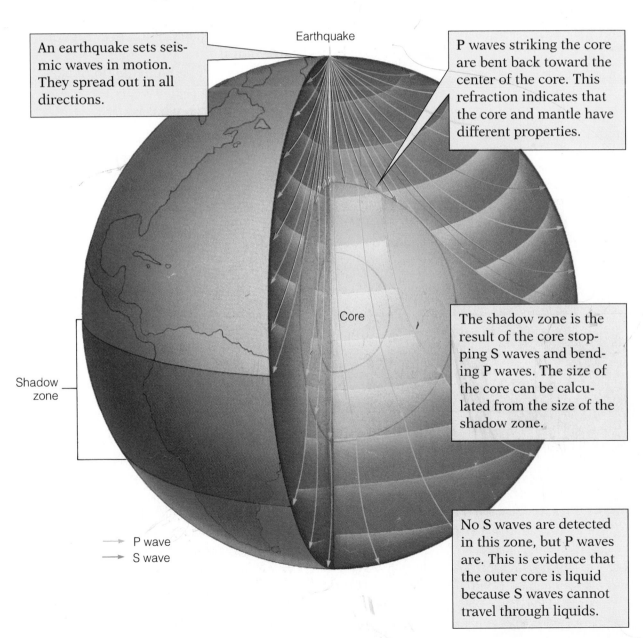

An earthquake sets seismic waves in motion. They spread out in all directions.

Earthquake

P waves striking the core are bent back toward the center of the core. This refraction indicates that the core and mantle have different properties.

Core

The shadow zone is the result of the core stopping S waves and bending P waves. The size of the core can be calculated from the size of the shadow zone.

Shadow zone

→ P wave
→ S wave

No S waves are detected in this zone, but P waves are. This is evidence that the outer core is liquid because S waves cannot travel through liquids.

Boiling Over

Without removing the cover from a pot cooking on the stove, how could you determine what was cooking inside? How might your method of determining the pot's contents be similar to the way scientists determine what is inside the earth?

SKILLS WORKOUT

Inferring the Chemical Makeup

Earth scientists cannot drill deep into the earth. So they make inferences about the chemical makeup of the earth's layers. Meteorites, pieces of rock or metal from space that strike the earth, are one important source of data. Some meteorites are made of iron and nickel. Scientists hypothesize that meteorites are the remains of the cores of planets that have broken apart. If this is true, then meteorites are further evidence that the earth's core is also made of iron and nickel.

Scientists also use measurements to infer the earth's chemical makeup. By dividing the earth's mass by its volume, they get an average density of about 5.5 g/cm^3. Scientists hypothesize that if the earth's mantle has a density of 3.5 g/cm^3, the core must be made up of very dense materials to bring the average density up to 5.5 g/cm^3. Based on these figures, what is the core's density?

Historical Notebook

The Mohole Project

The Moho is an important part of the earth's structure. Since Mohorovičić discovered it in 1909, earth scientists have dreamed of observing the Moho directly. In the 1950s, a group of scientists and engineers set out to achieve this goal. With money from the United States government, they set up the Mohole Project.

The goal of the project was to drill into the earth to sample all layers of the crust and reach the mantle. The first step was to decide where to drill the holes. Seismic studies indicated that the crust was thinnest under the ocean.

In 1961, the first drilling took place off the California coast. The purpose of this part of the study was not to reach the Moho, but to see if it was possible to collect crust samples located under thousands of meters of water.

The next stage was to build ocean drilling equipment that could actually drill deep enough to reach the Moho. It took four years to develop the technology for deep drilling. However, in 1966 the program was cancelled because of the high cost of the research. The Moho has never been observed directly.

1. Why would scientists want to directly observe the Moho?

2. What was the reason for choosing drilling sites that were beneath the ocean?

Science and Technology *Seismic Arrays*

Mohorovičić and other earth scientists who made the first major discoveries about the earth's interior used very simple seismographs to obtain their data. Since that time, the accuracy and sensitivity of seismographs have greatly increased. In addition, more seismographs have been placed all over the earth. As a result, earth scientists have been able to gain more and more detailed knowledge of the earth's interior.

One important advance in the detection of seismic waves has been the development of seismic arrays. A seismic array is a cluster of interconnected seismographs. For example, one seismic array in Montana is made up of 525 seismographs. They are linked together in 21 clusters. The clusters are arranged in a circle about 200 km in diameter.

With the help of computers, a seismic array can make very precise comparisons among the seismic data received by individual seismographs. Why is this interconnection important? It lets earth scientists filter out seismic "noise." Seismic noise is created by constant small movements of the crust. These movements are detected by seismographs and hide weak seismic waves from distant earthquakes. When the seismic noise is filtered out, seismographs in the array can better detect these faint seismic waves.

Figure 3.9 ▲

Comparison of data from different seismographs helps earth scientists interpret seismic waves.

Check and Explain

1. What are two types of seismic waves?

2. What is the shadow zone? What does the shadow zone tell scientists about the earth's core?

3. **Predict** A seismic wave passes at an angle from a dense rock layer into a denser rock layer. What will happen to the wave?

4. **Infer** Suppose you are given a sealed shoe box containing an object. What kinds of indirect observation can you use to learn about the object in the box?

Activity 3 *How does matter move in the mantle?*

Task 1 Prelab Prep
1. Collect the following items: hot plate, 250-mL or larger beaker, water, food coloring, dropper, spoon, rolled oats cereal.
2. Turn the hot plate on to medium heat.

Task 2 Data Record
1. On a separate sheet of paper, draw the outlines of two beakers, as shown below. Label one beaker *A* and the other *B*.

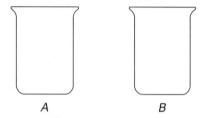

2. You will use the drawings to record your observations about the movement of two different substances in the beaker.

Task 3 Procedure
1. Fill beaker about two-thirds full of water. Place it on the hot plate. **CAUTION! Keep hair and loose clothing away from the hot plate.**
2. Wait about two minutes. Using the dropper, carefully add one drop of food coloring to the surface of the water near the side of the beaker. Try not to disturb the water.
3. Observe the path of the food coloring for as long as possible. Draw your observations of the movement of the food coloring in the beaker labeled *A* on your paper.
4. Repeat steps 2 and 3 if you have any difficulty observing the movement of the drop of food coloring.
5. Sprinkle one spoonful of the rolled oats evenly across the surface of the water in the same beaker. Observe the path of the rolled oats on the water.

6. Draw your observations of the movement of the rolled oats in the beaker labeled *B* on your paper.
7. Turn off the hot plate. Once the beaker has cooled, remove it from the hot plate and dispose of the contents.

Task 4 Analysis
1. Describe the path taken by the food coloring. What pattern did you see in its movement?
2. What part of the earth does the water represent?
3. Describe the path taken by the rolled oats. How does the movement of the rolled oats compare with the movement of the food coloring?
4. What part of the earth could the rolled oats represent? Why?
5. How is the water similar to the mantle? How is it different?
6. Once the water is completely heated, it no longer serves as an accurate model of the mantle. Why?

Task 5 Conclusion
Write a short paragraph explaining how the beakers of water model the movement of material in the earth's mantle.

Everyday Application
Convection is a common process of heat transfer in substances. You experience convection currents every day. Give three examples of convection that you have experienced. What type of matter is moving in each case?

Extension
The material in the mantle is much thicker and denser than water. Try heating a thick but flowing substance, such as cooked cereal or flour and water. Record your observations.

Chapter 3 Review

Concept Summary

3.1 Layers of the Earth

▶ The layers of the earth are classified into the crust, mantle, and core. They are made of different chemicals.

▶ Temperature and pressure differences cause the lithosphere, asthenosphere, mantle, inner core, and outer core to be solid, liquid, or in-between.

▶ The crust is composed of a dense layer called oceanic crust and a less dense layer called continental crust.

▶ Convection in the asthenosphere causes a circular flow of matter.

3.2 Studying the Earth's Interior

▶ Scientists use indirect observations from earthquake vibrations to study the interior of the earth.

▶ Earthquakes produce several kinds of seismic waves. P and S waves are the most useful to study Earth's interior.

▶ Seismic waves change speed when they encounter materials with different densities. They are refracted, or bent, if they pass at an angle through materials

▶ of different density.
The boundary between the mantle and the crust, the Moho, was discovered by

▶ studying the speed of seismic waves.
The shadow zone is an area of the earth's surface where no seismic waves are detected after an earthquake. The size of the core was determined from the size of the shadow zone.

Chapter Vocabulary

crust (3.1)	lithosphere (3.1)	convection (3.1)	Moho (3.2)
mantle (3.1)	asthenosphere (3.1)	seismic wave (3.2)	shadow zone (3.2)
core (3.1)			

Check Your Vocabulary

Use the vocabulary words above to complete the following sentences correctly.

1. The semiliquid layer of the earth between the lithosphere and deep mantle is the ____ .

2. The circular flow of matter in the mantle is called ____ .

3. The layer of the earth that lies above the mantle is the ____ .

4. The dense, metallic, innermost layer of the earth is the ____ .

5. A boundary called the ____ separates the crust and the mantle.

6. The cool, solid part of the earth that includes the crust and the upper part of the mantle is the ____ .

7. Geologists study the ____ produced by earthquakes to make inferences about the earth's structure.

8. Between the crust and the core is the ____ .

9. The earth's core produces a ____ on the other side of the earth from an earthquake.

Explain the difference between the words in each pair.

10. mantle, asthenosphere

11. P waves, S waves

12. lithosphere, crust

13. seismic wave, seismograph

Chapter 3 Review

Check Your Knowledge

Answer the following in complete sentences.

1. What are the three main layers of the earth?

2. What is the lithosphere?

3. Where does convection take place within the earth?

4. What produces seismic waves?

5. How was the Moho discovered?

6. What information does the shadow zone suggest about the core?

7. What is refraction?

8. What tool have scientists used to help them make inferences about the interior of the earth?

9. How does continental crust differ from oceanic crust?

10. List the five zones of the earth that differ in their physical properties.

Determine whether each statement is true or false. Write *true* if it is true. If it is false, change the underlined word(s) to make the statement true.

11. Scientists have drilled holes into the <u>core</u>.

12. The <u>core</u> floats on top of the asthenosphere.

13. The material in the asthenosphere flows by <u>convection</u>.

14. <u>Seismic waves</u> can pass from one side of the earth to the other.

15. Scientists think that the core is composed of iron and <u>magnesium</u>.

16. The continental crust is <u>less</u> dense than the oceanic crust.

Check Your Understanding

Apply the concepts you have learned to answer each question.

1. For each of the five zones of the earth, explain the relationship between temperature and pressure in that layer.

2. **Infer** How does convection in the asthenosphere affect the lithosphere above?

3. **Compare** Explain the difference between a direct observation and an indirect observation.

4. Explain why the core can make up 32 percent of the earth's mass but only 16 percent of its volume.

5. Instead of waiting for an earthquake to happen, how might earth scientists create seismic waves?

6. Why is the existence of iron-nickel meteorites evidence that the earth's core is made of iron and nickel?

7. Explain how the size of the core was determined.

8. **Extension** In a dictionary, look up the rocks granite and rhyolite, which make up the continental crust. Also look up the rocks basalt and gabbro, which make up the oceanic crust. Describe and compare each of the rocks.

9. **Mystery Photo** The photograph on page 54 shows a mineral hot spring. The water is heated by hot underground rock. The rock is heated by gases released from molten rock within the earth. Describe other ways in which the high temperatures in the mantle affect the surface of the earth.

Develop Your Skills

Use the skills you have developed in this chapter to complete each activity.

1. **Interpret Data** The graph below shows the relationship between depth and pressure within the earth.

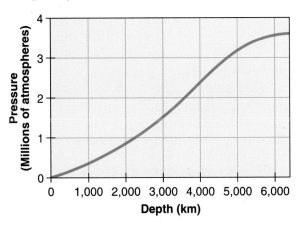

a. What is the pressure at 2,000 km?

b. Between what two depths is the rate of pressure change the greatest?

c. What happens to the change in pressure at depths greater than 6,000 km?

2. **Data Bank** Use the information on page 613 to answer the following questions.

a. How deep was the deepest well drilled into the earth?

b. How deep was the deepest mine drilled into the earth? How much deeper is the inner core than the deepest mine? The deepest well?

3. **Organize Data** Make a table comparing the core, mantle, and crust. Include columns listing percentages of the earth's mass and chemical makeup. What other columns will you include?

Make Connections

1. **Link the Concepts** Draw a concept map showing how the concepts below link together. Add terms to connect, or link, the concepts. Use the following words to construct your concept map:

crust	mantle
core	continental crust
convection	nickel
iron	oceanic crust

2. **Science and You** Study a world map. Do you live on continental or oceanic crust? How does the type of crust you live on affect your life?

3. **Science and Literature** Read the book *Journey to the Center of the Earth*, by Jules Verne. Based on what you have learned in this chapter, is the story scientifically accurate? Choose four or five excerpts from the book that are related to concepts from the chapter. Write about the scientific accuracy of these excerpts. Explain why this book is classified as a science fiction novel.

4. **Science and Math** Make a bar graph that shows the average temperature for the lithosphere, asthenosphere, mesosphere, outer core, and inner core. Be sure to label the x-axis and the y-axis.

5. **Science and Physical Education** Find a worn-out or torn baseball or golf ball. Determine its structure by removing the cover and taking the rest of it apart. How is its structure similar to and different from that of the earth?

Science and Literature Connection

In Spanish, Manzanar means "apple orchard." Great stretches of Owens Valley were once green with orchards and alfalfa fields. It has been a desert ever since its water started flowing south into Los Angeles, sometime during the twenties. But a few rows of untended pear and apple trees were still growing there when the camp opened, where a shallow water table had kept them alive. In the spring of 1943 we moved to block 28, right up next to one of the old pear orchards. That's where we stayed until the end of the war, and those trees stand in my memory for the turning of our life in camp, from the outrageous to the tolerable.

Papa pruned and cared for the nearest trees. Late that summer we picked the fruit green and stored it in a root cellar he had dug under our new barracks. At night the wind through the leaves would sound like the surf had sounded in Ocean Park, and while drifting off to sleep I could almost imagine we were still living by the beach.

Once the first year's turmoil cooled down, the authorities started letting us outside the wire for recreation. Papa used to hike along the creeks that channeled down from the base of the Sierras. He

Farewell to Manzanar

The following excerpt is from the novel Farewell To Manzanar *by Jeanne Wakatsuki Houston and James D. Houston.*

brought back chunks of driftwood, and he would pass long hours sitting on the steps carving myrtle limbs into benches, table legs, and lamps, filling our rooms with bits of gnarled, polished furniture.

He hauled stones in off the desert and built a small rock garden outside our doorway, with succulents and a patch of moss. Near it he laid flat steppingstones leading to the stairs.

He also painted watercolors. Until this time I had not known he could paint. He loved to sketch the mountains. If anything made that country habitable it was the mountains themselves, purple when the sun dropped and so sharply etched in the morning light the granite dazzled almost more than the bright snow lacing it. The nearest peaks rose ten thousand feet higher than the valley floor, with Whitney, the highest, just off to the south. They were important for all of us, but especially for the Issei. Whitney reminded Papa of Fujiyama, that is, it gave him the same kind of spiritual sustenance.

The tremendous beauty of those peaks was inspirational, as so many natural forms are to the Japanese (the rocks outside our doorway could be those mountains in miniature). They also represented those forces in nature, those powerful and inevitable forces that cannot be resisted, reminding a man that sometimes he must simply endure that which cannot be changed.

Skills in Science

Reading Skills in Science

1. **Infer** What "forces in nature" are referred to in the last paragraph of the selection?

2. **Find Context Clues** What is "Whitney"? Identify the clues you used to make this determination.

Writing Skills in Science

1. **Compare and Contrast** What do Whitney, Fujiyama, and Papa's rock garden have in common? Describe their symbolic meaning to Papa.

2. **Infer** Describe the importance of nature in the family's life while they were detained in the camp.

3. **Detect the Writer's Mood** How does the author feel about the camp she is in? How do you know?

Activities

Science and Art Draw or paint the natural surroundings described in this excerpt.

Communicate How did the Sierra Nevada mountain range form? Do research to find out the most current theory on the formation of these mountains. Make a poster that illustrates the formation.

Where to Read More

A Spit is a Piece of Land by Doris Coburn. New York: Julian Messner, 1989. This text examines various landforms in the United States and the forces that shaped them.

The Home Front by Conrad R. Stein. Chicago: Childrens Press, 1986. You can learn more about the treatment of Japanese-Americans during World War II through this text, which explores life on the home front.

Unit 2
The Dynamic Earth

Data Bank

Use the information on pages 612 to 625 to answer the following questions about topics explored in this unit.

Calculating

How much taller is Mt. Everest than Mt. McKinley?

Reading a Table

What was the magnitude of the earthquake that struck northwestern Argentina? When did it happen?

Organizing Data

List in order how long the epochs of the Cenozoic Era lasted. Begin with the epoch that was the longest.

Interpreting Data

What is the elevation of Mt. Kilimanjaro in Africa?

The photograph to the left shows an explosion of volcanic ash after the eruption of Mt. Pinatubo in the Philippines in 1991. What do you think caused the eruption?

Chapter 4 Time and Change

What Do You See?

66I see a fossil of a bird that looks like it might have been a flightless bird. It looks like it might have run to catch insects, small lizards, and small reptiles. It looks like it was an early form of the ostrich. I would say it is probably one to two million years old.99

Cliff Thompson
Kesner Junior High School
Salida, Colorado

To find out more about the photograph, look on page 88. As you read this chapter, you will learn about the earth's history.

4.1 Earth's History

Objectives

▶ **Describe** the origin and early history of the earth.

▶ **Describe** processes of change on the earth's surface.

▶ **Infer** how different sedimentary rock forms.

▶ **Communicate** in a diagram how processes of surface change are related.

How much will you change during the next year? You will probably grow several inches. You'll make new friends and learn new skills. In just ten years, you will change a great deal. Much about your family and community will change, too.

During those same ten years, will the earth change? Will its mountain ranges change in elevation? Will the oceans shrink in volume? Compared to changes in the human world, changes in mountains and oceans are small and unmeasurable. For this reason, you are used to thinking of the earth and its features as permanent and unchanging. And yet they are not.

The earth, oceans, atmosphere, and climate all undergo changes. The difference between change in your life and change in the earth is a matter of scale. Many important changes in and on the planet Earth take place very slowly, over enormous periods of time. Studying earth science, therefore, means adjusting the way you think about time.

Age of the Earth

How old are you? Most people can answer this question with a one- or two-digit number. How old is the earth? This question requires an answer with ten digits: 4,600,000,000 years.

Compare the age of the earth to a 24-hour day. Based on this time scale, how old are you? The correct answer is not hours, minutes, or even seconds. Even if you were 100 years old, your lifetime would be measured in only *fractions* of a second.

Figure 4.1 ▲
The human environment of a city changes much more rapidly than the natural earth on which it is built.

Figure 4.2 ▶

If the length of this soccer field stands for the age of the earth, how much of the field equals your lifetime?

For another comparison, look at Figure 4.2. It shows a soccer field, 100 m long. Imagine that this length represents the age of the earth. How "long" is your life in comparison? It would be much less than the thickness of one blade of grass.

As you can see, the earth's history is very long. This amount of time is so much longer than anything humans experience that scientists have given it a special name: **geologic time.** If the passage of geologic time were recorded in books so that each year was condensed into one letter, your life would be the length of an average sentence. The earth's history, in contrast, would fill not only this whole book, but a good-sized library *full* of books!

Figure 4.3 ▲

The earth began as a clump of matter spinning around a hot cloud of matter that would become the sun.

Origin of the Earth

Old as it is, the earth has not always existed. About 5,000 million years ago, a huge cloud of matter spinning in space began to collapse. Matter was drawn toward the center of the cloud by an ever-increasing gravitational pull. As the center increased in mass, it grew hotter and denser. Eventually, the center of the cloud became so hot and dense that individual atoms began to join, or fuse. This fusion of atoms released large amounts of heat and light. The sun was born.

The matter that still spun around the newly formed sun began to clump. Each clump drew the surrounding matter toward it. Over time, each clump became a planet. Earth is one of the nine clumps that became a planet.

Earth's Early History

During its first billion years or so, the earth was very different than it is now. At first, the hot surface had no oceans or continents. There was probably no atmosphere. Volcanoes erupted constantly, spewing gases. An atmosphere slowly formed, and some of the gases in the atmosphere began to condense, or turn to liquid. Much of this liquid was water, and it fell to the earth as rain. An ocean eventually covered the surface.

By about 3,800 million years ago, the first small landmasses had formed as a result of volcanic eruptions. Around the same time, the first living things came into being in the oceans. Some of these organisms began to produce oxygen as a by-product of their life processes.

By about 2,000 million years ago, the earth was much like it is today. Organisms did not yet live on land, but there were mountains and rivers on the continents. The atmosphere contained oxygen, and energy from the sun created weather patterns.

Changes on the Surface

Over the last 2,000 million years, the earth has continued to change. But unlike the changes that occurred in the earth's early history, these changes have followed regular patterns. The same patterns continue today.

Weathering and Erosion   One basic process that has shaped the earth's surface is the wearing away of rock. Rock wears down in two related steps. First, rock undergoes **weathering**, during which it is broken down into smaller particles. Second, these smaller particles are carried away by **erosion** (ee ROH zhuhn). Wind, waves, ice, flowing water, and gravity can all erode weathered rock particles. Particles carried away by erosion are called *sediment*.

Weathering and erosion work very slowly. Over long periods of time, however, weathering and erosion together cause major changes in the surface. They can make mountains disappear or carve canyons over 1 km deep.

Figure 4.4 ▲
The first landmasses on the earth may have formed in the way you see here.

Figure 4.5 ▲
Can you see the sediment that has eroded from this hillside?

Deposition   Because of gravity, particles of rock are carried by erosion to low places. These places include the bottoms of lakes and valleys, and the ocean floor. There, rock particles stop moving and collect. The buildup of eroded particles, or sediment, is called **deposition** (DEHP uh ZIH shuhn).

In contrast to the wearing-down processes of weathering and erosion, deposition is a building-up process. Deposition happens slowly all the time. It is another major cause of change on the earth's surface. At any one time, most parts of the earth's surface are either being eroded or having sediment deposited on them.

Figure 4.6 ▲
Eroded pieces of rock were deposited in this riverbed. Where did they come from?

Formation of Sedimentary Rock

Sediment builds up over long periods of time, forming horizontal layers. Newer layers form on top of older layers. The growing mass of the upper layers puts more pressure on the sediments in the lower layers. As pressure compacts the sediment particles and minerals cement them together, sediments become rock.

Rock that forms from sediment is called *sedimentary rock*. Sedimentary rock has formed on the earth for such a long time that in some places it is very thick. The Grand Canyon, for example, cuts through sedimentary rock over 1 km thick. Because of the way sedimentary rock forms, its layers vary in age. Like the bricks in the wall of a building, the lowest layers are laid down first. Therefore, the deeper a layer of sedimentary rock, the older it is.

Figure 4.7 ▲
What evidence of its formation does this sedimentary rock contain?

Uplift   What would happen if weathering, erosion, deposition, and the formation of rock from sediment were the only processes shaping the earth's surface? High places would wear down, and low places would fill up. Erosion and deposition would then stop. What prevents this from happening?

In a number of different ways, parts of the crust are raised above others in a process called *uplift*. Through uplift, mountains and plateaus form. Because uplift, like weathering and erosion, has been going on constantly over at least the last 2,000 million years, there are always new, elevated landforms to be worn away.

Changes in Life

Organisms have lived on the earth's surface millions of years. They are, therefore, an important part of the earth's history. Organisms that lived in the past have left evidence of their existence in the rocks of the crust. These traces of past life are called **fossils**.

Most fossils formed when an organism was buried in sediment. Over time, the remains of the organism became part of a layer of sedimentary rock. A fossil, therefore, is as old as the rock of which it is a part.

By studying fossils, scientists found that living things changed greatly over time. Most of the kinds of organisms, or species, that left fossils no longer exist today. They became extinct.

Over time, living things evolved. Through the process of evolution, the inherited traits of a species change, and new species arise. Therefore, as the earth's surface changed over time, so have the organisms living on it.

Figure 4.8 ▲

The organisms that left these fossils lived over 150 million years ago. They are now extinct.

Historical Notebook

The Discovery of Earth's Old Age

If you had lived 200 years ago, you would probably have learned in school that the earth was 6,000 years old. In fact, the accepted view of history was that humans had lived on the earth nearly all that time. Therefore, human history and the earth's history were the same.

In the late 1700s, however, this view was challenged by a group of Scottish scientists led by James Hutton. Hutton made observations of rocks that made sense only if the earth was far older than anyone had imagined. He observed that rocks were made of particles eroded from even older rocks.

Hutton saw that the earth's surface had changed gradually over a very long period of time. He based his ideas on the principle of uniformitarianism (YOO nih FORM uh TAIR ee uhn izm). According to this principle, the laws of nature do not change over time. Thus, the same processes that shaped the earth in the past are still at work today.

The idea that the earth was very, very old gave birth to the modern science of geology. It changed the way life scientists viewed organisms. And it changed forever the human concept of time.

1. What made Hutton believe the earth was very old?

2. What is the principle of uniformitarianism?

On Ice

When sheets of ice expand and advance from the poles, much of Earth's water is frozen in ice. What do you think might happen to the ocean levels? How might this affect shoreline erosion? State a hypothesis to explain your reasoning.

SKILLS WORKOUT

Changes in Climate

Throughout the earth's history, the climate of the planet as a whole varied considerably. At certain times, most of the planet was warm and wet. At other times, it was much drier and colder. During the dry, cold times, the polar ice caps increased in size. Huge sheets of ice spread from the poles into the middle latitudes. These periods are called *ice ages*.

Science and Technology
Are Humans Changing the Climate?

For most of the earth's history, natural processes caused slow changes in climate. However, scientists have evidence showing that human technology is changing the climate today. These changes may be both local and global.

On a local scale, cities cause changes in temperature. The average temperature in a large city is often slightly higher than in the surrounding countryside. Scientists also determined that cutting down large areas of forest in tropical regions changes rainfall patterns. The deforested areas hold less moisture, so more rainwater drains to the oceans, instead of evaporating slowly to form clouds. As a result, rainfall in these areas may decrease.

Scientists are also worried about global warming. The burning of fossil fuels for energy increased the amount of carbon dioxide in the atmosphere. This caused small increases in the average temperature of the earth.

Check and Explain

1. From what did the earth form?

2. What does erosion do to the earth's surface?

3. **Infer** How would a layer of sedimentary rock formed from mud be different from one formed from sand?

4. **Communicate** Using words and arrows, draw a diagram to show how weathering, erosion, deposition, sedimentary rock formation, and uplift are related.

Activity 4 *How can you measure time differently?*

Skills Measure; Collect Data

Task 1 Prelab Prep
Collect the following items: a book, a pencil, a piece of paper.

Task 2 Data Record
Copy the data table below on a separate piece of paper and use it to record your measurements.

Table 4.1 Time in Different Scales

Type of year	Number of years to walk across the room	Number of years to write my name
book years		
step years		
title years		
??? years		

Task 3 Procedure
1. You will investigate some different ways that you can measure time. You'll begin by measuring in "book years." A book year equals the time it takes to open and close a book. Walk across the room opening and closing a book. Count the number of book years it takes to cross the room. Record this number in your data table.
2. Measure the number of book years it takes to write your name by having one partner count book years, while the other partner writes. Record this measurement in the table.
3. Count the number of steps it takes you to cross the room. Each step counts as one year. Record the "step years" in the table.
4. Measure the number of step years it takes to write your name by having one partner walk across the room while the other partner writes your name. Count the step years as

your name is written. Record this number in the data table.

5. A "title year" is the amount of time it takes to read the title of this activity. Count how many times you say the title as you walk across the room. Record this number in the table.
6. Measure the number of title years it takes to write your name by having one partner count title years, while the other partner writes your name. Record this number in the table.
7. Make up a scale for a type of year. Record the name of your type of year in Table 4.1. Use your new time scale to measure the number of years it takes to walk across the room and to write your name. Record these numbers in the data table.

Task 4 Analysis
1. Compare each of the new time scales to the real time scale. Which time scale has the shortest year? The longest?
2. Which time scale do you think would be the best to use? Why?
3. Which time scale was the most difficult to use? Why?
4. Calculate your age using one of the time scales from the data table.
5. **Infer** Would any of the time scales in this activity be useful in measuring the age of the earth? Explain.

Task 5 Conclusion
Write a paragraph explaining the possible uses for different time scales. Include the advantages and disadvantages of each scale.

Extension

Use easily obtainable items to define several different scales for measuring length. Measure the length of your book, your height, and the length of an eraser using each of the measuring systems that you defined.

The Time of Your Life

Make a timeline showing the major events in your life.

Divide the timeline into stages based on these events. How many stages did you make? How did you decide what a stage was?

SKILLS WARMUP

4.2 Geologic Time Scale

Objectives

▶ **Explain** how scientists determine the relative age of sedimentary rocks and other rocks.

▶ **List** the order of events that may result in an unconformity being formed.

▶ **Describe** the major divisions of the geologic time scale.

▶ **Infer** the relationship between the fossil record and the geologic time scale.

W hat stages have you gone through in your life? First you were an infant. Then you learned to walk and talk to become a toddler. After a few more years, you went to elementary school. Now you're a teenager or about to become one.

The earth, too, has gone through stages. Like the stages in your life, each one began with some important event or change. But the stages in the earth's history took place in geologic time. Each stage stretched over enormously long periods of time.

Time Record in the Rocks

How have scientists learned enough about the earth's history to divide it into stages? How do they find out about events that took place millions or even billions of years ago? The rocks of the earth's crust hold all the evidence. Scientists simply learned how to "read" the record of time preserved in the rocks.

Rock Layering Layers of rock provide scientists with important evidence of past events. As you learned, layers of rock form one after another. They are stacked according to age, like a pile of old magazines. Older rocks are found under younger rocks. Therefore, going down into deeper layers of rock is like going back in time. This principle holds true as long as the rock layers were not turned upside down by intense folding. What do you think scientists can learn by studying the layering of rock?

Figure 4.9 ▲

As these people move down into the canyon, they will pass by older and older rocks.

Relative Age The position of rock layers allows earth scientists to determine the *relative age* of these rocks. They can say a certain layer is older or younger than other layers by comparing its position to other layers. The relative positions of layers also helps in the ordering of past events. For example, suppose a certain layer of rock formed from volcanic ash. Above it is a layer formed by sediment deposited in a shallow sea. What can you infer from this evidence?

◀ **Figure 4.10**
How are these rock layers an example of an unconformity?

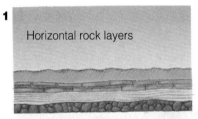

1 Horizontal rock layers

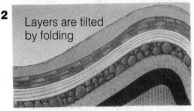

2 Layers are tilted by folding

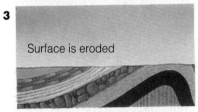

3 Surface is eroded

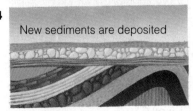

4 New sediments are deposited

Unconformities A break in the layering of rock can also be informative. Look at the photograph in Figure 4.10. Layers of rock tilted at an angle are covered by horizontal layers. An earth scientist knows that the tilted rock layers are much older than the horizontal layers. The line between them, called an *unconformity* (UHN kuhn FORM uh tee), represents a break in time.

Look at Figure 4.11 to see how an unconformity forms. Many different changes occurring over a long time period produce an unconformity. Geologists can infer what these changes were and when they occurred.

Absolute Age Geologists also have methods to determine the approximate age of rocks in years. These methods tell them the *absolute age* of rocks. The main method of determining absolute age is through radiometric dating. You will learn more about radiometric dating when you study fossils in Chapter 13. Through methods of absolute and relative dating, earth scientists have pieced together the earth's history.

Figure 4.11 ▲
An unconformity forms over a long period of time.

Divisions of Geologic Time

Scientists have divided geologic time into four large units. These units are called **eras** (AIR uhz). Each era covers one major stage in the earth's history. Look at Figure 4.12. It is a timeline showing the length of each era. Notice how the eras vary greatly in length.

Precambrian Era   The first era of the earth's history is the longest. It includes all the events from the earth's formation to a time about 640 million years ago. The Precambrian (pree KAYM bree uhn) Era ended when many new and different life forms began to appear.

Paleozoic Era   The 400 million years following the end of the Precambrian Era make up the Paleozoic (PAY lee UH ZOH ihk) Era. During this era, plants and animals began to live on land. The Paleozoic Era ended when many kinds of organisms became extinct.

SkillBuilder *Making a Graph*

Earth History Pie

A circle graph helps you to compare different amounts. You will make a circle graph that shows approximately how long each of the earth's eras lasted. Copy the table below.

Geologic Time Scale		
Era	Length (millions of years)	Percentage of Earth's History
Precambrian		
Paleozoic		
Mesozoic		
Cenozoic		

Using Figure 4.12 on page 85, determine how long each era lasted. Record the length for each era in the table.

Calculate the percentage of the total earth history that each era lasted. To do this, divide the era length by the age of the earth, then multiply by 100. The formula is

$$\frac{\text{era length}}{4{,}600} \times 100$$

Record the percentage for each era in the table.
   Using the percentages you recorded, draw and label a circle graph of the earth's history in geologic time. Then answer the questions.

1.   Which era occupies the smallest section of the circle graph? The largest?

2.   How might your circle graph change in ten million years? Work with a partner to construct a circle graph that represents the eras ten million years from now.

Mesozoic Era This era was the time of the dinosaurs. Most of the earth had a warm, wet climate. The Mesozoic (MEHZ uh ZOH ihk) Era ended when most of the dinosaurs and many other life forms died out. Many scientists hypothesize that mass extinctions occurred after a large asteroid, or rock from space, struck the earth.

Cenozoic Era Since the end of the Mesozoic Era, the earth has been in the Cenozoic (SEE nuh ZOH ihk) Era. During this time, the earth's climate became cooler and drier. Several ice ages have come and gone. Humans lived on the earth for only a small part of this era.

Periods and Epochs The Paleozoic, Mesozoic, and Cenozoic Eras are divided into smaller units called **periods**. Look at Figure 4.12. It shows these divisions of time on a small part of the geologic timeline. The periods of the Cenozoic Era, in turn, are divided into epochs (EHP uhks).

Periods and epochs help scientists locate more exactly the changes and events in the earth's history. When a scientist says a fossil is from the Devonian period, for example, other scientists know how long ago the organism lived.

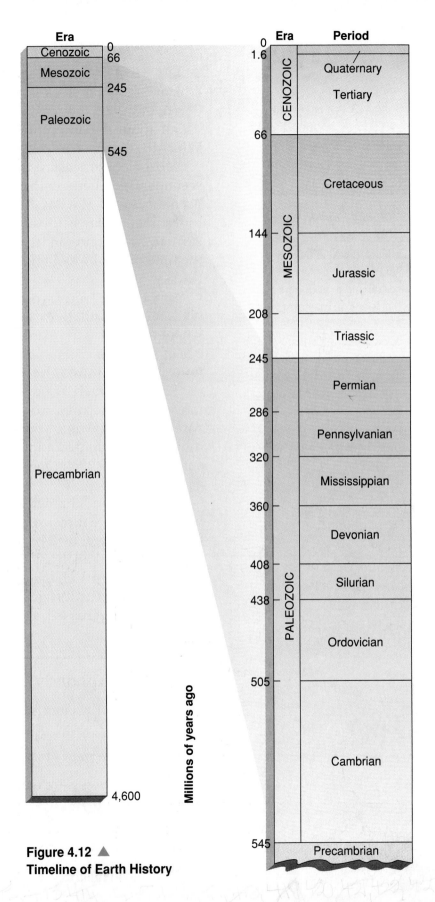

Figure 4.12 ▲
Timeline of Earth History

How do you tell time? Usually, you probably look at a clock. A clock is a mechanical or electronic device designed to measure units, or intervals, of time. Think about the different kinds of clocks you've seen. What do they have in common?

Most clocks measure time in hours, minutes, and seconds. But where do these units of time come from? An hour is 1/24 of a day. A day is defined by the earth's movement. A day is the amount of time it takes the earth to rotate once on its axis. You can get an idea of the time of day by looking at where the sun appears in the sky.

In a similar way, a year is the amount of time it takes for the earth to revolve around the sun. You know where the earth is in its revolution by the season. The age of the earth is equal to the total number of revolutions it made around the sun.

The earth, then, is the ultimate clock. The earth's movements determine how people experience and measure time. How would your life be different if the earth took half as long to complete one journey around the sun? What would change if one rotation took twice as long?

An important characteristic of a clock is that the intervals of time it measures stay the same. You trust that each day will be 24 hours and each year 365.25 days. You have this trust because the earth's rate of movement doesn't change. It would be more difficult to measure the earth's age if its revolving speed steadily increased or decreased.

▼ ACTIVITY

Observing

Something Old, . . .

Find something living or nonliving that is over 100 years old. You may find something in your home or outside. You may also look for pictures of objects in books or magazines. What evidence do you have that the object is old? How does it differ from a similar object that is much newer?

SKILLS WORKOUT

Check and Explain

1. How do earth scientists determine the relative age of rock layers?

2. What are the steps in the formation of an unconformity?

3. **Predict** If you were exploring the Grand Canyon, where would you find rocks from the Paleozoic Era?

4. **Infer** How are the fossil record and the geologic time scale related? Draw a diagram as part of your answer.

Chapter 4 Review

Concept Summary

4.1 Earth's History

▶ Geologic changes occur on a different time scale than the changes humans experience.

▶ The earth is about 4,600 million years old. This length of time is called geologic time.

▶ The sun and the earth formed from a spinning cloud of matter in space.

▶ It took over 1 billion years for the earth to form oceans, continents, and an atmosphere containing oxygen.

▶ For about the last 2 billion years, the processes of weathering, erosion, deposition, formation of sedimentary rock, and uplift have caused regular patterns of change on the earth's surface.

▶ Organisms living on the earth's surface have evolved over time. Their fossil remains have been left in layers of sedimentary rock.

4.2 Geologic Time Scale

▶ Sedimentary rocks form so that the oldest layers are below younger layers. The position of rock layers in relation to each other enables scientists to determine their relative ages.

▶ Unconformities form as a result of repeated cycles of sedimentation, sedimentary rock formation, and uplift.

▶ Geologic time is divided into four eras: the Precambrian, Paleozoic, Mesozoic, and Cenozoic.

Chapter Vocabulary

geologic time (4.1)	erosion (4.1)	fossil (4.1)	period (4.2)
weathering (4.1)	deposition (4.1)	era (4.2)	

Check Your Vocabulary

Use the vocabulary words above to complete the following sentences correctly.

1. Weathered particles of rock are carried away by _____ .

2. Geologic time is divided into four large units called _____ .

3. You can find the remains of ancient organisms, or _____ , in layers of sedimentary rock.

4. The buildup of sand on the bottom of a lake is an example of _____ .

5. The age of the earth is the length of time called _____ .

6. An era is divided into smaller units of time called _____ .

7. Rocks are broken down through the process of _____ and the particles are carried away by erosion.

Explain the difference between the words in each pair.

8. period, epoch

9. weathering, erosion

10. deposition, sediments

11. geologic time, relative age

Write Your Vocabulary

Write sentences using the vocabulary words above. Show that you know what each word means.

Chapter 4 Review

Check Your Knowledge

Answer the following in complete sentences.

1. How did oceans form in the early part of the earth's history?

2. What do fossils show about the organisms that lived long ago?

3. How do layers of sediment become rock?

4. What kinds of inferences can earth scientists make by observing layers of sedimentary rock?

5. Name four forces that cause erosion.

6. What geologic process creates elevated landforms that can be eroded?

7. Where on the earth are sediments commonly deposited?

Choose the answer that best completes each sentence.

8. Wearing-down processes include (deposition, uplift, formation of sedimentary rock, erosion).

9. The uppermost layer of sedimentary rock is (younger than, older than, the same age as, denser than) the layers of rock below it.

10. If geologic time were compressed into 24 hours, a human life span would be measured in (minutes, seconds, fractions of a second, hours).

11. Life has existed on the earth since the (Mesozoic, Cenozoic, Paleozoic, Precambrian) Era.

12. You live in the (Paleozoic, Mesozoic, Cenozoic, Precambrian) Era.

13. A fossil is (older than, the same age as, younger than, not related to) the rock layer in which it is found.

Check Your Understanding

Apply the concepts you have learned to answer each question.

1. If you could travel back in time, why would you not want to go back too far into the earth's past?

2. What do unconformities tell earth scientists about the earth's history?

3. How is geologic time different from time as you normally experience it?

4. **Application** Anne hasn't cleaned out her locker all year. Where will she find papers from the beginning of school? What is her locker modeling?

5. **Critical Thinking** Why are epochs used to measure geologic time in the Cenozoic Era but not in the other eras?

6. You find fossils of sea shells in rocks near the top of a mountain. Explain all the geologic processes that resulted in the fossils ending up in this location.

7. **Predict** Rivers carry large amounts of eroded sediments into the oceans. Predict what will happen to a river's sediments when a dam is built on the river.

8. The early earth has been compared to the moon as it is now. Explain the similarities on which this comparison is based.

9. **Application** You explore two mountain ranges. One has tall, jagged peaks. The other is lower and more rounded. Which mountain range is likely to be the older one? Why?

10. **Mystery Photo** The photograph on page 74 shows a bird fossil from the Tertiary period. It was discovered in Wyoming. What kinds of information might this fossil provide to scientists studying the earth's history?

Develop Your Skills

Use the skills you have developed in this chapter to complete each activity.

1. **Interpret Data** Study the graph below, which shows the decrease in the elevation of a mountain range over time due to erosion.

   a. How many million years does it take for the elevation to change from 3 km to 2 km? How long does it take to change from 2 km to 1 km?

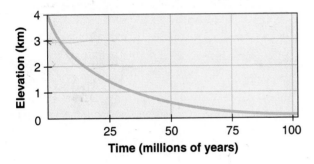

   b. Describe how the rate of erosion of the mountain range changes over time.

   c. Explain why a mountain range would erode more slowly the older it became.

2. **Data Bank** Use the information on page 612 to answer the following questions.

   a. Which epoch lasted the longest in the Cenozoic Era? How long did it last?

   b. How many millions of years ago did the Eocene epoch begin?

3. **Hypothesize** Fossils from the Precambrian Era are rare. In comparison, Paleozoic fossils are common. Suggest several explanations.

Make Connections

1. **Link the Concepts** Below is a concept map showing how some of the main concepts in this chapter link together. Only part of the map is filled in. Complete the map, using words and ideas from the chapter.

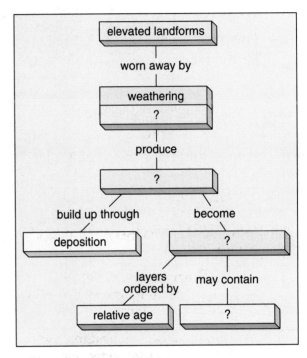

2. **Science and Technology** Do library research on the greenhouse effect. Write a report describing how global warming may affect the environment and human society over the next 50 years.

3. **Science and Geography** Go to places where you can see the landforms around your community. Then write a description of how you think the area looked 10 million years ago.

4. **Science and Social Studies** Find out how time is thought of in the traditions of Native Americans. How do Native-American concepts of time differ from yours?

Chapter 5

Plate Tectonics

What do you see?

❝I see a volcano eruption with lava flowing into the water and cooling off rapidly. A volcano must have erupted nearby because of the lava. Pressure and underground heat make it erupt. Volcanoes usually occur on or around plate boundaries.**❞**

Julie Lehman
Sequoyah Middle School
Edmond, Oklahoma

To find out more about the photograph, look on page 110. As you read this chapter, you will learn about the plates that make up the earth's crust.

5.1 Drifting Continents

Objectives

▶ **Describe** how the continents moved over the past 250 million years.

▶ **Explain** the evidence supporting continental drift.

▶ **Make a model** of the supercontinent Pangaea.

▼ **ACTIVITY**

Observing

A Puzzling World

Look at a globe or map of the world. Study the shapes of the continents closely. What do you notice about the shapes of the continents on opposite sides of the Atlantic Ocean?

SKILLS WARMUP

Hundreds of years ago, the first accurate maps were made of the continents on both sides of the Atlantic Ocean. Many people who looked at the maps noticed something interesting about the shapes of the continents. It seemed as if Africa and South America could fit together like pieces of a jigsaw puzzle. The coastlines of Europe and North America made a good match, too, if Greenland filled a gap between them.

This observation suggested that the continents on either side of the Atlantic Ocean were once joined. Few people, however, took the idea seriously. How could the continents have moved? They were solid rock! Yet a few scientists dared to suggest that this movement, or continental drift, had actually happened.

Theory of Continental Drift

During the 1800s, scientists studying rocks and fossils found bits of evidence that seemed to support the idea of moving continents. In the early 1900s, Alfred Wegener, a German meteorologist, collected all this evidence and made observations of his own. In 1912, he proposed the first complete, scientific theory of continental drift. He claimed that all the world's landmasses had once been joined in a giant supercontinent he called **Pangaea** (pan JEE uh).

For many years, most scientists rejected Wegener's theory. But in the 1950s, scientific ideas about the structure of the earth's crust began to change completely. Because of new discoveries, continental drift began to seem possible. Scientists soon agreed that the continents had moved as Wegener proposed.

Figure 5.1 ▲
Do you think that the two landmasses shown here were connected at one time?

The Breakup of Pangaea

From years of study, scientists collected large amounts of data on how the continents moved. From this information, they pieced together a history of the continents. They now have a good idea of how Pangaea split up and how the parts became the present-day continents. The maps you see in Figure 5.2 show how the earth's landmasses changed over the last 250 million years.

Pangaea began to break apart across its middle during the Mesozoic Era, about 200 million years ago. Two major continents formed: a southern continent called Gondwanaland (gahnd WAH nuh LAND) and a northern continent called Laurasia (lawr AY zhuh).

About 135 million years ago, Gondwanaland began to break up into smaller pieces that would become Africa, South America, Antarctica, India, and Australia. By about 40 million years ago, Laurasia had broken apart, forming landmasses that would become North America, Europe, and most of Asia. A little later, India, which was drifting north for 100 million years, finally collided with Asia. How have the earth's continents changed since then? Do you think they will change in the future?

Figure 5.2 Stages in Continental Drift ▼

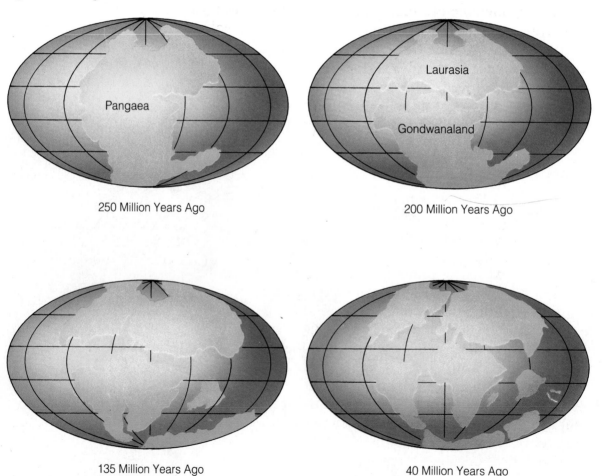

250 Million Years Ago

200 Million Years Ago

135 Million Years Ago

40 Million Years Ago

Evidence for Continental Drift

Why are scientists now sure that the continents moved over time? They collected much evidence supporting two related conclusions:

▶ Continents now separated by wide oceans were once joined.

▶ Since the Mesozoic Era, each continent's location on the earth's surface changed.

Fossil Evidence Scientists know that a new kind of organism, or species, appears on the earth only in one area and then spreads outward. Animals that swim and plants with windblown seeds can spread across an ocean. Many other living things, however, can only spread across land.

Paleontologists found fossils of an ancient fernlike plant called *Glossopteris* in South America, Africa, India, Australia, and Antarctica. The seeds of *Glossopteris* are too heavy to have blown across oceans by wind. Scientists infer from this evidence that all these continents were connected at one time.

Fossils of several other species have the same pattern, as you can see in Figure 5.3. None of these organisms could spread across an ocean. So how did the organisms end up on different continents? They must have lived on one large continent that later broke up.

Fossil evidence also shows that the continents moved over the earth's surface. Antarctica now lies at the South Pole, covered with ice. But fossils found there show that it once supported vast green swamps and forests full of plant and animal life. This evidence suggests that Antarctica was once much closer to the equator.

Figure 5.3 Fossil Evidence for Continental Drift ▼

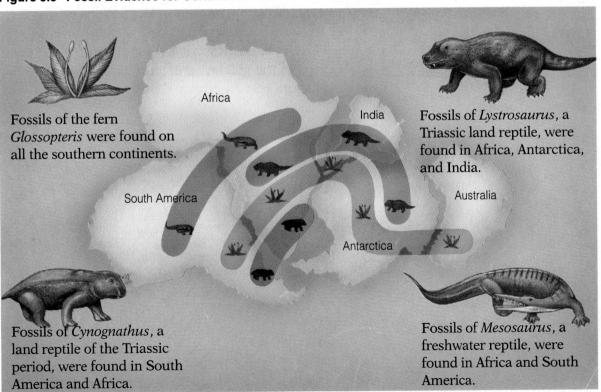

Fossils of the fern *Glossopteris* were found on all the southern continents.

Fossils of *Lystrosaurus*, a Triassic land reptile, were found in Africa, Antarctica, and India.

Fossils of *Cynognathus*, a land reptile of the Triassic period, were found in South America and Africa.

Fossils of *Mesosaurus*, a freshwater reptile, were found in Africa and South America.

Africa

India

South America

Australia

Antarctica

Figure 5.4

Present-day evidence for glacial movement is shown on the left. The hypothesized position of the continents during the time of glaciation is shown on the right. ▼

Rock Evidence   Geologists studying South America and Africa found many similarities in the rocks and landscapes of the two continents. On both continents, for example, there are mountain ranges formed by folding of the crust. If the two continents are fitted together, the two mountain ranges line up. In addition, the mountains in South America are made up of rocks similar in age and type to those in Africa. Scientists hypothesize that the two mountain ranges were once one. They formed when Africa and South America were connected as part of Gondwanaland.

Evidence from Ancient Glaciers   Glaciers are huge masses of ice that move slowly over land. During the ice ages, glaciers spread outward from the poles. Rocks found in parts of South America, Africa, India, and Australia all show evidence of glaciers at the end of the Paleozoic Era. For these places to have glaciers, they had to be closer to the South Pole.

The rocks also show the direction in which the glaciers traveled. These directions are shown by arrows in Figure 5.4. You can see that in most cases the ice-age glaciers moved away from present-day oceans. This doesn't make sense because glaciers always move toward oceans. The movement of the ice-age glaciers could be explained, however, if Africa, South America, India, Australia, and Antarctica were all part of the same landmass when the glaciers existed. Figure 5.4 shows how the glaciers spread outward on Gondwanaland.

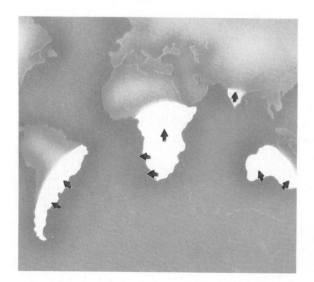
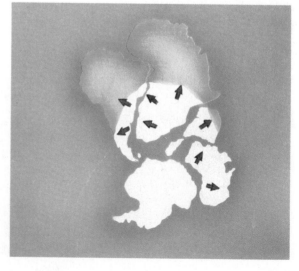

Science and Society *Accepting New Ideas*

In 1923, Alfred Wegener traveled to the United States to present his theory of continental drift to other scientists. Most of the people who heard his talks refused to accept his ideas. In fact, many scientists thought he was crazy! One earth scientist exclaimed, "Wegener . . . is blind to every fact and argument."

Why did scientists react this way? It was probably because Wegener's ideas were not only new, they were upsetting. At that time, the idea that the continents were solidly anchored in the earth's crust was very important. Much of the knowledge scientists had about the earth was understood in terms of this idea. If the continents had drifted, it meant that many facts had to be questioned and many theories thrown out. Accepting the idea of continental drift was something like believing that space aliens control the earth!

Most scientists, therefore, did not look at Wegener's evidence objectively. They had already decided that the continents could not move. They rejected any evidence that suggested otherwise.

Many other scientists have had experiences similar to Wegener's. The astronomer Copernicus, for example, proposed in 1543 that the sun was the center of the solar system. Scientists at that time believed the planets and sun revolved around the earth. They refused to consider the evidence and reasoning behind Copernicus' theory. The theory contradicted much of what they believed to be true about the universe. Only with time was Copernicus proved correct.

▼ **ACTIVITY**

Reasoning by Analogy

Is It True?

Recall a time when someone told you that something you believed to be true, wasn't really true. How did you react? How was your reaction similar to the way scientists reacted to Wegener's theory?

SKILLS WORKOUT

Check and Explain

1. Which present-day continents or pieces of continents were once part of Gondwanaland?

2. List two types of evidence that support the idea of continental drift.

3. **Predict** What will happen to the size of the Atlantic Ocean during the next 50 million years?

4. **Make a Model** Paste a map of the world on heavy paper. Cut out the landmasses and fit them together to form the supercontinent Pangaea.

Moving Plates

Use a dictionary to find the meaning of the words *plate* and *tectonic*. Based on the definitions, explain what you think the two words mean together. What do you think the theory of plate tectonics is about? Do you think using a dictionary is enough to get a good idea about the theory of plate tectonics?

SKILLS WARMUP

5.2 Theory of Plate Tectonics

Objectives

▶ **Describe** the process of sea-floor spreading.

▶ **Identify** different types of plate boundaries.

▶ **Explain** what happens where plates come together.

▶ **Infer** from observation of a large surface feature what kind of plate boundary process produced it.

Have you ever wondered what lies at the bottom of the ocean? Imagine what you would see if you could travel into the cold, dark depths of the ocean in a submarine and shine lights on the bottom. Would it be flat? Or would it have valleys and mountains like the continents?

Until the 1950s, scientists could only guess about the deep ocean bottom. It was impossible to explore and map this large part of the earth's crust. To understand the crust's structure, they had to rely on their knowledge of continents. They didn't know that the key to understanding continental drift lay on the ocean floor.

Ocean-Floor Discoveries

In the 1950s, scientists finally had the tools they needed to learn about the ocean floor. One of the most important tools was sonar. Sonar devices bounced sound waves off the ocean bottom, providing scientists with data about its topography.

Scientists used sonar and other tools to make the first reliable maps of the ocean floor. They discovered long underwater mountain ranges. These ranges formed one long ridge snaking through all the oceans like the seams of a baseball. This mid-ocean ridge had one remarkable feature: a deep valley running the length of its crest.

Scientists found that the rocks of the ocean bottom were very young compared to rocks in the continents. They also discovered that the rocks were youngest near the mid-ocean ridge. Scientists puzzled over this new information.

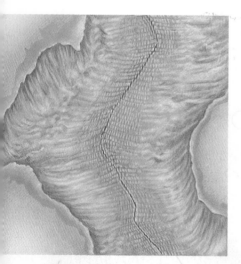

Figure 5.5 ▲
Discovery of the mid-ocean ridge helped scientists understand continental drift.

Sea-Floor Spreading

In 1960, American geologist Harry Hess proposed the theory of **sea-floor spreading** to explain these discoveries about the ocean floor. He claimed that the mid-ocean ridge was a huge crack in the crust where the hot mantle pushed upward. The pieces of crust on each side of the crack were moving slowly away from each other. As they moved, molten rock from the mantle welled up between them, forming new ocean crust. This spreading process is shown in Figure 5.6.

At the same time, old ocean crust was being swallowed up in deep ocean trenches. In this way, the total amount of oceanic crust stayed the same. The ocean bottoms were remade every 300 million years or so.

Other scientists soon provided convincing evidence for Hess' theory. They sampled rocks on both sides of the mid-ocean ridge. They found a pattern of parallel magnetic "stripes" that was identical on each side. This striping pattern is shown in Figure 5.7. The stripes were formed when the earth's magnetic field caused mineral crystals in rocks to line up in a certain way when the rock was still young and not yet solid. The stripes were different because the earth's magnetic field reversed itself many times in the past. The stripes showed that new ocean crust was being added to both sides of the mid-ocean ridge at the same rate.

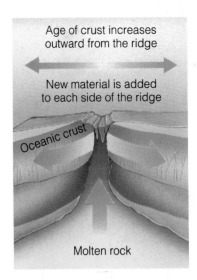

Age of crust increases outward from the ridge

New material is added to each side of the ridge

Oceanic crust

Molten rock

Figure 5.6 ▲
New crust is produced at the mid-ocean ridge.

Figure 5.7
When new rock is formed at the mid-ocean ridge, it is affected by the polarity of the earth's magnetic field at that time. The resulting patterns are evidence for sea-floor spreading. ▼

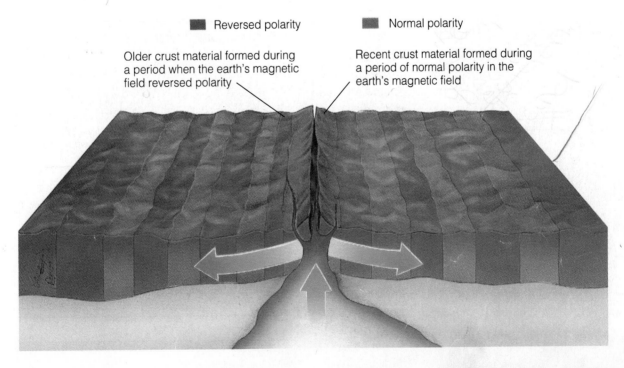

■ Reversed polarity   ■ Normal polarity

Older crust material formed during a period when the earth's magnetic field reversed polarity

Recent crust material formed during a period of normal polarity in the earth's magnetic field

Tectonic Plates

Sea-floor spreading was the missing piece of information scientists needed to accept the theory of continental drift. It provided a way for pieces of the crust to move. With this new knowledge, scientists had to develop a new model of the structure of the earth's crust.

The new model that arose came to be known as the theory of **plate tectonics** (tehk TAHN iks). According to the theory, the entire lithosphere of the earth is divided into pieces called plates. The plates are constantly moving, each at a different rate and direction. Because the plates are parts of the lithosphere, they are often called lithospheric plates.

Recall that the earth's lithosphere is a cool, rigid layer about 100 km thick on average. It sits atop the asthenosphere, a hot layer of partially molten rock. A lithospheric plate moves as a unit, "floating" on top of the asthenosphere like a flat rock on wet cement.

SkillBuilder *Interpreting Data*

Magnetic Patterns on the Ocean Floor

Using the data in the table, make a scale map of magnetic striping on the ocean floor. Place the mid-ocean ridge in the center of the map at distance zero. On each side of the ridge, make a scale in kilometers. Then color in areas where you think the rocks will show normal magnetic alignment and reversed magnetic alignment. Remember that each side of the ridge has the same pattern.

Now use the data to calculate the rate at which the ocean floor spreads. The formula for this is

$$\text{rate} = \frac{\text{distance}}{\text{time}}$$

From the table, choose four measurements. Calculate the rate of spread in km/million years for each. Record each number. Average these four values.

1. What is the average rate of ocean-floor spreading at this mid-ocean ridge?

2. Convert your average rate to cm/year.

3. The distance from a point on the coast of Africa to the mid-ocean ridge is 2,500 km. How long ago was that point at the ridge?

Write a report explaining how magnetic polarity on the ocean floor supports the plate tectonic theory.

Distance from Ridge (km)	Magnetic Polarity	Age (millions of years)
6.5	Normal	0.5
7.7	Normal	0.6
10.0	Reversed	0.8
20.5	Reversed	1.6
24.5	Normal	1.9
28.5	Reversed	2.2
29.6	Reversed	2.3
34.0	Normal	2.6

The Structure of Plates

Each lithospheric plate is made up of both crust and mantle. However, there are two different kinds of crust: oceanic and continental. Oceanic crust material is mainly made up of two types of rock: basalt and gabbro. Continental crust is less dense, made up mainly of granite and rhyolite. The earth's lithospheric plates can be classified according to the kinds of crust they contain.

Continental Plates   The earth has seven major plates, six of which are continental plates. Continental plates carry mostly continental crust material and consist of one continent and a large section of oceanic crust. In the bottom part of Figure 5.8 you can see a diagram of a typical continental plate.

The continental crust material of a continental plate can be in the center of a plate or at one side. Some continental plate edges, therefore, have both oceanic and continental crust. This kind of edge interacts with other plates differently than an edge made up of oceanic crust alone.

Oceanic Plates   One major plate and several smaller ones are oceanic plates. They contain little or no continental crust material. They are made up entirely of oceanic crust, as you can see in Figure 5.8.

▼ **ACTIVITY**

Making a Model

A Mountain of Plates

Use sheets of foam, corrugated cardboard, clay, or other materials to make models of an oceanic plate and a continental plate. How does your model distinguish among the different layers making up each plate? If you use a combination of materials, explain why your materials are appropriate for the layers they represent.

SKILLS WORKOUT

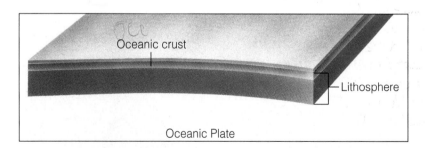

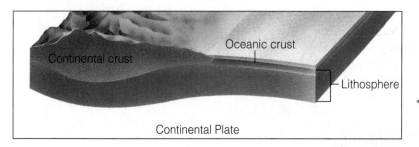

◀ **Figure 5.8**
What is the difference between the two types of tectonic plates?

Plate Boundaries

What happens where plates meet? Three kinds of interactions are possible at plate boundaries. Plates can move away from each other, they can collide, and they can slide past each other. To picture the interaction of plates, imagine yourself riding in a bumper car at the amusement park. You may collide with other cars in front and move away from cars behind you. And you may slide past or be bumped by cars on the side. What actually happens is determined not just by how you move, but by how all the other cars move too. The earth's lithospheric plates interact in a similar way, except that each plate is always in contact with other plates on all of its sides. Most plates have all three types of boundaries around them.

Divergent Boundaries

Any boundary where plates move away from each other is called a **divergent boundary**. These are places where new crust is being created. The mid-ocean ridges are all divergent boundaries. Divergent boundaries also occur in continents, where they signal the beginning of the continent's breakup. ▼

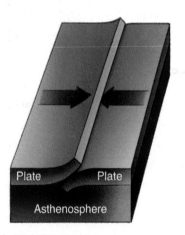

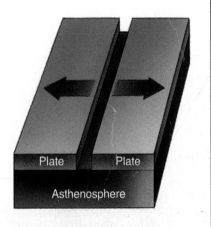

Convergent Boundaries ▲

A boundary where two plates come together, or collide, is called a **convergent boundary**. At most convergent boundaries, one plate moves under another, and crust material is destroyed. Convergent boundaries produce many different kinds of features on the surface of the earth.

Transform Boundaries

At the third type of boundary, two plates slide in opposite directions beside each other. Such a boundary is called a **transform boundary**. Crustal material is not created or destroyed along a transform boundary. The break or crack along which movement occurs is called a transform fault. ▼

Convergent Boundaries

The collision of two plates releases huge amounts of energy. This energy causes many important geologic processes to take place at and near convergent boundaries. These processes include volcanic activity and mountain building. What occurs at a particular convergent boundary is determined by the kinds of plates that meet there. Three kinds of convergent boundaries exist.

Oceanic-Oceanic Where two oceanic plates meet, one plate is pushed down under the other. This process of one plate moving under another is called **subduction** (suhb DUHK shuhn). It takes place in what is called a subduction zone.

As you can see in Figure 5.9, the lower, or subducting plate, descends into the asthenosphere. There it melts and is absorbed into the mantle. The melting of the subducting plate causes molten rock to rise up through the other plate. Volcanoes form on the ocean bottom and build a chain, or arc, of volcanic islands. As the subducting plate sinks into the earth, it also creates a deep ocean valley, or **trench**. Trenches are the deepest parts of the ocean.

Oceanic-Continental Subduction also occurs where an oceanic plate meets a plate with continental crust material. Because the oceanic plate is denser, it is always subducted under the continental plate. The oceanic plate melts in the asthenosphere, causing molten rock to rise up through the continental plate. A mountain range forms, usually containing volcanoes.

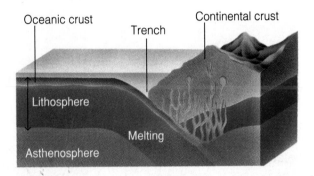

Figure 5.10 ▲
An oceanic plate is subducted under a less-dense continental plate.

Continental-Continental A third and very different process occurs where two continental plates collide. Because both are thick and have similar densities, neither can move under the other. Instead, they compress and buckle each other, forming tall mountains. The plates become joined in a single continental block.

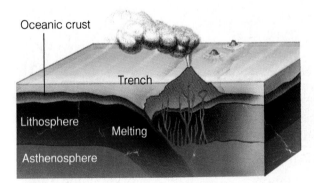

Figure 5.9 ▲
Where two oceanic plates converge, one is subducted under the other.

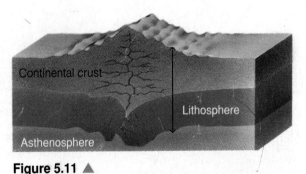

Figure 5.11 ▲
Where two continental plates converge, both buckle, producing a mountain range.

Plate Geography

The movement and location of plates helps explain many of the earth's features. Movement at plate boundaries creates mountain ranges, forms ocean basins, makes continents grow, and splits them apart. It causes earthquakes and volcanoes. The earth's tectonic plates and the boundaries between them are shown below.

Figure 5.12 ▶
Tectonic Plates of the Earth

The volcanic activity at the convergent boundary of a continental plate and an oceanic plate produced the Aleutian Islands of Alaska.

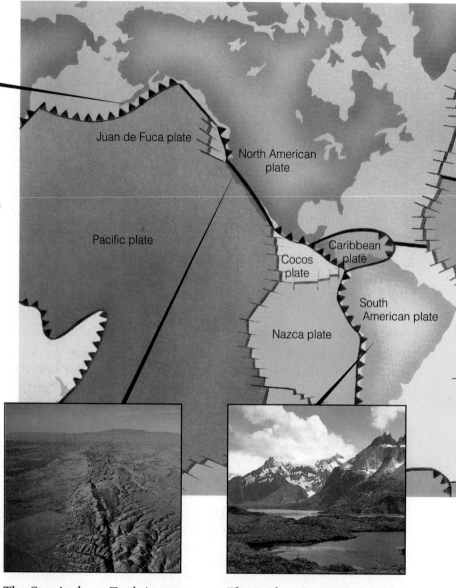

Juan de Fuca plate

North American plate

Pacific plate

Caribbean plate

Cocos plate

South American plate

Nazca plate

Key

Divergent plate boundaries

Convergent plate boundaries

Transform plate boundaries

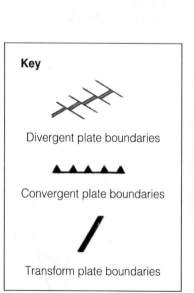

The San Andreas Fault is one of the few transform boundaries on land. Its movement causes severe earthquakes.

The Andes Mountains were built as a result of the Nazca plate subducting under the South American plate.

Plate Movement

The very slow movements of the plates are detected and measured by certain instruments. Scientists have determined the speed and direction of most of the earth's plates. They used this information to reconstruct the locations of the plates in the past and to predict their locations in the future.

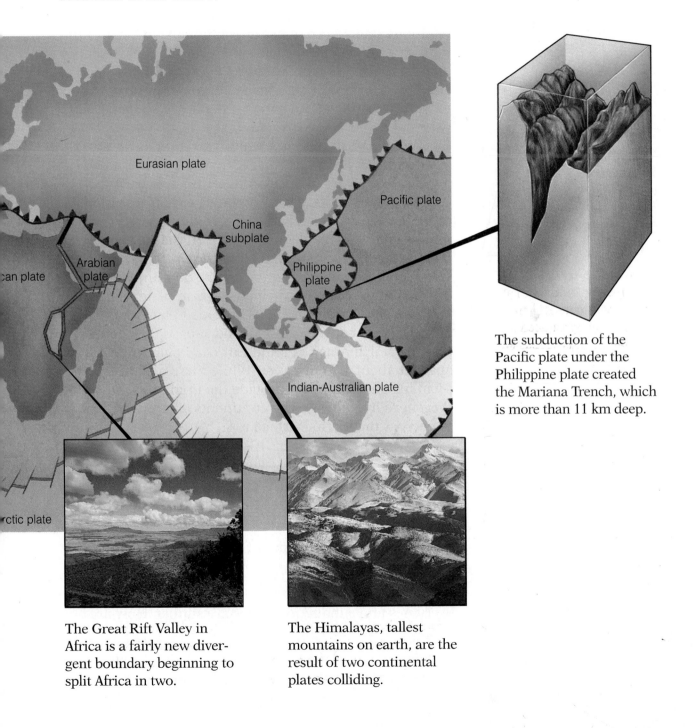

Eurasian plate

China subplate

Pacific plate

Arabian plate

Philippine plate

can plate

Indian-Australian plate

rctic plate

The subduction of the Pacific plate under the Philippine plate created the Mariana Trench, which is more than 11 km deep.

The Great Rift Valley in Africa is a fairly new divergent boundary beginning to split Africa in two.

The Himalayas, tallest mountains on earth, are the result of two continental plates colliding.

Science and Technology
Measuring Plate Movement

Figure 5.13 ▲
Radio telescopes collect data that are used to measure plate movement.

From the time that Alfred Wegener proposed his hypothesis of continental drift, scientists have searched for new and better ways to find out about movement of the earth's crust. You may be surprised to know that some of the most useful data about this movement was collected with the help of signals from deep in space.

Today scientists can use a technique known as VLBI to make very precise measurements of the earth's shape and the motion of its plates. VLBI stands for very long baseline interferometry. This technique uses radio signals from distant stars, known as quasars, to help scientists make their measurements.

To make VLBI measurements, two stations far apart on the earth's surface receive signals from the same quasar. Using very precise atomic clocks, scientists compare the signals. The tiny differences from when the signals are received are converted into a precise measurement of the distance between the stations. By making these measurements at different times, very small changes in the distance can be determined.

VLBI measurements helped confirm plate tectonics theory. Using VLBI, scientists observed plate motion of 8.3 cm a year between Hawaii and Japan. They found that the North American and Eurasian plates move apart at about 1.7 cm a year. While these distances may seem insignificant, they provide the final proof of Wegener's hypothesis. The continents are, indeed, drifting across the earth's surface.

Check and Explain

1. What happens during sea-floor spreading?

2. Describe the three types of plate boundaries, and give an example of each.

3. **Compare and Contrast** Explain how mid-ocean ridges and subduction zones are similar. How are they different?

4. **Infer** Japan is made up of a long chain of islands formed from volcanoes. What kind of plate boundary do you think is nearby? Why?

Activity 5 *What happens at a divergent boundary?*

Skills Model; Observe; Infer

Task 1 Prelab Prep

1. Collect the following items: shoe box, metric ruler, scissors, white paper, two wide-tip markers in different colors.
2. Cut two identical strips of white paper, each 7 cm wide by 30 cm long.
3. Cut an 8 cm-long slit in the bottom of the shoe box. Look at Figure 5.14 to see how it should look.

Task 2 Data Record

1. Title a separate sheet of paper *Model of a Divergent Plate Boundary*.
2. Use this data sheet to record all your observations about the model you create.

Task 3 Procedure

1. Put the two strips of paper together and push one end through the slit in the box.
2. Place the shoe box bottom-up as shown in Figure 5.14. Let about 5 cm of the paper strips stick out of the slit.
3. Separate the strips and hold each one down against the surface of the box as shown.
4. Take one of the markers and mark across the paper strips where they come out of the box. Make sure each strip gets colored with a stripe about 1 cm wide.
5. Pull the strips evenly so that another 1 cm comes out of the slit on each side.
6. Use the second marker to color all the new white paper now visible above the slit. On your data sheet, describe what is happening in the model.
7. Repeat steps 5 and 6 until both strips of paper are pulled out of the box. Use a different color marker each time.
8. When you're done, draw on your data sheet a picture of how the strips appear.

Figure 5.14 ▲

Task 4 Analysis

1. What part of the earth do the construction paper strips represent?
2. What do the markers represent? What do the different colored stripes on the paper strips represent?
3. What part of the earth does the slit in the box represent?
4. What type of plate boundary did you model?
5. How does your model differ from the actual movement of plates at this type of boundary?

Task 5 Conclusion

Write a short report explaining how your model shows that oceanic crust is created. Discuss how it models the creation of magnetic patterns in the rock of the ocean floor. Describe how the actual earth differs from the model that you built.

Extension

Create models for the different kinds of convergent plate boundaries. Use different materials if you think they will work better.

5.3 Physics of Plate Movement

ACTIVITY

Generalizing

Convey the Concept

Describe how a conveyor belt works. Make a list of where conveyor belts are used. What happens to objects placed on a conveyor belt?

SKILLS WARMUP

Objectives

▶ **Describe** two models of how convection occurs in the earth's mantle.

▶ **Explain** how a tectonic plate may move as part of a convection cell.

▶ **Evaluate** models explaining plate movement by convection.

▶ **Compare** and **contrast** two models for how convection results in the movement of the plates.

Fifty years after Alfred Wegener presented his theory, the scientific community came to accept the idea of moving continents in the form of plate tectonic theory. Since then, earth scientists collected more and more information about plates. They know how fast plates move, which directions they move in, and how they interact at boundaries. However, even today, one question remains only partly answered: What is the driving force that moves the plates?

Convection in the Mantle

The question is partly answered because earth scientists do know that the driving force has something to do with movement within the mantle. Recall that heating of rock material within the partially melted zone of the mantle causes the material to move in a circular motion, the movement called convection. It occurs in circular units of movement called convection cells.

Although most earth scientists agree that convection causes plate movement, there is no agreement on exactly how convection occurs in the mantle. Earth scientists have two basic models. Look at Figure 5.15. In the model shown on the right side, convection occurs mainly in the asthenosphere. In the model shown on the left, the convection cells are much larger. They include the entire mantle. There is strong evidence for both models.

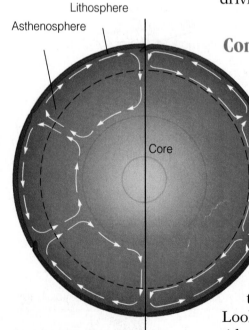

Figure 5.15 ▲
This diagram shows two different models describing how convection occurs inside the earth.

Lithosphere
Asthenosphere
Core

Models for Plate Movement

Earth scientists also disagree about how convection moves the plates. In one model proposed, the plates are carried along by the movement of convection. In other words, the plates are like passengers on giant conveyor belts. Where convection pushes material upward, divergent boundaries form. Where convection goes downward back into the mantle, convergent boundaries form. Many earth scientists still think this is the best model for explaining plate movement.

According to a newer model, the plates themselves have an active role in convection. Each plate is thought to be part of a convection cell. Because a plate is cooler and more dense than the hot asthenosphere below, it tends to sink. Its sinking in a subduction zone "pulls" the rest of the plate down, helping create the circular movement of convection. Scientists observed a similar process in pools of molten lava.

Consider This

Should Geothermal Power Plants Be Built?

Geothermal energy is another name for the earth's internal heat. Geothermal energy can be used to produce electricity for human use. In geothermal power plants, steam from water heated deep in the earth moves turbines connected to electric generators.

Geothermal power has some advantages. Unlike coal and oil, geothermal energy is constantly renewed. Compared to the cost of electricity made by burning coal or oil, geothermal power is inexpensive. Many possible geothermal sites could be developed.

There are limits to the usefulness of geothermal power. Only a few geothermal power plants have been built so far. But even if all geothermal sites were used, the power would only supply a small amount of our energy needs.

Also, geothermal power has some drawbacks. For example, the hot water contains minerals and toxic metals that must be disposed of. Toxic hydrogen sulfide gas, which smells like rotten eggs, is also released in the steam.

Think About It Is geothermal power a good alternative to burning coal and oil? Should geothermal energy be used more than it is now?

Write About It Write a paper stating your position for or against building geothermal power plants.

you dumbass
why you listen
to me.
Do your fuckin
work Bitch

You have probably had direct experience with convection without even knowing it. For example, when you take a shower, cold air blows into your warm environment under the bottom of the shower curtain. The invasion of the cold air is caused by a convection current. The hot water heats the surrounding air in the shower. The hot air rises and escapes through the opening above the shower curtain. Denser, colder air replaces the warm air by entering under the shower curtain. A convection cell is created.

Rooms in your home may be heated by convection, too. Warm air enters the room through a heating vent or a radiator. The warm air rises. Colder air moves in to take its place and is heated by the radiator or heating vent. A convection current forms that moves heat throughout the room.

As in the mantle, convection also moves matter in liquids. For example, if you place a pan of water on the stove, convection heats the water. Look at Figure 5.16. The heat from the stove burner transfers to the bottom of the pan. Water at the bottom of the pan becomes hot and decreases in density. The hot water moves upward. Cold, denser water moves downward. The convection cell created in the pan spreads heat throughout the water, until all the water is heated equally.

Convection moves heated matter in both liquids and gases. In your home, there are many places where liquids and gases become heated. Where are some places where convection cells may form in your home?

Figure 5.16 ▲
Next time you heat water on the stove, watch for convection.

Check and Explain

1. What are two models for convection in the mantle?

2. If convection cells in the mantle are like conveyer belts, what are plates like?

3. **Evaluate** Which model do you think best explains how convection moves the plates? Explain the reasons for your choice.

4. **Compare and Contrast** What are the similarities and differences between the two major models explaining how convection causes plate movement?

Chapter 5 Review

Concept Summary

5.1 Drifting Continents
▶ Alfred Wegener proposed the first scientific theory of continental drift.
▶ 250 million years ago, the continents were joined in the supercontinent Pangaea and have since drifted apart.
▶ The theory of continental drift is supported by evidence from fossils, land formations, and glacial movement.

5.2 Theory of Plate Tectonics
▶ Sea-floor spreading occurs at the mid-ocean ridge, where molten material from the mantle forms new crust.
▶ The theory of plate tectonics states that the entire lithosphere is divided into moving pieces called plates.

▶ The earth has seven major plates and several smaller plates. The plates are classified as continental plates or oceanic plates.
▶ Plates meet at divergent, convergent, and transform boundaries.
▶ Different kinds of convergent boundaries create ocean trenches, volcanic islands, and mountain ranges.

5.3 Physics of Plate Movement
▶ Convection in the mantle causes plate movement.
▶ According to two different models, plates are either carried along by convection, or they are parts of convection cells.

Chapter Vocabulary

Pangaea (5.1)   sea-floor spreading (5.2)   plate tectonics (5.2)
divergent boundary (5.2) convergent boundary (5.2)   transform boundary (5.2)
subduction (5.2)   trench (5.2)

Check Your Vocabulary

Use the vocabulary words above to complete the following sentences correctly.

1. At the mid-ocean ridge, ____ occurs because of the welling up of molten material from the mantle.

2. The process of one plate moving under another is ____.

3. Any plate boundary where the plates move away from each other is called a ____.

4. All of the earth's landmasses were once joined in the supercontinent ____.

5. A plate boundary where two plates slide past each other is a ____.

6. The theory of ____ states that the lithosphere of the earth is divided into moving pieces.

7. When a plate is subducted, a deep ocean valley, or ____, is formed.

8. A plate boundary where two plates come together is called a ____.

Explain the difference between the words in each pair.

9. convergent boundary, divergent boundary

10. subduction zone, trench

11. lithosphere, tectonic plate

Write Your Vocabulary

Write sentences using the vocabulary words above. Show that you know what each word means.

Chapter 5 Review

Check Your Knowledge

Answer the following in complete sentences.

1. What is the theory of continental drift?

2. How does the age of rocks found at the bottom of the ocean compare to the age of rocks found on the continents?

3. How did scientists prove that sea-floor spreading occurs?

4. List the three kinds of convergent boundaries.

5. Explain the two models proposed for how convection moves plates.

6. What two continents were formed when Pangaea broke apart? During which era of geologic time did this occur?

7. How do the marks left by ancient glaciers provide evidence for continental drift?

8. List the three ways in which plates can interact with one another.

9. What landforms can result when two plates meet at a convergent boundary?

Determine whether each statement is true or false. Write *true* if it is true. If it is false, change the underlined term to make the statement true.

10. The present-day continents of Africa, South America, Australia, India, and Antartica were once joined as the continent of <u>Laurasia</u>.

11. Tectonic plates "float" on the <u>lithosphere</u>.

12. The density of oceanic crust is <u>greater than</u> the density of continental crust.

13. The mid-ocean ridges are all <u>subduction</u> boundaries.

Check Your Understanding

Apply the concepts you have learned to answer each question.

1. Discuss the evidence that scientists gathered to support the theory of continental drift. Why is it important to have more than one type of evidence?

2. Discuss how the theory of plate tectonics relates to the theory of continental drift.

3. Which type of plate boundary formed each of the following?

    a. Mariana Trench

    b. Himalaya Mountains

    c. San Andreas fault

    d. Andes Mountains

4. If new oceanic crust is constantly being added to the sea floor, why is the earth not getting larger?

5. **Critical Thinking** Why does continental crust material always stay at or near the surface of the earth?

6. **Application** The Ural Mountains are a very old mountain range separating Europe and Asia. Suggest a way in which they might have formed.

7. **Calculate** If the plates on which Hawaii and Japan sit are moving toward each other at the rate of 11 cm a year, how much closer will these two places be 1 million years from now?

8. **Mystery Photo** The photograph on page 90 shows molten lava from a volcanic eruption pouring into the sea. What might be one cause for the release of molten rock at the earth's surface? Predict what type of landform this lava might form after many years.

Develop Your Skills

Use the skills you have developed in this chapter to complete each activity.

1. **Interpret Data** The table below shows the rate of movement between certain locations on the earth's surface. A negative number means the distance between the two places is shrinking.

Locations	Movement (cm/year)
Hawaii—Japan	−11
Hawaii—Alaska	−4
Florida—Germany	+1
Florida—Sweden	+1
Alaska—California	−8

   a. How fast are Hawaii and Alaska moving toward each other?

   b. How many years will it take for Florida and Sweden to move 1 km farther apart?

   c. Using these data and a world map, infer whether California and Japan are moving toward each other or away from each other.

2. **Data Bank** Use the information on page 619 to answer the following questions.

   a. Give the location and magnitude of four major earthquakes.

   b. Use a world map to locate where ten major earthquakes have occurred. Explain the relationship between their locations and plate boundaries.

Make Connections

1. **Link the Concepts** Below is a concept map showing how some of the main concepts in this chapter link together. Only part of the map is filled in. Finish the map, using words and ideas from the chapter.

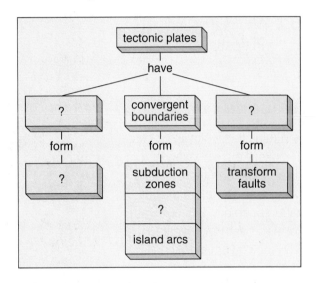

2. **Science and Art** Make a flip book that illustrates continental movement from Pangaea to the present. Obtain a dozen small pieces of paper the same size. On one piece of paper, draw Pangaea. On another piece of paper, draw the continents in their current location. On the other pieces of paper, draw separate moments in the movement of the continents, using Figure 5.2 as a guide. Stack the papers in order, and staple them together at one end. Flip through the pages to see the movement of the continents through time.

3. **Science and Society** Through library research, find out what happened when the Italian astronomer Galileo claimed that the sun, not the earth, was the center of the solar system. How was Galileo similar to Wegener?

Chapter 6

Movement of the Crust

Chapter Sections

6.1 Folding and Faulting

6.2 Mountains and Plateaus

What do you see?

"I think this looks like rocks. It looks like a side view of a large rock formation. It looks very neat. There are a lot of different colors. I think it was formed over many years. The rock layers slowly built up because of powerful forces in the earth."

Emily Vella
The MacDuffie School
Springfield, Massachusetts

To find out more about the photograph, look on page 130. As you read this chapter, you will learn about forces that change the earth's surface.

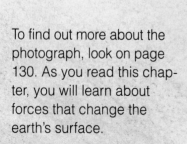

6.1 Folding and Faulting

Objectives

▶ **Identify** three types of stress that deform the crust.

▶ **Describe** three types of folding.

▶ **Distinguish** between normal, reverse, and lateral faults.

▶ **Make a model** showing how stress affects different materials.

▼ **ACTIVITY**

Observing

Does It Stack Up?

1. Make a stack of about 20 half-sheets of construction paper.

2. Hold the stack in both hands and apply force to the edges in different ways.

3. Describe the different ways you can get the stack to bend.

SKILLS WARMUP

Imagine you're a piece of rock lying quietly inside the earth's crust. Things would be pretty boring if you experienced the passage of time the way you do now. But if you were very patient, and if a million years were like a single day, you would experience all sorts of changes. You might be tilted, even turned upside down. Neighboring rocks might slide past you. Or they might squeeze you from two sides. You might even be stretched out and broken into pieces.

The rocks and rock layers that make up the earth's crust undergo similar changes all the time. Usually the change is very, very slow. But it produces mountains, valleys, and other features that make the earth's varied topography.

Change in the shape or structure of the earth's crustal material is called **deformation**. Deformation includes bending, folding, breaking, sliding, and tilting. Often you can see evidence of past deformation at the surface of the earth.

Deformation of the Crust

How can something as solid and hard as rock bend and break? Rocks in the earth's crust are subjected to enormous forces. Many of these forces are related to the movement of tectonic plates. In addition, parts of the crust have high temperatures and pressures. These conditions can make rocks behave differently than you might expect.

Under certain conditions, many rocks become *ductile*; that is, they can change shape without breaking. Rocks may also simply break or crack when the stress

Figure 6.1 ▲
These rock layers have been both tilted and broken.

Figure 6.2

Three basic types of stress act on the rocks of the crust. ▼

on them is great enough. The physical properties of each kind of rock and the surrounding conditions determine how it will be affected by the forces acting upon it.

Recall that much of the earth's crust is made up of layers of sedimentary rock. Each layer formed at a different time during the earth's history. When first formed, each layer was usually flat, horizontal, and of even thickness. Deformation of this layered structure produces patterns that earth scientists can recognize. They can infer from the patterns what kind of deformation occurred. The patterns can also help scientists determine how landforms were produced.

Crustal Stresses

The forces acting on the rocks of the crust are forms of what earth scientists call *stress*. Stress causes rocks to move and to change shape and volume. Three main types of stress are at work in the crust.

One type of stress is **compression**. Compression is the squeezing together of rocks. The second type of stress is **tension**. Tension is the stretching, or pulling apart, of rocks. The third type of stress is **shear**. Shear is the pushing of rocks in different horizontal directions. Compare the different types of stress in Figure 6.2. What changes in the rock do you think each type of stress can produce?

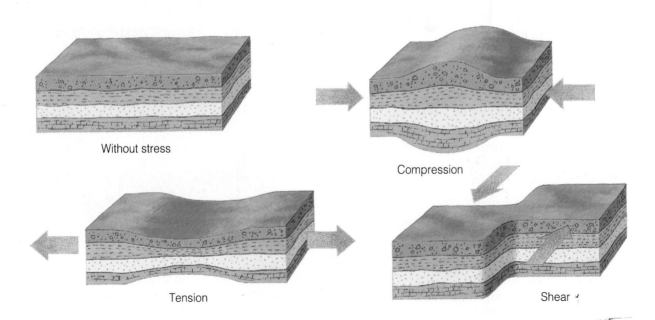

Without stress

Compression

Tension

Shear

Folding

Place a blank sheet of paper on your desk. Push forward on one end of the paper while a partner pushes on the other end. What happens? By applying compressional stress, you created a kind of fold. Layers of rock often behave similarly. Folding of rocks is a result of compressional stress.

Compression can cause either folding or breaking of rock. Compressed rocks tend to fold rather than break when they are under high temperature or pressure. Under these conditions, rocks are more ductile. Rock type also affects whether folding will occur. Folds in rocks range in size from microscopic to as large as a mountain. Whatever their size, folds can be divided into three basic types.

Monocline ▶

The simplest fold has only one bend. Rock layers on one side of the bend are higher than on the other side. This fold is a **monocline** (MAHN oh klyn), which is similar in shape to a sliding board in a playground.

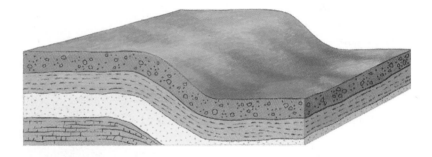

◀ **Anticline**

A fold producing an upward bulge is an **anticline** (ANT ee klyn). The center part of an anticline is higher than either edge. Often, however, the raised center part of an anticline is worn away by erosion.

Syncline ▶

A fold producing a downward bulge is a **syncline** (SIHN klyn). The center part of a syncline is lower than either edge. So that you're not confused by the different names, remember a *sync*line as something that "sinks."

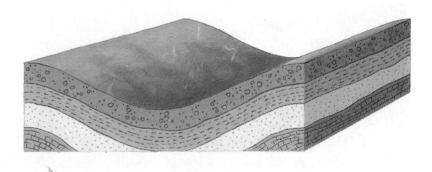

Folded Sheets

Collect newspaper, water, and soil for a model you will construct outdoors.

1. Cut the newspaper into several 25 by 35 cm sheets.

2. Use the water to moisten the soil and the newspaper.

3. Construct a layer cake, alternating layers of wet newspaper with 1 to 2 cm-thick layers of moistened soil.

4. Compress these layers from two sides.

What happens? Can you form both anticlines and synclines?

SKILLS WORKOUT

Figure 6.3 ▶
Erosion changes folds in characteristic ways (right). How can you tell this landscape (bottom) was produced by folding? ▼

Folded Topography

Much of the earth's crust has been folded at one time or another, often in complex ways. Synclines and anticlines may be combined together. Folds can be pushed on top of other folds, and a group of small folds can become part of a much larger fold.

Folds, however, are not always visible at the surface. They may be eroded or covered by newer layers of rock or sediment. Together, folding and erosion produce a great variety of landforms and features, including mountains, valleys, jagged ridges, and rounded hills. Look at Figure 6.3. How is the folded surface changed by erosion? What evidence is left of the original folding?

Many parts of the crust have been gently folded into a rolling landscape of anticlines and synclines. Anticlines form long hills or ridges. Synclines form low areas called basins. Over time, anticlines erode to reveal the upward-tilting rock layers.

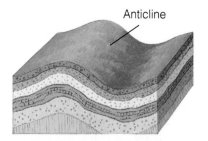
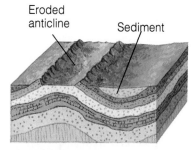

Faulting

Stress can cause rocks to break, or fracture. Fracturing occurs as a result of tension or shear. Fracturing also happens under certain conditions when the stress is compressional. A fracture becomes a **fault** when the rocks on either side of the fracture move in relation to each other. Much deformation of the crust occurs through the process of faulting. Faulting can transform horizontal stress into vertical movement.

Faults vary in many ways. To make them easier to classify, earth scientists named their parts. The fracture line of a fault is called the *fault plane*. The fault plane may slope at any angle from horizontal to vertical. Look at the fault in Figure 6.4, and find the fault plane. When the fault plane is inclined, or at any angle other than vertical, there is rock above it and below it. The rocks above the fault plane form the *hanging wall*. The rocks below the fault plane form the *footwall*. Two of the main types of faults are distinguished by the direction the hanging wall moves in relation to the footwall.

Figure 6.4 ▲
The hanging wall is on the upper side of the fault plane, and the footwall on the lower side.

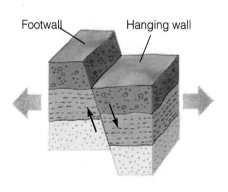

Normal Fault ▲
When the hanging wall moves downward in relation to the footwall, the fault is a **normal fault**. Normal faults occur when the stress is from tension. The fault plane in a normal fault is usually steeply inclined.

Reverse Fault
When the stress is from compression, the hanging wall moves upward in relation to the footwall. The result is a **reverse fault**. If the hanging wall rides up and over the footwall, it is called a *thrust fault*. ▼

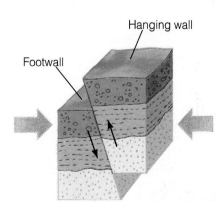

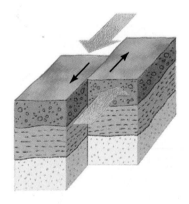

Lateral Fault ▲
Shear stress causes side-to-side movement, resulting in a **lateral fault**. Unlike normal and reverse faults, there is little or no up-and-down movement along a lateral fault. In addition, the fault plane of a lateral fault is usually vertical.

Studying Faults

Earth scientists are very interested in faults because they help form some of the earth's most important surface features. In many areas, faulting is the major force shaping the crust and the surface topography. By studying faults, earth scientists can learn how blocks of the crust moved in the past. The main principle earth scientists follow in studying faults is that a fault is always younger than the rock it passes through.

Often, upward-moving blocks are no higher in elevation than downward-moving blocks because of erosion. In addition, the blocks on each side of the fault may be tilted in such a way that past movement is hard to determine by looking at the surface. In such cases, earth scientists must rely on the relative positions of the rock layers on each side of a fault to infer how the fault has moved.

Figure 6.5 ▲
The structures produced by fault movement are not always easy to interpret.

SkillBuilder *Inferring*

Interpreting Faults

Faults are geologic puzzles. The relative positions of rock layers on each side of a fault provide clues for inferring how the rocks have moved. Study the diagram at the right, and then answer the following questions:

1. Which layers in the diagram match up?

2. Where is the fault plane? How can you tell?

3. Which layers make up the hanging wall? The footwall?

4. Which direction is the hanging wall moving? Which direction is the footwall moving?

5. What kind of fault is this?

6. Which layer above the fault plane is the oldest? The most recent?

7. Why doesn't layer E match up with any other

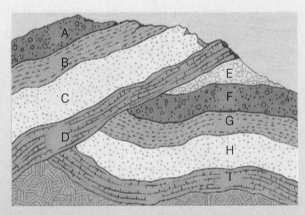

layer shown?

8. What kind of deformation occurred here besides faulting?

In one or two paragraphs, explain what happened to the rock layers in the diagram. Include a description of what the rock layers looked like before the faulting occurred.

Science and Society   *Faulty Theories*

Faults in the crust and the stress caused by plate movement create much of the earth's varied topography, such as hills, mountains, and valleys. Today this idea is logical and easy to understand. However, it has been accepted for less than 100 years. Before then, many other theories were proposed to explain the formation of different landforms.

In the 1600s, most people believed that the earth's landforms were created in one terrible event, or catastrophe. Thomas Burnet, a clergyman, suggested that mountains were the result of a giant flood. He believed that the earth was a smooth shell before the flood. When the shell cracked apart, it released water that covered the surface. Mountains were the pieces left from the cracks in the shell.

In the 1800s, the shrinking earth theory became popular. The shrinking earth theory was proposed by James Dwight Dana, a geology professor at Yale University. Dana thought the earth had once been a hot ball of semimolten rock. As the earth cooled, it shrank and created wrinkles on the surface. The wrinkles were the earth's mountains. His idea was easily demonstrated by observing the wrinkles formed on the skin of an apple as it dried.

These two theories remained popular for many years. After earth scientists better understood the structure and age of the earth, these theories were discarded. Faulty theories may remain popular only until new theories are backed by a great amount of evidence.

▼ ACTIVITY

Inferring

A One Time Deal

What observations and evidence might have convinced people that the earth's landforms were all formed during one catastrophic event? Explain.

SKILLS WORKOUT

Check and Explain

1. Describe the three types of stress that can deform rocks in the crust.

2. What is an anticline? How does it differ from a syncline?

3. **Compare and Contrast**   How are normal, reverse, and lateral faults similar? How are they different?

4. **Make a Model**   Find a substance that will fold when you apply compression. Use layers of it to make a model of folding in the earth's crust.

Activity 6 How does stress cause movement along faults?

Skills Model; Observe; Measure; Interpret
Data; Infer

Task 1 Prelab Prep

1. Collect the following items: sheet of corru-
    gated cardboard, scissors, pencil, paper,
    metric ruler.
2. Cut out pieces of cardboard to match the
    five shapes in Figure 6.6. Each piece should
    be about 6 cm tall. Together they should
    form a straight line about 25 cm long.
3. Label the shapes with letters as shown in
    Figure 6.6.

Task 2 Data Record

On a separate sheet of paper, copy Table 6.1.
Use your copy of the table to record your observations and measurements in this activity.

Table 6.1   Models of Movement Along Faults

Type of Faulting	Length at Start	Length after Movement
Normal faulting		
Reverse faulting		

Task 3 Procedure

1. On a flat surface, fit the cardboard pieces
    together as shown in Figure 6.6. Move the
    pieces together to remove all gaps.
2. Measure the total length of the assembled
    pieces, from the left edge of the first *A* piece
    to the right edge of the last *A* piece. Record
    this measurement in both boxes of the first
    column of your data table.
3. Model normal fault movement by sliding all
    three *A* pieces down about 1 cm in relation
    to the *B* pieces.
4. Measure the total length of the assembled
    pieces, and record this measurement in your
    data table.

5. Model reverse fault movement by sliding all
    three *A* pieces up about 1 cm in relation to
    the *B* pieces.
6. Measure the total length of the assembled
    pieces, and record this measurement in your
    data table.

Figure 6.6 ▼

Task 4 Analysis

1. How did the length of the assembled pieces
    change when you modeled normal fault
    movement? What kind of stress would pro-
    duce this change in length?
2. How did the length of the assembled pieces
    change when you modeled reverse fault
    movement? What kind of stress would pro-
    duce this change in length?
3. What results would you get using cardboard
    pieces shaped as squares?

Task 5 Conclusion

Write a short paragraph explaining how tension
and compression can produce up-and-down
movement in blocks of the earth's crust. Include
an explanation of the importance of the angle of
the fault planes.

Extension

Experiment with differently shaped blocks of
crust. Try making cardboard pieces that increase
and decrease the angle of the fault planes. Can
you model thrust faulting?

6.2 Mountains and Plateaus

Objectives

▶ **Identify** four mountain-building processes.

▶ **Distinguish** between folded and fault-block mountains.

▶ **Relate** mountain-building processes to different kinds of plate boundaries.

▶ **Classify** types of mountains according to how and where they formed.

▼ **ACTIVITY**

Observing

Mountain Building

Look at a globe or a map of the world. Locate mountain ranges on all seven continents. Can you detect any patterns in their shape or location? What inferences can you make about how mountains are formed?

SKILLS WARMUP

You feel like you can't take another step. The trail is steep and crumbly. You're breathing hard, and your heart is pounding. But you look up and see you're near the top. You make your legs work again and trudge on up. Finally you reach the rocky summit. You climb atop the highest rock and gaze at the world stretched out at your feet.

If you've ever climbed a tall mountain, you know the feeling of awe you get viewing the earth from such a high perch. Mountains have always had a special meaning to people. Many cultures consider mountains to be sacred places. Mountains have also been a source of valuable metal and mineral resources.

Mountain Building

Mountains are evidence that incredibly powerful forces are at work shaping the crust. What produces these forces? Forces powerful enough to raise huge blocks of rock kilometers above sea level are the result of the movement of tectonic plates. Recall that the places where tectonic plates collide are called convergent boundaries. Most active mountain building occurs at or near convergent plate boundaries. Mountains can also be produced at divergent plate boundaries.

Because it is related to plate boundaries, most mountain building happens on a huge scale. Whole mountain belts, made of many mountain ranges, are produced. If you look at a globe, for example, you can see that a mountain belt stretches all along the western edge of both North and South America.

Figure 6.7 ▲
Have you ever wondered how mountains are built?

Figure 6.8 ▲
From high up, the Appalachian Mountains look like folds in the earth's crust. This photograph was taken with special equipment sensitive to infrared light.

Folded Mountains

You just learned that folding of the crust is the result of compression. When the compressive force is very powerful, the folding is great enough to produce mountains. At what type of convergent boundary do you think this type of mountain building occurs? It happens where two continental plates collide.

Two of the world's tallest mountain ranges—the Alps and the Himalayas—were built up as a result of two continental plates colliding. Another folded mountain range is the Appalachians in North America. Notice the folds in the Appalachians shown in Figure 6.8. The Appalachians were uplifted long ago, during the Paleozoic Era, and have undergone much erosion. They are no longer at a convergent plate boundary.

Thrust faults are common in folded mountain ranges. This makes sense if you remember that both folding and thrust faulting are the result of compressional stress. Because thrust faulting pushes rocks on top of other rock layers, it helps in the mountain-building process.

Figure 6.9 ▶
In parts of the Canadian Rocky Mountains, folded rock layers are clearly visible.

Fault-Block Mountains

Tensional stress, or the stretching out of the crust, can also create mountains. This may seem impossible unless you remember that tensional stress causes up-and-down movement along a normal fault. The footwall moves upward as the hanging wall moves downward.

Look at Figure 6.11. As you can see, a block of crust may have normal faults on either side and be the footwall of both sides. This block will therefore move upward, while the two blocks of crust on either side move downward. As a result of these movements, the block of crust becomes a fault-block mountain.

In the eastern part of Africa, the crust is stretching in a somewhat narrow area along a divergent plate boundary. The result is a long *rift valley*. It is surrounded on both sides by fault-block mountains.

In the Great Basin of western North America, a wider zone of crust has stretched from east to west. Over time, the area has become wider. In fact, it is now 50 percent wider than it was 30 million years ago. As a result of this tensional stress, a series of long fault-block mountain ranges was created. Can you infer which direction these fault-block mountain ranges run?

Figure 6.10 ▲
The Grand Tetons of Wyoming are fault-block mountains.

Figure 6.11
Movement along normal faults makes some blocks of crust rise in relation to others. ▼

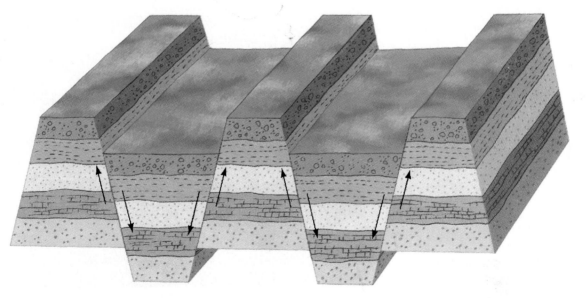

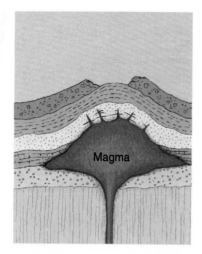

Figure 6.12 ▲

When a pool of magma collects under the surface, rock layers above are lifted. When it solidifies, the magma becomes a pluton.

Figure 6.13

Batholiths form large areas of mountain ranges in western North America (left). The Sierra Nevada batholith (right) includes many mountains rising above 3,300 m. ▼

Plutonic Mountains

Fault-block mountains and folded mountains differ in that they are caused by different types of stress. Both compression and tension, however, are horizontal forces. Another type of mountain-building process, in contrast, involves a direct vertical force. This force is the upward movement of molten material from the mantle.

Recall that one place where molten material rises through the crust is near the boundary between an oceanic and a continental plate. At this type of plate boundary, oceanic crust subducts and melts deep in the earth. This molten material then rises through the crust of the continental plate. In some places, the magma breaks the surface to form volcanoes. But much of the time, a large pool of molten rock builds up under the surface. It raises the surface above it and then solidifies, forming a *pluton*. This process is shown in Figure 6.12. Large plutons exposed at the surface by erosion are called *batholiths*.

Many mountain ranges in western North America are made up of batholiths. These include the Sierra Nevada and the Coast Ranges of British Columbia and Baja California. Locate these batholiths on the map in Figure 6.13. Uplift from plutonic activity often occurs before, during, or after other forms of mountain building. For example, a rising pool of magma may raise a folded mountain range even higher.

Volcanic Mountains

Magma reaching the surface can form another type of mountain called a volcano. Volcanoes occur at the convergent boundary formed by two oceanic plates or an oceanic and a continental plate. At both kinds of plate boundaries, entire mountain ranges are formed by volcanic activity. Because they are made by the vertical force of rising magma, volcanic mountains are similar to plutonic mountains. In fact, volcanoes are often found in mountain ranges uplifted by plutonic activity.

Volcanic mountains are often cone-shaped. Some of the world's best-known mountains, such as Mt. Fuji in Japan and Mt. Kilimanjaro in Tanzania, are volcanoes. The mountains on the Hawaiian Islands and the Aleutian Islands of Alaska are all volcanic in origin. Many earth scientists think that volcanoes created the first continents early in the earth's history. You will learn more about volcanoes in the next chapter.

Figure 6.14 ▲
Japan's Mt. Fuji is a volcanic mountain.

Career Corner *Field Geologist*

Who Infers the History of the Landscape?

Your mission is to map the geology of a remote mountain range in the desert of Nevada. You have four months to cover 100 km². You load camping supplies, shovels, picks, and hammers onto your horses and head out. You'll live in a tent most of the time, leaving your study site only a few times for supplies.

Many field geologists spend their summers this way. Their job is to observe, infer, and collect all sorts of data in the field. Their findings are then used for locating valuable resources, or simply for understanding how the varied geologic processes have shaped the crust.

Most field geologists also work in laboratories some of the time. There they analyze rock samples and other data, draw up maps, and write reports. But the focus of their work is outdoors.

Field geologists may work for oil or mining companies, government agencies, or universities. Most have advanced degrees in geology, but there are some job opportunities for people with four-year college degrees.

If you might be interested in being a field geologist, high

school courses in mathematics, physics, geology, and chemistry are good preparation. You should also practice outdoor skills such as rock climbing, camping, and map reading.

Plateaus

In many parts of the world, areas of the crust have been uplifted without forming mountains. Instead, the land has stayed relatively flat. Recall that this kind of elevated, level area is called a plateau.

There are two basic types of plateaus. The most common type of plateau is formed next to a mountain range by the same forces that produced the mountains. The largest of these plateaus include the Andean Altiplano in South America, the Tibetan Plateau in Asia, and the Colorado Plateau in North America.

The other type of plateau is formed by a flood of molten rock pouring through cracks or fractures in the earth's surface. This type of plateau is called a basalt plateau. Two of the world's largest basalt plateaus are the Deccan Plateau in India and the Columbia Plateau in the western United States.

Figure 6.16 ▲
What do you notice about the rocks in this part of the Columbia Plateau?

Because plateaus are usually made up of flat rock layers and are high above neighboring regions, they tend to erode in characteristic patterns. Streams carry away the softer material and leave the harder materials exposed as cliffs. Streams and rivers carve deep canyons.

Figure 6.15 ▲
Rivers have cut deep canyons into the Colorado Plateau.

Floating Crust

Mountains don't last forever. After their uplift stops, weathering and erosion slowly reduce their elevation. However, after erosion wears away much of a mountain range, it may be slightly uplifted again. This upward movement is the result of *isostasy* (eye SAHS teh see).

Isostasy is the balancing of two basic forces. Because the crust has mass, gravity pulls it down into the mantle. But the crust is also less dense than the mantle, giving it buoyancy. So, while gravity pulls the crust down, the force of buoyancy pushes it up. These forces balance at different points depending on the mass of the crust.

Because mountains have great mass, they sink deeper into the mantle than other parts of the crust. However, as a mountain range erodes, it loses mass. The upward force of buoyancy becomes greater, making the crust "spring back." The springing back, or rebounding, of the crust makes the mountain regain some elevation. This process is shown in Figure 6.17.

◄ **Figure 6.17 Isostasy at Work**

A newly uplifted mountain range sinks deeply into the mantle because of its great mass. Erosion begins to slowly wear it away.

After many years, erosion greatly reduces the elevation and mass of the mountain range. The upward force of buoyancy now increases.

The mountain range rises upward, once again gaining some elevation. The downward force of gravity and the upward force of buoyancy come back into balance.

Science and You *Into Thin Air*

If you travel to the top of a mountain, you may notice changes occurring in your body. Maybe your ears pop. When you try to run or walk, you may have difficulty breathing. Although these changes may seem strange, they are your body's normal response to changes in altitude. At high altitudes, air pressure is lower and the amount of oxygen in the air is less than at low altitudes.

When you go from low to high elevation, your body must adjust. Some adjustments occur quickly. Others take days or weeks. Your ears adjust quickly. There must be equal pressure on both sides of the eardrum for it to move freely. The sensation of popping ears is the ear balancing the pressures by letting some air out of the inner ear through the auditory tube.

Your body adjusts to the reduced amount of oxygen in several different ways. The first response is rapid: an increase in the rate and depth of breathing. When you breathe more quickly and more heavily, your oxygen intake increases.

A slower adjustment is the creation of more red blood cells. Since red blood cells carry oxygen, an increase in their numbers helps your other cells get the oxygen they need. Your body releases some extra red blood cells from storage areas, such as the spleen. But it also produces red blood cells at a more rapid rate. If you try to exercise at high elevation before your body is fully adjusted, you'll tire easily, and you may get dizzy.

Figure 6.18 ▲
Tibetans are adapted to living where the air contains much less oxygen than it does at sea level.

Check and Explain

1. What are four ways in which mountains can be formed?

2. How do folded and fault-block mountains differ? What do they have in common?

3. **Infer** What type of mountain is produced at a convergent boundary between two oceanic plates?

4. **Classify** In a table, classify each type of mountain by the kind of stress or force that produces it, and by the kind of plate boundary at which it is produced.

Chapter 6 Review

Concept Summary

6.1 Folding and Faulting

▶ Compression, tension, and shear are three types of stress that deform the rocks of the crust.

▶ The crust responds to stress by folding and by faulting.

▶ Folding produces monoclines, anticlines, and synclines.

▶ Faulting is a result of the fracturing and movement of pieces of crust. Depending on the type of movement that occurs along a fault, it is classified as normal, reverse, or lateral.

6.2 Mountains and Plateaus

▶ Most mountain building is related to the movement of the earth's tectonic plates.

▶ Powerful stress in the form of compression produces folded mountains.

▶ Stress in the form of tension creates fault-block mountains.

▶ Plutonic mountains are formed by the upward movement of molten rock from the mantle.

▶ Volcanic mountains are built up by molten material reaching the surface and solidifying.

▶ Plateaus can be formed by some of the same processes that produce mountains and mountain ranges.

▶ Once a mountain range loses much of its mass from erosion, it may uplift slightly because its smaller mass gives it increased buoyancy.

Chapter Vocabulary

deformation (6.1)   compression (6.1)   tension (6.1)   shear (6.1)
monocline (6.1)   anticline (6.1)   syncline (6.1)   fault (6.1)
normal fault (6.1)   reverse fault (6.1)   lateral fault (6.1)

Check Your Vocabulary

Use the vocabulary words above to complete the following sentences correctly.

1. The simplest kind of fold is a(n) _____ .

2. The force that pulls or stretches rock is _____ .

3. In a _____ , the footwall moves down in relation to the hanging wall.

4. A fold with an upward bulge is a(n) _____ .

5. Two pieces of crust move in opposite horizontal directions along a _____ .

6. Two kinds of _____ are folding and faulting.

7. When rock is stressed by _____ , folding or reverse faulting occurs.

8. The type of stress that causes movement along a lateral fault is _____ .

9. A fold with a downward bulge is a(n) _____ .

10. When rocks on either side of a fracture move in relation to each other, a _____ results.

11. In a _____ , the footwall moves up in relation to the hanging wall.

Write Your Vocabulary

Write sentences using the vocabulary words above. Show that you know what each word means.

Chapter 6 Review

Check Your Knowledge

Answer the following in complete sentences.

1. What is a fault-block mountain? How does it form?

2. In what two ways can compression deform the crust?

3. At what type of plate boundary are folded mountains produced?

4. What conditions make rock more ductile?

5. How does a plateau differ from a mountain?

6. List four types of mountain-building processes.

7. What is the difference between a monocline and an anticline?

8. When is a fracture not a fault?

9. How are plutonic and volcanic mountains similar?

Choose the answer that best completes each sentence.

10. If you're standing on a footwall, and the hanging wall in front of you has moved up, you're at a (normal, reverse, lateral, transform) fault.

11. One way mountains are built up by a direct upward force is through (folding, volcanic activity, faulting, erosion).

12. A thrust fault is a type of (normal, transform, lateral, reverse) fault.

13. A rift valley is produced as a result of (tension, compression, folding, movement of lateral faults).

14. A mountain range sinks deep into the mantle because of its (mass, size, elevation, buoyancy).

Check Your Understanding

Apply the concepts you have learned to answer each question.

1. Why do anticlines and synclines occur together?

2. What kind of plate boundary would you expect to produce a lateral fault?

3. Why do thrust faults occur in folded mountain ranges? Suggest a way in which a fold could become a thrust fault.

4. Explain why a mountain range may be uplifted slightly after much of its mass has been eroded.

5. **Critical Thinking** Why does mountain building usually occur at the edge of a continent? Why are most mountain ranges much longer than they are wide?

6. Explain how tensional stress can cause up-and-down movement of the crust.

7. **Critical Thinking** Some areas of land that were covered by thick glaciers during the last ice age are now slowly rising in elevation. Explain why this may occur.

8. **Application** What kinds of evidence would you look for to determine if the crust where you live had been folded at some time in the past? What kinds of evidence would you look for to find a fault?

9. **Mystery Photo** The photograph on page 112 shows folded layers of rock in Death Valley, California. What type of stress produced these folds?

Develop Your Skills

Use the skills you have developed in this chapter to complete each activity.

1. Read a Map The map below is a view from above of three faults separating four blocks of crust. The direction of stress on each block is shown by the arrows.

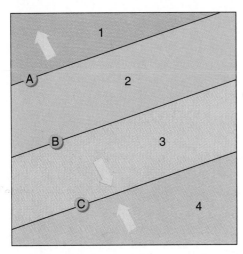

a. What type of fault is A? What type is C? Is fault B the same type as A or C?

b. How does the elevation of block 2 compare to that of block 3? Explain your reasoning.

c. How would these faults appear viewed from the side, in cross section? Draw a diagram that illustrates the information on the map.

2. Data Bank Use the information on page 618 to answer the following questions.

a. What is the world's tallest mountain? What is its elevation? In what mountain range is it found?

b. What is the tallest mountain in North America? How does its elevation compare to that of the tallest mountain in the world?

Make Connections

1. Link the Concepts Below is a concept map showing how some of the main concepts in this chapter link together. Only part of the map is filled in. Finish the map, using words and ideas from the chapter.

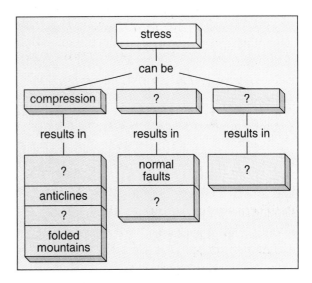

2. Science and Social Studies Do library research to find out about the people who live high in the Andes Mountains of Ecuador or Peru. How does the high elevation affect their lifestyle, culture, and food crops?

3. Science and Geography Is there a mountain range near where you live? If so, observe its shape and relationship to the surrounding land. Infer how it formed. Then do research to find out which mountain-building processes contributed to its formation.

4. Science and Writing Write a short story about a long trip during which you explore new places with different landscapes. Use as many vocabulary words from this chapter as you can to describe the landscape and how it was formed.

Chapter 7

Earthquakes and Volcanoes

What do you see?

66This picture is lava flowing from a nearby volcano or volcano spout. The tremendous heat and pressure under the volcano force this lava out onto the earth's surface. The lava or magma (as it is called when it is underground) can cause vast changes in the earth's appearance. The Hawaiian Islands were all formed by lava like this. The next day this place probably looked like a mass of black rock, just like the Hawaiian Islands.99

Derek Smiley
Patrick Henry Middle School
Sioux Falls, South Dakota

To find out more about the photograph, look on page 152. As you read this chapter, you will learn about volcanoes and earthquakes.

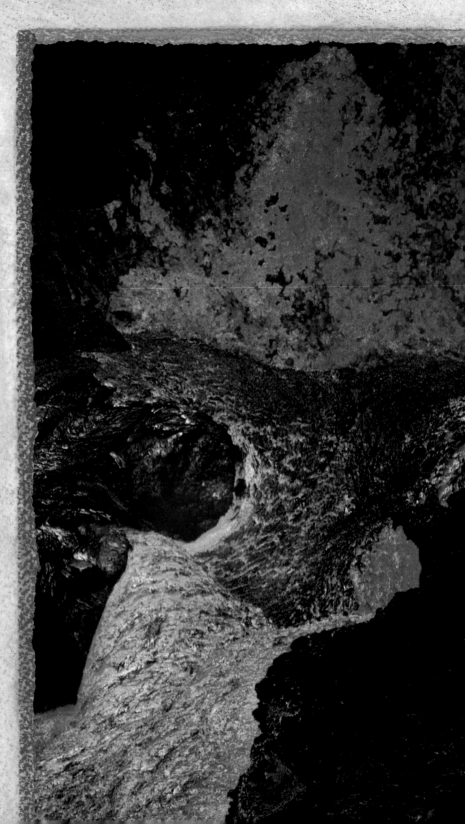

7.1 Earthquakes

Objectives

▶ **Describe** what happens during an earthquake.

▶ **Explain** the difference between an earthquake's focus and epicenter.

▶ **Compare** and **contrast** the three types of waves produced by earthquakes.

▶ **Infer** the number of seismograph stations needed to locate an earthquake's epicenter.

Imagine you and a friend are standing on a sidewalk. Suddenly the pavement seems to move under your feet. You grab your friend to avoid falling. In front of you, a streetlight sways wildly. You feel dizzy and scared. Neither of you has experienced this before, but you both yell, "Earthquake!"

In less than a minute, the shaking stops. You and your friend look at each other with relief. You feel a small earthquake later that day, but it passes almost before you notice it. As the days go by, you begin to forget the terrifying feeling of the earth moving. Yet you often find yourself wondering when the next earthquake will strike. You also find yourself curious to know why earthquakes occur.

Energy of Earthquakes

Movements of the earth's crust that occur when plates shift and release stored, or potential, energy are called **earthquakes**. The energy quickly travels outward in waves from the point of breakage. The energy of an earthquake can break and move rock and soil. Most earthquakes occur at depths less than 100 km, where rocks are brittle.

Earthquakes can be dramatic events, or they can be so small that most people don't notice them. Most earthquakes result from movements of the earth's crust along faults. As you learned in Chapter 6, a fault is a fracture in the earth's crust. The two sides of a fault move in different directions. These opposing movements set the stage for earthquakes to occur.

Figure 7.1 ▲
In 1989, the Loma Prieta earthquake in California caused the collapse of this building in San Francisco.

▼ ACTIVITY

Making Analogies

Making Waves

Briefly describe the movement of the waves in the following situations:

1. A pebble drops into a puddle.

2. A string is pulled on one end and the other end is loose.

3. A spring scale is held and a heavy object is attached to the bottom of the spring. Which situation is most like a P wave? S wave? L wave?

SKILLS WORKOUT

Figure 7.2
Earthquake Epicenter ▼

Physics of Earthquakes

In Chapter 6, you learned about the types of force, or stress, in the earth's crust. These forces are at work along faults. They cause the two sides of a fault to move past each other. Sometimes the rocks along the two sides of a fault may snag and remain locked. Tremendous stress builds in these areas as the two sides of the fault attempt to move past each other.

The limit to how much stress a material can absorb is called its *elastic limit.* For example, if you stretch a rubber band too far, it will break and snap back. When rocks are strained beyond their elastic limit, the rocks break and grind past each other, releasing huge amounts of energy.

Look at Figure 7.2. As the rocks break and move, potential energy is transformed into kinetic energy in the form of **seismic waves**. Recall that seismic waves are the vibrations produced by earthquakes. Earthquakes produce three main types of seismic waves: primary, secondary, and surface.

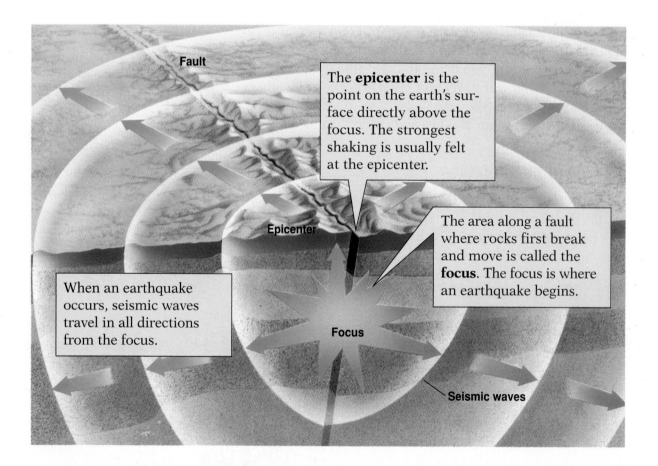

Fault

The **epicenter** is the point on the earth's surface directly above the focus. The strongest shaking is usually felt at the epicenter.

Epicenter

The area along a fault where rocks first break and move is called the **focus**. The focus is where an earthquake begins.

When an earthquake occurs, seismic waves travel in all directions from the focus.

Focus

Seismic waves

Primary waves, or P waves, are the fastest seismic waves. P waves are *longitudinal waves*. Figure 7.3 shows the movement of a longitudinal wave. In a longitudinal wave, the material through which the wave is traveling moves in the same direction as the wave. P waves compress and stretch the earth in the direction of the wave.

The second waves to arrive at a given point are secondary waves, or S waves. S waves are *transverse waves*. You can see how a transverse wave moves in Figure 7.3. It is similar to the up and down movement of a rope wave. In a transverse wave, the material moves at right angles to the wave direction.

P waves and S waves travel from the focus, through the earth's interior. Waves that travel along the surface are called L waves. L waves cause the most damage during an earthquake because they cause the earth's surface to move up and down or side to side.

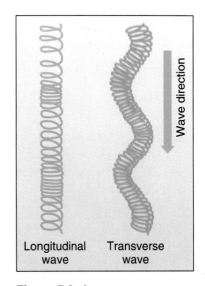

Figure 7.3 ▲
Which wave represents the movement of a P wave? An S wave?

Detecting Seismic Waves

You have learned that seismographs are used to detect and record seismic waves. The seismograph, shown in Figure 7.4, has a pen attached to a weight and a sheet of paper on a revolving drum. Seismic waves from earthquakes cause the pen to vibrate and record a wavy line on the paper as the drum revolves. The height of the peaks of the wavy line indicates the strength of the earthquake. Notice the pattern in the seismograph's record below.

Figure 7.4
Study the printout at left. It shows seismic wave activity from the Landers earthquake in southern California. The earthquake was recorded on June 2, 1992. ▼

Locating an Epicenter

Because P, S, and L waves travel at different rates, they reach a seismograph at different times. The difference between the arrival times of the waves enables scientists to find the epicenter's distance from the seismograph.

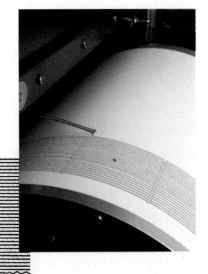

Figure 7.5 ▲

The epicenter is the point at which the three circles intersect.

The calculated distance to the epicenter becomes the radius of a circle that is then plotted on a map. The epicenter lies somewhere on the circle. As shown in Figure 7.5, plotting circles from three different seismograph stations pinpoints the epicenter.

Rating Earthquakes

The strength of an earthquake, or its magnitude, is often described in terms of numbers on the Richter scale. The *Richter magnitude* is based on the amount of shaking caused by an earthquake. On the scale, each increase of 1 magnitude number equals an increase of 10 in ground motion caused by seismic waves. A magnitude 7 earthquake causes 10 times more ground motion than a magnitude 6 and 100 times more than magnitude 5.

Earthquakes are also rated on the Mercalli intensity scale. This scale is based on earthquake intensity, which includes ground motion and damage.

SkillBuilder *Reading a Table*

Comparing Earthquake Scales

The Mercalli scale and the Richter scale for rating earthquakes are based on different factors. The Richter scale is based on energy released by an earthquake, whereas the Mercalli scale is based on personal observations of earthquake intensity.

The table shows a rough relationship between the two scales. Study the table, then answer the following questions:

1. How are the two scales similar? How are they different?

2. What occurs during a Richter magnitude 8.0 earthquake? What is the measurement for the same quake on the Mercalli scale?

3. At which measurement on each scale does damage to buildings begin?

4. Why are two different scales used for measuring earthquakes?

Measurement		Earthquake Effects
Richter Scale	**Mercalli Scale**	
3	III	Felt slightly in areas near epicenter, no damage
4	V	Felt by most people up to several miles from earthquake, some objects upset
5	VI–VII	Strongly felt, some damage to weak buildings
6	VII–VIII	Moderately destructive, some severe damage to weak buildings
7	IX–X	Major earthquake, destructive to many buildings
8	XI–?	Very destructive, some structures destroyed

Earthquake Zones

Some parts of the earth's crust are more stable than others and have few, if any, earthquakes. Other regions are under enormous stress and have many quakes. Figure 7.6 shows that most of the world's earthquakes occur along or near the edges of plate boundaries, where stress is greatest.

The earth has three major earthquake zones. The most active of these zones is the Ring of Fire, shown in Figure 7.6. It accounts for 80 percent of the world's seismic activity. The Ring of Fire extends nearly all the way around the Pacific Ocean and includes the eastern coast of Asia, and the western coasts of North America and South America. Along the ring, some plates are being subducted. In a subduction zone, one plate is forced under another plate. Some plates along the ring are scraping past each other. In the United States, the most active earthquake region is in Alaska along the volcanoes of the Aleutian Islands. Another very active earthquake region is California.

The other main earthquake zones are the mid-Atlantic ridge and the Mediterranean-Asiatic belt. Scientists hypothesize that new ocean crust is being created along the mid-Atlantic ridge, causing the region's many earthquakes. Along the Mediterranean-Asiatic belt, continental plates are colliding, often causing very destructive earthquakes.

A small number of the world's earthquakes occur far from plate boundaries. For example, some of North America's strongest quakes have struck the eastern United States. These include the New Madrid, Missouri, quakes of 1811 and 1812 and the Charleston, South Carolina, quake of 1886. The activity in Missouri and South Carolina shows that even quiet parts of the earth's crust may conceal large amounts of stress.

Figure 7.6
Major Earthquake Zones ▼

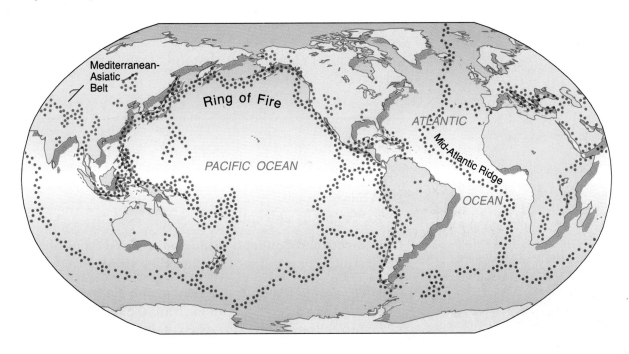

Shaky Ground

Use resources at your school's library to research historically strong earthquakes. Make a line graph to illustrate the magnitudes of the ten most powerful earthquakes of the twentieth century. Identify the earthquakes by their epicenter. How many of these earthquakes occurred in the earth's major earthquake zones?

SKILLS WORKOUT

Physical Science
L I N K

As fault blocks slide past each other, they may lock or stick together due to friction along the fault. Collect the following items: 2 shoe boxes, 10 wide rubberbands, glue, and scissors.

1. Cut the rubberbands into 2 to 5 cm pieces. Glue the pieces to the bottoms of the shoe boxes. Allow glue to dry.

2. With a partner, press the bottoms of the shoe boxes together, sliding the boxes past each other with differing amounts of effort.

How much effort was needed to move the "blocks" past each other? How strong was the force of friction along your "fault"?

A C T I V I T Y

Science and Technology
What Fault Is This?

In 1983, a Richter magnitude 6.7 earthquake struck Coalinga, California. Coalinga is midway between Los Angeles and San Francisco. The earthquake surprised seismologists for three reasons. First, though the area's geology had been studied as a result of oil drilling, no active faults had been mapped. Second, there was no recorded history of any large quakes in the area. Third, studies showed no sign of hidden faults capable of large quakes. Yet a large quake struck Coalinga. In fact, the damage from the quake was so great that it was easier to tear down many buildings than to repair them.

How could the Coalinga earthquake have happened? Should residents expect future tremors? Many scientists studied damage to buildings. They examined the oil wells in the area. They also searched the town's historical records. They hoped to find evidence of previous earthquakes in the area.

The work of seismologists, geophysicists, and others finally revealed the truth. Several faults exist 6 to 10 km beneath Coalinga. The faults had not been detected because they are deeper than the deepest oil wells. Also, the faults are hidden by folds. Many geologists were surprised that active faults could be hidden in folds.

In the end, the scientists' investigations found that the Coalinga faults are not very active. They concluded that future earthquakes are more likely to occur on more active faults, such as the San Andreas. But the events in Coalinga are a reminder that unknown faults can surprise residents and scientists alike.

Check and Explain

1. Explain what causes earthquakes.

2. What is the difference between an earthquake's focus and its epicenter?

3. **Compare and Contrast** How do the three types of seismic waves differ? How are they similar?

4. **Infer** Would using four seismograph stations to locate the epicenter of an earthquake be any more accurate than using three? Explain.

Activity 7 *How can you model the Richter scale?*

Skills Model; Infer

Task 1 Prelab Prep
1. Collect the following items: three blocks of wood with the following relative sizes: $3 \times 3 \times 3$ cm, $3 \times 3 \times 15$ cm, $3 \times 3 \times 25$ cm; piece of cardboard large enough to hold the blocks; masking tape; pencil.
2. Place the cardboard on a desk or table. Be sure the desk is level.
3. With the tape, label the longest block *1*, the medium-sized block *5*, and the smallest block *9*.
4. Place the three blocks on the cardboard with the long side facing up.

Task 2 Data Record
1. On a separate sheet of paper, copy Table 7.1.
2. In the data table, record all your observations and measurements about the movement of the blocks.

Task 3 Procedure
1. Move the cardboard to create a gentle shaking for 5 seconds.
2. Record any observations about the blocks.
3. Repeat the gentle shaking for about 65 seconds. Record your observations.

4. Repeat steps 1 through 3 and carefully use moderate force and violent force to shake the blocks.

Task 4 Analysis
1. Identify the variables in this activity.
2. Which block was the hardest to knock down? The easiest?
3. Which had a greater impact on the blocks, the length of the shaking or the strength of the shaking? Why?
4. The label on each of the blocks corresponds to a reading on the Richter scale. The energy it takes to knock over each block relates to an earthquake of that size on the Richter scale. Which block was the hardest to knock down? What is the Richter scale number for an earthquake of that size?

Task 5 Conclusion
How does your model compare to the Richter scale? Write a short paragraph comparing the earthquake energy that relates to the different numbers on the Richter scale.

Extension
Calculate the size of the blocks needed to represent earthquake energies for the rest of the Richter scale. Make enough blocks to complete an entire Richter scale set. Test the set that you make.

Table 7.1 Earthquake Energy Table

Type of Shaking		Movement		
Strength	Length (sec)	Block 1	Block 5	Block 9
Gentle	5			
	65			
Moderate	5			
	65			
Violent	5			
	65			

Traveling Waves

Collect the following items: rubber band, cardboard tube, paper towel, and sand or rice.

1. Using the rubber band, cover one end of the card-board tube with a paper towel.

2. Fill the tube with sand or rice.

3. Push down on the sand with your finger. Try to push the sand out through the paper towel.

What happens? Infer how you think seismic waves move through soft materials, such as sand.

7.2 Earthquake Evidence

Objectives

▶ **Describe** some features produced by earthquakes.

▶ **Discuss** factors that determine earthquake damage.

▶ **Explain** what causes tsunamis.

▶ **Make inferences** about ways to build structures that could withstand major damage from earthquakes.

Look at Figure 7.7. How do you think the road became separated? What powerful forces can cause the earth's surface to separate in this way? You can probably easily guess that an earthquake caused the separation.

Evidence of the powerful force of earthquakes occurs in many forms. Some of these forms may be permanent, such as ground movement. Others are temporary, such as damage caused to a road that is quickly repaired. Scientists learn a lot about earthquakes by studying the evidence the quakes leave behind.

Ground-Level Evidence

Evidence from earthquakes is sometimes preserved in vertical or horizontal changes in ground level near a fault. The road in Figure 7.7 was separated by movement along the San Andreas fault in California. Strong, abrupt earthquakes generally leave more dramatic evidence than small earthquakes.

Along some active faults, ground-level changes occur slowly but nearly continuously whether or not an earthquake occurs. This type of slow, steady motion is called *creep*. Even at the creep rate of only 1 cm per year, ground levels on either side of a fault would be displaced by 1 m after about 100 years. If a house or fence sat on the fault, the creep would become evident within a decade or two. The reason is that the ground displacement caused by creeps eventually breaks buildings and other structures located on the fault.

Figure 7.7 ▲
What kind of evidence was left behind after an earthquake struck this area?

Landscape Evidence

Powerful earthquakes can cause permanent changes in an area's landscape. One of the most dramatic examples occurred in Alaska in 1964. The 8.4 magnitude of this earthquake caused the upheaval of over 260 000 sq km of ground. The city of Anchorage was actually moved sideways!

Earthquake movements especially affect poorly compacted sediments, such as sands, silts, and clays. When seismic wave energy is more powerful than the compacted sediments, the sediments may fracture or slide. You can see examples of sudden movements that uplift parts of the earth's crust below.

Slides ▲

Earthquakes often trigger slides, or rapid downslope movements of soil, debris, and rock. A 1985 earthquake in Mexico caused the slide shown above. Slides can occur on a fault or a long distance away. Large sections of mountains may fracture and race downward, coming to rest where the slope ends. Some slides continue for many kilometers, often destroying everything in their path, including houses and roads.

Scarps

Sudden earth movements along a fault may create a scarp, or cliff. A scarp's height depends on the type of materials uplifted and the amount and frequency of uplift. Some scarps may be as high as 1,500 m. Scarps, like most steep hillsides, are subject to erosion. Over time, a scarp may become so eroded that its origin is difficult to recognize. The scarp shown below occurred along the San Andreas fault in California. ▼

Fissures ▲

Earthquakes can produce fissures, or long cracks, in soil or rock. In rocky areas, these cracks may extend for many kilometers. Massive landslides may result if the fissures occur on a hill or mountainside. The fissures in the photograph above are located near the San Andreas fault in California.

Earthquake Damage

The enormous forces that cause landslides and uplift scarps can seriously damage human-built structures. In fact, earthquakes can level entire towns. What determines how much damage a quake causes?

Perhaps the most important factor that determines earthquake damage is how close an earthquake epicenter is to a populated area. In fact, a moderate quake that occurs in a crowded city is more likely to cause damage than a large quake in a desert.

The type of ground on which structures are built also influences damage. Soft, wet, loose soils can increase seismic waves several fold. In 1985, an earthquake that occurred in Mexico City caused major destruction and many deaths. Most of the buildings in Mexico City were built on loose soil. Buildings on loose soils have less of a chance of surviving earthquakes than buildings on solid ground.

Figure 7.8 ▲
The earthquake that caused the collapse of the middle building occurred in Managua, Nicaragua, in 1972. How do the materials used in a building's construction affect its ability to withstand an earthquake?

Damage also depends on building design and materials. Wood-frame structures may be able to move with and withstand ground motion. Unreinforced brick and cement structures are likely to sway and collapse during large quakes. An earthquake in Peru in 1970 destroyed most buildings made of adobe (uh DOH bee), a soil-clay mixture from which bricks are formed. The adobe structures could not withstand the earthquake vibrations.

People who live near the seashore face another threat from quakes. An offshore earthquake can cause movements in the ocean floor that create a **tsunami** (soo NAHM ee). A tsunami is an ocean wave caused by earthquakes.

In deep water, tsunamis are low and fast-moving. In shallow water, they begin to slow down and increase in height, to as much as 30 m. When the wave breaks, the tsunami releases tremendous energy. Few structures can survive a large tsunami. Figure 7.9 shows the damage caused by a tsunami.

Figure 7.9 ▲
The 1964 earthquake that struck Alaska unleashed a series of tsunamis. Waves crossed the Pacific Ocean and damaged areas as far away as California, Japan, and Hawaii. Here you can see some of the damage that occurred.

Earthquake Prediction

For centuries, people have tried to predict earthquakes by observing changes in animal behavior and well levels, among other things. Today, seismologists use more sophisticated prediction techniques. They look at evidence of former quakes to predict future ones. Changes in creep rates and lower water levels in wells may also tell of future quakes.

In 1981, seismologists predicted that a quake was likely in the Santa Cruz Mountain area of the San Andreas fault within 15 years. When moderate earthquakes rocked this area in 1988 and 1989, scientists identified these as foreshocks. The devastating Loma Prieta quake in October of 1989 proved them correct.

Science and Society *Earthquake Safety*

If you live near an active fault, you and your family may already know about the importance of preparing for possible earthquakes. In some earthquake-prone areas, such as California, city officals are encouraging families and communities to develop earthquake disaster plans. These plans include what to do during an earthquake, where to meet after one, and how to communicate if telephones don't work. Table 7.2 lists some ways in which people can prepare for earthquakes.

In a number of earthquake-prone areas, strict building and zoning laws are enforced to reduce seismic risks. Many public facilities are built to survive the largest earthquakes expected.

Check and Explain

1. What are some changes caused by earthquakes?

2. What factors determine the amount of damage caused by an earthquake?

3. **Predict** Describe the hazards you might face if an earthquake struck while you were asleep in bed; standing next to a tall building; at the beach; skiing.

4. **Infer** If you were an architect in an earthquake-prone area, what could you do to reinforce structures to reduce hazards?

Table 7.2 Earthquake Safety

Outside the Home	Inside the Home
Add internal or external braces to weak structures.	Anchor hot water heaters and bookshelves to walls.
Anchor house or building to its foundation.	Use flexible connectors on gas appliances.
Know where the main gas valve is and have tools to turn it off.	Store emergency supplies in a safe location.
Make plans to meet at a specific location outdoors if your home is destroyed.	Install latches on cabinets to protect dishes and other valuables.

The Pressure is Mounting

What happens when you blow up a balloon or inflate a tire and put in too much air? What happens when heat and pressure build up in a closed space and the pressure is suddenly released? How might these pressure situations be similar to a volcano that is about to erupt? Explain.

SKILLS WARMUP

7.3 Volcanoes

Objectives

▶ **Describe** how volcanoes form.

▶ **Explain** why volcanoes erupt.

▶ **Compare** the three main types of volcanoes.

▶ **Make a model** of the structure of a volcano.

D o you think you know what a volcano looks like? You can probably easily identify the conical, snow-covered peak in Figure 7.10 as a volcano. Some of the world's most beautiful mountains, such as Mt. Fuji in Japan, Mt. Rainier in Washington state, and Mt. Etna in Sicily, are volcanoes. Any opening in the earth's crust that has released molten rock is a **volcano**. The mountain that builds up from volcanic eruptions is also referred to as a volcano.

Formation of a Volcano

Magma, or molten rock, is under tremendous pressure deep inside the earth. Magma forms deep pockets called magma chambers in some places. Sometimes the magma cools and hardens deep within the crust. However, if the pressure and heat are great, magma tends to force its way upward through the earth's crust.

The more heat and pressure acting on magma, the more potential energy it contains. The higher the potential energy, the more likely the magma will force its way to the earth's surface. Magma that reaches the earth's surface is called **lava**. When lava or other volcanic materials reach the earth's surface, the event is called an eruption.

Volcanoes that have erupted in the past century are considered to be active. Those that haven't erupted in hundreds of years are considered to be dormant, or inactive. Volcanoes that haven't erupted in thousands of years are considered extinct. The eruptive life of a volcano may span hundreds of thousands of years, including periods of dormancy. Study Figure 7.11, which shows the major parts of an active volcano.

Figure 7.10 ▲
This active volcano is located in the Lake District of southern Chile.

Figure 7.11
Parts of a Volcano ▼

Vent
All volcanic material that reaches the surface emerges through some sort of **vent**, or opening. Vents are common at the tops of volcanoes, but they may also appear along the sides.

Crater
    The steep, hollowed-out area surrounding a vent at the top of a volcano is called a **crater**. A crater usually forms after a very explosive eruption.

Pipe
A pipe is a long, nearly vertical crack in the crust through which magma moves. A pipe may be thousands of meters long and only a few meters wide. Magma travels through a pipe until it reaches a vent on the earth's surface.

Magma Chamber
Large pockets of magma form underground magma chambers. When magma is hot or powerful enough, it makes its way toward the earth's surface through cracks in the crust.

Volcanic Eruptions

Volcanic eruptions range from quiet outpourings of lava to violent explosions of rock particles, steam, and gas. The chemistry, temperature, and pressure of the magma inside a volcano determine whether an eruption will be explosive or quiet. Volcanoes that erupt quietly generally make better neighbors than those that explode. However, even slow-moving lava flows can destroy towns and villages.

Lava Flows A common type of eruption for some volcanoes, especially those in Hawaii, is a lava flow. A lava flow is a stream of lava that flows from a vent. The stream may be narrow, or it may spread out. On steep slopes, some lava flows can reach speeds as high as 30 to 40 km per hour. As the lava moves, it cools and hardens.

Volcanic Explosions When volcanoes erupt explosively, they mainly give off rock particles. These particles, called volcanic debris, contain a range of airborne materials including dust, ash, cinders, and bombs. The kinds of volcanic debris are identified by the size of their particles. With an average particle the size of a flour grain, dust is the finest volcanic debris. The largest are called bombs, which measure at least 64 mm in diameter.

River of Lava
This lava flow comes from Mauna Loa (MOW nuh LOH uh), an active volcano on the island of Hawaii. This stream of lava is traveling at about 10 km per hour. When it hardens, it will form an uneven surface of very rough boulders and rocks. ▼

Bombs ▶
Hurled from the vent as molten or semimolten masses, volcanic bombs cool as they sail through the air. Some bombs are as large as cars. This bomb is from a volcano on the Hawaiian island of Maui (MOW ee).

Ash
◀ Volcanic ash can cover the landscape many meters deep. Fine-grained ash may be carried hundreds of kilometers by wind before it settles to the earth's surface. If hot enough, ash will ignite trees, plants, and animals. This ash is erupting from the small volcanic island of Krakatoa (KRAH kuh TOH uh) in Indonesia.

Types of Volcanoes

The different types of volcanic eruptions and explosions produce different types of volcanoes. Each type is named for its shape or structure.

Cinder Cone Volcanoes

Volcanoes that form from the products of explosive eruptions are called **cinder cone volcanoes**. Ash, cinders, and other volcanic debris mound up around the vent, forming a cone. Cinder cones have steeply sloping upper slopes, but their bases usually slope gently. They generally form from wet, silica-rich magmas. These cinder cone volcanoes are located on Java, an island in Indonesia. ▼

Shield Volcanoes ▲

Volcanoes that have flat-top, shieldlike shapes are called **shield volcanoes.** The lava that forms shield volcanoes is runny and flows easily when it reaches the surface. As a result, most lava flows away from the vent. As the lava cools, it becomes thicker, then slows down and collects. One of the largest shield volcanoes in Hawaii, Mauna Loa, is shown above. Many ocean islands are the tops of large shield volcanoes.

Composite Volcanoes

Volcanoes that contain alternating layers of volcanic debris and lava are called **composite volcanoes.** Usually, composite cones are formed from many cycles of eruptions. Most have steep tops but gently sloping bases. Mt. Rainier, shown below, and Mt. Fuji are composite volcanoes. ▼

Areas of Volcanic Activity

You know that most earthquakes occur along plate boundaries. Most of the earth's volcanic activity also occurs in the same regions. In fact, volcanic activity can often produce earthquakes. As magma moves upward, it may fracture rocks or buckle the overlying crust. The resulting earthquakes often serve as warnings to scientists that volcanic eruptions may occur.

Ring of Fire Look at Figure 7.12. Like earthquakes, the major zone of active volcanoes is along the Ring of Fire that encircles the Pacific Ocean. As you know, oceanic plates along the Ring of Fire are subducting. In this area, volcanoes occur in long chains that stretch for hundreds of kilometers. One major chain runs along the western coasts of North and South America. Where is another major chain located?

Oceanic Ridge Systems The oceanic ridge systems are the earth's longest volcanic zones. Here, plates are moving apart along ocean ridges, forming cracks called rifts. As magma rises from the rifts, the ocean water cools it. Lava builds up from the ocean bottom, forming volcanoes. Most volcanic eruptions along the ridge systems happen deep beneath the ocean's surface. However, along the mid-Atlantic ridge, volcanoes have risen above sea level, forming the island of Iceland. Iceland has many active volcanoes.

Hot Spots In Figure 7.12, you can see that volcanic activity called *hot spots* occurs in some areas. Notice that many of the hot spots are located far from plate boundaries. Scientists hypothesize that hot spots develop in parts of the earth's mantle that are especially hot. As the hot spots melt the surrounding rock, the rock changes into magma and rises to the surface. The Hawaiian Islands are an example of a volcanic island chain formed over a hot spot.

Figure 7.12
Map of Volcanic Activity ▼

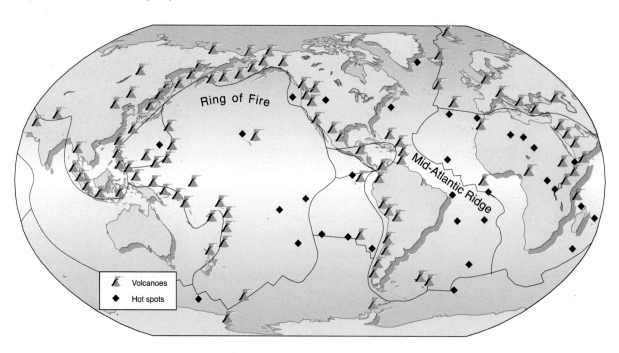

Historical Notebook

The Great Vesuvian Eruption

On August 24, AD.79, none of the residents of Pompeii and Herculaneum in what is now Italy imagined that nearby Mt. Vesuvius would erupt. The volcano had been peaceful for over 300 years. Most people who lived in the area probably didn't suspect that the mountain was a volcano. They also didn't know about the relationship between earthquakes and volcanoes. If they had, they would have realized that a nearby earthquake 17 years earlier was a warning of the renewed activity in the volcano.

The great eruption rained hot ash, mud, and stones upon the residents of Pompeii and Herculaneum. As the ash piled deeper, many people tried to save themselves by climbing to the second stories of buildings. Many did not escape. Some accounts of the event claim that 80 percent of the population perished. The two towns completely disappeared under about 20 m of ash and stone. About 1,500 years later, the forgotten towns were discovered.

1. What warning did residents of the two towns have of a volcanic eruption?

2. **Research** Find out about the discovery of Pompeii and Herculaneum. Who discovered the ruins? What did they find?

Life on a Volcanic Island

Organisms cannot survive on molten rock, where temperatures are sometimes above 1,000°C. Yet many of the world's volcanic islands are filled with life. How does a volcanic island, which was once covered with life-destroying lava, become a home for organisms?

The slow process begins as moisture from rain and fog reacts chemically with the exposed lava. Over time, soil develops. Wind, waves, and birds scatter microbes, plant spores, and pollen. Lichens and mosses appear and break down rock. Ocean currents deliver marine organisms, including algae, seaweed, kelp, corals, mollusks, insects, fish, and marine mammals.

Although new volcanic eruptions may wipe out this progress, the process begins again when the new layer of lava cools. Eventually, most volcanic islands will have a community of plants and animals.

Figure 7.13 ▲
Surtsey, Iceland, is a volcanic island that was built by a series of eruptions that began in 1963. Just a few weeks after its first eruption, Surtsey showed signs of life.

Science and Technology
Predicting and Monitoring Eruptions

In the past, volcanic eruptions often took people by surprise, sometimes at the cost of many lives. Today, advances in technology can give people warnings about eruptions. For example, when seismic activity, surface temperatures, and gas venting increased on Mt. Pinatubo in May 1991, Philippine authorities began to evacuate neighboring areas. Their actions probably saved many lives.

Fifty years ago, few instruments existed to detect volcanic activity. Those that did were inaccurate, heavy, and inefficient. Most required a person to operate them from potentially dangerous locations. Today, sophisticated devices can monitor volcanoes from safer distances. They also detect changes, such as when magma accumulates underground, increased seismic activity, changes in temperature, and gas emissions.

Advances in photography and satellite imaging also help monitor volcanic activity. They enable volcanologists to study eruptions in remote parts of the world. Infrared photography reveals minor differences in surface temperatures, even through thick cloud layers. This makes it possible to track volcanic activity in any type of weather.

With these developments in predicting and monitoring volcanic activity, scientists hope to save lives and protect property. In addition, scientists are gathering valuable information about the powerful processes that take place within the earth.

Figure 7.14 ▲
A scientist from the Hawaii Volcano Observatory dips hot lava out of a lava flow for research purposes.

Check and Explain

1. What is a volcano? How does it form?

2. Explain the differences between shield volcanoes, cinder cones, and composite volcanoes.

3. **Infer** Volcanic activity has been known to trigger tsunamis. Explain how this is possible.

4. **Make a Model** Use a large sheet of paper to draw a diagram of a volcano. Be sure to label its parts.

Chapter 7 Review

Concept Summary

7.1 Earthquakes

▶ Earthquakes are movements of the earth's crust that occur when rocks break and release energy in the form of seismic waves.

▶ An earthquake's focus is the point in the earth's crust where rock first breaks. The epicenter is the point on the surface above the focus.

▶ The strength of an earthquake is usually given in terms of its Richter magnitude.

7.2 Earthquake Evidence

▶ Earthquakes can cause changes in ground level near a fault. Ground-level changes can be vertical or horizontal.

▶ Earthquakes can trigger slides, create scarps, and cause fracturing.

▶ Tsunamis are ocean waves that are caused by earthquakes on the ocean floor.

7.3 Volcanoes

▶ Volcanoes are vents in the earth's crust that have released molten rock. The mountain that builds up is also called a volcano.

▶ Volcanic eruptions can be quiet or explosive. Volcanoes may give off lava, gas, steam, and other volcanic debris.

▶ The three main types of volcanoes are cinder cones, shield volcanoes, and composite volcanoes.

Chapter Vocabulary

earthquake (7.1)	seismic wave (7.1)	lava (7.3)	cinder cone volcano (7.3)
epicenter (7.1)	tsunami (7.2)	vent (7.3)	shield volcano (7.3)
focus (7.1)	volcano (7.3)	crater (7.3)	composite volcano (7.3)

Check Your Vocabulary

Use the vocabulary words above to complete the following sentences correctly.

1. Any opening on the earth's surface that has emitted lava is a ____ .

2. A volcano that forms from layers of slow-moving lava is a ____ .

3. A volcano that forms from alternating layers of lava and volcanic debris is a ____ .

4. The point on the earth's surface where an earthquake's shaking is generally the strongest is the ____ .

5. The ____ of an earthquake is the point within the crust where breakage occurs.

6. A volcano with steeply sloping sides that forms from explosive eruptions is a ____ .

7. Magma that has reached the earth's surface is called ____ .

8. The vibrations produced by an earthquake are ____ .

9. Earthquakes can trigger huge ocean waves called ____ .

10. A hollowed-out area at the top of a volcano is called a ____ .

11. Lava usually emerges from a ____ at the top of a volcano.

12. An ____ releases energy in the form of seismic waves.

Write Your Vocabulary

Write sentences using the vocabulary words above. Show that you know what each word means.

Chapter 7 Review

Check Your Knowledge

Answer the following in complete sentences.

1. Describe what happens during an earthquake.

2. Explain the difference between an earthquake's focus and its epicenter.

3. List the three types of seismic waves. Which type is the fastest moving? Which is the slowest moving?

4. Which type of seismic wave causes the most damage? Why?

5. How many seismograph readings are needed before an earthquake's epicenter can be located? Why?

6. Name some different types of surface changes that an earthquake can cause.

7. List factors that influence how much damage an earthquake causes.

8. What is the relationship between tsunamis and seismic activity?

9. Describe a magma chamber and its relationship to a volcano.

10. What are the different types of volcanoes? How does each form?

Choose the answer that best completes each sentence.

11. Molten rock within the earth is called (magma, lava, volcanic debris).

12. The fastest moving seismic waves are (S waves, P waves, L waves).

13. A cliff created by an earthquake is a (slide, scarp, fracture).

14. Rocks in the earth's crust can store a great deal of (elastic limit, stress, potential energy, seismic waves) before they fracture.

Check Your Understanding

Apply the concepts you have learned to answer each question.

1. **Compare and Contrast** Why do some volcanoes erupt explosively whereas others erupt quietly?

2. Why does soil type have an effect on how much damage a building sustains during an earthquake?

3. Explain how a seismograph works.

4. **Application** Describe the methods used to rate earthquakes. Explain why a single earthquake can have many ratings on the Mercalli intensity scale.

5. **Mystery Photo** The photograph on page 132 shows a volcanic eruption and lava flow. The red material is the lava. What is lava? What do you think happens to lava when it cools?

6. **Extension** The soils of volcanic islands are often very rich in minerals. Explain why this is so.

7. Explain how volcanoes can cause earthquakes.

8. **Infer** Many people in Pompeii and Herculaneum died as a result of suffocation during the eruption of Mt. Vesuvius. What might have caused their suffocation?

9. What is a slide? Explain how an earthquake can trigger a slide.

10. **Application** How is it possible that a volcanic island, such as Surtsey, is now home to many organisms? Explain.

Develop Your Skills

Use the skills you have developed in this chapter to complete each activity.

1. **Interpret Data** The graph below shows the time and distance that seismic waves travelled from the focus of an earthquake. Study the graph, then answer the questions that follow.

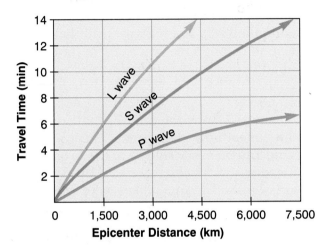

a. How far did the P wave travel in 6 minutes?

b. How far did the S wave travel in 14 minutes?

c. At 2,000 km, approximately how much faster was the P wave than the S wave?

2. **Data Bank** Use the information on page 619 to answer the following questions.

a. What was the magnitude of the quake that occurred in Guatemala?

b. In what country did the earthquake with the highest magnitude occur?

c. **Infer** Some earthquakes with high magnitude ratings caused many deaths. Others didn't. List two or three reasons why the statistics differ.

Make Connections

1. **Link the Concepts** Draw a concept showing how the concepts below together. Add terms to connect, or the concepts.

seismic waves	seismograph
earthquakes	P waves
scarps	Mercalli scale
L waves	Richter scale
fractures	S waves
	tsunamis

2. **Science and Social Studies** Find out about the last major volcanic eruption in the United States excluding Alaska and Hawaii. When and where did it occur? Did scientists gather data that suggested an eruption would occur? How has the area recovered from the eruption?

3. **Science and Literature** Do some research at your school library to find out about Pele, the Hawaiian goddess of volcanoes. How do the legends about Pele describe her? What purpose do these legends serve? Make up your own legend that explains the origin of volcanoes.

4. **Science and Society** Iceland is home to tremendous volcanic activity and geothermal energy, or heat, trapped within the earth's crust. In fact, over half the homes on Iceland are heated by geothermal energy. Find out about the practical applications of geothermal energy. How can it be used? What are its advantages and disadvantages? Is geothermal energy used in the United States?

Science and Literature Connection

By autumn their travois was loaded with pemmican, and the time had come for them to follow the animals north and to pick a good camping place where they might find protection from the howling blizzards and snows of winter. The sun glowed orange and golden in the midafternoon as shadows crossed the silent grasses, bringing night earlier and earlier each day. It was a sad time for the women, for now they faced a long and lonely winter of solitude. It was also a sad time for Amana. For as many seasons as she could recall, her tribe had always assembled into a vast winter encampment. All the small bands that spent the summer alone in their far-flung hunting grounds joined together in a glistening community of tipis, sending up smoke and the sounds of laughter and winter games. How nice it used to be when all the people gathered together in the time of the Cold-Maker.

"Aih," Grandmother Weasel Woman exclaimed as she embraced Amana with an expression of sorrow in her face, "but we are alone now. All the people were taken by the sickness and we are alone. So we must fend for ourselves through the hard wintertime."

They broke camp before sunrise, and in a cool breeze that pressed hard upon them from the mountains, they started on their way. Amana and blind

---

Legend Days

The following excerpt is from the novel Legend Days *by Jamake Highwater.*

Weasel Woman pulled the heavy travois while Crow Woman, with the aid of a cottonwood cane, stumbled along after them, singing into the wind.

They left the shelter of their handsome valley in the mountains and followed a shady forest trail that wound through the rusty-brown foothills. Already the first frosts had turned the grasses umber and dry. Then they descended over high ridges and turned northward along the prairies that spread out beneath the giant peaks. The crickets sang and on every side were the broad meadows and rolling swells of brown grasslands. The small lakes were filled with noisy flocks of ducks and geese pausing on their southward migrations.

On their journey the women followed the Old North Trail, the most traveled of all the ancient routes of the Northwest. It ran along the great chain of mountains called the Backbone of the World, winding over the smooth, rounded ridges and then down long slopes, through wide meadows, and across blue streams and gray rivers, clear and icy cold.

At the head of a broad and windy valley they saw the peak of Chief Mountain, a lone spur of rock, a huge wall rising into the clouds above the surrounding plain.

The women were exhausted from their long, hard journey. Each day they pressed forward, and at night they made camp in groves of shaking aspen, among big cottonwoods in river valleys, and on the banks of swift-flowing streams. But during all these difficult days they saw no one. They found no tracks of other travelers. And they could hear no trace of human voices in the wind that brought the smallest and most distant sound across the great plains.

Then one evening, when they were searching for a camping place, Amana thought she heard an unfamiliar noise. It came from very far away and was very faint, but she was certain that it was a dog or a horse or perhaps a person. Without saying a word she dropped her burden and ran ahead of the old women, peering into the darkening landscape. In the distance, where the endless plains reached the sky,

she thought for a moment that she saw a whiff of smoke. But she was not certain. It could have been just a cloud or dust devil.

Skills in Science

Reading Skills in Science

1. **Find Details** Why did Amana and the other women go on this journey? What had happened to the other members of Amana's tribe? How do you know?

2. **Find the Main Idea** Describe the relationship that exists between the type of landforms that make up the setting of the passage and the reason for the women's journey.

Writing Skills in Science

1. **Predict** Imagine that you are Amana. Write an entry in your diary describing what caused the whiff of smoke referred to at the end of the passage. Then add an entry that describes a day in your life one month from now.

2. **Find Causes** Choose two topographical features described in this passage and explain how they may have formed. Give evidence for your response.

Activities

Communicate If you lived in a tipi at the location you live now, would you be protected from howling blizzards and winter snows? Is there a nearby location where the natural land features would help protect you from harsh winters? Imagine that you had to set up a winter encampment using a tipi. Describe the best place to set up camp. Explain why you chose the location.

Make a Model Make a topographical map of the region where the women traveled. You will need to use your imagination to fill in some parts of the map.

Where to Read More

The Shape of the World. Chicago: Rand McNally, 1991. This beautifully illustrated text is a companion volume to a six-part PBS series telling the story of the exploration, mapping and measurement of earth. Complete with pictures of the earth as viewed from space.

Composition of the Earth

Data Bank

Use the information on pages 612 to 625 to answer the following questions about topics explored in this unit.

Classifying

What kinds of minerals are classified as sulfides? What kinds of minerals are classified as silicates?

Comparing

Which rock is more common in the United States, metamorphic rock or igneous rock?

Reading a Table

What are the chemical symbols for the minerals gold, calcite, and gypsum?

Interpreting a Map

List the classes of rocks that are found in Alaska.

The photograph to the left is of metamorphic and other types of rocks in Alaska. What else do you see in the photograph?

Chapter 8 Earth Chemistry

What do you see?

66The picture resembles frost on a window. You can see many crystal shapes, and there are convoluted spiderlike branches pressed against the glass. The frost probably formed when the dew on a window froze. The sunlight is shining through the ice giving the appearance of the yellow color.99

Mark Adato
Hanby Junior High School
Wilmington, Delaware

To find out more about the photograph, look on page 182. As you read this chapter, you will learn about the chemistry of the earth.

8.1 Structure of Matter

Objectives

▶ **Describe** the structure of atoms.

▶ **Explain** what an element is.

▶ **Compare** and **contrast** three kinds of chemical bonds.

▶ **Communicate** the information contained in chemical formulas.

What is everything on the earth made of? You probably think that there isn't just one answer to that question. After all, there are plants, animals, rocks, mountains, oceans, and many other different things on the earth. But, in spite of the differences, everything on the earth is made of **matter**. Matter is anything that takes up space and has mass. Mass, measured in kilograms, is the amount of matter making up an object.

If you look around, you see examples of matter everywhere. In fact, you are made of matter. Your chair, desk, textbook, pencil, and lunch are made of matter. The classroom windows, and the trees and buildings you see outside, are also made of matter. Even the air you breathe is made of matter.

Look at Figure 8.1. What examples of matter do you see? You may think that matter is only found on the earth, but look at the sky one night. Did you know that the stars are made of matter, too?

Properties of Matter

Because the properties of matter are different, it's easy to tell them apart. For example, rocks are usually solid, hard, and heavy. Water is a clear liquid that sometimes turns into ice or steam. Wood and coal are solids that burn easily. Apples, cheese, and peanuts are forms of matter that are good to eat.

You can probably think of many other properties of matter. All of the properties of matter fall into one of two categories. They are either physical properties or chemical properties.

Figure 8.1 ▲
This landscape is made of many different kinds of matter. How do they differ from each other?

Figure 8.2 ▲
The interaction of oil and water reveals properties of the oil.

Physical Properties Imagine going for a walk along a beach or stream and finding an unusual rock. How would you describe the rock to others? You might mention its color, shape, texture, or hardness. These are all examples of physical properties of matter.

Other physical properties of matter include density, ductility, buoyancy, and solubility. Density is the amount of matter in a given volume of a substance. *Buoyancy*, which depends on density, is the ability of a substance to float in water. *Ductility* is the ability of a metal or other solid to be stretched, shaped, or bent without breaking. *Solubility* is the amount of a substance that will dissolve in another substance.

Look at Figure 8.2. Describe the physical properties of the oil pouring into the water. Now observe the masks in Figure 8.3. How do their physical properties differ?

Chemical Properties Every substance has an important set of properties called its chemical properties. Chemical properties describe how a certain substance reacts chemically with other substances. For example, substances such as gasoline or wood combine easily with oxygen in a reaction that produces heat and light. You recognize substances that combine with oxygen this way as substances that burn, or combust. One chemical property of these substances is that they are combustible. Other substances, such as helium gas, aren't combustible.

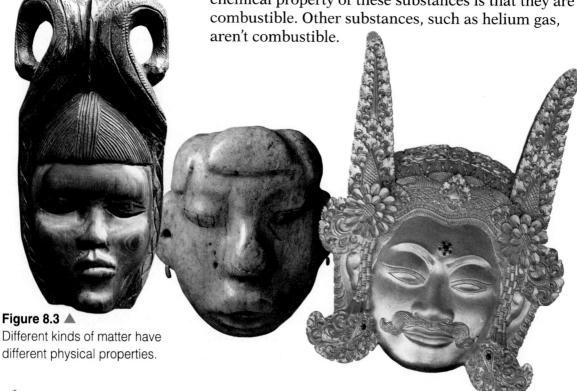

Figure 8.3 ▲
Different kinds of matter have different physical properties.

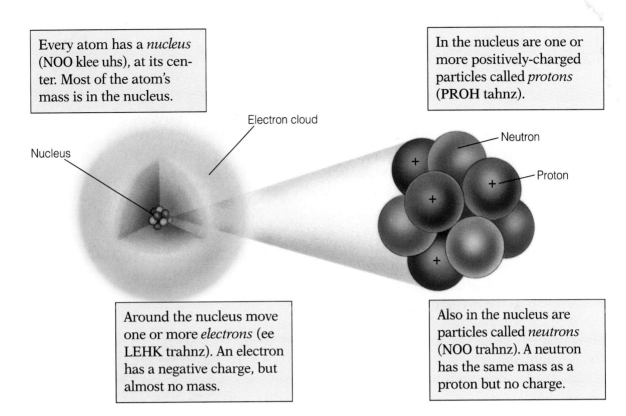

Every atom has a *nucleus* (NOO klee uhs), at its center. Most of the atom's mass is in the nucleus.

In the nucleus are one or more positively-charged particles called *protons* (PROH tahnz).

Electron cloud

Nucleus

Neutron

Proton

Around the nucleus move one or more *electrons* (ee LEHK trahnz). An electron has a negative charge, but almost no mass.

Also in the nucleus are particles called *neutrons* (NOO trahnz). A neutron has the same mass as a proton but no charge.

Figure 8.4 ▲
Structure of the Atom

Atoms

What makes each kind of matter different? Each kind of matter has a unique structure. Anything with a structure is built of smaller parts that serve as building blocks. For example, your school may be built out of bricks or wooden boards. Similarly, your body is built out of cells.

What smaller parts is matter made of? All matter is made of very tiny particles called **atoms**. An atom is much smaller than the smallest speck of dust you can see with your eyes. Each kind of atom has specific properties that make it different from other kinds of atoms. An atom can't be broken down into smaller pieces without losing its properties.

Atomic Structure An atom contains even smaller particles called subatomic particles. Study the model of an atom in Figure 8.4. Every atom has a nucleus containing protons, and most also contain neutrons. Moving rapidly around the nucleus are one or more electrons. Since the location of the electrons always changes, an atom's electrons are modeled as an electron cloud.

An atom is electrically neutral, or without an overall charge, because it has the same number of electrons and protons. Sometimes, an atom can gain or lose electrons and become an **ion** (EYE ohn). An ion is an atom with an overall positive or negative charge. An ion with one extra electron has a charge of minus one (-1). What would be the charge of an ion that has lost one electron?

Elements In nature, there are about 90 different kinds of atoms. Although all atoms have a nucleus and an electron cloud, the number of subatomic particles varies. Each kind of atom, called an **element**, has a different number of protons in its nucleus.

The number of protons in the nucleus is an element's *atomic number*. Elements have been found or created for every atomic number from 1 to 109. Some of the most common elements and their atomic numbers are shown in Table 8.1. For example, an atom with 6 protons in its nucleus has an atomic number of 6. It is known as the element carbon. An atom of carbon also has six electrons. How many protons are in an atom of the element sulfur?

Every element has a unique set of physical and chemical properties. If you think of atoms as building blocks of matter, then elements are the different kinds of building blocks available. One of the most important facts you can know about a type of matter is what elements make it up. Look at the items in Figure 8.5. What elements make up each one?

Plant
• Carbon
• Oxygen
• Hydrogen

Plastic
• Carbon
• Hydrogen
• Chlorine

Amethyst
• Silicon
• Oxygen

Figure 8.5 ▲
Different kinds of matter are made of different elements.

Table 8.1 Common Elements

Element	Atomic Number	Element	Atomic Number
Hydrogen	1	Chlorine	17
Carbon	6	Calcium	20
Nitrogen	7	Iron	26
Oxygen	8	Silver	47
Sodium	11	Gold	79
Silicon	14	Lead	82
Sulfur	16	Uranium	92

Isotopes All atoms of the same element aren't exactly alike. Although they have the same number of protons, the number of neutrons can vary. For example, most carbon atoms have 6 neutrons. However, some have 7 or 8 neutrons. Atoms of the same element that have different numbers of neutrons are called **isotopes** (EYE soh tohpz).

Different isotopes can be identified by their *mass number*. Mass number is the total number of protons and neutrons in an atom's nucleus. For example, the most common isotope of carbon has 6 protons and 6 neutrons. Therefore, it has a mass number of 12 and is called carbon-12. What would be the name of a carbon isotope that has 8 neutrons?

Chemical Bonding

Most of the matter around you has atoms joined to other atoms. The atoms are held together by **chemical bonds**. In a chemical bond, two atoms are held together by interactions between their electrons.

Atoms form chemical bonds because of the way their electrons are arranged. Electrons move around the atom's nucleus in regions called energy levels. Generally, lower energy levels are closer to the nucleus and higher energy levels are farther away. Each energy level has room for a certain number of electrons. The lower energy levels fill up first.

Only a few elements have the right number of electrons to completely fill all their energy levels. The atoms of most elements have either too few or too many electrons. The highest energy level of these atoms isn't filled. Atoms with unfilled energy levels are less stable than atoms with filled energy levels.

An atom can fill an energy level with electrons by making a chemical bond with another atom. Therefore, forming a chemical bond makes both atoms more stable. For this reason, most atoms bond with other atoms, rather than exist as separate atoms. Three major types of chemical bonds join atoms together: ionic bonds, covalent bonds, and metallic bonds.

Ionic Bonds   An ionic (eye AHN ihk) bond forms when one or more electrons actually move from one atom to another. One atom gives up electrons so that its highest remaining energy level is full. The loss of electrons causes this atom to become a positive ion. The other atom accepts the electrons to fill up its highest energy level. The gain of electrons causes the second atom to become a negative ion. The attraction between the two oppositely-charged ions forms an ionic bond.

Substances made up of atoms joined by ionic bonds are called ionic solids. One ionic solid that you use every day is table salt, or sodium chloride. Look at the structure of sodium chloride in Figure 8.6. Notice the many pairs of positive and negative ions inside a sodium chloride crystal.

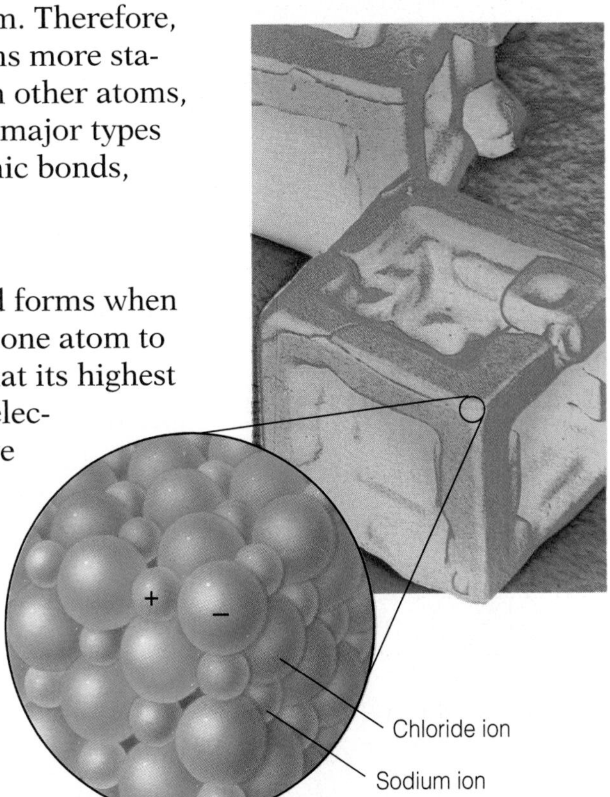

Chloride ion

Sodium ion

Figure 8.6 ▲
Ionic bonds join the sodium and chloride ions in grains of salt.

Covalent Bonds A covalent (koh VAY lehnt) bond forms when two atoms share one or more electrons. The electron clouds of the two atoms overlap. Then, electrons in the highest energy levels can move around both atoms. Each atom is more stable because the shared electrons help fill their highest energy levels. Two or more atoms joined together by covalent bonds form a **molecule** (MAHL ih KYOOL).

Some atoms form covalent bonds with more than one other atom. Look at Figure 8.7. A molecule of water has one oxygen atom bonded to two hydrogen atoms. Most common substances, including air, wood, food, and the cells of your body, are made up of molecules.

Figure 8.7
Covalent bonds join the atoms in molecules of water. ▼

Covalent bonds

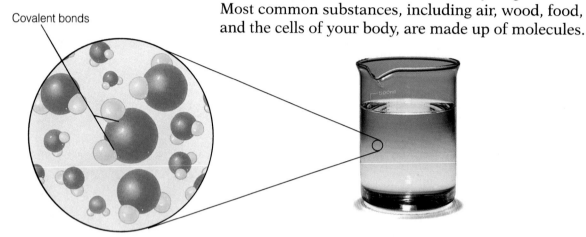

Metallic Bonds Atoms of certain elements, called metals, bond together with metallic bonds. In metallic bonding, many atoms share many electrons. The electrons move freely among all the atoms.

Pieces of gold, iron, aluminum, and other metals contain atoms joined by metallic bonds. Metallic bonds give metals some of their physical properties. For example, metals can bend without breaking. Their many shared electrons allow metals to conduct electricity.

Figure 8.8
Metallic bonding holds together the atoms in pieces of metal. ▼

Freely moving electrons

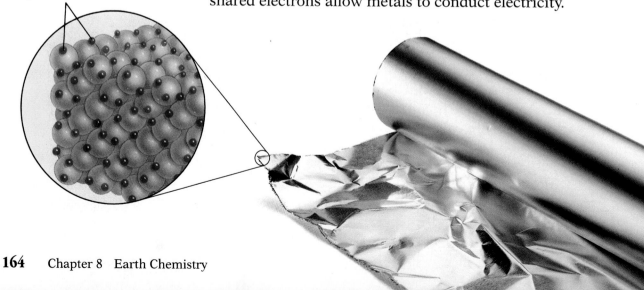

Chemical Reactions

A chemical reaction is another name for a chemical change. Chemical reactions occur constantly in the earth's atmosphere, in the oceans, in rocks, and in soil. In your body, chemical reactions change the food you eat into substances your body's cells can use.

In any chemical reaction, starting materials, called reactants, are changed into products. The same atoms are present in the reactants and products, but they are combined differently. Chemical bonds in the reactants are broken. New chemical bonds are formed to create the products. For example, when elemental iron combines with oxygen gas, the product is iron oxide, or rust.

The product of a chemical reaction has different chemical and physical properties than the reactants do. For example, chlorine is a poisonous gas. Sodium is a soft, shiny metal. But sodium and chlorine combine in a chemical reaction to form ordinary table salt.

Chemical Equations A chemical reaction can be expressed in a kind of sentence called a chemical equation. Chemical equations use chemical formulas to represent the reactants and the products. Study the chemical equation shown in Figure 8.16. Notice that reactants and products have the same number and kinds of atoms, but in a different arrangement.

Figure 8.15 ▲
What substances combine in this chemical reaction?

Figure 8.16   Example of a Chemical Equation ▼

Reactants
On the left side of a chemical equation are the starting materials, or reactants. When there is more than one reactant, a plus sign separates them.

Yield Sign
The arrow means "yields" or "produces." It shows the direction of the change.

Products
New substances formed in a chemical reaction are its products. The products are shown at the right of the yield sign. What are the products of this chemical reaction?

$$NaOH + HCl \rightarrow NaCl + H_2O$$

Inferring

Up in Flames

Make a list of ten substances that have the chemical property of being combustible. What do you think the molecules of all these substances have in common?

SKILLS WORKOUT

Energy in Chemical Reactions Energy is absorbed or released in a chemical reaction. Chemical bonds in the reactants break and new chemical bonds form to make the products. Energy changes occur in this process because each kind of chemical bond contains a certain amount of energy. Sometimes, the chemical bonds of the products contain less energy than those of the reactants. Then the reaction releases energy, usually in the form of heat or light. For example, combustion is a chemical reaction that releases both kinds of energy. Sometimes, the chemical bonds of the products contain more energy than the chemical bonds of the reactants. Then the reaction absorbs energy.

Energy also affects the speed of chemical reactions. Generally, chemical reactions occur faster at higher temperatures. The heat energy makes the particles of the reactants move about faster. They are more likely to collide with each other and start a reaction.

Consider This

Should People Be Warned About Harmful Chemicals?

Every day, many people are exposed to harmful chemicals. The health effects of these chemicals may not show up for many years. So, scientists cannot easily link chemicals to health problems. However, cases of illness and death probably caused by chemicals in food, water, and air have increased as the general use of chemicals has grown.

Because of health concerns, some workers have demanded that they be told if harmful chemicals are in their workplace. Consumers have demanded that products include warning labels telling of any risks. In response, state governments passed a number of "right to know" laws. Such laws are necessary, say their supporters, for people to be able to protect their health.

Others argue, however, that such laws may go too far. It is very difficult to determine whether many chemicals actually are harmful, or at what levels people should be concerned. Also, the laws are very expensive for companies to obey. The more warnings and labels that are required, the higher the cost of products.

Think About It Do you support "right to know" laws? Would you pay higher prices for products in order to be better informed of dangers?

Write About It Write a paper discussing your position on the issue of "right to know" laws.

Science and Technology *Buckyballs*

Imagine designing and building a custom-made molecule. You could design matter with unique and useful physical or chemical properties. Scientists have discovered many ways to make custom-made molecules from carbon atoms. A carbon atom can form up to four covalent bonds with other atoms. Carbon atoms can combine to make straight chains, branched chains, and rings.

In 1985, scientists discovered how to link 60 carbon atoms together to form a structure shaped like a hollow soccer ball. They named the new substance buckminsterfullerene. The name honors the scientist R. Buckminster Fuller, who designed a building with a similar shape called a geodesic dome. Molecules of the substance are sometimes called buckyballs.

The unusual structure of buckyballs gives them many important uses. Buckyballs link together in different ways to create new materials. Atoms of other elements can be placed inside or on the surface of the hollow buckyballs.

One use of buckyballs is to create substances called superconductors. Superconductors let an electric current flow with little resistance. Buckyballs coated with atoms of fluorine produce a heat-resistant lubricant. A larger buckyball containing 70 carbon atoms has been used to grow thin films of diamond. These diamond films could be produced cheaply as tough coatings for tools, ball bearings, and surgical blades. Buckyballs may have many other possible uses.

Figure 8.17 ▲
A computer helped create this image of a buckyball molecule.

Check and Explain

1. Describe two examples of a physical change.

2. How is a chemical change different from a physical change?

3. **Compare and Contrast** Describe two kinds of phase changes. How are they alike? How are they different?

4. **Infer** You observe that when two liquids are mixed together, they become warm. What can you infer is happening to the molecules in each liquid?

Activity 8 *How can you measure energy changes?*

Skills Measure; Make a Graph; Interpret Data

Task 1 Prelab Prep

1. Collect the following items: labels, calcium chloride, baking soda, 3 plastic or foam cups, 2 spoons, water, a graduated cylinder, a thermometer, a timer or clock, paper towels, graph paper, a pencil, 3 different colored pencils.
2. Label one cup *baking soda,* one cup *calcium chloride,* and one cup *baking soda + calcium chloride + water.*

Task 2 Data Record

1. On a separate sheet of paper, copy Table 8.4.
2. Record your temperature measurements for the three chemical reactions in the data table.
3. You will use the data you collect in the table to graph the energy changes in the three chemical reactions.

Table 8.4 Temperature Changes During Chemical Reactions

Reactants	Temp (°C)					
	0 min.	1 min.	2 min.	3 min.	4 min.	5 min.
Baking Soda + Water						
Calcium Chloride + Water						
Baking Soda + Calcium Chloride Water						

Task 3 Procedure

1. Measure 15 mL of water in the graduated cylinder and add it to the baking soda cup.
2. Place the thermometer in the cup.
3. Measure one spoonful of baking soda and place it in the cup with the water.
4. Immediately measure the temperature of the combined reactants and record it in the data table.
5. Continue to measure the temperature at one minute intervals for five minutes. Record your temperature measurements in the data table.
6. After five minutes, remove the thermometer and wipe it clean with a paper towel.
7. Repeat steps 1 to 6 for calcium chloride + water, and for baking soda + calcium chloride + water.
8. On the graph paper, prepare a line graph with temperature on the vertical axis and time on the horizontal axis. Graph the temperature measurements for all three chemical reactions on the same graph, using a different color pencil for each.

Task 4 Analysis

1. Which chemical reaction gave off the most energy? How could you tell?
2. Which chemical reaction absorbed the most energy? How could you tell?
3. Describe the graph for the chemical reaction that included both baking soda and calcium chloride. What does this tell you about the chemical reaction?
4. Identify the independent and dependent variables in this activity.

Task 5 Conclusion

Write a short paragraph explaining how energy changes relate to chemical reactions.

Extension

Test each of the three chemical reactions to find out how much gas each produces. Conduct each of the chemical reactions in self-lock plastic bags. Try to write simple chemical equations for each of the reactions. Use the equations to reveal the gas produced.

8.3 The Earth's Elements

Objectives

▶ **Describe** the organization of the periodic table.

▶ **List** elements that are most common in the crust, atmosphere, and ocean.

▶ **Generalize** about the location of metals and nonmetals in the periodic table.

▶ **Interpret data** contained in the periodic table.

If you had a collection of 90 different tapes or CDs, how would you organize them? One possible way would be to put them in rows on shelves, in alphabetical order. Then you could find any CD quickly. Or you could organize them by type of music. Whichever way you choose, some kind of organization is useful. It would take a long time to go through a stack of 90 CDs that were in no order at all.

Organization is also useful in understanding the chemical elements. However, in the case of the elements, the goal of organization is different. The goal is to make sense of patterns that the elements show in their chemical and physical properties.

Patterns in the Elements

Many years ago, scientists noticed that certain elements had very similar properties. The elements with atomic numbers 2, 10, 18, and 36 all existed as gases and didn't react chemically with other elements. The metals lithium, sodium, and potassium were all so reactive they never existed as pure metals. Scientists thought that each set of similar elements should be grouped together. They also thought that elements should be organized in order of increasing atomic number.

Look at the calendar in Figure 8.18. The dates increase by one each day. Also notice that all the dates in a single column have a similar "property." They are the same day of the week. The elements can be arranged in a calendarlike way to form what is called the periodic table of the elements.

Figure 8.18 ▲
How does a calendar organize the days of a month?

The Periodic Table

On these pages, you will tour the periodic table. During the tour, you will learn more about how the table is put together and the patterns that make it useful. The periodic table is an important tool in the study of earth science.

Figure 8.19
Periodic Table of the Elements ▶

Groups Vertical columns are called groups. Elements within a group can have many similar properties. Their properties are similar because their atoms have a similar arrangement of electrons.

Group Number Groups of elements are identified by numbers from 1 to 18, beginning at the left side of the table.

Periods The seven horizontal rows are called periods. Period 1 contains only hydrogen and helium. Elements 57 to 70 and 89 to 102 fit into periods 6 and 7.

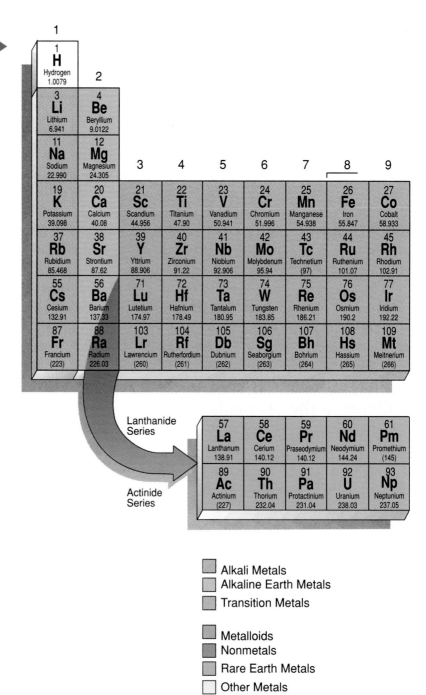

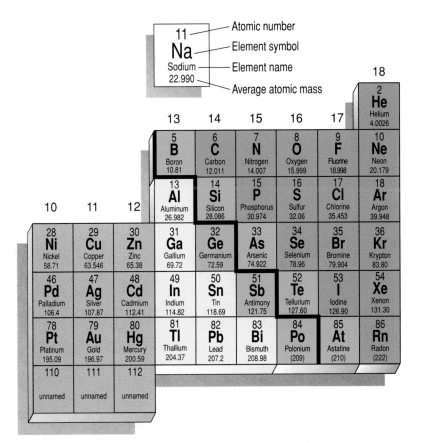

Atomic number — 11
Element symbol — Na
Element name — Sodium
Average atomic mass — 22.990

Nonmetals Nonmetals occupy the upper-right corner of the periodic table. All nonmetals, except hydrogen, are to the right of the zigzag line.

Metals Most of the elements are metals. They occupy the space in the periodic table to the left of the zigzag line.

Metalloids Elements that have properties of both metals and nonmetals are metalloids (MEHT uh LOYDZ). Metalloids border both sides of the zigzag line that separates the metals from the nonmetals.

Rare Earth Metals The two rows of elements from periods 6 and 7 are separated from the rest of the table to make it a more convenient size. These are the rare earth metals.

Elements of the Earth's Crust

Most of the elements in the periodic table are found in the earth's crust. Some elements are very common, and others are very rare. Look at Figure 8.20. It show the chemical makeup of the earth's crust. How much of the crust is made of just oxygen and silicon?

Most of the atoms of silicon and oxygen in the crust are chemically bonded together. Silicon and oxygen, alone or com bined with one or more metallic elements, form compounds called silicates. Silicates are the most common compounds in the rocks of the earth's crust.

The thin layer of soil on the surface of the crust is different in makeup from the crust itself. In addition to tiny bits of rock, soil contains **organic matter.** Organic matter comes from, or is produced by, living or dead organisms. All organic matter contains the element carbon, a nonmetal. Other elements in organic matter include the nonmetals oxygen, hydrogen, and nitrogen.

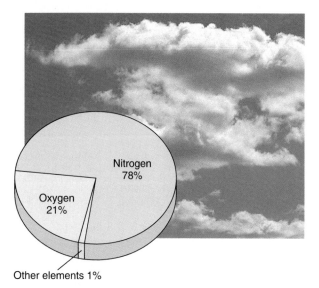

Figure 8.21 ▲
What two elements are most abundant in the atmosphere?

Elements of the Atmosphere

Elements found in the atmosphere are usually in the gas phase. Look at Figure 8.21. What elements are most common? Nitrogen gas exists as molecules of two nitrogen atoms each, shown by the chemical formula N_2.

Oxygen is also common in the atmosphere. Unlike oxygen in the crust, most oxygen in the atmosphere exists as elemental matter. Molecules of oxygen gas, O_2, contain two oxygen atoms. Oxygen gas in the atmosphere is important to many living organisms. Some oxygen is chemically combined with hydrogen in the form of water molecules. Water in the gas phase is invisible, but tiny droplets of water in the atmosphere form clouds.

Carbon in the atmosphere is contained in molecules of carbon dioxide, or CO_2. Plants use CO_2 and energy from sunlight to make glucose. Glucose made by plants is the source of much of the carbon in the organic matter of the soil and in living organisms.

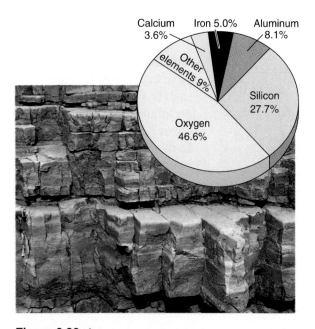

Figure 8.20 ▲
What do calcium, iron, and aluminum have in common?

Elements of the Ocean

If you've tasted ocean water, you know it's not pure water. Ocean water is a mixture of gases and solids dissolved in water. Most of the solids are salts. Salts are ionic compounds containing a metal and one or more nonmetals.

The most abundant salt in ocean water is sodium chloride, or table salt. It is made up of ions of the metal sodium and ions of the nonmetal chlorine. Look at Figure 8.22. What are the most common elements in ocean water?

The gases dissolved in ocean water are the same ones that make up the atmosphere. They are nitrogen (N_2), oxygen (O_2), and carbon dioxide (CO_2). The amount of dissolved gases varies greatly by depth and water temperature. Ocean organisms remove dissolved O_2 from the water for use in their life processes just as you remove O_2 from the air you breathe.

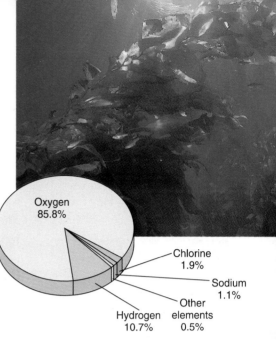

Oxygen 85.8%
Chlorine 1.9%
Sodium 1.1%
Other elements 0.5%
Hydrogen 10.7%

Figure 8.22 ▲
In what chemical form does most of the ocean's oxygen and hydrogen exist?

SkillBuilder *Interpreting Data*

Using the Periodic Table

The periodic table contains a great deal of information packed into a small space. For example, if you know the name of an element, the periodic table will tell that element's symbol and atomic number. Practice using the periodic table on pages 176–177 by answering the questions below.

1. List all the elements in Group 17.

2. Find sodium (Na) in the periodic table. How many protons does an atom of sodium have in its nucleus? How do you know?

3. Find nickel (Ni). How many electrons does an atom of nickel have?

4. Which is likely to have the greater mass, a cubic centimeter of titanium, or the same volume of zirconium?

5. Use the periodic table to complete the table below.

Make a list of the different kinds of information you can get from the periodic table. Give an example of each.

Symbol	Name	Atomic Number	Group Number
H			
		6	
		8	
Mg			
		13	
	Silicon		

Where's My Iridium?

Find iridium in the periodic table. What is its group number? What familiar elements are in the same period as iridium?

SKILLS WORKOUT

Science and Society *Chemical Clues*

Did you know that many of the earth's secrets have been unlocked by studying an element or compound? For example, the element iridium (Ir) occurs around the world in a thin layer of clay about 65 million years old. Iridium is also found in asteroids. The earth's iridium layer provides evidence that an asteroid collided with the earth 65 million years ago. U.S. scientists Luis and Walter Alvarez proposed that the collision may have caused the extinction of the dinosaurs.

Other elements also provide clues to the earth's past. For example, silicon, iron, oxygen, and many other elements occur in rocks and soil. Carbon has been found in wood, bones, and carbon dioxide bubbles in ancient ice. These elements provide evidence that the earth's atmosphere has changed. The amount of oxygen gas (O_2) has increased greatly over the last 2.8 billion years. This change had a major effect on living organisms, climate, and the earth's crust.

Studying chemical compounds is also important in understanding changes taking place on the earth today. Since the 1970s, the amount of ozone (O_3) in the upper parts of the atmosphere has decreased. Ozone is a form of oxygen that blocks out harmful ultraviolet radiation from the sun. Ozone is destroyed by chemical compounds released into the atmosphere by people. Finding out which compounds destroy ozone is an important step in solving the problem.

Check and Explain

1. How are the elements organized in the periodic table?

2. Which two elements are most abundant in the earth's crust? In what form do atoms of these elements exist in the crust?

3. **Generalize** Where are metals located in the periodic table? Where are nonmetals located?

4. **Interpret Data** What other elements are in the same period as sulfur? What other elements are in the same group? Which elements are likely to have properties similar to those of sulfur?

Chapter 8 *Review*

Concept Summary

8.1 Structure of Matter

▶ All things are made of matter. Matter is anything that takes up space and has mass. Each type of matter has unique chemical and physical properties.

▶ Atoms are the building blocks of matter. Atoms are made up of electrons, neutrons, and protons.

▶ The number of protons in an atom's nucleus determines what element it is.

▶ Atoms of the same element with different numbers of neutrons are isotopes.

▶ Atoms are joined together by ionic, covalent, and metallic bonds.

▶ Matter exists as elemental matter, compounds, and mixtures.

8.2 Energy and Changes in Matter

▶ A physical change in matter is a change in its physical properties.

▶ A chemical change alters the chemical bonds joining the atoms of matter.

▶ Matter on the earth exists in the solid, liquid, or gas phase. A change in phase is a physical change caused by the addition or removal of heat energy.

8.3 The Earth's Elements

▶ The elements are organized in a systematic way in the periodic table.

▶ The earth's crust, atmosphere, and oceans vary in the elements that make up their matter.

Chapter Vocabulary

matter (8.1)
atom (8.1)
ion (8.1)
element (8.1)

isotope (8.1)
chemical bond (8.1)
molecule (8.1)

compound (8.1)
phase change (8.2)
organic matter (8.3)

Check Your Vocabulary

Use the vocabulary words above to complete the following sentences correctly.

1. Two or more atoms joined by covalent bonds form a(n) _____ .

2. Everything you can touch is made of _____ .

3. Matter created or derived from living things is _____ .

4. A nucleus surrounded by electrons makes up a(n) _____ .

5. A substance made of two or more elements chemically bonded is a(n) _____ .

6. Two atoms with 6 protons each but different numbers of neutrons are examples of a(n) _____ .

7. Interactions between two atoms or ions create a(n) _____ .

8. Hydrogen, oxygen, and iron are examples of _____ .

9. Water undergoes a(n) _____ when it becomes ice.

10. When an atom loses or gains an electron, it becomes a(n) _____ .

Write Your Vocabulary

Write sentences using the vocabulary words above. Show that you know what each word means.

Chapter 8 Review

Check Your Knowledge

Answer the following in complete sentences.

1. Name four properties of solids.

2. What element is most abundant in the crust, atmosphere, and oceans?

3. Name the four phases of matter.

4. What is the difference between an atom and an ion?

5. What kind of bond holds together the atoms of a metal?

6. How are groups of elements arranged in the periodic table? How are the groups identified?

7. What subatomic particle carries a positive charge?

8. What phase of matter has neither a definite volume nor a definite shape?

9. What are the three basic parts of a chemical equation?

Choose the answer that best completes each sentence.

10. An oxygen atom with a mass number of 16 has 8 protons and (0, 8, 9, 16) neutrons.

11. A liquid (evaporates, melts, condenses, freezes) to form a gas.

12. Atomic number describes the number of (electrons, neutrons, protons, nuclei) in the atoms of an element.

13. An ionic solid is (elemental matter, a compound, a mixture, an isotope).

14. In the chemical formula of a compound, the number of atoms of each element is shown by (chemical symbols, subscripts, charges, yield signs).

Check Your Understanding

Apply the concepts you have learned to answer each question.

1. Can two negative ions be joined by a chemical bond? Explain.

2. When the pressure of a certain substance is increased, it becomes more dense. Is it a solid, liquid, or gas? Explain how you know.

3. Compare and contrast the movement and arrangement of H_2O molecules in water, ice, and water vapor.

4. **Application** You have two blocks of metal that look the same and have the exact same size and shape. How can you determine if the two blocks are the same metal or different metals?

5. Arrange the following by size, from smallest to largest: molecule, proton, atom, nucleus.

6. **Classify** The following are properties of iron. Which are chemical properties? Which are physical properties?

   a. Density is 7.87 g/cm^3.
   b. Combines with oxygen to form rust.
   c. Shiny.
   d. Melts at 1,535°C.

7. For each particle described below, give the name of the element and tell whether it is an atom, a negative ion, or a positive ion.

   a. 11 protons, 10 electrons.
   b. 17 protons, 18 electrons.
   c. 10 protons, 10 electrons.

8. **Mystery Photo** The photograph on page 158 shows ice crystals on a window. Where do you think the molecules making up the crystals came from?

Develop Your Skills

Use the skills you have developed in this chapter to complete each activity.

1. **Interpret Data** The graph below shows the atomic number and mass number of the most common isotopes of the first eight elements.

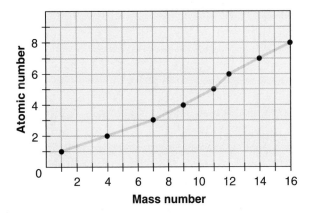

a. What is the mass number of the element with an atomic number of 4? How many neutrons are in the nucleus of this isotope of the element?

b. Describe the relationship between atomic number and mass number.

c. Why do you think the isotopes on the graph don't line up to form a straight line?

2. **Data Bank** Use the information on page 622 to answer the following questions.

a. By measuring the amounts of certain unstable isotopes contained in rocks and fossils, scientists can determine their age. Which element and isotope is used to date fossils containing organic matter?

b. How many protons and how many neutrons do atoms of this isotope contain?

Make Connections

1. **Link the Concepts** Below is an incomplete concept map showing how some of the main concepts in this chapter link together. Copy the map, then complete it, using words and ideas from the chapter.

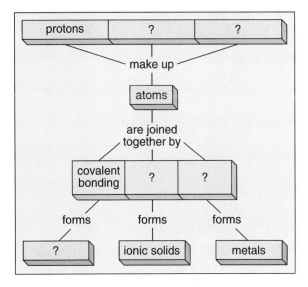

2. **Science and Technology** Buckyballs are one kind of substance being used to make superconductors. Research other types of superconducting materials and find out their possible uses.

3. **Science and Social Studies** Find out how the model of the atom has changed over time. Focus your research on the scientists John Dalton, J. J. Thomson, Ernest Rutherford, and Niels Bohr.

4. **Science and Society** Contact your local water department or water company and ask for the latest chemical analysis of the drinking water supplied to your home. Use this information to make a wall chart for your classroom showing the substances contained in your water and their amounts. Identify any substances that might be harmful.

Chapter 9   Minerals

What do you see?

"I see an amethyst cut crosswise. It was formed like all crystals, through many years. The colors are caused by different elements when it was being formed."

Eliza Bivins
Westwood Center for
*   Health and Science*
Grand Rapids, Michigan

To find out more about the photograph, look on page 206. As you read this chapter, you will learn about the composition and uses of minerals.

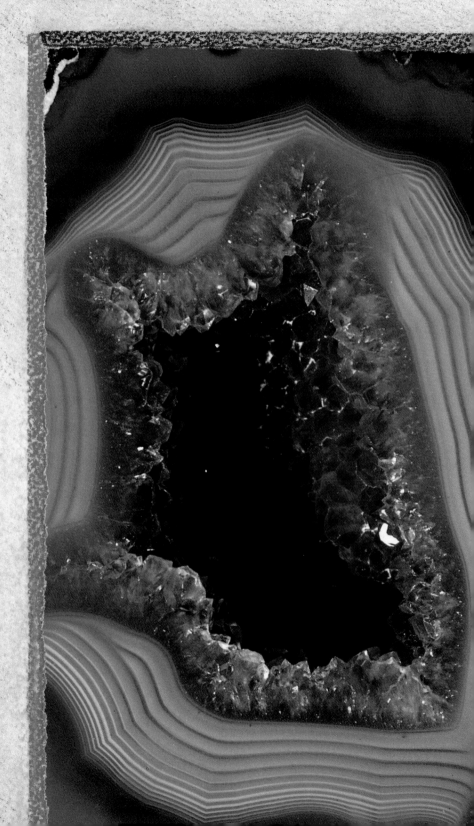

Crystal Structure

The crystal shapes of most of the earth's minerals are classified into six different groups. Each group of crystal shapes is called a crystal system. The six crystal systems are shown in Table 9.2. Each crystal system is defined by a certain arrangement of three or four lines called axes. Each axis represents one dimension of the crystal's three-dimensional shape. The relationship of the axes to one another determines the three-dimensional shape.

Crystal shape is determined by the arrangement of the atoms that make up a mineral. A mineral's characteristic crystal shape is the most stable way its atoms can arrange. The shape of a mineral's crystals is the same no matter how large they are. Sometimes crystals become very large, so the crystalline arrangement is easy to see. These beautiful minerals are valuable because they are rare. However, most crystals are very small. Some are so small that microscopes or X-rays are needed to reveal the crystal's pattern.

Table 9.2 Basic Crystal Systems

Cubic	Tetragonal	Orthorhombic
Three axes of equal length intersect at 90° angles.	Same as cubic, except the vertical axis is longer or shorter than the others.	Three axes of different lengths intersect at 90° angles.
Examples: halite, galena, pyrite	Examples: cassiterite, chalcopyrite	Examples: olivine, topaz
Monoclinic	**Triclinic**	**Hexagonal**
Same as orthorhombic, except one axis is oblique, or not at a 90° angle, to the others.	Three unequal axes intersect at oblique angles to one another.	Three equal horizontal axes intersect at 60° angles. The vertical axis is longer or shorter than the others.
Examples: mica, gypsum	Examples: plagioclase feldspar, turquoise	Examples: calcite, quartz

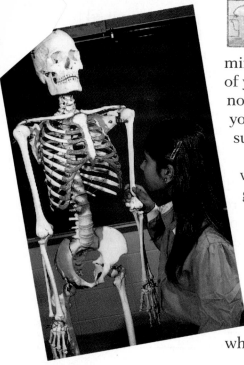

Figure 9.4 ▲

Bones contain large amounts of calcium and phosphorus, elements which come originally from minerals in the earth.

Science and You   *Minerals for Life*

If you read the labels on food products and vitamins, you may know that minerals are a necessary part of your diet. However, the minerals your body needs are not the same as the minerals you just read about. What you need are certain elements that come from minerals, such as iron, calcium, phosphorus, and iodine.

In the earth, these elements are usually combined with other elements to form minerals in rocks. But to get them into your body, you can't simply eat rocks! Instead, you eat parts of plants that extracted these elements from mineral particles in the soil. You can also get these elements by eating parts of animals that have eaten plants.

Iron is necessary for the formation of red blood cells. Red blood cells carry oxygen throughout your body. When you eat meat, liver, nuts, and whole-grain cereal, you get the iron you need.

Calcium and phosphorus help your body produce healthy bones and teeth. They also aid in blood and tissue formation. These elements are present in whole-grain cereal, meat, milk, and vegetables.

A chemical released by your thyroid gland regulates many of the processes that occur in your body. This gland depends on iodine for proper functioning. Foods containing iodine include seafood and iodized salt. You and rocks do have something in common: You are both formed from some of the same elements.

Check and Explain

1. Write a definition of *mineral* that includes all five characteristics.

2. Describe the chemical composition of each major mineral group.

3. **Reason and Conclude**   Explain why each of the following is not a mineral.

   a. Clam shell   c. Brick
   b. Iron nail   d. Concrete

4. **Make a Model**   Using cardboard and tape, make three-dimensional models of two of the basic crystal systems.

Activity 9 *How do you grow crystals?*

Skills Measure; Observe

Task 1 Prelab Prep

1. Collect the following items: 2 beakers, water, 2 pipe cleaners, spoon, hot plate, oven mitt or tongs, 2 pencils, 2 pieces of masking tape, alum (potassium aluminum sulfate), table salt (sodium chloride), safety goggles.
2. With the masking tape and pencil, label one beaker *Alum* and the other *Sodium chloride*.
3. Put on your safety goggles.

Task 2 Data Record

1. On a separate sheet of paper, copy Table 9.3.
2. Throughout the next several weeks, record your observations in the data table.

Table 9.3 Observations of Crystal Growth

Date	Alum Crystals	Sodium Chloride Crystals

Task 3 Procedure

1. Fill the beaker labeled *Alum* half full of water.
2. On the hot plate, heat the water to boiling. With the oven mitt or tongs, remove the beaker from the hot plate. **CAUTION! Be careful when handling a beaker of hot water.** Set the beaker on a heat-resistant surface.
3. Slowly add alum to the beaker of hot water, stirring constantly. Keep adding alum until no more of the chemical will dissolve.
4. Allow the solution to cool for several minutes.
5. Dampen a pipe cleaner. Roll the pipe cleaner in the remaining powdered alum.

6. Wrap one end of the pipe cleaner around the middle of a pencil. Place the pencil on the rim of the beaker so that the pipe cleaner hangs in the center of the solution.
7. Repeat steps 1 to 6 for sodium chloride.
8. Set the beakers where they will not be disturbed.
9. Observe the beakers every school day for the next two weeks. Each time you make an observation, examine the crystals, and record what you see in your data table.

Note: If no crystals form after several days, remove the pipe cleaner, roll it again in the powdered chemical, and put it back in the solution.

Task 4 Analysis

1. Did crystals form in each beaker?
2. If crystals grew, where did they form in each beaker? Why?
3. How do the crystals of alum differ from the crystals of sodium chloride?
4. Did the alum and the sodium chloride crystals grow at the same rate?

Task 5 Conclusion

Write a short report describing the growth of crystals. Include drawings in your report.

Everyday Application

Try making rock candy using the same procedure for growing crystals. Use sugar for your chemical and use heat-resistant kitchenware instead of labware. Compare the shape of the sugar crystals to the shape of the alum and sodium chloride crystals.

Extension

Do crystals formed in nature grow like the crystals you made in this activity? Discuss possible ways that a solution of a mineral and water could form and then dry out to form crystals.

Scratch Tests

What do you think will happen when you scratch a mineral with a penny? Will you get different results with different minerals? How might the results of such a test be useful?

SKILLS WARMUP

9.2 Mineral Identification

Objectives

▶ **List** the six properties of all minerals.

▶ **Identify** special properties of minerals.

▶ **Compare** and **contrast** mineral cleavage and fracture.

▶ **Measure** the hardness of minerals.

P icture a snake in your mind. You probably imagined an animal with scales and no legs. If you were to describe your snake, it would be different from the ones your classmates might describe. In nature, too, each kind of snake has unique characteristics that distinguish it from other snakes. What characteristics distinguish the snake you imagined? Physical properties, such as color, shape, and size, are useful for identifying snakes. Certain physical properties are also useful for identifying minerals.

Properties of Minerals

A prospector panning for gold in a stream collects some shiny gold-colored nuggets. Can the prospector be sure the nuggets are gold? Many gold miners have been fooled by pyrite, a mineral that's also called "fool's gold." Look at Figure 9.5 and notice the similarities between these two minerals.

Pyrite and gold are both shiny and have similar colors. But by testing other properties, the prospector can tell whether the mineral is pyrite or gold. Other physical properties that the prospector may test include streak, luster, cleavage or fracture, specific gravity, and hardness.

How do you identify a mineral you find in the field or laboratory? First, you can ask a series of questions about the mineral. The questions can be answered by performing simple tests or making observations. Each test determines one of the mineral's important properties that will help identify the mineral. Since each mineral has a unique set of properties, you can identify the mineral that you find.

Figure 9.5

Which is pyrite and which is gold? ▼

Luster How does the mineral reflect light? Some minerals are shiny and others are dull. The way light reflects from the mineral's surface is called **luster**. If a mineral is shiny like a metal, it has a *metallic* luster. The galena in Figure 9.6 has a *metallic* luster.

All other types of luster are grouped together. They are called *nonmetallic* lusters. Nonmetallic lusters include pearly, silky, glassy, dull, and greasy. Describe the luster of the olivine in Figure 9.6.

Galena   Olivine

Figure 9.6 ▲
Minerals vary in their luster.

Streak What color mark does the mineral leave on a tile? Many minerals make a mark when rubbed on a piece of unglazed porcelain tile called a streak plate. The mark is some of the mineral in powdered form. The color of the powder left on the streak plate is called the mineral's **streak**. What is the color of the streak of the mineral hematite in Figure 9.7?

Unlike color, the streak of a mineral does not vary, so streak is often a good identification test. Hematite varies in color from red to brown, but its streak is always red. A streak test is one way to distinguish between pyrite and gold. Gold has a gold streak, and pyrite has a black streak.

Color What color is the mineral? Color may be the first property you notice about a mineral. However, very few minerals can be identified by their color. Most minerals vary greatly in color because of small amounts of impurities. For example, the mineral quartz comes in a variety of colors, including pink, brown, purple, white, and clear.

Color can often tell you if a certain element is contained in a mineral. Copper, for example, produces a green or blue color in a mineral. You can infer that most green or blue minerals, such as the azurite and malachite in Figure 9.8, contain copper. Knowing that a mineral contains a certain element greatly narrows down what it might be.

Figure 9.7 ▲
Why is streak a more reliable property than color for mineral identification?

Figure 9.8 ▲
You can see both azurite (blue) and malachite (green) in this sample.

Cleavage and Fracture How does the mineral break? The broken surfaces on a mineral can be an important clue to identification. There are two types of mineral breakage: fracture and cleavage. A mineral that breaks along a flat surface, or plane, has **cleavage**. Minerals can have cleavage in one, two, three, four, or six directions. The mineral mica cleaves in one direction, forming flat, thin sheets. Halite cleaves in three directions. It breaks into smaller cubes.

Some minerals do not form smooth surfaces when they break. A mineral that leaves an uneven surface when it breaks has **fracture**. Fracture surfaces may be curved, splintery, or fibrous.

Minerals that break to form curving surfaces have *conchoidal* (kahn KOYD uhl) fracture. Quartz, shown in Figure 9.9, is one common mineral with conchoidal fracture. Minerals with conchoidal fracture have been used by people for thousands of years for making cutting tools and arrowheads.

Specific Gravity How dense is the mineral? Recall that density is how much matter is contained in a certain volume. Density is expressed as g/cm^3.

The densities of minerals can also be compared by using the measure of **specific gravity**. Specific gravity is the ratio of a mineral's density to the density of water. Water is used as a basis of comparison because its density is $1\ g/cm^3$. A mineral with a density of $5.3\ g/cm^3$, for example, has a specific gravity of 5.3. It is 5.3 times more dense than water.

The specific gravity of most minerals varies from 2 to 5. Minerals made mostly of metal elements, however, may have a much higher density. The specific gravity of pure gold, for example, is 19.3.

In the field, specific gravity is hard to measure, so heft is used instead. *Heft* is measured by picking up the mineral, feeling its mass, and comparing it to an equal volume of another mineral. A prospector would find that gold has more heft than pyrite.

Figure 9.9

The type of cleavage or fracture a mineral shows can help in its identification. ▼

Halite
Cleavage along three planes

Mica
Cleavage along one plane

Quartz
Conchoidal fracture

Hardness How hard is the mineral? Hardness is an important property for identifying minerals. Hardness is the ability of a mineral to resist being scratched. Harder minerals scratch softer minerals.

To make it easier to compare the hardness of different minerals, a German earth scientist named Friedrich Mohs (MOHZ) set up a hardness scale in the early 1800s. He arranged ten minerals in order of increasing hardness and assigned each a number from 1 to 10. These reference minerals are used to test and describe the hardness of minerals. This scale is called the **Mohs scale** of hardness.

Look at the Mohs scale in Table 9.4. Which mineral has a hardness of 10? Which mineral has a hardness of 1? The softest mineral, talc, can be scratched by all other minerals. Talc is in crayons and talcum powder. Diamond, the hardest known mineral, can scratch all other minerals.

When you test hardness, don't confuse a scratch with a streak. A soft mineral such as talc cannot scratch a harder mineral. But it may leave a streak that looks like a scratch!

In the field, you can test hardness with the field tests shown in the right-hand column of the table. Field tests do not require the test minerals from the Mohs scale. Instead, common items, such as a steel knife, are used.

Figure 9.10 ▲
Diamond is the hardest known mineral. What number is it given on the Mohs scale?

Table 9.4 Mohs Scale of Mineral Hardness

Mineral	Hardness	Field Test
Talc	1	Easily scratched by a fingernail
Gypsum	2	Can be scratched by a fingernail
Calcite	3	Barely scratched by a copper penny
Fluorite	4	Easily scratched by a steel knife blade
Apatite	5	Can be scratched by a steel knife blade
Feldspar	6	Easily scratches glass
Quartz	7	Easily scratches glass and steel
Topaz	8	Scratches quartz
Corundum	9	No simple test
Diamond	10	No simple test

Chemistry

L I N K

The cleavage of a mineral provides clues to how the mineral is structured. Collect some toothpicks, glue, and a butter knife.

1. Using the toothpicks and glue, build a "mineral" that you think will cleave in only one direction.

2. Allow the glue to dry, then test the cleavage of your mineral by trying to pry it apart with a butter knife or other flat instrument.

3. Draw a picture of your mineral and label the cleavage plane.

Why does your mineral break along this plane?

A C T I V I T Y

Figure 9.11 ▲
Willemite shows the special property of fluorescence.

Special Properties

All minerals have the physical properties of color, streak, luster, cleavage or fracture, specific gravity, and hardness. Some minerals have additional properties that can be used for identification. One special property is smell. Other special properties include magnetism and fluorescence (flor EHS uhns).

Magnetism Minerals containing iron or nickel are attracted to magnets. Some of these minerals can even act as magnets themselves. Magnetite is a magnetic mineral. Magnetite is also an important source of iron.

Fluorescence Some minerals display interesting characteristics when they interact with light. Exposure to ultraviolet light will make some minerals fluoresce, or glow. In Figure 9.11, the mineral willemite is shown fluorescing bright green after exposure to ultraviolet light.

SkillBuilder *Classifying*

ACTIVITY ACTIVITY

Identifying Common Minerals

Unknown minerals can be identified by testing the minerals' properties. Copy the table to the right. Obtain a streak plate, a copper penny, a kitchen knife, a piece of glass, and unknown mineral samples for identification. Give a number to each sample, and label it with that number.

1. In your table, observe and record the color of each mineral.

2. Test each mineral's streak using a streak plate. Record the color of the streak for each mineral in your table.

3. Test each mineral's hardness using the field tests in Table 9.4. Record the hardness results in your table.

4. Try to identify each mineral by comparing your results to the chart of mineral properties on pages 624–625 of the Data Bank.

5. Based on the three properties you tested, could you identify any of your samples? If not, what additional properties do you need to test in order to identify the samples?

6. Which property was most helpful in identifying the minerals?

Write a short report describing how you would identify an unknown mineral you found while walking home from school.

Sample Number	Color	Streak	Hardness
1			
2			
3			

Mineral Properties and Chemical Structure

Minerals are made of different chemical elements. But chemical makeup alone doesn't explain all the variations in minerals' properties. What matters most is a mineral's structure—the arrangement of its atoms or ions.

The effect of chemical structure on physical properties is easily seen in the silicates. All silicates contain silicon and oxygen. So they are similar in chemical makeup. However, silicates vary greatly in their properties.

All silicates share a structural unit called the silicon–oxygen tetrahedron (TEH truh HEE druhn). You can see in Figure 9.12 that this unit is made up of four oxygen atoms covalently bonded to one atom of silicon.

Silicon–oxygen tetrahedra bond to each other and to atoms or ions of other elements in many different ways. The tetrahedra can form single chains, double chains, sheets, and three-dimensional networks. Each type of structure results in a different set of physical properties. Study Figure 9.13. It compares two different types of structures.

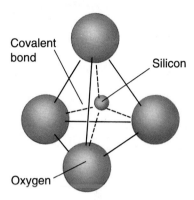

Figure 9.12 ▲
The silicon–oxygen tetrahedron is the building block of all silicate minerals.

**Figure 9.13
Silicate Structures** ▼

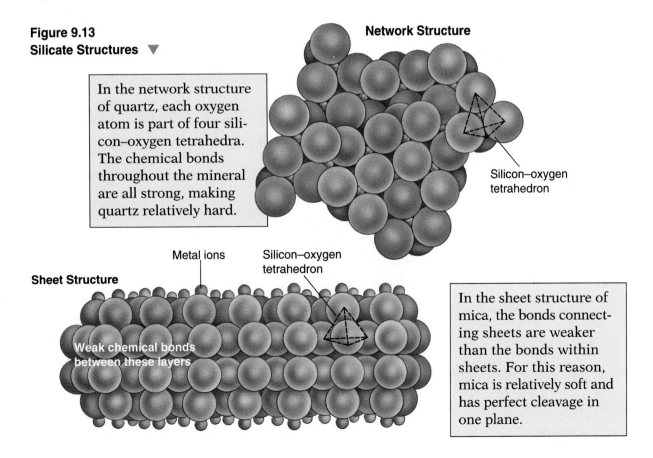

Network Structure

In the network structure of quartz, each oxygen atom is part of four silicon–oxygen tetrahedra. The chemical bonds throughout the mineral are all strong, making quartz relatively hard.

Silicon–oxygen tetrahedron

Sheet Structure

Metal ions

Silicon–oxygen tetrahedron

Weak chemical bonds between these layers

In the sheet structure of mica, the bonds connecting sheets are weaker than the bonds within sheets. For this reason, mica is relatively soft and has perfect cleavage in one plane.

Common Rock-Forming Minerals

Of the thousands of minerals in the earth's crust, only about 20 are common. They are called the rock-forming minerals because they make up most of the earth's rocks. Some important rock-forming minerals are described in Table 9.5. The 11 rock-forming minerals listed in the table make up about 90 percent of the mass of the earth's crust. Why do you think that most of the rock-forming minerals are in the silicate group? Recall that almost three-fourths of the earth's crust is made of oxygen and silicon.

Figure 9.14 ▲

Common rock-forming minerals include feldspar (front), olivine (center), and mica (rear).

Table 9.5   Major Rock-Forming Minerals

Mineral	Composition	Mineral Group	Hardness	Color
Quartz	SiO_2	Silicate	7	Varies
Potassium feldspar	$KAlSi_3O_8$	Silicate	6	Pink
Plagioclase feldspar	Varies from $NaAlSi_3O_8$ to $CaAl_2Si_2O_8$	Silicate	6	Varies
Mica	Contains Si, O, Al, K, and other elements	Silicate	2.5	White to dark
Olivine	$(Mg, Fe)_2SiO_4$	Silicate	6.5	Olive, yellowish, greenish
Pyroxene	Contains Si, O, Fe, and Mg	Silicate	5–6	Dark green to black
Amphibole	Contains Si, O, H, Fe, and Mg	Silicate	5–6	Dark green to black
Calcite	$CaCO_3$	Carbonate	3	White, grey, yellow, colorless
Dolomite	$CaMg(CO_3)_2$	Carbonate	3.5–4.0	Varies
Halite	NaCl	Halide	2.5	White, colorless
Gypsum	$CaSO_4 \bullet 2H_2O$	Sulfate	2	Reddish, white, grayish, yellowish,

Science and Technology
Drilling with Diamonds

When you think of diamonds, you probably imagine the glistening gems embedded in jewelry. But diamonds are also used for industrial purposes. Because of their hardness, diamonds can cut and drill through substances, such as rock, that are relatively hard.

The diamonds used in industry are not the same as those chosen for fine jewelry. Industrial diamonds have impurities or flaws, so they cannot be used as gems. Most industrial diamonds are also very small, like grains of sand.

Diamonds are most commonly used to coat the cutting surfaces of drill bits. Diamond drill bits for cutting through rock are ring-shaped hollow cylinders set with diamonds. The drill bit is attached to a drill that rotates at high speed. The bit penetrates the rock, leaving a sample of the rock inside it. The rock is then removed.

Diamond drill bits cut through rock much faster than bits made of other materials. They also last much longer. A high-grade steel bit cuts a path 8 km long before wearing down. A diamond bit, in contrast, cuts a path 2,000 km long before wearing down. You can see why diamonds are important for reasons other than just their brilliant luster.

Figure 9.15 ▲
This diamond-tipped drill can cut through the hardest of rocks.

Check and Explain

1. List the six properties that can be tested for identification of a mineral.

2. What is the property of fluorescence? How may it be used to identify a mineral?

3. **Compare and Contrast** Discuss the similarities and differences between cleavage and fracture.

4. **Measure** Using the Mohs scale of hardness on page 195, determine the hardness number for each of the following minerals.

   a. Scratches feldspar, but not topaz

   b. Scratched by your fingernail

   c. Scratches all the other minerals

   d. Scratched by a penny

Jewels

1. Make a list of all the valuable stones and gems you can think of that are used in jewelry.

2. Classify the items on your list into two or more groups.

Why did you choose the groups you did?

9.3 Uses of Minerals

Objectives

▶ **Describe** the use of ores.

▶ **List** some common uses of minerals.

▶ **Distinguish** between precious and semiprecious gems.

▶ **Infer** why metals are usually not found in their pure form in the earth's crust.

Did you know that every time you drink from a glass or bottle, you are using a product made from sand? Sand is a very plentiful material. Sand is mostly made of the mineral quartz, or SiO_2. Sand is melted down and molded or blown to make glass.

The quartz in sand is just one of the minerals of the earth that people use. Substances and products that come from minerals are all around you. You couldn't live your life without them.

Figure 9.16

The iron in steel comes from iron-containing minerals. ▼

Metals from Minerals

People use minerals as a source of metals. Only a few metals, such as gold, silver, and copper, exist as pure metals in the earth's crust, and even these are rare. Most of the metals people use, therefore, must come from minerals or rocks that contain metal elements.

A mineral or rock that contains usable amounts of an earth material is called an **ore**. Bauxite, for example, is an ore of aluminum. Feldspar also contains aluminum. But feldspar is not an ore because it contains too little aluminum to make extracting it worthwhile.

The process of removing a metal from its ore is called smelting. The ore is broken down into small particles and then heated to a high temperature. The atoms of metal separate from the rest of the mineral or rock and join in a molten mass. The molten metal is then collected.

Iron is produced by smelting the mineral hematite and other iron-containing minerals. Once extracted from its ores, iron can be processed to make steel. Many different industries use steel. For example, steel is used to build bridges, machine parts, and the frames of large buildings.

Useful Minerals

Look at Table 9.6. It lists just a few of the many uses of minerals. As you can see, many products you use every day contain minerals.

The mineral gypsum is present in the walls of most modern houses and other buildings. Gypsum is mined in large, open pits. It is crushed and then used to make wallboard, or drywall. If you can easily push a tack into a will, the wall is probably made of gypsum-filled wallboard.

Sulfur is a very useful mineral. In addition to the uses listed in Table 9.6, sulfur is important in the making of dyes, paints, fertilizers, insecticides, and plastics. Some of the world's richest sulfur deposits are on the Gulf Coast in Louisiana and Texas. Many deposits of sulfur are no easily mined because they are deeply buried. Gulf Coast sulfur is removed from the earth, however, without digging. Hot water, pumped into the sulfur deposit, melts the sulfur. It is then pumped to the surface and dried.

Some minerals are not in a usable form when they are mined from the earth. They are contained in ores that must be processed to separate the useful substances from the waste rock. Asbestos, for example, is separated from the mineral sepentinite.

Figure 9.17 ▲
What mineral is used to make glass?

Life Science
L I N K

Research what types of minerals are important for human health.

In a data table, list at least five different minerals, where or how the minerals can be obtained, and which bodily functions the minerals help to perform.

A C T I V I T Y

Table 9.6   Mineral Uses

Mineral	Used to Make
Borax	Soaps, cleansers, porcelain, dyes, inks
Calcite	Medicines, toothpaste
Feldspar	Pottery, glass, scouring powder, porcelain
Graphite	Pencils, dry lubricant, battery electrodes
Gypsum	Wallboard, plaster of Paris, fertilizer
Halite	Table salt, food preservatives, glass, paper
Mica	Glossy makeup, electronic parts, insulation
Quartz	Glass, watches, radios, televisions
Sulfur	Matches, medicines, rubber, gunpowder
Talc	Talcum powder, crayons, paints, soap

Quartz Vibrations

Quartz has many useful properties. It is very common, relatively hard, and can be melted down to make glass. Quartz also has an unusual property that has many important uses. Pressure produces electric charges across a quartz crystal. Because of this property, quartz is used as a *transducer* (tranz DOOS ur). A transducer is a device that changes one form of energy into another.

Scientists found that this special property of quartz also works in reverse. When an electrical charge is placed across a quartz crystal, the crystal changes shape slightly in one direction. If the electrical field is reversed, the crystal changes shape in the opposite direction. Therefore, if the electrical field alternates, the crystal will vibrate.

The number of vibrations per second stays constant if the frequency of the electrical current stays constant. This property is used to control the frequency of radio and television waves. It also makes a good timekeeper.

There is a quartz crystal inside this gas igniter. When the button is pushed, the crystal is squeezed, producing an electric charge. This charge causes a small spark. The spark lights the gas from the burner quickly and safely. ▼

Have you seen a wristwatch with the word quartz on it? A thin slice of quartz in these watches helps keep accurate time. Electrical current from the watch battery makes the crystal vibrate at a constant frequency of over 30,000 times a second. ▼

▲ Electronic equipment may use oscillators made from slices of quartz. An oscillator vibrates. Oscillators in radios control the frequency of the radio waves received by the radio.

Gems

Rare and beautiful minerals that are cut and polished for use as ornaments are called **gems**. Gems are divided into two groups: precious and semiprecious. Precious gems are rare and valuable. Diamonds, rubies, sapphires, and emeralds are precious gems. Semiprecious gems include garnet, jade, opal, topaz, and certain kinds of quartz. Semiprecious gems are usually not as rare as precious gems, so they are not as valuable.

Gems are valued for their color, luster, and hardness. In jewelry, diamonds are treasured for their ability to break up light into dazzling colors. They are also used in drills and abrasives because of their hardness. Jade's silky luster makes it a valued mineral for ornaments, such as vases and sculptures. For centuries, gems have adorned many temples, homes, and people.

Figure 9.18 ▲
Gems decorate fine jewelry.

Historical Notebook

Mineral Use Through Time

For thousands of years, people have known that minerals provide many useful materials. Minerals have been used in their original forms and as sources for metals.

Copper was the first metal extracted from a mineral. Over 7,000 years ago in the Middle East, people found they could put the mineral malachite into fire to remove its copper. The molten copper was collected, cooled, and hammered into tools, ornaments, and containers.

About 3800 B.C., people discovered that adding tin to copper made bronze, an alloy harder than either of the two metals. After its discovery in the Middle East, the secret of bronze-making traveled to other parts of the world. In China, bronze was used for weapons, everyday items, and sculptures like the one shown here.

Iron was discovered much later than copper because it is more difficult to extract from its

ores. Iron was first refined in Egypt about 3,500 years ago. Because iron is a hard, durable metal, it became an important metal for making tools and weapons.

1. Why was bronze more useful than copper?
2. Why was copper discovered before iron?

Science and Technology
Improved Minerals

Did you know that pure metals are often recombined with other metals and nonmetals? The result of this combination is called an alloy. In many ways, an alloy is like an artificial mineral.

Alloys have different properties from the elements that make them up. An alloy may be stronger, lighter, or more resistant to corrosion or rusting than a pure metal. For these reasons, alloys are more widely used in commercial products than pure metals.

Steel is an alloy made by combining iron and carbon. Different kinds of steel with special properties are produced by adding elements to the iron and carbon. For example, extremely sharp blades are made from a kind of steel that contains titanium. These blades are so sharp that they are used to cut regular steel.

A kind of steel that contains manganese hardens with impact. Earth-moving equipment contains this alloy because it can withstand continuous pounding. Stainless steel is a familiar kind of steel that resists corrosion. Stainless steel contains chromium and nickel.

Duraluminum® is an alloy of aluminum, copper, magnesium, and manganese. This alloy is hard, light, and able to withstand much tension without tearing apart. Because of this quality, duraluminum is used for many aircraft parts.

Another important alloy is brass. Brass is used in musical instruments, jewelry, and electrical appliances. Brass is a combination of copper and zinc.

Figure 9.19 ▲
Because they have to be light yet strong, aircraft are made of many different alloys.

Check and Explain

1. What is an ore?

2. Make a list of products or substances you've used in the past week that contain minerals.

3. **Compare and Contrast**   Explain the difference between precious and semiprecious gems.

4. **Infer**   Why do most metals in the crust not exist in their pure form?

Chapter 9 Review

Concept Summary

9.1 Mineral Formation and Structure

▶ A mineral is a natural, inorganic solid with a definite chemical composition and a particular crystalline structure.

▶ Minerals are formed when magma solidifies and when minerals precipitate from solutions.

▶ Most minerals are classified as silicates, carbonates, oxides, sulfates, sulfides, or halides.

▶ Most minerals are classified into one of six basic crystal systems.

9.2 Mineral Identification

▶ Minerals have six basic properties that help in their identification: color, streak, luster, cleavage or fracture, specific gravity, and hardness.

▶ Hardness is measured on the Mohs scale.

▶ The most common minerals in the earth's crust are the rock-forming minerals.

9.3 Uses of Minerals

▶ Most metals come from minerals in the earth that have high metal content called ores.

▶ Some minerals are used in their original form to make a variety of products.

▶ Gems are cut or polished minerals valued for their rarity or beauty.

Chapter Vocabulary

mineral (9.1)	cleavage (9.2)	Mohs scale (9.2)
streak (9.2)	fracture (9.2)	ore (9.3)
luster (9.2)	specific gravity (9.2)	gem (9.3)

Check Your Vocabulary

Use the vocabulary words above to complete the following sentences correctly.

1. The color of a mineral may vary, but the color of its ____ does not.

2. Minerals have either metallic or nonmetallic ____ .

3. Hardness is measured on the ____ .

4. Feldspar is a ____ , but coal and concrete are not.

5. When a mineral breaks along flat planes, it has ____ .

6. Minerals that break to form curved surfaces and jagged edges have conchoidal ____ .

7. A cut diamond is an example of a precious ____ .

8. Metals are separated from minerals called ____ .

9. The density of different minerals may be compared by measuring their ____ .

Explain the difference between the words in each pair.

10. cleavage, fracture
11. gem, crystal
12. specific gravity, density

Write Your Vocabulary

Write sentences using the vocabulary words above. Show that you know what each word means.

Chapter 9 Review

Check Your Knowledge

Answer the following in complete sentences.

1. What are the materials you need to perform field tests for hardness?

2. Name six rock-forming minerals.

3. How is a metal separated from its ore?

4. Why is color an unreliable property to use for mineral identification?

5. Describe two ways that minerals form.

6. What is a crystal system? Describe one.

7. Why must a mineral be solid to be called a mineral?

8. Name two kinds of nonmetallic luster.

9. What is the highest measure of hardness on the Mohs scale? What mineral has this hardness?

10. What elements do minerals in the halide mineral group contain?

Determine whether each statement is true or false. Write *true* if it is true. If it is false, change the underlined word to make the statement true.

11. Most of the earth's crust is made up of minerals in the <u>sulfate</u> group.

12. The mineral sulfur has <u>few</u> uses.

13. The streak left behind by a mineral on a streak plate is the mineral in its <u>powdered</u> form.

14. The axes of a triclinic crystal all meet at <u>90°</u> angles.

15. Hard organic matter <u>may</u> be classified as a mineral.

16. Not all minerals have the special property of <u>luster.</u>

Check Your Understanding

Apply the concepts you have learned to answer each question.

1. Why is a mineral containing the element aluminum not necessarily an ore of aluminum?

2. What do the minerals amphibole, pyroxene, and olivine have in common?

3. How do carbonates and silicates differ in their chemical composition?

4. Why are the crystals of a mineral always the same shape, no matter what their size?

5. **Application** You have two mineral samples that vary in color but are identical in all other properties. What can you infer about the two samples?

6. **Classify** Each chemical formula below represents a particular mineral. Identify the mineral group to which each belongs.

   a. $NaAlSi_3O_8$

   b. $MgSO_4$

   c. CaF_2

   d. AlO_3

   e. ZnS

7. **Mystery Photo** The photograph on page 184 shows the polished cross section of a geode. The crystals on the inside of the geode are amethyst, a type of quartz. How do you think the purple bands surrounding the amethyst crystals were formed?

8. A sample of a mineral has a mass of 64 g and a volume of 16 cm^3. What is its density? What is its specific gravity?

9. **Application** Why is a mineral with conchoidal fracture useful for making stone tools?

Develop Your Skills

Use the skills you have developed in this chapter to complete each activity.

1. **Interpret Data** The table below shows the specific gravity of different substances.

Substance	Specific Gravity
Aluminum	2.7
Diamond	3.5
Gold	19.3
Mercury	13.5
Oak wood	0.85
Talc	2.7
Water	1.0

   a. How much denser is gold than water?

   b. Which of the substances listed will float in water? Which will float in the liquid metal mercury?

2. **Data Bank** Use the information on pages 624–625 to answer the following questions.

   a. What mineral has a hardness of 5, a white streak, and a specific gravity of 3.2?

   b. Name two minerals with a specific gravity higher than 5.0. What do they have in common?

3. **Make a Map** In an atlas, find a map showing the location of important mineral deposits in the world. Make your own map, using this information.

Make Connections

1. **Link the Concepts** Below is a concept map showing how some of the major concepts in this chapter link together. Only parts of the map are filled in. Complete the map, using words and ideas from the chapter.

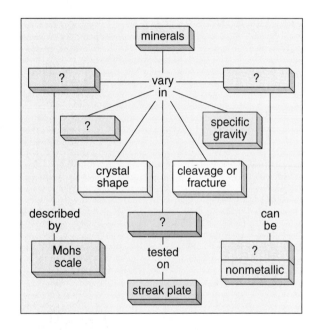

2. **Science and You** Compare the labels on three or more daily multiple-vitamin products. Make a chart that shows the minerals each product contains and their amounts.

3. **Science and Technology** Research how synthetic diamonds are made. In a few paragraphs, explain how these diamonds are created and their uses.

4. **Science and Economics** Find out what minerals, ores, or gems are mined in your state. Write a short report on the economic importance of these mining operations.

Chapter 10

Rocks and the Rock Cycle

What do you see?

❝I see a rock's surface. I think it shows some type of erosion by rain. I think there was also wind erosion. I think that it will become soil for a plant.❞

Latrina Young
Edison Learning Center
Dallas, Texas

To find out more about the photograph, look on page 232. As you read this chapter, you will learn about different types of rocks and the rock cycle.

10.1 Rocks

Objectives

▶ **Identify** and **classify** the three types of rocks.

▶ **Explain** the role of heat in the rock cycle.

▶ **Describe** the main characteristics of rocks.

▶ **Make a model** of the rock cycle.

Have you ever made peanut brittle? What ingredients are needed to make this treat? Peanut brittle is made of nuts, butter, sugar, boiling water, and corn syrup. The mixture is heated, then spread to cool and harden. Once hard, it can be broken into pieces. Like peanut brittle, rocks contain different ingredients. In rocks, the "ingredients" are minerals. Unlike peanut brittle, rock formation takes millions of years.

Types of Rocks

A rock is a made of one or more minerals. In Figure 10.1, you can see three rocks that contain the minerals feldspar and quartz. Although these rocks contain similar minerals, they formed in different ways. Rocks are classified according to how they formed. Rhyolite is classified as an **igneous** (IHG nee uhs) **rock**. Sandstone is a **sedimentary rock**. Quartzite is a **metamorphic rock**. Igneous, sedimentary, and metamorphic are the three main types of rocks.

Deep within the earth, high temperatures melt minerals to form magma. When magma cools and solidifies, igneous rock forms. Some magma solidifies beneath the surface. Some reaches the surface before hardening.

On the earth's surface, wind and water carry away pieces of minerals, rocks, and the remains of organisms. These particles settle to form layers of sediment. Over time, the sediment compacts, cements together, and hardens into sedimentary rock.

Through a series of changes involving heat and pressure, buried rock may form metamorphic rock. The original rock changes in appearance, structure, and composition.

Quartzite

Rhyolite

Sandstone

Figure 10.1 ▲
Each of these rocks belongs to a different group. Sandstone is sedimentary; rhyolite is igneous; quartzite is metamorphic.

The Rock Cycle

Cycles occur in many places on the earth. For example, during a frog's life cycle, the frog changes from a tadpole into an adult frog through a process called metamorphosis. Many insects go through a similar process as eggs develop into adults.

Rocks also go through cycles. The **rock cycle** is a series of processes in which rocks continuously change from one type to another. The rock cycle is shown in Figure 10.2. Follow the cycle as you read how rocks change form.

Heat and Pressure When rock is buried under the surface, heat and pressure may change the structure and appearance of the rock's minerals. Metamorphic rocks, such as marble or slate, may form.

If deeply buried sedimentary, igneous, or metamorphic rocks are exposed to even greater heat and pressure, the rocks melt to form magma. The rock cycle continues.

Figure 10.2
The Rock Cycle ▼

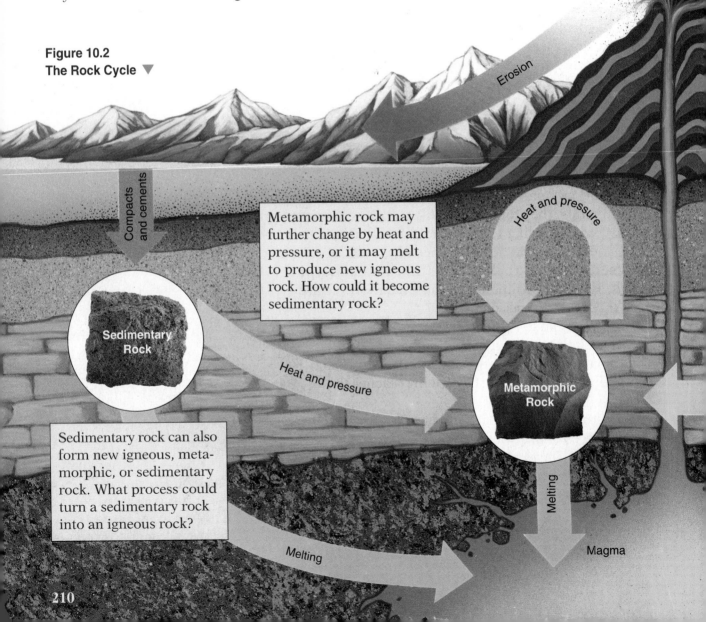

Compacts and cements

Erosion

Heat and pressure

Metamorphic rock may further change by heat and pressure, or it may melt to produce new igneous rock. How could it become sedimentary rock?

Sedimentary Rock

Heat and pressure

Metamorphic Rock

Sedimentary rock can also form new igneous, metamorphic, or sedimentary rock. What process could turn a sedimentary rock into an igneous rock?

Melting

Melting

Magma

Melting and Cooling Inside the earth, great pressures and high temperatures melt rocks and minerals. Here, igneous, sedimentary, and metamorphic rocks become magma. Some magma reaches the surface as lava. The lava cools and hardens, forming new igneous rock from the melted rock material.

Some magma pushes its way up through the surrounding rock. As it rises, the magma cools slowly. Eventually it hardens and forms new underground igneous rocks. Forces within the earth may push up great mountains of underground igneous rock.

Sedimentation Sedimentary, igneous, and metamorphic rocks located near the surface are exposed when topsoil washes or blows away. Rain, wind, and running water break down surface rocks into tiny particles. The particles of many different rocks form layers of sediment. As new layers of sediment form, they push down on the older layers. Over time, the weight of the overlying layers presses the particles below tightly together. The buried sediments harden into new sedimentary rock. The type of sedimentary rock formed depends on the kinds of particles that collect in the sediments.

Cools

Heat and pressure

Igneous Rock

Bits of igneous rock may become part of new sedimentary rock. Heat and pressure may change igneous rock into metamorphic rock. Melted igneous rock may form new igneous rock.

Melting

Characteristics of Rocks

Deep into Rocks

1. Start a rock collection by gathering rock samples from places near where you live.

2. Use a hand lens to examine each rock.

3. Use a rock field guide to identify your rocks.

4. Classify the rocks as igneous, sedimentary, or metamorphic.

If you try to find your friend in a crowd, you probably look for certain physical characteristics. You might look for hair style or body build. Physical characteristics are important in identifying your friend. To identify a rock, you'd also examine its physical characteristics.

The texture of a rock is an important physical characteristic. The size, shape, and arrangement of the mineral grains that make up a rock determine its texture. Notice the different textures of the rocks in Table 10.1.

The size of the mineral grains in a rock helps determine the texture. Mineral grains that are large enough to see without a microscope give rocks a coarse-grained texture. These rocks look and feel rough. Some particles of coarse-grained rocks may come off when you rub or scrape them. Which rocks in Table 10.1 have coarse-grained textures?

Table 10.1   Common Rock Textures

Grain Size	Example	Grain Shape	Example	Grain Pattern	Example
Coarse	Sandstone, granite	Smooth and round	Conglomerate	Banded	Gneiss
Fine	Shale, basalt	Sharp and angular	Breccia	Nonbanded	Granite
Glassy	Obsidian	Elongated	Slate		

In Table 10.1, you can see shale. Shale is a sedimentary rock that forms from clay sediments. It has a fine–grained texture. The tiny grains can be seen only with a magnifying glass or a microscope.

Some igneous rocks, such as obsidian, don't contain any mineral grains. These rocks have a glassy texture. Obsidian is smooth and looks like dark glass.

Look at the conglomerate rock in Table 10.1. It is a sedimentary rock made of different kinds and sizes of rock. The grain shape in conglomerate affects the rock's texture. The large particles in conglomerate have smooth, rounded edges. In contrast, the particles in breccia (BREHCH ee uh) have sharp, angular edges.

Describe the grain pattern for each rock in Table 10.1. In most rocks, the grain pattern is random. In some rocks, such as slate and sandstone, the grains are spread evenly through the rock. These grains appear to line up in one direction. Other rocks, such as gneiss (NYS), have a banded pattern.

SkillBuilder *Classifying*

Rock Groups

Copy the flowchart onto a sheet of paper. Use a hand lens to examine ten different rock samples that are identified with a number. Divide the ten rocks into three groups based on their texture. Record each sample number in the appropriate circle on the flowchart. Further divide the rocks in each texture group. Record the sample numbers and the characteristic you used for each new group. Compare your system of classification with the systems used by your classmates.

1. Which texture was the easiest to identify?

2. Which texture group had the most rocks?

3. What characteristics did you use for the additional groups? Why?

4. If you knew the minerals present in each rock, would you group them differently? Why?

Write a paragraph describing how a rock's physical characteristics help to identify it.

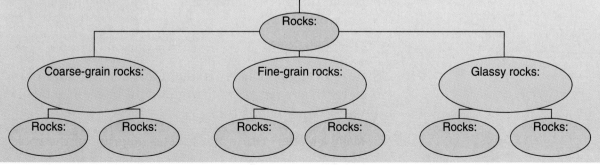

Figure 10.3 ▲

What types of rock materials were used to construct these row houses in Philadelphia, Pennsylvania?

Science and You
Is Your Home Made of Stone?

Think about the outside and inside of your home, school, and other buildings in your neighborhood. What kinds of rock materials were used to construct these buildings? Some buildings have an exterior of brown sandstone, often called brownstone. Others are made of bricks, which are manufactured from clay or shale. Perhaps the outside walls of some buildings in your neighborhood are covered with stucco. Stucco is a mixture of sand, water, and cement.

Is there a fireplace in your home? What is it made of? Most likely, it is made of bricks or stones held together by cement. The cement used to bind together bricks, tiles, and stones begins as a mixture of limestone and shale or clay. The mixture is ground, heated, and then crushed into a fine, gray powder. Powdered cement was probably also used to build the foundation of your house. When water, sand, and gravel are added to powdered cement, the mixture forms concrete. The concrete is poured into wooden foundation forms, where it hardens. Houses and buildings are then built on top of this sturdy material.

Gypsum is a sedimentary rock that is heated to produce plaster of Paris. You may have used plaster of Paris in art class or to create scientific models. But did you know that plaster is also used in building construction? Plaster is mixed with water and sand or other materials, and then covered with cardboard to make wallboard. Wallboard is commonly used for the inside walls of houses, apartments, and offices.

Check and Explain

1. Name the three main types of rocks, and give an example of each type.

2. How is heat involved in the formation of rocks?

3. **Reason and Conclude** Explain how the mineral particles in a piece of sandstone might have once been part of an igneous rock.

4. **Make a Model** Draw and label a diagram of the rock cycle. Use arrows to show how rocks are related.

10.2 Igneous Rocks

Objectives

▶ **Name** the two kinds of igneous rocks.

▶ **Explain** how igneous rocks form.

▶ **Classify** igneous rocks by characteristics.

▶ **Infer** what minerals are present in an igneous rock.

What image comes to mind when you think about the word "ignite"? Perhaps you imagine something being set on fire or bursting into flames. "Ignite" and "igneous" both come from the Latin word *ignis*, meaning "fire." In the formation of igneous rocks, heat plays an important role.

Formation of Igneous Rocks

Recall that the rock-forming process determines the rock type. Rocks produced by the cooling and solidifying of magma are classified as igneous. Igneous rocks form either underground or on the earth's surface. Thus igneous rocks are further classified by where they form.

Lava on the surface solidifies to form **extrusive rock**. At or near the surface, lava cools rapidly, leaving little time for large grains to form. As a result, extrusive rock tends to have a fine-grained or a glassy texture. Rhyolite, basalt, and pumice (PUHM ihs) are examples of extrusive rocks.

Magma that solidifies beneath the surface forms **intrusive rock**. Deep magma cools very slowly, producing rocks with large grains of uniform size. Coarse-grained texture is characteristic of intrusive igneous rocks, such as granite and gabbro.

Notice the grains in the porphyritic (POR fuh RIHT ihk) rock shown in Figure 10.4. The grains are different sizes. The large crystals formed from magma cooling beneath the earth's surface. However, before the magma completely hardened, it was forced out. On the surface, the rest of the magma cooled rapidly, producing the fine grains.

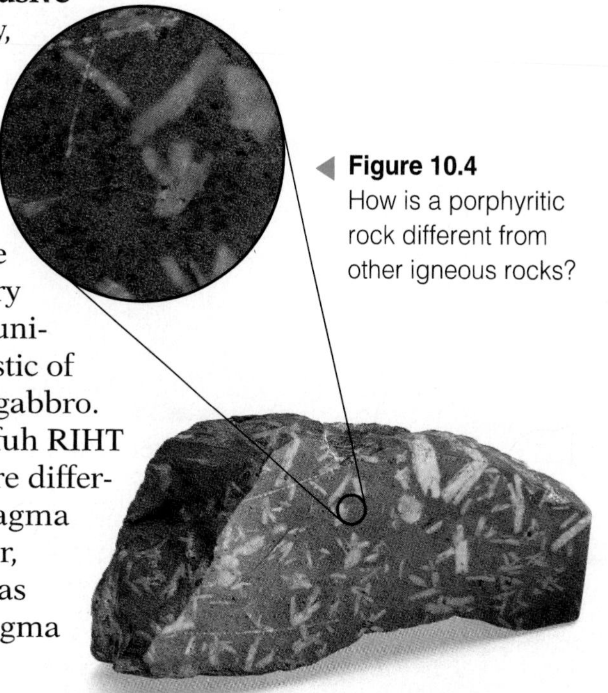

◀ **Figure 10.4**
How is a porphyritic rock different from other igneous rocks?

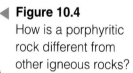

Figure 10.5
Formation of Extrusive and Intrusive Rocks ▼

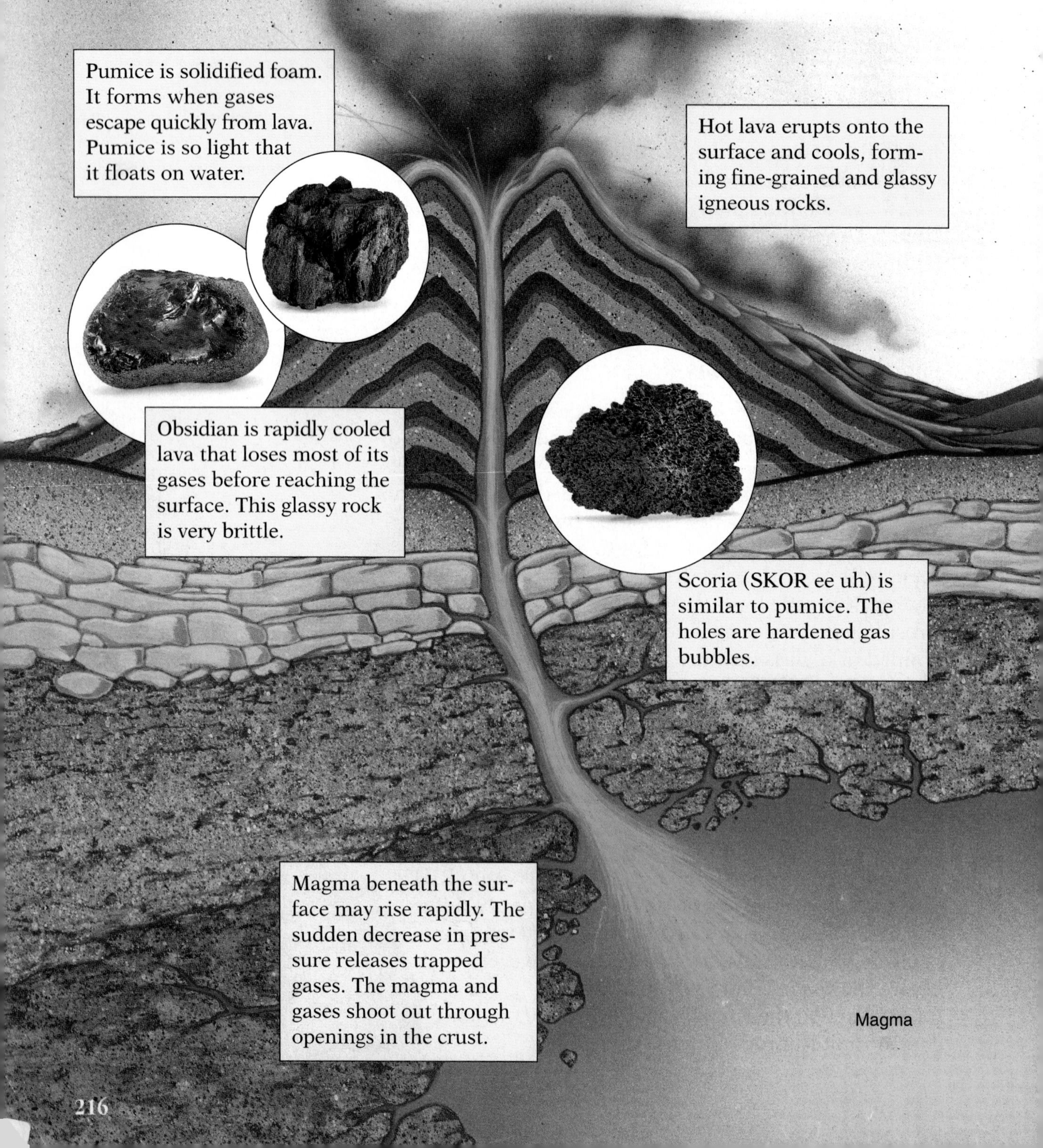

Extrusive Rocks

Recall that extrusive rock forms from lava. When you hear the word "lava," you probably immediately think of volcanoes. Volcanoes are important in extrusive igneous rock formation. For this reason, extrusive rocks are also known as volcanic rocks.

Pumice is solidified foam. It forms when gases escape quickly from lava. Pumice is so light that it floats on water.

Hot lava erupts onto the surface and cools, forming fine-grained and glassy igneous rocks.

Obsidian is rapidly cooled lava that loses most of its gases before reaching the surface. This glassy rock is very brittle.

Scoria (SKOR ee uh) is similar to pumice. The holes are hardened gas bubbles.

Magma beneath the surface may rise rapidly. The sudden decrease in pressure releases trapped gases. The magma and gases shoot out through openings in the crust.

Magma

Intrusive Rocks

According to Greek myths, Pluto was the ruler of the Underworld. This Kingdom of the Dead was located "beneath the secret places of the earth." Because intrusive rocks form deep inside the earth, they are also called plutonic (ploo TAHN ihk) rocks.

Recall that a body of intrusive rock is called a pluton. Plutons are usually composed of granite. Plutons have an irregular shape and form the core of great mountain ranges. Huge bodies of intrusive rock are called batholiths.

Sometimes magma intrudes layers of existing sedimentary rock. The force of the magma pushes up part of the rock, causing it to bulge. As the magma cools, it forms an irregular or mushroom-shaped body called a *laccolith*. Locate the laccolith in Figure 10.5.

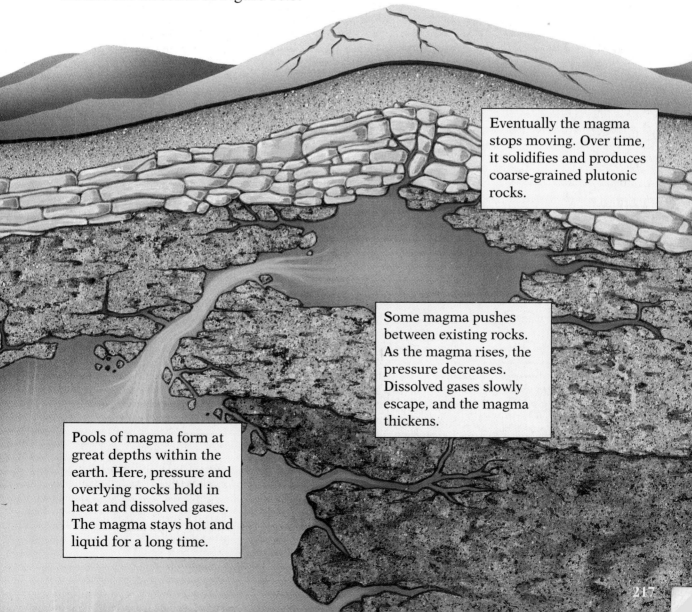

Eventually the magma stops moving. Over time, it solidifies and produces coarse-grained plutonic rocks.

Some magma pushes between existing rocks. As the magma rises, the pressure decreases. Dissolved gases slowly escape, and the magma thickens.

Pools of magma form at great depths within the earth. Here, pressure and overlying rocks hold in heat and dissolved gases. The magma stays hot and liquid for a long time.

Feldspar

Biotite

Quartz

Figure 10.6 ▲
The crystals in granite reveal its mineral composition. Different kinds of granite contain different minerals.

Igneous Rock Identification

Igneous rocks are identified by texture and mineral composition. The minerals present in the magma that forms a rock determine its composition. Texture depends on how fast the magma cools.

Texture In coarse-grained rocks, the grains can be as wide as a pencil. You can easily see the grains. In fine-grained rocks, the grains are no wider than the thickness of paper. The grains are visible with a hand lens or a microscope. Rocks with glassy texture contain no grains. Many igneous rocks are porphyritic. Recall that porphyritic rocks have large crystals embedded in fine-grained rock. What texture is shown in Figure 10.6?

Composition The major minerals found in igneous rocks are quartz, feldspar, muscovite, biotite, pyroxene, olivine, and hornblende. Notice the mineral colors for granite in Figure 10.6. The colors in igneous rock are a clue to its mineral composition. Quartz, feldspar, and muscovite are light-colored minerals. The dark-colored minerals are pyroxene, olivine, biotite, and hornblende.

Examples of Igneous Rocks

Figure 10.7
Different igneous rocks vary in texture, color, and mineral composition. ▼

Compare the different igneous rocks shown in Figure 10.7. All three rocks are formed from magma, but no two look alike. The texture and the mineral composition vary for each rock.

Diorite
Diorite is coarse-grained. It is gray or gray-green with white speckles. Its color comes from biotite, hornblende, and pyroxene.

Gabbro
Gabbro is coarse-grained. It is dark gray to black. It mainly contains pyroxene. Other minerals, such as olivine, may be present.

Basalt
Basalt is a fine-grained rock with the same mineral composition as gabbro. It is medium gray to gray-black in color.

Science and Society *Rock Architecture*

Granite, gabbro, and basalt are hard, dense igneous rocks. The minerals in these rocks make them resistant to erosion and give them a pleasing appearance. Because rain and wind have little effect on these rocks, they have been used as building materials for thousands of years. For example, many European castles and churches were constructed from gabbro. Some roads in ancient Rome were paved with basalt. Although they were built centuries ago, many of the structures still stand. These roads and buildings remain as evidence of the durability of igneous rock.

In the 1800s and early 1900s, many buildings in the United States were built mainly of granite. The state capitol buildings in Arizona, Arkansas, California, Maine, and Vermont were built of granite native to those areas. Today few buildings are constructed of igneous rock. Although igneous rock is available in many regions, high removal and processing costs restrict its use for entire buildings. Granite, for example, must first be blasted or drilled out of the ground. The stone must then be cut and polished.

Some igneous rock is still used as decoration. Public buildings, such as libraries and courthouses, are partially constructed from or decorated with granite and gabbro. Is any part of the capitol building in your state built of igneous rock? How are these rocks used in other public buildings in your city or town?

Figure 10.8 ▲
Many old buildings, such as this castle in France, are constructed from igneous rock.

Check and Explain

1. What are the two kinds of igneous rocks? How do igneous rocks form?

2. How does the texture of an igneous rock help identify its origin?

3. **Classify** What two main characteristics are used to identify igneous rocks? Give examples of rocks in each category.

4. **Infer** Suppose you see an old building made from very dark, almost black, coarse-grained rock. What minerals would the rock most likely contain? Explain your reasoning.

10.3 Sedimentary Rocks

Objectives

▶ **Describe** the stages of sedimentary rock formation.

▶ **Identify** and **describe** the three types of sedimentary rocks.

▶ **Compare** and **contrast** the physical characteristics of sedimentary and igneous rock.

▶ **Make a model** of the sedimentation process.

Imagine you're on a beach along a rocky cliff. Near the cliff base are large boulders, stones, and pebbles. Some are as big as your fist and have sharp edges. These recently broke off the cliff. Others are no larger than dimes and have rounded edges worn by waves. Your feet move through tiny sand grains. Where the water meets the beach, you notice shells and seaweed. If you could see the ocean bottom, you'd find silt and mud forming a thick ooze. These are some of the various materials that make up sedimentary rock.

Formation of Sedimentary Rocks

Sedimentary, igneous, and metamorphic rocks are all present on the earth's surface. An existing body of rock on the earth's surface is subjected to various forces of weathering and erosion. Rain, sun, wind, ice, pollution, and organisms break down exposed rock. What forces are acting on the rock shown in Figure 10.9?

Moving water transports rock particles of all sizes and deposits them as sediment. Rivers and streams carry loose sediment to lakes or oceans. As a water current slows, it drops sediment.

The size and density of the rock particles determine the order of the sediment deposited. Pebbles and gravel-sized particles are the first ones moving water deposits. Sand-sized particles are deposited next. Clay-sized particles and silt are the last particles that moving water deposits.

Layers of sediment slowly build up. The first sediment deposited is buried as more and more layers of sediment cover it. Over time, pressure from the stack of sediment hardens lower, older layers into sedimentary rock.

Figure 10.9 ▲

Many different forces slowly break down this rocky cliff into sediment.

Sedimentary Rock Processes If you step on paper in a wastebasket to make more room, you use weight to decrease the paper volume. The same thing happens to sediment in water. Newly deposited particles don't fit together tightly, so the spaces fill with water. As more sediment deposits, the weight of new layers presses on underlying sediment. As the water squeezes out, the spaces get smaller, and the particles pack tightly together. The process of particles pressing together is called *compaction*.

During compaction, minerals dissolved in water may be left behind. The minerals form a thin film around the particles and bind them together. The process of sediment spaces filling and binding together with minerals is called *cementation*. Calcite and silica are common mineral cements.

You can see the processes of compaction and cementation represented in Figure 10.10. They are part of the lithification of sedimentary rock. *Lithification* is the hardening of sediment into rock.

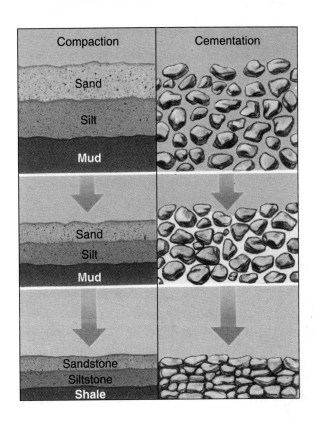

Figure 10.10 ▲
Compaction presses sediments tightly together. Cementation glues the sediment into one mass.

Figure 10.11 ▲
Mud cracks may form as fine-grained sediment dries out (above); water currents can produce ripple marks (below).

Sedimentary Rock Structures Different structures, such as layering, ripple marks, and mud cracks form in sedimentary rock.

▶ Horizontal layering occurs in sediment laid down in calm water. Particle size, composition, and thickness may vary in each layer.

▶ Permanent ripple marks, such as those in Figure 10.11, form when wind or water constantly move over sediment.

▶ Cracks form on the rock's surface as muddy sediment dries and shrinks. You can see cracks in Figure 10.11.

▶ Fossils that form from the remains of organisms buried in sand, silt, clay, or mud may also become part of sedimentary rock.

Classification of Sedimentary Rocks

Sedimentary rocks are grouped by their composition and the way they were formed. Compacted and cemented particles form clastic sedimentary rock. Living things or their remains may form organic sedimentary rock. Minerals that were once dissolved in water make up chemical sedimentary rock.

Clastic Rock   Particles of eroded and weathered rock and mineral grains that compact and cement together form **clastic rock**. Particles in clastic rock range from coarse boulders to a fine sediment of silt and clay. The particle size determines the type of clastic rock.

▶ Conglomerate rock and breccia are made of various large rock fragments. In conglomerates, the fragments are smooth with round edges. In breccia, the fragments are sharp and angular. The spaces between fragments fill with material that cements them into a single rock.

▶ Grains of sand can become sandstone, as shown in Figure 10.12. Sandstone textures vary from coarse to fine. Many sandstones are almost all quartz grains. However, sandstone may also contain feldspar, biotite, pyroxene, or olivine. The color of sandstone depends on its mineral grains and the impurities in the cement that binds the grains together.

▶ Silt and clay are composed of tiny mineral particles. Silt and clay mixed together with water make mud. When mud with a lot of clay compacts, it hardens into shale. Because plant or animal remains buried in mud preserve well, you can often find fossils in shale.

Figure 10.12 ▲
When sand cements together, it forms the clastic rock, sandstone. Sandstone formations, like these in Bryce Canyon, can extend for many kilometers.

Organic Rock Sedimentary rock that is formed from living things or their remains is called **organic rock.** Limestone is the most common organic rock. Coal is also an organic rock.

Limestone is mainly made of calcium carbonate. Ocean organisms, such as coral, clams, and mussels, extract calcium carbonate from water to form their shells and other hard parts. When these organisms die, layers of shells deposit on the ocean bottom. Over time, the fragments compact and cement together, forming limestone.

Chalk is a fine-grained, white limestone that formed on the bottom of ancient seas. Unlike most limestones, chalk is soft and rubs off easily. Figure 10.13 shows chalk deposits located near Dover, England.

Coal forms in swamps from the decayed remains of land plants. As plants die, they gradually form thick layers that harden into peat. The peat deposits become buried under sediment of sand and clay. Over time, pressure changes peat into lignite, a dark-brown type of coal. With increased time and pressure, black coal forms.

Figure 10.14 ▲
The Bonneville Salt Flats exist in land-locked Utah. How can you explain their formation?

Chemical Rock When minerals come out of solution and crystallize, they form **chemical rock**. Most chemical rocks are formed by the evaporation of water. When water evaporates, the dissolved minerals are left behind.

Rocks formed by water evaporation from oceans or desert lakes are called *evaporites*. Like igneous rocks, evaporites and other chemical rocks are held together by tightly interlocking mineral crystals.

You are probably familiar with the chemical rock halite, which you know as table salt. Large halite deposits may form when water in a sea inlet evaporates faster than water can enter. When saltwater lakes evaporate, they may leave behind large, flat deposits of halite, such as the Bonneville Salt Flats in Utah, shown in Figure 10.14. Ancient salt deposits exist in Kansas, Michigan, New Mexico, and Oklahoma.

Ocean water evaporation also causes the crystallization of the mineral gypsum. Gypsum is therefore usually found with deposits of halite. Gypsum is used in making cement, plaster of Paris, and wallboard. Gypsum deposits are found in Iowa, California, Michigan, Texas, New York, and New Mexico.

Figure 10.13 ▲
What do these chalk formations tell you about the history of this area in England?

Science and Technology
History in Sediment

One of the biggest challenges for scientists studying the earth is finding out about its early history. How do scientists learn about the earth's history? Sedimentary rock holds the key to many unanswered questions about the earth.

One important way sedimentary rock is used to study the earth is through core sampling. Since the late 1960s, several ocean-drilling projects have collected cores from layers of sediment and oceanic crust more than 1,000 m below the ocean floor. The cores are valuable because ocean sediments are not affected by many of the processes that change sediments and sedimentary rocks at the earth's surface. In recent years, scientists have studied core samples from the Indian Ocean.

From the core samples, they learned that the gradual formation of the Himalaya Mountains from plate collisions actually occurred 10 million years earlier than they had originally hypothesized.

Sediments from core samples also helped scientists discover that the climate in Antarctica has not always been cold. In fact, they discovered that Antarctica was warm and populated with ferns and beech trees until about 40 million years ago. The evidence for an iceless Antarctica came mainly from sediment deposits beneath the polar seas.

Figure 10.15 ▲
The long tubes will drill deep into the Mediterranean Sea to remove core samples.

Check and Explain

1. Where can you observe the beginning stages of sedimentary rock formation? Give several examples.

2. Identify and describe the three kinds of sedimentary rocks. Give an example of each kind.

3. **Compare and Contrast** Suppose you find a coarse-grained rock while walking in the mountains. How could you tell that the rock is sedimentary rather than igneous?

4. **Make a Model** Construct a model that shows how sedimentary layers form in a lake. What materials did you use to make the model?

Activity 10 *How do sedimentary layers form?*

Skills Model; Hypothesize; Observe; Infer

Task 1 Prelab Prep

1. Collect the following materials: gravel, sand, clay, graduated cylinder, jar, water, timer with a second hand, spoon, cup, diluted white glue solution, several toothpicks.
2. Crumble the clay into particles.

Task 2 Data Record

On a separate sheet of paper, copy Tables 10.2 and 10.3. In Table 10.2, keep a record of any changes in the layers you observe.

Task 3 Procedure

1. Fill the jar 3/4 full of water.
2. Drop in a pinch of one type of sediment. Watch it fall. Time the length of the fall. Record the settling rate in your data table.
3. Repeat step 2 for the other two types.
4. Hypothesize what would happen if you poured a mixture of the three types of sediment into the jar. Record your hypothesis on a separate piece of paper.
5. Measure three spoonfuls of each sediment. Mix them together and pour the mixture into the water. Record the settling order in your data table.
6. Pour out the excess water from the jar. Measure 50 mL of the diluted white glue solution. Evenly distribute the solution over the sediment layers in the jar.
7. Set the jar in a warm, dry place.

Table 10.2 Sediment Characteristics

Sediment Type	Sediment Size	Settling Rate	Settling Order
Gravel			
Sand			
Clay			

8. The next day, use toothpicks to test the hardness of the layers. Continue to keep the jar in a warm, dry place. Observe the layers each day for several days. Record your observations in Table 10.3.

Table 10.3 Observations

Day 1	Day 2	Day 3

Task 4 Analysis

1. **Observe** What happened to the glue solution after several days?
2. What did the glue solution represent?
3. What happened to the sediment layers after several days? Which layer was the first to harden?
4. Did the water in the jar represent fast- or slow-moving water? Why?
5. What kinds of sedimentary rock did you form for each layer?

Task 5 Conclusion

Write a paragraph describing how this model is similar to the natural processes involved in the formation of sedimentary rock layers. How is it different?

Everyday Application

The compaction and cementation of sediments in the activity are similar to the formation of concrete. How are they alike? How do they differ?

Extension

Develop a model using simple materials to show how igneous rock forms. Compare this model to your model for sedimentary rock formation.

Find It Under "M"

Use a dictionary to look up the meaning of the prefix *meta.* Also find the meaning of the suffix *morph.* Using these two definitions, define the word "metamorphic."

SKILLS WARMUP

10.4 Metamorphic Rocks

Objectives

▶ **Identify** common metamorphic rocks and their parent rocks.

▶ **Describe** the conditions necessary for metamorphism to take place.

▶ **Compare** and **contrast** contact and regional metamorphism.

▶ **Predict** the conditions necessary to form foliated or nonfoliated metamorphic rock.

When you see a butterfly, it's hard to imagine it was once a caterpillar. What happened to its many legs and its jaws? A butterfly is the result of a process called metamorphosis. During metamorphosis, the caterpillar's structure and appearance change to form a butterfly.

Rocks also go through a type of metamorphosis. In fact, both igneous and sedimentary rock can change into metamorphic rock. The texture, color, and composition of the original rock differ greatly from the new metamorphic rock formed.

Formation of Metamorphic Rocks

Changes in structure, appearance, and composition of rock beneath the surface is called **metamorphism.** Metamorphism is caused by intense heat and high pressure acting on rock.

Magma may partially melt a rock mass. Under heat and pressure, the minerals recrystallize and small mineral grains enlarge. New minerals replace the original minerals. Mineral grains may pack more tightly and align, creating bands.

Shale is a fine-grained, clastic rock that contains clay. During metamorphism, the mineral mica replaces some of the clay to form slate. With continued heat and pressure, the mica grains enlarge, and new minerals are added. The minerals form bands. The rock changes to schist (SHIHST). Schist is shown in Figure 10.16. Schists are coarse-grained metamorphic rocks derived from slate or shale.

Figure 10.16

Shale may first change to slate, before changing into schist, the rock shown below. ▼

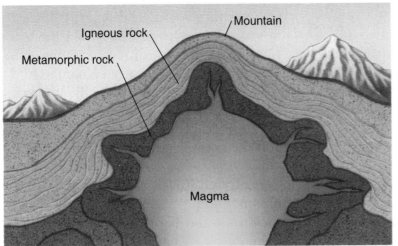

Figure 10.17
During contact metamorphism, rocks near the magma are altered.

Contact Metamorphism What happens to an egg when it's fried? As it fries, an increase in temperature causes chemical changes in the egg. The part closest to the heat cooks first. The egg changes color and texture. Even if the outside of the egg looks done, the inside may have just begun to cook. During contact metamorphism, rocks go through a similar process.

Contact metamorphism takes place when magma intrudes country rock. The heat from the magma alters the rock. The rock in contact with the magma "cooks" first. Which rock in Figure 10.17 would the magma affect first? Minerals in the magma and the rock mix. New mineral combinations form in the country rock.

Different changes take place farther from the heat source. Rocks composed mainly of one kind of mineral recrystallize with little mixing.

Regional Metamorphism Small areas of rock are affected by contact metamorphism. In contrast, regional metamorphism affects thousands of kilometers of rock. Regional metamorphism occurs at the margins of continents, where large areas of rock become deeply buried. Intense forces act on the buried rock. Pressure may cause rocks to buckle and fold. Heat and pressure cause minerals to recrystallize and change structure.

Deeply buried rocks may come into contact with a magma chamber. Some rocks may melt completely, forming intrusive igneous rocks. Other rocks altered by contact with the magma form metamorphic rocks.

Figure 10.18
Regional metamorphism occurs at continental plate boundaries. ▼

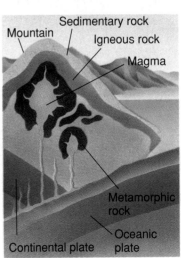

Metamorphic Rock Classification

Metamorphic rock grains have uniform size. They are arranged either randomly or in parallel bands. Metamorphic rocks are classified according to the arrangement of their mineral grains.

Foliated Rocks The pressures that accompany metamorphism affect grain structure. The grains in sedimentary and igneous rocks tend to be random. Look at Figure 10.19. What happens to the grain arrangement when pressure is applied from one direction? The grains line up and lock together in bands.

Metamorphic rock with grains arranged in parallel bands are **foliated.** Banding gives foliated rocks a striped appearance. In rocks that contain several minerals, the grains may separate into bands of different minerals. The presence of sheet minerals, such as mica, causes foliated rocks to break into smooth plates. This property makes slate a useful rock for chalkboards and roofing material.

Foliated rocks differ from layered sedimentary rocks. The separate layers in sedimentary rock consist of different sized particles, not different minerals. Clastic rock particles are cemented and compacted, not interlocked like the minerals in foliated rock. Chemical rocks have mineral crystals, but the size varies, and the crystals are random.

Nonfoliated Rocks In contact metamorphism, equal pressure surrounds the rock mass. Little or no grain rearrangement occurs. These metamorphic rocks are nonfoliated. Nonfoliated rocks don't have bands. Most nonfoliated rocks originate from single-mineral rocks.

Because the grains in nonfoliated rocks form at the same time, the grains are similar in size. This property can distinguish metamorphic rock from igneous rock. Compare the grains in the igneous rock granite shown below on the left, with those in the nonfoliated rock marble in Table 10.4. Igneous rock grains form at different times, producing various grain sizes. The metamorphic rock grains are more uniform in size.

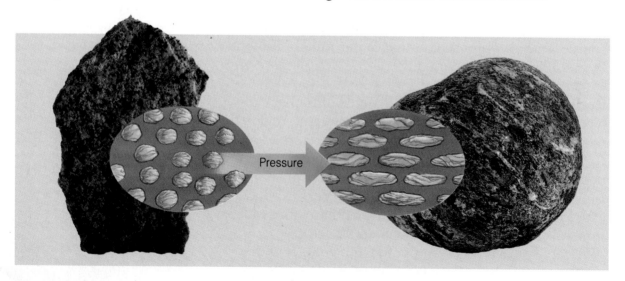

Figure 10.19 ▲
The random arrangement of minerals in rocks rearranges under pressure to form bands.

Examples of Metamorphic Rocks

You can identify some metamorphic rocks by observing the parent rocks from which they formed. Compare the metamorphic rocks to the parent rocks in Table 10.4. How do they differ?

Marble is coarser-grained than its parent rock, limestone. Layers or fossils that were in limestone are not seen in marble, but impurities can form patterns.

The sedimentary rock sandstone changes into quartzite. It is a hard rock with tightly linked quartz sand grains.

Regional metamorphism changes shale into slate. Clay and mudstone also change into slate. Unlike its parent rock, slate contains mica and splits into thick slabs.

Table 10.4 Metamorphic Rocks and Their Parent Rocks

Parent Rock	Metamorphic Rock
Limestone	Marble
Sandstone	Quartzite
Shale, clay, mudstone	Slate

Historical Notebook

Marbles from the Past

Marble is a metamorphic rock that has been valued by people for centuries for its beautiful textures and colors. The Taj Mahal in India, shown at the right, is a famous monument made of a variety of marbles. It was completed in 1643 by Emperor Shah Jahan in memory of his wife.

The main building, or mausoleum, of the Taj Mahal complex is made of pure white marble. This type of marble is the most valuable marble. The mausoleum stands on a marble block 7 m high. The main arch rises to 33 m. Inside the mausoleum, the marble tombs of the emperor and his wife are carved and decorated with precious stones.

The marble and materials for the Taj Mahal came from all over India and central Asia. More than 20,000 workers labored daily for nearly 22 years to complete the Taj Mahal complex.

A huge marble building like the Taj Mahal would be nearly impossible to build today because of the high cost of extracting marble. Today marble is mainly used for interior decorations, tabletops, and other small items.

1. Why do you think Emperor Jahan chose marble to build the Taj Mahal?

2. **Research** Find out the history of another famous building that was made from marble, such as the Parthenon in Greece.

Science and Technology
Building on Bedrock

How can a tall building like the Empire State Building stand without toppling over? The reason is because the building is built on a layer of solid rock called bedrock. Because few materials are strong enough to support the great weight of a tall building, bedrock is very important in construction.

Bedrock can be igneous, metamorphic, or sedimentary in origin. It can be located below or at the earth's surface. When choosing a building site, builders must locate and identify the bedrock.

To locate bedrock, detailed geological maps are studied. Sonar, a device that uses reflected sound, may help detect bedrock. In some cases, bedrock is located by measuring the speed of seismic waves as they move through the earth. If the bedrock is difficult to identify, engineers must sometimes drill into the earth. A camera is then used to take photographs that will help identify the bedrock.

Before laying a foundation, workers may drive steel pipes, called piles, into the bedrock. The piles are then filled with concrete. For skyscrapers and other tall buildings, the concrete may be reinforced with steel rods called footings. The piles and footings are important because they support the weight of the entire building. Once they are in place, construction can begin.

Figure 10.20 ▲
Before a large structure can be built, piles are driven into the bedrock for support.

Check and Explain

1. Name four examples of metamorphic rocks, and identify their possible parent rocks.

2. What conditions are necessary before metamorphic rock will form?

3. **Compare and Contrast** How are contact and regional metamorphism similar? How are they different?

4. **Predict** Suppose you are searching for metamorphic rocks for your rock collection. Where would you most likely find samples of foliated and nonfoliated rock on the earth's surface?

Chapter 10 Review

Concept Summary

10.1 Rocks
▶ The main types of rocks are igneous, sedimentary, and metamorphic.
▶ The rock cycle is a series of processes that recycle rocks.
▶ Depending on the conditions, a rock may change into another type of rock.
▶ Rocks are identified by their texture and grain size. Rock textures include coarse-grained, fine-grained, and glassy.

10.2 Igneous Rocks
▶ Igneous rock forms from magma.
▶ Extrusive igneous rock comes from magma cooling on the surface. Intrusive igneous rock forms by magma solidifying beneath the surface.
▶ Igneous rocks are identified by texture and mineral composition.

10.3 Sedimentary Rocks
▶ When loose sediments settle, compact, and cement together, sedimentary rock forms.
▶ Layers, ripples, and mud cracks are found in sedimentary rocks. Fossils occur in sedimentary rocks.
▶ Sedimentary rock can be clastic rock, organic rock, or chemical rock, depending on the origin of the rock particles.

10.4 Metamorphic Rocks
▶ Heat and pressure can change any rock into metamorphic rock.
▶ Metamorphic rock can form by contact or regional metamorphism.
▶ Metamorphic rocks are classified as foliated or nonfoliated.

Chapter Vocabulary

igneous rock (10.1)   extrusive rock (10.2)   chemical rock (10.3)
sedimentary rock (10.1)   intrusive rock (10.2)   metamorphism (10.4)
metamorphic rock (10.1)   clastic rock (10.3)   foliated (10.4)
rock cycle (10.1)   organic rock (10.3)

Check Your Vocabulary

Use the vocabulary words above to complete the following sentences correctly.

1. Rocks can change from one type into another type during the ____ .

2. Rocks formed by the compaction and cementation of sediments are ____ .

3. Changes in the appearance, structure, and composition of rocks is ____ .

4. Rocks formed from the cooling and hardening of magma are ____ .

5. Minerals coming out of solution and crystallizing form ____ .

6. Country rock exposed to heat and pressure may change to ____ .

7. A sedimentary rock made of compacted and cemented particles is ____ .

8. Magma that reaches the surface, then cools and hardens, makes ____ .

9. Metamorphic rocks that have mineral grains arranged in bands are ____ .

10. Magma that cools and hardens under the surface forms ____ .

11. Rock made from living organisms or their remains is called ____ .

Chapter 10 Review

Check Your Knowledge

Answer the following in complete sentences.

1. List three ways that rock breaks down to form sediment.

2. What are the different rock textures?

3. List the processes involved in forming sedimentary rock.

4. What is a fossil?

5. Name the two ways that metamorphic rock can form.

6. What is another name for extrusive igneous rock? Why?

7. Give an example of a nonfoliated metamorphic rock.

8. List three sedimentary rock structures.

9. What kind of sedimentary rock is coal?

10. What is another name for intrusive igneous rock? Why?

11. How is chemical rock typically formed?

Choose the answer that best completes each sentence.

12. Chalk is an example of (clastic, organic, chemical, igneous) rock.

13. Rocks that don't contain any mineral grains have a (coarse-grained, fine-grained, mixed-grain, glassy) texture.

14. Foliated rocks have (layers, cracks, bands, ripples).

15. Volcanic lava that cools and solidifies forms (metamorphic, intrusive, extrusive, organic) rock.

16. The process of minerals filling the spaces between sediments to bind them together is called (cementation, sedimentation, compaction, lithification).

Check Your Understanding

Apply the concepts you have learned to answer each question.

1. Describe the different kinds of extrusive rocks that can form from a volcanic explosion.

2. Explain why fossils are commonly found in sedimentary layers.

3. Discuss how the texture and mineral composition of shale changes to form schist.

4. How can you tell if an igneous rock is extrusive or intrusive by looking at it?

5. Explain why the name "metamorphic" is appropriate for this type of rock.

6. Explain how the composition of sedimentary rocks reveals their origin.

7. **Compare** Discuss how the formation of igneous rock is similar to the formation of metamorphic rock. How is it different?

8. If all igneous rocks are formed from magma, why don't they look the same?

9. **Extension** Imagine you are a little blob of magma floating beneath the earth. Discuss all the possible changes you could go through during your very long life.

10. **Application** You find an interesting rock while walking home from school. Discuss how you could determine whether it is an igneous, sedimentary, or metamorphic rock.

11. 📷 **Mystery Photo** The photograph on page 208 shows the surface of a sedimentary rock. The stripes are areas where the rock is harder than the rest of the cemented particles. List features common to sedimentary rocks that you can see in this photograph.

Develop Your Skills

Use the skills you have developed in this chapter to complete each activity.

1. **Interpret Data** The graph below shows the effect of burial depth and temperature on various rocks.

   a. At what ranges of depth and temperature are sedimentary rocks found?

   b. At what ranges of depth and temperature are igneous rocks found?

   c. Name the metamorphic rocks listed in the graph. What are the depth and temperature ranges for these rocks?

   d. What is the relationship between the types of rocks formed and depth? Temperature?

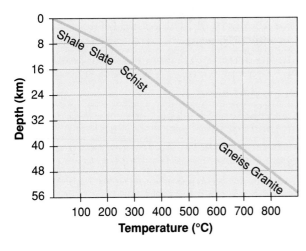

2. **Data Bank** Use the information on page 617 to answer the following questions.

   a. What is the most common class of rock found in the United States?

   b. What is the most common class of rock found in Canada?

   c. List the classes of rocks that are found in Mexico.

Make Connections

1. **Link the Concepts** Draw a concept map showing how the following concepts from the chapter link together. Add terms to connect, or link, the concepts.

   rocks
   chemical rock
   extrusive
   intrusive
   clastic rock
   metamorphic

   igneous
   sedimentary
   nonfoliated
   organic rock
   foliated

2. **Science and You** Make a list of all the building materials in your home and your school that contain rock. Then identify each of the building materials as igneous, sedimentary, or metamorphic rock.

3. **Science and Art** Make a rock sculpture using the sedimentary rock material, plaster of Paris. Decorate your sculpture with pebbles. Use the sedimentary rock, chalk, to color your sculpture.

4. **Science and Home Economics** Make peanut brittle, chocolate chip cookies, or banana nut bread. Describe how the steps in cooking one of the above recipes is similar to the formation of a conglomerate rock.

5. **Science and Social Studies** The Stone Age was a period in human history that lasted over 2 million years. Research how ancient people living during the Stone Age used rocks as tools. Make a replica or drawing of one of the stone tools. Present your replica or drawing to the class, and explain how the tool was used.

Science and Literature Connection

"Now, Harry," cried the Professor, in an enthusiastic tone of voice, "we are truly about to take our first step into the Interior of the Earth; never before visited by humans since the first creation of the world. You may consider, therefore, that at this precise moment our travels really commence."

As my uncle made this remark, he took in one hand the Ruhmkorf coil apparatus, which hung around his neck, and with the other he put the electric current into communication with the worm of the lantern. And a bright light at once illuminated that dark and gloomy tunnel!

The effect was magical!

"Forward!" cried my uncle. Each took up his burden. Hans went first, my uncle followed, and I going third, we entered the sombre gallery!

Just as we were about to engulf ourselves in this dismal passage, I lifted up my head, and through the tube-like shaft saw that Iceland sky I was never to see again!

Was it the last I should ever see of any sky?

The stream of lava flowing from the bowels of the earth in 1229 had forced itself a passage through the tunnel. It lined the whole of the inside with its thick and

A Journey to the Centre of the Earth

The following excerpts are from the novel A Journey to the Centre of the Earth *by Jules Verne.*

brilliant coating. The electric light added very greatly to the brilliancy of the effect.

The great difficulty of our journey now began. How were we to prevent ourselves from slipping down the steeply-inclined plane? Happily, some cracks, abrasures of the soil, and other irregularities, served the place of steps; and we descended slowly, allowing our heavy luggage to slip on before, at the end of a long cord.

But that which served as steps under our feet became in other places stalactites. The lava, very porous in certain places, took the form of little round blisters. Crystals of opaque quartz, adorned with limpid drops of natural glass suspended to the roof like lustres, seemed to take fire as we passed beneath them.

"Magnificent, glorious!" I cried, in a moment of involuntary enthusiasm. "What a spectacle, uncle! Do you not admire these variegated shades of lava, which run through a whole series of colors, from reddish-brown to pale yellow—by the most insensible degrees? And these crystals—they appear like luminous globes."

"You are beginning to see the charms of travel, Master Harry," cried my uncle. "Wait a bit, until we advance farther. What we have as yet discovered is nothing— onward, my boy, onward!"

We had journeyed the entire day through this gallery when we noticed a difference in the walls of the gallery. It was a glorious sight to see how the electric light brought out the sparkles in the walls of the calcareous rocks and the old red sandstone. Some magnificent specimens of marble projected from the sides

of the gallery; some of an agate gray with white veins of variegated character, others of a yellow spotted color, with red veins; farther off might be seen samples of color in which cherry-tinted seams were to be found in all their brightest shades.

Skills in Science

Reading Skills in Science

1. **Classify** Classify this passage as either fiction or nonfiction. Provide evidence for your classification.

2. **Find Context Clues** In which country did the explorers enter the center of the earth? Identify the sentence from the passage that contains this information

Writing Skills in Science

1. **Infer** Imagine you are accompanying the narrator in his journey to the center of the earth. What do you see? Write an entry in your diary describing your experiences.

2. **Classify** Write a paragraph identifying the rock types viewed by the explorers on their journey. Provide evidence for your classification.

Activities

Find Causes The passage describes lava having a great variety of color. Use reference tools to determine the cause of this color variation.

Communicate The country in which the explorers began their journey is unique in that it uses the heat of volcanic material as an energy source. Use reference materials to find out how this is accomplished. Make a diagram to illustrate your findings with the class.

Where to Read More

Digging Deeper by Sandra Markle. New York: Lothrop, Lee and Shepard Books, 1987. Learn more about various topics such as plate tectonics, erosion, and mineral resources by reading this text, complete with experiments and activities!

Unit 4

Changes on the Earth's Surface

Chapters

Data Bank

Use the information on pages 612 to 625 to answer the following questions about topics explored in this unit.

Interpreting a Diagram

In which climate does the regolith reach a depth of about 15 meters?

Inferring

Why do you think the Ganges River has the highest silt load shown?

Interpreting a Table

How many years ago did the Miocene epoch begin? What is the most recent epoch?

Reading a Map

What is the approximate silt load of the Amazon River?

The photograph to the left is of Arches National Park in Utah. How did this unusual rock structure form?

Chapter **11**

Weathering and Soils

What do you see?

❝I see caves, a rock structure. It looks like one of the caverns in Carlsbad Caverns. They were made some billions of years ago when the water table lowered. Water penetrated through the hairline cracks in an immense block of limestone, gradually forming chambers and corridors. Calcium carbonate deposits formed from evaporating lime-laden ground water.❞

April Stachura
Carman Ainsworth Junior
High School
Flint, Michigan

To find out more about the photograph, look on page 260. As you read this chapter, you will learn about weathering and soils.

11.1 Weathering

Objectives

▶ **Describe** the causes of mechanical weathering.

▶ **Describe** the causes of chemical weathering.

▶ **Compare** and **contrast** mechanical and chemical weathering.

▶ **Predict** rates of weathering.

▼ **ACTIVITY**

Predicting

Not in a Million Years

Imagine that you can travel through time. What do you think the earth's surface will look like after one million years? What do you think causes these changes?

SKILLS WARMUP

Think about an area of pavement near your home or school. Over time, cracks develop. Sometimes tiny plants grow in the cracks. Ants and other insects often build their homes under the cracks. If left alone and not repaired, the pavement eventually crumbles apart as a result of the constant action of the rain, sun, plants, and animals.

The changes in the pavement over time are caused by a process called weathering. Weathering is the process by which exposed rocks and other materials break down. The surface of the earth is constantly wearing away due to the process of weathering.

Mechanical Weathering

Breaking rock into smaller pieces by mechanical or physical means is called mechanical weathering. You can see the effects of mechanical weathering if you break a rock into small pieces with a hammer. Mechanical weathering results in smaller pieces of rock, but the rock type doesn't change.

Most rocks break into small, irregularly shaped pieces. But some rocks break off in large sheets, leaving a rounded surface underneath. For example, look at the granite dome in Figure 11.1. The granite originally formed underground, under great pressure from overlying rock. Over time, the ground above the granite wore away, and the pressure on the granite decreased. As a result, the outer layers of granite expanded, cracked, and flaked off in a process called **exfoliation** (EHKS foh lee AY shuhn). Extreme changes in temperature can also cause exfoliation.

Figure 11.1 ▲
Half Dome, in Yosemite National Park, is an example of an exfoliation dome.

Causes of Mechanical Weathering

Mechanical weathering occurs in many different ways. Study the causes of mechanical weathering on these pages. An important cause of mechanical weathering is the freezing and thawing of water. Recall that water expands when it freezes. If you fill a jar with water, cap it with a lid, and put it in the freezer, the expanding ice will break the glass or push the lid off. Water breaks rocks apart in the same way.

Ice Wedging

Water from rain or melting snow enters the cracks in a rock. If the air temperature drops below freezing, the water in these cracks changes into ice. The expanding ice slowly pushes the cracks farther apart. Over a long period of time, the cracks widen so much that the rock can split apart. ▼

Plant Weathering ▲

The wind carries seeds from plants into cracks in the rocks. The seeds sprout, and the plants begin growing. As each plant grows, the roots exert pressure on the sides of a crack. Over time, the root pressure causes the crack to widen.

Small weedy plants often grow in the rock cracks. But even large trees can grow right out of rocks!

Animal Weathering

Animals dig into rocky areas to search for food or to build homes. For example, insects such as ants and termites split rocks apart as they constantly dig and burrow in cracks. The insects carry rock and dirt particles to the surface, sometimes forming a hill or mound. Animal burrows allow air and water inside the rock, so it weathers faster. What other ways might animals cause weathering? ▼

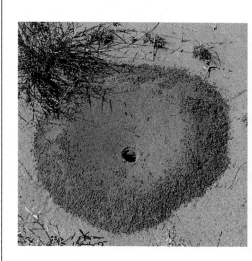

Temperature changes make rocks expand and contract. Where there are extreme daily temperature changes, such as in a desert, expansion and contraction can help make rocks break apart. Another important mechanical weathering process is called abrasion. Think about what happens when you use sandpaper to smooth a piece of wood or an emery board to file your fingernails. When gravity, wind, or moving water causes rocks to rub against each other, the rocks wear down or break into smaller pieces.

Water Abrasion

Rivers and streams carry particles of sand or rock. The particles scrape and tumble against other rocks as the water moves by. The abrasion wears down the rocks over a period of time.

On the coast, ocean waves also carry particles of sand and rock. As the waves strike the shoreline, the particles scrape and smooth the rocks on shore. ▼

Temperature Change ▲

The sun warms up the surface of rocks. The heat causes the surface layer of each rock to expand. The inside of the rock remains cool. At night, this process is reversed. The surface layer of the rock gets cold and contracts. The inside of the rock is warmer than the outside. This daily expansion and contraction can help cause the weakened surfaces of exposed rocks to slowly crack and flake off.

Wind Abrasion ▲

Wind can carry sand, dust, and small rock particles over long distances. In dry regions, the wind easily picks up loose sand and dust. As the particle-laden wind blows against exposed rocks, the particles scrape against the rock surfaces. Over a long period of time, wind abrasion can polish and flatten the windward sides of rocks.

Chemistry LINK

ACTIVITY

Obtain two pieces of uncoated steel wool, water, and a sheet of white paper.

1. Wet one piece of wool.

2. Set both pieces of steel wool out for two days.

3. The following day, place the pieces on the sheet of paper and grind them firmly for two minutes.

Which piece of wool gave off more debris? Why?

Chemical Weathering

Weathering that changes the chemical composition of rock is called chemical weathering. You can see chemical weathering at work if you look at old building stones or tombstones made of marble or granite. The surface of the stones is dissolved by a weak acid in rainwater. The acid eats away the stone, rounding the edges, smoothing away areas of lettering, and forming surface pits and holes.

Causes of Chemical Weathering

The most common causes of chemical weathering are water, oxygen, and carbon dioxide from the air. Study the causes of chemical weathering shown below.

Oxidation ▲

What happens if you leave a steel hammer outside for a few days? It develops rust. Rust is the result of a type of chemical weathering called **oxidation**. Iron combines with oxygen in the air to form a substance called iron oxide, or rust. Rust isn't as strong as iron. Rust crumbles easily. When exposed to air, rocks containing iron become "rusty" and eventually fall apart.

Water ▶

Water can dissolve many minerals. Water also combines with gases in the air to form acids that can dissolve or change the composition of rocks.

As water dissolves the minerals, rocks either change in composition or fall apart. As shown in the photograph to the right, feldspar minerals combine with water to become clay minerals. The clay mineral kaolinite is an important ingredient of fine porcelain. ▶

Chemical weathering breaks down minerals. Recall that minerals are the chemical compounds that make up rocks. Even though minerals are solids, many dissolve in water. A rock that contains a water-soluble mineral will slowly dissolve when the rock is exposed to water.

Acids also dissolve many minerals. Acids form when gases in the air dissolve in rainwater. For example, carbon dioxide dissolves in rainwater to form carbonic acid. Acids produced by plants and fungi break down rocks and help to form soil.

Rainwater carries dissolved minerals deeper into the ground in a process called **leaching**. Leaching changes the chemical composition of a soil. Leaching makes the surface soil mineral-poor. The leached minerals are deposited deeper down, forming a mineral-rich layer.

▼ ACTIVITY

Observing

The Acid Test

Observe the effect of weak acids on chalk. You can make a solution of carbonic acid by blowing through a soda straw into a glass of water. Lemon juice and vinegar are other weak acids you can try. What do your observations tell you about weak acids and chemical weathering?

SKILLS WORKOUT

Sulfuric Acid

Burning coal and natural gas release sulfur dioxide gas into the air. Water vapor in the air combines with sulfur dioxide to form sulfuric acid. Sulfuric acid is a strong acid that easily dissolves rock and metals. When sulfuric acid falls to the earth as acid rain, it can harm plants and fishes. ▼

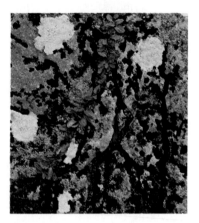

Plant and Fungal Acids ▲

Some plants and fungi make acids that dissolve rocks and minerals. For example, the root tips of some plants produce a weak acid. The acid helps the roots burrow into cracks in the rock.

Lichens sometimes hug the surface of rocks. They often look like green, orange, or brown patches. Lichens contain fungi that produce a weak acid. The acid dissolves the surface of the rock beneath them.

Carbonation ▲

Weathering produced by carbonic acid is called **carbonation**. You can see the effects of carbonation on limestone and marble. The rock develops small pits or holes. Underground, carbonic acid dissolves limestone deposits. As the rock is eaten away, caverns and sinkholes form.

Figure 11.2 ▲
Over time, the inscriptions on this granite obelisk have nearly disappeared.

Science and Society *Lost Inscriptions*

Ancient peoples around the world built monuments and buildings of stone. Many monuments are covered with detailed inscriptions carved thousands of years ago. The inscriptions record information about events and people in the distant past.

Ancient Egyptians inscribed stone temples and pointed stone towers called obelisks. Ancient people in Central America inscribed stone pyramids, temples, and pillars called stelae. In Asia, people inscribed stone pillars and temples, such as the one at Angkor Wat in Cambodia.

Exposed stone monuments are subject to weathering. Over time, weathering can wear away inscriptions, and the information they contain may be lost. The speed of weathering depends on the climate. Look at Figure 11.2. The granite obelisk now called Cleopatra's Needle was carved in Egypt more than 3,500 years ago. Very little weathering took place in Egypt's hot, dry climate.

In 1881, the obelisk was given by the Egyptian government as a gift to the people of New York City. When the obelisk arrived in New York, its inscriptions were clear and readable. But New York's temperate, humid climate weathered the stone quickly. Extremes of heat and cold caused mechanical weathering. City air caused chemical weathering by carbonation and sulfuric acid. After 100 years in New York City, the obelisk's inscriptions have almost disappeared.

Check and Explain

1. What are the causes of mechanical weathering? Explain the effects of each cause.

2. What are the causes of chemical weathering? Explain the effects of each cause.

3. **Compare and Contrast** How are mechanical and chemical weathering different? How are they alike?

4. **Predict** Which rock would weather faster, a smooth rock or one with many cracks? Explain your choice. How would climate affect the rate of weathering? Explain.

Soil Organisms

Think about the smell of freshly turned soil. The earthy odor you think of as the smell of soil is produced by a soil organism called *Streptomyces*. In addition to supporting plant growth, soil itself contains a large number of organisms. Some soil organisms are large enough to see, but most are microscopic. The most common soil organisms are bacteria and fungi. Just 1 g of soil may contain several million bacteria, an equal amount of fungi, and more than 100,000 protozoa.

Larger, but still tiny soil organisms include mites, springtails, nematodes, and insect larvae. Some examples are shown in Figure 11.7. Study Table 11.1 to compare the numbers of organisms in an area of soil 1 m² at the surface and extending down to the bedrock. Most soil organisms feed on organic matter in the soil, or on other soil organisms. The number of organisms living in the soil varies with local conditions. For example, fungi are the most common organisms in the acid soil of a forest, but bacteria are more common in neutral grassland soil.

Many larger animals also live in the topsoil. Worms, insects, grubs, slugs, gophers, moles, groundhogs, and rabbits are just a few of them. These animals perform several important functions. By digging through the soil, animals help to maintain the flow of water and air into the soil. Through their bodily functions—such as eating, digesting, and excreting—the animals help change the soil chemically. Finally, when they die, they become part of the soil itself as their bodies decay into humus.

Table 11.1 Soil Organisms

Organism	Number per m²
Bacteria	2.6×10^{14}
Fungi	8×10^{12}
Algae	3×10^{10}
Protozoa	7×10^{12}
Nematodes	250,000
Springtails	100,000
Mites	50,000
Crustaceans	4×10^{13}

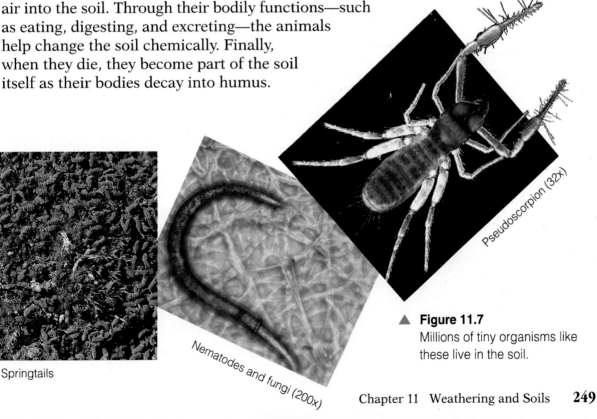

Springtails

Nematodes and fungi (200x)

Pseudoscorpion (32x)

▲ **Figure 11.7**
Millions of tiny organisms like these live in the soil.

Soil Ecology

Figure 11.8   Role of Soil ▼

Soil plays an important role in energy flow and nutrient cycling. Study Figure 11.8. Plants, which depend on mineral nutrients from soil, capture the sun's energy and store it. Animals use the captured energy, in the form of plant material, as food. For this reason, plants are called producers, and animals are called consumers.

Soil organisms, such as bacteria and fungi, are called decomposers. They break down dead leaves, wood, and animal remains, releasing mineral nutrients back into the soil.

Soil bacteria are part of the global nitrogen and phosphorus cycles. One group of soil bacteria releases phosphorus from organic matter. Another group of soil bacteria takes in nitrogen gas from the air and puts it in the soil.

Sun

Energy

Plants move water up from the soil and out through their leaves.

Plants use energy from the sun and minerals from the soil to produce plant materials. They also take in carbon dioxide from the air and release oxygen.

Animals take in oxygen and release carbon dioxide. They get energy from eating plant material or other animals.

Consumers

Carbon dioxide

Oxygen

Producers

Water

Dead plants and animals are decomposed by soil organisms, releasing plant nutrients.

Soil organisms break down organic matter, releasing nitrogen and phosphorus.

Producers

Energy

Nitrogen

Water

Soil minerals

Phosphorus

Decomposers

Historical Notebook

Ancient Agriculture

In prehistoric times, people hunted animals and gathered wild plants for food. But at least 18,000 years ago, people began farming. Ancient farmers poked holes in the ground with sticks and planted seeds they collected from wild grass. They farmed areas such as river deltas, where the ground was soft and easy to work. Wheat, barley, lentils, and chickpeas were grown in Africa 18,000 years ago. Corn was grown in North America 7,000 years ago. Rice began to be cultivated in Asia about 6,000 years ago.

As farming became a way of life, people developed farming technology. By 6,000 years ago, farmers were plowing their fields using animals dragging logs. About 4,800 years ago, the sickle was developed. The sickle, used for harvesting, had a curved handle made of wood or bone and a flint stone for a blade. About 3,500 years ago, metal plows began to be used.

1. Why did ancient people farm river deltas? What other areas might they have used as farm technology improved? Explain.

2. **Research** Many farmers still use sickles, plows, and other tools developed thousands of years ago. Do library research on farming techniques in other parts of the world. Write a one-page report.

Science and You *Everyday Uses of Soil*

You may eat from dinner plates made from a soil component, clay. Clay is easy to shape and hardens when dry. When fired at high temperatures, clay becomes very hard and shiny. You may attend classes in a brick building. Bricks are also made from fired clay. Even your pencil contains clay. The clay is mixed with graphite, a soft black mineral, and then fired to make pencil lead. Clay also coats the shiny paper you see in magazines.

Check and Explain

1. List three important properties of soil.

2. Describe how a soil forms.

3. **Generalize** Why do different locations have different kinds of soil?

4. **Model** Draw or make a soil profile of a mature soil.

▼ ACTIVITY

Observing

Down in the Dirt

Obtain a sample of fresh soil.

1. Using a hand lens, examine the soil closely.

2. Describe the types of soil particles you observe and any soil organisms you find.

3. Make a drawing to record your observations.

SKILLS WORKOUT

Activity 11 How permeable is it?

Skills Model; Observe; Interpret Data

Task 1 Prelab Prep
1. Collect the following items: 3 paper cups; pencil; scissors; 3 pieces of filter paper or coffee filters; one sample each of sand, soil, and gravel; metric ruler; measuring cup; water; clock or watch; 3 small blocks of wood or 3 small rocks; a shallow dish or saucer.
2. Using your pencil point, make eight small holes in the bottom of each cup. Label the cups *Sand, Soil,* and *Gravel.*
3. Cut circles from the filter paper to fit into the bottom of each cup.

Task 2 Data Record
1. Copy Table 11.2. Record the amount of water poured into each cup and the time the water takes to drain.
2. After the experiment, calculate the drainage rate for each type of soil. Record the drainage rate in your table.

Task 3 Procedure
1. Mark a line 5 cm up from the bottom of each cup. Fill to this line with the sand, soil, or gravel, according to the label on the cup.
2. Look at Figure 11.9. Set the sand-filled cup in the dish on top of the blocks or rocks. Be sure the blocks don't cover the holes.
3. Measure out 100 mL of water. Start timing as you pour the water into the cup. Finish timing when no more water drains from the cup. Record the time on your chart.

Figure 11.9 ▲

4. Pour the water in the shallow dish into your measuring cup. Record this amount.
5. Repeat steps 2, 3, and 4 with the other two cups.

Task 4 Analysis
1. In Table 11.2, calculate the drainage rate for each sample. Divide the amount of water that drained into the saucer by the time it took to drain. Record the drainage rates.
2. Which sample had the highest drainage rate? Which sample had the lowest rate?
3. List the samples in order of particle size from largest to smallest.
4. If a sample with the highest drainage rate is the most permeable, order the samples from most permeable to least permeable.

Task 5 Conclusion
Write a short paragraph explaining how particle size can affect the permeability of a soil sample.

Extension
How might permeability be affected if the samples were mixed together? Propose a hypothesis, and test it.

Table 11.2 Permeability Data

Soil Type	Time	Amount of Water	Drainage Rate
Sand			
Soil			
Gravel			

11.3 World Soil Types

Objectives

▶ **Describe** seven types of soil.

▶ **Identify** soil types by geographic location and climate.

▶ **Compare** and **contrast** the major soil types

▶ **Classify** soils by their characteristics.

▼ **ACTIVITY**

Classifying

I Just Mopped the Floor

What type of soil is usually found near a beach? What type of soil would you find in a swamp? If your shoes were covered with dark, slimy mud, which area did you walk through, a beach or a swamp? Explain.

SKILLS WARMUP

Did you know that detectives can use soil samples from suspects' shoes to prove they were at the scene of a crime? How does identifying soil help solve a crime? The reason is that soil varies from place to place.

Although there are thousands of different soils, people have developed ways to classify soils into groups. One way to classify soils is by the environment in which the soil was formed. For example, soil formed in a tropical environment differs from soil formed in a desert environment. Look at Figure 11.10. Notice the distribution of soil types formed in different environments around the world.

Figure 11.10 Map of Soil Types ▼

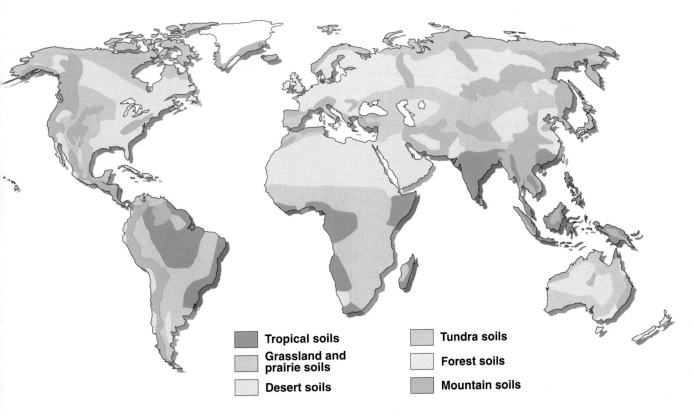

Legend:
- **Tropical soils**
- **Grassland and prairie soils**
- **Desert soils**
- **Tundra soils**
- **Forest soils**
- **Mountain soils**

Forest Soils

Forest soils occur in areas of heavy rainfall and changing temperatures. Look at the soil profile of a forest soil in Figure 11.11. Above the topsoil is a layer of dead leaves, needles, and twigs. Rainwater leaches organic acids from the dead plant material into the topsoil. The acidic water leaches minerals and clay particles out of the topsoil. As a result, the lower part of the *A* horizon of a forest soil is usually thin, sandy, and light-colored.

Insoluble iron, aluminum, and clays build up in the *B* horizon. Therefore, the *B* horizon is usually red or brown in color. Although the composition of forest soils varies, the acidic leaching causes a similar

Figure 11.11 ▲
What materials help produce forest soils?

soil profile to form. A soil formed in this way is called a **podsol**. Podsols are generally not very fertile because of the thin topsoil. Trees can grow because they have deep roots.

Consider This

Should the Cutting of Forests Be Restricted?

All over the world, people have been cutting down forests. Sometimes, the forests have grown back. But worldwide, about 30 to 50 percent of the forests that were cut down have not grown back.

People cut down forests mainly to clear land for farming and to obtain firewood and lumber. As the world's population grows, people need more farmland to grow food. In many areas, firewood is essential for cooking and heating. People need lumber to build homes. In rural areas, the lumber industry provides needed jobs.

Forests play an important role in the environment. The trees give off oxygen and take in carbon dioxide. They also move water up from the soil into the atmosphere. Through these processes, a forest helps maintain the balance of gases and moisture in the air. When a forest is cut down, the balance of gases in the air is affected. After a forest is cut down, newly exposed soils can blow or wash away. Also, cutting forests destroys the homes of other plants and animals.

Think About It
What might happen to people and the environment if the cutting of forests is restricted? If people cut as much as they want?

Debate It Find out more about all sides of the forest-cutting issue. Choose a position.

Prairie Soils

Prairie soil regions don't get quite as much rain as forest soil regions. So there is less leaching of minerals, and the topsoil is very deep and rich in humus and nutrients. Look at Figure 11.12. Prairie soils are fertile and productive soils. A major crop grown in prairie soil regions is corn.

Prairie soil regions in the central United States contain deposits of fine-grained angular particles called *loess* (LOH ehs). The particles were produced as moving glaciers scoured rocks during the last ice age. As the glaciers retreated, meltwater formed many streams and deposited glacial sediments in front of the melting ice. Strong winds picked up and carried away silt-sized particles and piled them up into thick layers.

Winds can carry the fine prairie soil particles away if they are not held together by plant roots. For example, during a drought in the 1930s, the dry, bare soils were blown away by the wind. The area in which this disaster occurred was named the Dust Bowl. The land lost all of its topsoil, so no crops could grow.

Grassland Soils

Grassland soils get even less rain than prairie soils. Because of the smaller amount of rainfall, the grassland topsoil isn't leached very much. The soil mineral calcium isn't dissolved away. The calcium remains in the *A* horizon, giving the topsoil a whitish color. Look at the soil profile of a grassland soil in Figure 11.13. Soils in drier grassland regions often contain whitish calcium deposits.

The thick grassland topsoil is rich in humus from decaying grass stems and leaves. Food crops that are grasses, such as wheat and rye, grow well in grassland areas around the world. Grassland areas also support large herds of grazing animals, such as buffalo, cattle, and sheep. Important grassland areas around the world include the Great Plains region of North America, the pampas region in South America, and the steppes regions of central Asia.

Figure 11.12 ▲
This tallgrass prairie has soil with a very thick layer of organic matter.

Figure 11.13 ▲
A grassland soil has less organic matter than a prairie soil.

Desert Soils

In areas of little or almost no rainfall, desert soils form. Desert soils are only slightly weathered and leached. As a result, desert soils are rich in minerals. Look at the profile of a desert soil in Figure 11.14. Only plants adapted to dry conditions, such as cacti, grow in deserts. Because of the scarcity of plants, there is little organic matter available to form humus.

Despite the lack of humus, desert soils can be very fertile because of the high mineral content. Farmers in the western United States use irrigation to add water to the desert soil. With water, sunshine, and minerals, crops grow easily. But years of irrigation can make the soil become salty. Fresh water contains salts. As the water evaporates, it leaves the salt behind. Crops don't grow well in salty soil. The flow of irrigation water also leaches out the needed soil minerals.

Figure 11.14 ▲
A desert soil has very little organic matter and is rich in minerals.

Figure 11.15 ▲
A thin layer of rocky soil can form on the slopes of mountains.

Mountain Soils

In the mountains, the soils are usually rocky and thin. Mountain slopes are too steep for mature soils to develop. As soon as soil builds up, gravity starts to pull it downhill. Look at the mountain in Figure 11.15. On the high slopes, there are only weathered chunks of rock, with little organic matter. Where trees and shrubs grow, organic matter can build up in depressions, producing a thin rocky layer of acidic soil.

Rainfall and wind cause soil conditions to vary from one side of a mountain to the other. On the side facing the wind, there is usually more rainfall. The rainy side can usually support the growth of trees and shrubs. But on the opposite side, there will be almost no trees or shrubs.

Mountain soils aren't usually good places to grow crops because of the steep slopes and thin soil. But in tropical mountain areas, thicker soils can develop. In South America and Africa, farmers grow coffee in the mountain soil.

Tundra Soils

In polar regions with very cold temperatures and little rainfall, tundra soils form. The deep layer of subsoil in polar regions is permanently frozen and is called *permafrost*. Above the permafrost is a soil layer that freezes in the winter and thaws out in the summer. When it thaws, the soil stays waterlogged because the water can't drain off through the permafrost. Evaporation occurs very slowly because of low air temperatures. Humus forms very slowly in these conditions. Therefore, tundra topsoil is usually black or brown and contains undecayed plant material. Look at the soil profile of a tundra soil in Figure 11.16.

Plants that grow in tundra soil are usually small with shallow roots. Tundra plants must grow quickly to take advantage of the short summer. Because only a small amount of organic matter is produced each year, tundra soils take a long time to build up. If disturbed, tundra soils recover very slowly.

Tropical Soils

Tropical soils form in areas of heavy rainfall and year-round warm temperatures. Chemical weathering occurs rapidly, and very thick layers of mineral soil build up. But the frequent rains cause heavy leaching. Almost everything, including the quartz, is leached out. Only aluminum clays and iron oxide, or rust, remain. These two minerals don't dissolve easily in water. The resulting soil, called **laterite** (LAYT er IGHT), is rusty red in color, due to the iron oxide.

The topsoil of laterites contains little humus. Humus can't build up because organic matter decays quickly in a tropical environment. The nutrients are immediately used for new plant growth. Look at the soil profile of a tropical soil in Figure 11.17. The topsoil lacks minerals because of the leaching.

If the tropical rain forest is cut down, the soil changes dramatically. Without the trees, the clay-rich soil bakes in the sun to a bricklike hardness.

Figure 11.16 ▲
Tundra soils have a layer of undecayed plant material on top of permafrost.

A
B
C

Figure 11.17 ▲
Tropical soils have thick layers of leached clays.

Science and Society
Overgrazed Grasslands

Do you think a Dust Bowl disaster could happen today? What might happen to cause one to occur? Drought is an important factor. But people learned from the Dust Bowl disaster of the 1930s that the way they manage the land has an important impact. For example, they learned that fields need some sort of plant cover, such as grass or clover, when no crops are growing. Plant roots help hold the soil in place. Today many farmers follow this plan to protect their soil.

People use grasslands to graze herds of cattle and sheep. When a small number of animals graze over a large area, the grass can grow back, and the grasslands aren't damaged. But if there are too many animals in an area, they can damage the grasslands. They eat too much of the grass, destroy its roots, and trample it under their hooves. Look at Figure 11.18. Too many grazing animals can strip large areas of grass. Without the grass, the bare topsoil blows away in the wind. A once productive grassland can turn into a desert.

In Africa, overgrazing and droughts have caused serious problems in the last few years. Parts of Australia and the United States also suffer from overgrazing. A recent study by the United States government found that more than half of the grazing land now in use is in poor or fair condition due to overgrazing.

Figure 11.18 ▲
Cattle have overgrazed the grasses on one side of the fence. No plants remain to hold the soil in place.

Check and Explain

1. List seven types of soil. Where in the world is each type found?

2. What is a laterite?

3. **Compare and Contrast** Describe two soils that undergo extensive leaching of minerals. Compare them to two soils in which less leaching occurs. What conditions seem to cause leaching?

4. **Classify** You have been given a soil sample from an unknown location. It is composed of fine-grained angular fragments, and the soil is somewhat leached. The topsoil is rich in humus and nutrients. What type of soil is your sample?

Chapter 11 Review

Concept Summary

11.1 Weathering

▶ Mechanical weathering breaks rock into pieces by physical means.

▶ The causes of mechanical weathering include ice wedging, plant weathering, animal weathering, temperature change, water abrasion, and wind abrasion.

▶ Chemical weathering alters the chemical composition of rock.

▶ The causes of chemical weathering include oxidation, water dissolving and leaching minerals, carbonation, sulfuric acid, and plant and fungal acids.

11.2 Soils

▶ Soil, the upper part of the regolith, is a mixture of parent rock, decayed plant and animal matter called humus, and rock fragments.

▶ Soils have measurable properties that include particle shape, particle size, fertility, and acid level.

▶ A soil profile shows the distinct layers, or horizons, present in soil. Mature soils have three horizons.

▶ Soil supports the survival of plants and many other living organisms.

11.3 World Soil Types

▶ Soil is classified by mineral and humus composition, and the environment where the soil was formed.

▶ The seven different world soil types are forest soils, prairie soils, grassland soils, desert soils, mountain soils, tundra soils, and tropical soils or laterites.

Chapter Vocabulary

exfoliation (11.1)	carbonation (11.1)	soil profile (11.2)	podsol (11.3)
oxidation (11.1)	regolith (11.2)	horizon (11.2)	laterite (11.3)
leaching (11.1)	parent rock (11.2)	humus (11.2)	

Check Your Vocabulary

Use the vocabulary words above to complete the following sentences correctly.

1. Iron combining with oxygen to form rust is a type of chemical weathering called ____ .

2. All of the loose, weathered material on the earth's surface is the ____ .

3. The decayed plant and animal matter in soil is called ____ .

4. The process of mechanical weathering when rock cracks and flakes off is called ____ .

5. Forest soils are usually ____ .

6. The process of dissolving and moving minerals from the upper soil is ____ .

7. The cross section of soil that shows distinct layers is a ____ .

8. A type of chemical weathering caused by carbonic acid is ____ .

9. The rock that breaks down to produce soil particles is called ____ .

10. Red soils often found in tropical regions are ____ .

11. The distinct layers seen in a soil profile are called ____ .

Write Your Vocabulary

Write sentences using the vocabulary words above. Show that you know what each word means.

Chapter 11 Review

Check Your Knowledge

Answer the following in complete sentences.

1. List three causes of mechanical weathering.

2. What are the properties of soil?

3. What are the seven different types of soil found around the world?

4. List four causes of chemical weathering.

5. What is permafrost?

6. How many horizons exist in mature soils? Name the horizons.

7. List five different types of organisms found in soil.

8. What is another name for acidic forest soils?

9. What chemical is found in acid rain?

10. What are the two types of weathering?

11. List the six important plant nutrients.

Choose the answer that best completes each sentence.

12. Ice wedging is a type of (mechanical, chemical, plant, animal) weathering.

13. Humus is found in horizon (A, B, C, D).

14. The most common soil organisms are (bacteria and fungi, protozoa, bacteria and nematodes, mites).

15. Temperature changes cause (exfoliation, chemical weathering, oxidation, carbonation).

16. The top layer of regolith is (bedrock, humus, soil, parent rock) that extends down to 3 m below the surface.

17. The particle shape of soils determines the amount of (clay, water, sulfur, living things) the soil can hold.

Check Your Understanding

Apply the concepts you have learned to answer each question.

1. Explain how industrial society increased the weathering of rocks.

2. What type of soil is common in the area where you live?

3. Compare water and wind abrasion. How are they the same? How are they different?

4. Explain how animals cause both chemical and mechanical weathering.

5. If you wanted to smooth the edges of a sharp stone, what types of chemical and mechanical weathering could you use?

6. Describe the events that take place to change parent rock into soil.

7. Why is the acid level in soil important to farmers?

8. Explain the role of plants and organisms in soil ecology.

9. **Extension** Make a list of the ways in which soil affects your life every day. How would your life be different if the soil were removed and replaced with concrete?

10. **Application** Describe the different types of weathering you see occurring as you travel from your home to school. How will the effects of weathering change the landscape in 100 years? In 1,000 years?

11. **Mystery Photo** The photograph on page 238 shows stalactites formed by water dissolving, leaching, and redepositing minerals. What might the soil be like above these underground caverns? Why?

Develop Your Skills

Use the skills you have developed in this chapter to complete each activity.

1. **Interpret Data** The drawings below show different soil profiles.

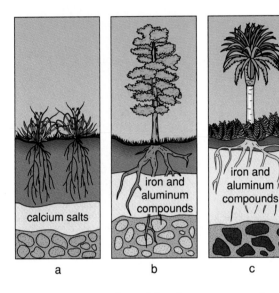

a. Which soil profile shows a grassland soil. Why?

b. Which soil profile has the most humus? The largest *B* horizon?

2. **Data Bank** Use the data on page 613 to answer the following questions.

a. In which climate is the regolith deepest? How deep is the regolith?

b. **Infer** How are precipitation and temperature related to depth of weathering?

3. **Classify** Make a table listing the seven major continents. Use Figure 11.10 to find the most common and the least common soil types for each continent.

4. **Compare and Contrast** What processes are probably most responsible for creating desert soils? Compare these to the processes most likely to create forest soil.

Make Connections

1. **Link the Concepts** Below is a concept map showing how some of the main concepts in this chapter link together. Only part of the map is filled in. Finish the map, using words and ideas from the chapter.

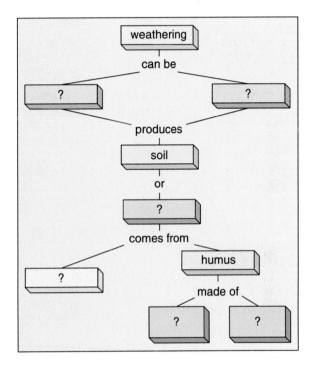

2. **Science and Society** Use recent magazines and newspapers to find out the impact of desertification on many African communities.

3. **Science and Literature** In John Steinbeck's novel, *The Grapes of Wrath*, a family is displaced from their home because of the Dust Bowl disaster. Read this book to find out how soil changed the lives of many people and the history of the United States.

4. **Science and Art** Jewelry often contains polished rocks. Obtain an unpolished rock. Use different types of abrasion processes to make a polished stone.

Chapter 12 Forces of Erosion

What do you see?

❝I see weathered rocks. It also looks like a cave. So it's a weathered cave. The rock looks like sandstone. The weather made it this way by breaking down the earth's surface.**❞**

Phillip Jackson
Bingham Middle School
Kansas City, Missouri

To find out more about the photograph, look on page 286.
As you read this chapter, you will learn how erosion and deposition change the surface of the earth.

12.1 Gravity and Erosion

Objectives

▶ **Explain** the difference between erosion and deposition.

▶ **Name** the agents of erosion.

▶ **Predict** what conditions cause mass movement.

▶ **Compare** and **contrast** the different types of mass movement.

▼ **ACTIVITY**

Predicting

How to Make Mud

What happens to a pile of dirt if you water it with a hose? Where will the dirt go when the water is turned off? What will happen to the dirt if the water comes out powerfully? Does the speed of the water affect the amount of dirt moved? Explain.

SKILLS WARMUP

I magine what the area where you live looked like 1,000 years ago. How do you think it differed from the way it looks today? For one thing, buildings and streets wouldn't have existed. The land may have had more hills. Since that time, human activity or natural causes may have worn away the hills. Maybe the land was more flat than it is today. Machines or wind and water may have deposited sediments to build up the land. You may not know it, but the land in your area is still changing. How do you think it will look 1,000 years from now?

Erosion and Deposition

The materials on the surface of the earth are always changing. How has the structure in Figure 12.1 changed over time? Recall that rock is broken down by mechanical and chemical weathering. Weathered materials are picked up and transported to other places. The action of picking up and moving materials is called **erosion**. The agents of erosion are water, wind, ice, and gravity. Erosion results in the wearing away of the land.

The degree of erosion that occurs in an area depends on the amount of rain, the looseness of the soil, and the slope of the land. Therefore, a bare hillside erodes faster than a grass-covered hill or a flat field.

The dropping of weathered materials somewhere else is called **deposition** (DEHP uh ZISH uhn). Deposition aids in the creation of new landforms. Sometimes deposition occurs over a long period of time. Sometimes deposition moves materials rapidly over a short time.

Figure 12.1

What agent of erosion weathered this Egyptian sphinx? ▼

Mass Movement

Gravity pulls downward on all objects. Gravity moves loose material on a slope. When gravity moves rocks or soil down a slope, it is called **mass movement**. Types of mass movements are classified by the size of material moved down the slope or by the speed of the movement.

Landslides ▲

The rapid movement of large amounts of rock and soil is a landslide. Landslides often occur after heavy rains or after earthquakes loosen materials on a steep slope. Landslides that occur on the sides of mountains can destroy entire towns. Piles of material at the bottom of a slope indicate a landslide location, as shown in the photograph above. Warning signs are often placed in landslide areas.

Creep ▲

The gradual downslope movement of soil is called creep. Creep happens too slowly to notice while it's occurring. But over time, the results of creep can be seen. How can you tell from the photograph that creep is taking place?

Slump

◀ When weak layers of underlying materials move downslope as a single unit, slump occurs. Water and gravity acting together cause slump. Slump can occur in soil or bedrock cliffs. Slumps often leave curved scars.

Mudflows

In dry areas, fine sediment can collect in thick layers. When it rains, water loosens the sediment and increases its weight. As a result, after a heavy rainfall, the sediment mixed with water washes down the slope. This movement is called a mudflow. Mudflows are rapid movements that sometimes destroy everything in their path. How did the mudflow in the photograph affect the area? ▼

Science and You
You: An Agent of Erosion

Have you ever thought of yourself as an "agent of erosion"? Probably not, but you are one. Here are a few examples. As you're walking home from school, you decide to take your usual shortcut through a field or yard. You notice that the grass where you walk is beginning to wear away. Soon there will be no grass at all, and you will have worn away a path. Your feet acted as agents of erosion by slowly wearing away the grass and topsoil.

When you get home, you turn on the hose to wash your bicycle. As you rinse your bicycle, you notice that water from the hose collects in small streams that run down the gutter on the side of the street. When the water stops moving or slows down, you notice that piles of dirt and leaves build up in the gutter. The water from the hose you are using acts as an agent of erosion when it removes soil and dirt from the ground. It also causes deposition, when the water slows down and creates piles of material.

When you finish, you climb on your erosion machine —or your bicycle—and ride to the park for a softball game. Over a long time, even the hard concrete of the sidewalk will slowly erode under the movement of your bicycle tires.

During the softball game, you get a chance to steal second base. You are called "safe" as you "erode" into second base!

Figure 12.2 ▲
How do you think the paths in this forest setting were created?

Physical Science
L I N K

Collect the following: sand, water, a medium-sized bucket, a large plastic bag, and a sheet of graph paper.

1. Fill the plastic bucket with sand. Add just enough water to make the sand clump together.

2. Freeze the container of sand for a few hours.

3. Place the frozen sand onto the plastic bag.

4. Draw a profile of the frozen sand mass.

5. Repeat step 4 at one-hour intervals for four hours.

What geologic processes are modeled? How does gravity affect geologic features on the earth's surface?

A C T I V I T Y

Check and Explain

1. How is erosion different from deposition? Give examples.

2. What are the four agents of erosion?

3. **Predict** Suppose you want to build a house on the side of a hill. What preparations would ensure that mass movement wouldn't affect your house?

4. **Compare and Contrast** Describe how the speed of the movement compares for each type of mass movement. Describe how the size of material moved varies for each type of mass movement.

Mud Pies

Collect some grass straw, two small pans filled with soil, a bucket, and about 300 mL of water.

1. Cover the soil in one pan with straw.

2. Hold the soil-only pan at a slight angle over the bucket.

3. Pour 150 mL of water over the soil. Observe the water in the bucket.

4. Repeat the process with the other pan.

How does the straw affect the amount of erosion?

SKILLS WARMUP

12.2 Water Erosion

Objectives

▶ **Describe** how a river forms.

▶ **Relate** the stages of a river to water erosion.

▶ **Classify** wave formations according to the type of shoreline.

▶ **Compare** and **contrast** stream and wave deposits.

A fter a hard rain, you've probably seen muddy water running down your street or road. Dirt moves from place to place in moving water. When the water stops or slows down, the sediment forms piles. You may have seen piles of sand and dirt building up in gutters or ditches next to the street.

Stream Erosion

As rainwater flows downhill, it forms **rills**, or small channels in the dirt. Look at Figure 12.3. Rills join to form larger channels called *gullies*. Water flows through rills and gullies carrying sediment downslope.

Once gullies reach a stream, more erosion occurs. A stream moves sediment. This constant motion erodes the stream bottom and sides, forming a valley. When streams enter rivers, the water slows and drops sediment.

Figure 12.3

How are rills different from gullies? ▼

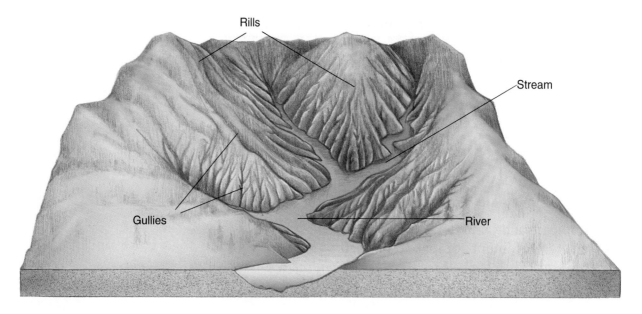

Rills

Stream

Gullies

River

Stages of River Erosion

Rivers are classified by how much they erode the areas around them. The three stages of river erosion are referred to as young, mature, and old. These stages are shown in the photographs at right.

Young River Young rivers are often found in mountains. Downcutting and erosion of the landscape are very visible around a young river. Young rivers flow swiftly and they are very powerful agents of erosion. A young river has a lot of energy that creates rapids and waterfalls. The energy is often used to generate electricity. Features of young rivers include steep slopes and V-shaped valleys.

Mature River A mature river moves more slowly and its slope is gentler than a young river. Energy in a mature river is just great enough to carry its load. A mature river continues to erode the bottom of the riverbed. It also begins to erode its sides. As the riverbed shifts toward the outside of a bend in the river, the river forms a series of curves called **meanders**. Meanders erode the valley sides and widen the valley floor of a mature river. During heavy rains, the river sometimes overflows its banks to create a *floodplain* on the valley floor.

Old River In an old river, the water moves very slowly. An old river carves its way over the land, widening the broad, flat floodplain. Sometimes during a flood, the river cuts across a meander loop and forms a new path. Sediments build up at both ends of the meander loop, cutting it off from the rest of the river. In time, a separate lake, called an *oxbow lake*, forms.

Figure 12.4a ▲
This young river flows quickly to erode through Yellowstone Canyon in Wyoming.

Figure 12.4b ▲
The Koyukuk River in Alaska is a mature river. How is a mature river different from a young river?

Figure 12.4c ▲
The Chena River is an old river located near Fairbanks, Alaska. Notice the many meanders.

Stream and River Deposition

When a stream or river slows down, it loses energy. The energy loss causes a stream or river to drop the sediment it is carrying. The sediment may deposit on the sides of the river, within the channel, or at the mouth. As the river slows, large coarse materials are the first sediment to deposit. Fine sediment, like silt and clay, deposit last. The size of the sediment and the location of the deposit determine the types of landforms that are created. You can see examples of these landforms in the photographs below.

Delta

◀ At the mouth of a river, a triangular-shaped deposit called a *delta* may form. A delta forms when the river flows into a quiet, still body of water, such as a gulf, lake, or inland sea. Because the river almost comes to a complete standstill, most of its sediment deposits at the mouth. The delta shown here is located in Alaska. Large deltas also exist at the mouth of the Mississippi River and Nile River.

Alluvial Fan ▶

Sometimes water leaves a steep mountain slope and flows onto a flat area. The water slows down and drops its load, forming a thick wedge at the mountain base. This type of sediment deposit is called an **alluvial** (uh LOO vee uhl) **fan**. Alluvial fans commonly form in arid regions where streams flow onto the desert floor.

Flood Control

Flooding occurs naturally as streams develop and river systems mature. However, flooding can cause problems for cities and farmlands located on floodplains. Some flooding is controlled naturally. During floods, sediment deposits in a long ridge, called a **levee**, next to mature or old rivers. Levees help prevent a river from spilling over its banks.

People also help control flooding by creating artificial lakes and levees. Artificial levees are built from dirt or concrete. People can also help by keeping fields covered with plants and by conserving forests. Soil conservation prevents excess runoff during heavy rainfall.

Floodplain ▶

Sediment builds up on floodplains after repeated flooding. Floodplains can be narrow or many kilometers wide. Floodplains are often excellent agricultural areas because flood deposits add nutrients and minerals to the soil on both sides of the river. The floodplain in this photograph is located in Kenya, Africa.

Levee

◀ Levees are composed of large grain sediment that deposits first when the river overflows its banks. The deposits build up and eventually raise the river banks. In this way, levees help control future floods. If repeated flooding occurs along a river, the natural levees may be quite high. The natural levee shown here is located near the Green River in Utah.

▼ ACTIVITY

Inferring

Erosion Control

Waves pounding on a shoreline can cause damage to roads and buildings nearby. Infer how wave erosion could be controlled. Compare your ideas to various methods that people actually use to control wave erosion.

SKILLS WORKOUT

Wave Erosion

A physical process called hydraulic action occurs when waves pound on cracks in rocks. First, a wave fills a crack with water. Before the water drains from the crack, another wave forces more water into the crack. This pressure causes the crack to get bigger. Eventually the rock breaks apart into smaller pieces that are further eroded by waves.

Another physical process that breaks up rocks is abrasion. The waves roll and tumble rocks against each other and break them into smaller pieces. These pieces are then eroded. The sediment carried by the waves can act like sandpaper, rubbing away at the rocks.

Finally, ocean water can chemically weather the rocks. The ocean water dissolves minerals in the rock, causing the rock to fall apart. These smaller pieces are picked up by the waves and further eroded.

SkillBuilder *Interpreting Data*

Sedimentation and Sorting

When a river enters an ocean, the water slows down and drops its sediments. These sediments are then moved along the shore by the waves. The sediments drop out of the waves according to the density and size of the different sediment particles.

The graph shows the average sediment sizes of samples taken along a 1.6 km stretch of beach next to the mouth of a river. Study the graph, then answer the questions.

1. List the sites in order, from the largest to the smallest sediment size.

2. Which sample came from the site closest to the river's mouth? Why?

3. Which sample came from the site farthest away from the river's mouth? Why?

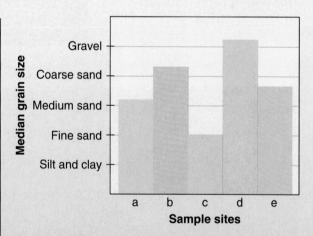

4. Where would you expect to find sediment sizes even smaller than these samples?

5. Where would you expect to find sediment sizes larger than these samples?

Write a short report explaining how waves sort sediments by size.

Formations from Wave Erosion

Have you ever seen any of the shoreline formations below? Waves constantly change the shape of the shoreline. Both sand on a beach and rocky shorelines are eroded continuously by the waves. Along a rocky coast, wave erosion results in beautiful landforms.

Sea Cave

◀ When a coastal area consists of several types of rock that erode at different rates, landforms develop. Waves pounding against a cliff that contains weak rock may hollow out a hole. This rock cavity is called a sea cave. Find the sea cave in the photograph.

Sea Arch ▶

If the rock in a sea cave becomes eroded through, a natural arch may form. This natural arch is called a sea arch. Compare the sea arch in this photograph to the sea cave shown above. If erosion continues, the sea arch may collapse and leave behind a column of rock, or a sea stack.

Sea Stack ▲

A sea stack is a tall tower of resistant rock standing offshore. It is the rock left standing from a steep wall of rock, or a sea cliff, after the waves eroded all of the weaker surrounding rock. Locate a sea stack in the photograph.

Sea Cliff

◀ When a rocky shore erodes at approximately the same rate all along an area, a steep wall of rock forms. This wall is called a sea cliff. Sea cliffs may extend along a rocky coast for many kilometers. At the base of a sea cliff, a platform called a sea terrace may form.

Wave Deposits

Sediment is constantly deposited by waves. This material was eroded from the coastline or brought to the ocean by rivers. These sediments deposit as the water slows down. Over a long period of time, the deposited sediments collect along the shore. A shoreline that is covered with sand, gravel, or other sediment forms a *beach*.

Looking at Figure 12.5, you might think that beach sediment stands still. However, if you could color some of the sand and watch it over a period of several hours or days, you would see that the sand actually moves along the beach. The sand is continuously eroded and deposited along the shoreline by waves and currents.

Currents are like rivers that flow offshore in the water along a beach. Currents move large amounts of sediment parallel to the shore. When these currents meet a change in the direction of the shoreline or deeper water, they suddenly slow down and deposit the sediment. This deposit is called a *spit*. Look at an example of a spit in Figure 12.6. A spit extends out from a beach across a bay or inlet.

Sand bars are features similar to spits but not connected to the beach. Sand bars may form offshore when breaking waves pull the sand from the beach into the water. This creates sand bars that are parallel to the beach.

Sand carried by waves and currents to the head of a bay or inlet may form small pocket beaches. Over a long period of time, the deposition of spits and beaches fills in the bays and inlets with sand, making the coastline more regular. This deposition of sediment straightens out the coastline.

Waves are most commonly found in the ocean. However, large lakes, such as the Great Lakes, also have waves. Large lakes create some of the same landforms that oceans do.

Figure 12.5 ▲
Although this beach in Kauai, Hawaii looks quiet, the sand is actually being moved along the shoreline by the pounding waves.

Figure 12.6 ▲
The Dungeness Spit in the state of Washington is a large natural spit. How does a spit differ from a sand bar?

Science and Society *Harbor Dredging*

Wave erosion and deposition move sand from one place to another. Sand often deposits in bays where the water has less energy to move the sediment. Over time, bays fill with sand deposits.

Bays are important sites for shipping. Bays provide ships with harbors for loading and unloading cargo. Therefore, the natural filling-in of the bay with wave deposits interferes with shipping. Sand bars can block the entrance to the harbor, and the bottom of the bay can become too shallow for large ships. New shipping channels are created by removing sediment that settled on the bottom of the harbor.

Figure 12.7 ▲
Dredges can be stationary or mobile. This floating dredge deepens shipping channels.

Many communities that surround harbors rely on dredging to keep the harbors operating. A dredging operation consists of a barge or platform that sits out in the bay. A large pump connects to several pipes. The pump sucks up the sediments on the bottom of the bay through one pipe. It then pumps out the collected sediment, either offshore or downshore through another pipe. The redepositing of sediments can cause changes in the natural erosion and deposition patterns in other areas of the shoreline.

How often dredging is done depends on how much sediment is deposited. In some harbors along sandy coastlines, such as Florida's, dredges operate nonstop.

Check and Explain

1. Using drawings and words, describe how a river forms from runoff.

2. How does a river's pattern of erosion change as it develops through the young, mature, and old river stages?

3. **Classify** Would you find each landform on a rocky or sandy shoreline: spit, sea stack, sea cliff, beach, or sea arch?

4. **Compare and Contrast** How are wave and river deposits similar? How are they different?

▼ ACTIVITY

12.3 Ice Erosion

Objectives

▶ **Explain** how glaciers form.

▶ **Describe** the process of ice erosion.

▶ **Classify** landforms as the result of glacial erosion or glacial deposition.

▶ **Make a model** of a valley glacier and label its parts.

L ike giant bulldozers, glaciers move very slowly. But they are capable of eroding and depositing large amounts of materials. Glacial movement produces many distinctive landforms.

Glaciers

When the amount of snow is so great that it can't completely melt, **glaciers** form. As the layers of snow pile up, the weight on the underlying snow increases. Eventually this weight tightly packs the snow underneath, forming glacial ice. The pressure on the ice at the bottom becomes so great that it partially melts. The entire ice mass starts moving. A glacier is formed.

The two types of glaciers are shown below. Glaciers that form in high mountain valleys are called *valley glaciers*. Glaciers that cover large areas in polar regions, like Antarctica, are called *continental glaciers*.

Figure 12.8
The photograph on the left shows a valley glacier. The one on the right shows a continental glacier. ▼

A glacier moves by sliding over the thin layer of water due to melting on the bottom of the ice mass. Once the glacier starts to slide, gravity pulls the ice mass downhill. Gravity moves glaciers a few meters to 100 m per year.

Ice Ages

Glaciers have been a feature on the earth's surface for a long time. In the past, the climate of the earth has been cooler, and large glaciers covered much of the earth. These periods of cooling are referred to as ice ages. Look at Figure 12.9. Where did glaciers cover the earth in the recent past?

During the last ice age, continental glaciers covered the northern part of North America. The western United States had many valley glaciers at the same time. The glaciers of the last ice age caused many of the landforms in these areas.

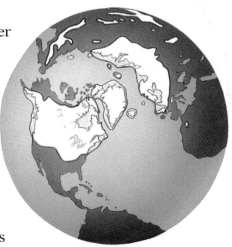

Figure 12.9 ▲
During the last ice age, did glaciers cover the area where you live?

Historical Notebook

Ice Age Societies

If you imagine Ice Age culture, you may think of people dressed in animal hides standing around a cave fire. However, scientific findings show that Ice Age people had a complex society. Evidence from Ice Age base camps reveals that these people lived in dwellings, made clothing, and created art.

Ice Age people probably didn't live in caves at all. In fact, an excavation site in the Ukraine uncovered a village built from the bones of wooly mammoths. At other sites, archeologists discovered wood and stone that may have been used for housing.

Caves were an important part of Ice Age culture, however. Many caves have been found decorated with art. Caves may have served as sacred places or places to record history.

Engravings and cave drawings give clues to Ice Age clothing. Ice Age art shows people wearing parkas, collared shirts with sleeves, and boots.

Site findings of beads and shark teeth suggest that they also adorned themselves with jewelry.

1. What findings suggest that Ice Age people had a complex culture?

2. **Write** Describe a typical day if you lived during the Ice Age.

Glacial Erosion

As a glacier moves, it causes erosion. The melted water from the glacier's surface or bottom seeps into cracks in rock and freezes. Ice wedging causes the rock to break apart. The rock fragments stick to the glacial ice and are plucked out as the glacier moves. These pieces of rock stuck to the bottom and sides of a glacier act like sandpaper. As the glacier moves, it scrapes and scratches the bedrock and soil underneath and along its sides. As shown in Figure 12.10, many landforms result from glacial erosion.

Unlike valley glaciers, continental glaciers tend to level large surface areas through the scraping and grinding of thick ice. Large areas carved out by continental glaciers can fill with water when the glaciers retreat. The Great Lakes along the Canadian border and the Finger Lakes in New York are examples of this process.

Figure 12.10
Landforms from Glacial Erosion ▼

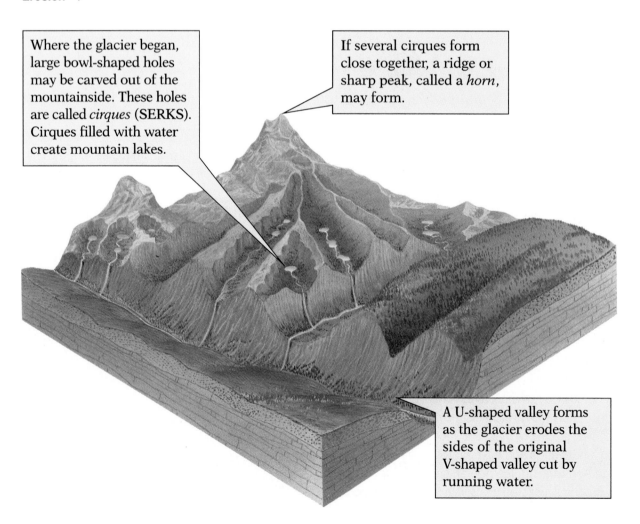

Where the glacier began, large bowl-shaped holes may be carved out of the mountainside. These holes are called *cirques* (SERKS). Cirques filled with water create mountain lakes.

If several cirques form close together, a ridge or sharp peak, called a *horn*, may form.

A U-shaped valley forms as the glacier erodes the sides of the original V-shaped valley cut by running water.

Glacial Deposits

Landforms also result from glacial deposits, as shown in Figure 12.11. As the ice moves to the front of the glacier, it carries along rocks and other sediments. The glacier drops some rocks as it moves. However, much sediment is carried to the front of the glacier. The meltwater streams that flow from the glacier carry some of the sediment. Deposits from meltwater streams are similar to an alluvial fan. The heaviest sediments drop out before the lighter ones, resulting in a sorted and layered deposit. This sorted and layered sediment is called **outwash**.

If the weather warms up, the glacier begins to melt faster than the ice accumulates. The glacier retreats and drops its sediment load in a big pile or ridge called a **moraine**. Moraines left behind during the last ice age helped to form Long Island, Cape Cod, and Nantucket. A moraine contains an assortment of sediment sizes. This mixture of sediments in a moraine is called **till**. When cemented together, till forms conglomerate sedimentary rock.

Figure 12.11
Landforms from Glacial Deposition ▼

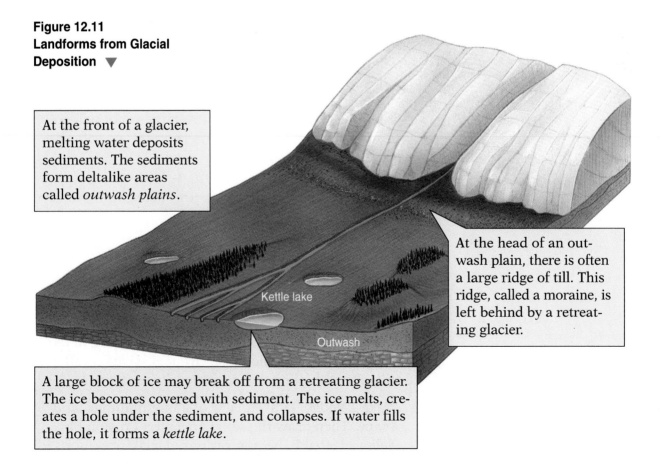

At the front of a glacier, melting water deposits sediments. The sediments form deltalike areas called *outwash plains*.

At the head of an outwash plain, there is often a large ridge of till. This ridge, called a moraine, is left behind by a retreating glacier.

Kettle lake

Outwash

A large block of ice may break off from a retreating glacier. The ice becomes covered with sediment. The ice melts, creates a hole under the sediment, and collapses. If water fills the hole, it forms a *kettle lake*.

Science and Technology
Working in Antarctica

Imagine your classroom is as cold as your freezer on warm, sunny days. That is actually the normal summertime climate for the nearly 4,000 scientists who live and work in Antarctica. Imagine what it's like in the winter! The scientists must bundle up to avoid frostbite. They pull their instruments on sleds and often ski or travel by snowmobile to their testing sites. For studies in more remote areas, scientists travel in airplanes equipped with skis for landing.

In Antarctica, scientists study glaciers, earth history, the atmosphere, wildlife, and volcanoes. Much of the research involves direct observation and sample collecting. Many Antarctic studies use remote-controlled equipment. Instruments are set up at the testing site. Probes collect information and beam it to satellites, which relay the information back to the scientists. This type of technology is very important for conducting year-round research, since the winter temperatures in Antarctica can drop lower than –57°C.

In one Antarctic study, scientists are using a roving robot. The robot has eight walking legs and high-resolution cameras for eyes. The robot is attached by a cable to a transporter. It will send information to the transporter for storage in case the robot is destroyed during its mission. If all goes well, however, the robot will collect samples and return to the transporter for a safe trip back to camp.

Figure 12.12 ▲
Scientists need special tools to study the extreme conditions in the Antarctic.

Check and Explain

1. How do glaciers form?

2. Explain how glaciers erode a mountain.

3. **Classify** Make a table with one column labeled *Glacial Deposition* and the other column labeled *Glacial Erosion*. Classify each of the following in the proper column in the table: cirque, U-shaped valley, till, outwash plain, horn, kettle lake, moraine.

4. **Make a Model** Draw a view of a mountainous landscape. Then draw the same area after erosion by a valley glacier. Label the various glacial formations.

Activity 12 *How can you model a glacier?*

Task 1 Prelab Prep
Collect the following materials: a large piece of ice, paper towel, a piece of wire, a square of hard plastic, a handful of sand.

Task 2 Data Record
On a sheet of paper, copy Table 12.1. Record all your observations in the table.

Table 12.1 Glacial Erosion Model

Event	Observations
Inserting wire quickly	
Inserting wire slowly	
Smooth ice on plastic	
Picking up sand quickly	
Picking up sand slowly	
Sandy ice on plastic	

Task 3 Procedure
1. Place the paper towel on your desk. Put the piece of ice on the paper towel. Try to quickly force the wire into the ice. Record your observations.
2. Slowly but firmly push the end of the wire against the ice. Hold it there for several minutes. Record your observations.
3. Place the plastic square on your desk. Rub the piece of ice back and forth on the plastic square. Observe the surface of the plastic. Record your observations.
4. Place the sand in a layer on the plastic square. Try to quickly pick up the sand with the ice. Record your observations.
5. Slowly but firmly push the ice down onto the sand. Leave the ice on the sand for several minutes. Remove the ice from the sand, and record your observations.
6. Clean the plastic square of sand. Rub the sandy side of the ice back and forth on the plastic square. Observe the surface of the plastic. Record your observations.

Task 4 Analysis
1. Which method worked the best for pushing the wire into the ice? How did inserting the wire demonstrate how glaciers melt?
2. Which method worked best for picking up the sand?
3. How could you remove a wire stuck in ice without destroying the ice block?
4. What was happening at the site where the wire or sand was slowly pushed into the ice?
5. What happened when you released the slow steady pressure?
6. Which caused the greatest change on the surface of the plastic, the smooth ice or the ice embedded with sand? How did this model demonstrate the effect of glaciers upon bedrock?

Task 5 Conclusion
Write a short paragraph explaining how your glacier model is similar to actual glaciers.

Everyday Application
Explain how inserting the wire into the ice is similar to the process that enables a figure skater to move across the ice.

Extension
Design a model that shows glacial deposition. Test the model that you design. Decide how it is similar to actual glacial deposition and how it is different.

▼ ACTIVITY

Predicting

Sandblasting

Rub the painted ridges of your pencil across a small piece of sandpaper. What happened to the paint? What does the surface of the pencil feel like? Explain what happened. How could wind do the same thing?

SKILLS WARMUP

12.4 Wind Erosion

Objectives

▶ **Describe** the conditions necessary for wind erosion to occur.

▶ **Explain** how sand particles move.

▶ **Compare** and **contrast** abrasion and deflation.

▶ **Make models** of the different types of sand dunes.

If you have ever gotten dirt or sand in your eyes on a windy day, you know that the wind can move dirt. Wind causes erosion, just like running water, waves, and glaciers do. Wind not only erodes areas, it also deposits materials to make unique landforms. If you have ever been to a beach, you probably have seen the most common landform deposited by winds: the dunes.

Energy in Wind

As with running water and waves, the energy of the wind determines the size of the materials it carries. As wind blows across the ground, it lifts and moves dry, loose surface materials. Weak winds have little energy, so they carry only small particles like dust. Strong winds have more energy. The energy creates more of an uplifting force. Strong winds are often more turbulent. The more turbulent the wind, the more sediments it carries. Just as the turbulence of running water prevents sediments from dropping out, the turbulence of strong wind prevents heavier particles from dropping. A constant, strong wind can develop a large dust cloud, like the one shown in Figure 12.13.

Most wind erosion occurs in the dry areas of the world, such as deserts. In wetter areas, water causes the soil particles to clump together, forming pieces that are too heavy for the wind to pick up. However, if a drought causes the ground to dry out and the soil is bare, wind erosion can occur anywhere. Wind erosion can also occur if the soil is left unplanted for a long period of time. Plants keep the soil from being blown away.

Figure 12.13 ▲
Beside strong winds, several other factors contribute to dust storms, such as arid climates, droughts, and poor planting practices.

Particle Movement

Follow the movement of the sand grains shown in Figure 12.14. How would you describe the movement of the particles? Sand particles are too heavy to be held up in the air for a long time. The sand grains are lifted into the air by the wind. Then they roll forward and collide with other sand grains. The collision sends the first grains up and over the other grains. The wind provides a horizontal force that sends the grains forward. Gravity pulls the grains back down to the ground. The result is that the sand grains follow a rounded path as they leap-frog along.

When a sand grain lands on the ground, it is picked up again by the wind or buried in the loose sand, which throws other grains in the air. This occurs simultaneously with many other sand grains, producing a cloud-like layer of moving sand just above the ground, as shown in Figure 12.14.

This type of movement also separates the sediment into different sizes. Large particles are left behind, close to their source. Medium-sized particles only move a short distance away. The smallest particles are carried the farthest. In both strong and weak winds, however, particles are carried only a few centimeters to a meter above the ground. The movement of particles over a distance is due to the energy transfer from one particle to another.

▼ **ACTIVITY**

Making a Model

Sand Dunes

1. Cover a hard surface, such as your desk or a section of the floor, with paper towels.

2. Place a small pile of sand in the center of the towels.

3. Using a drinking straw, slowly and carefully blow the sand across the towels. What happens to the sand? Do shapes form? What would happen if you blew hard? How is this a model of sand dune formation by wind?

SKILLS WORKOUT

Figure 12.14
Wind causes sand particles to move in little leaps. What happens to the sand particle followed by the green arrow? What happens to the sand particle followed by the red arrow? ▼

Abrasion   If you've ever felt the sand whip across your legs on a windy day at the beach, you have experienced abrasion. Sand grains wear away the surface of buildings, telephone poles, and rocks by abrasion. The sand-filled air is like a moving piece of sandpaper.

The effect of windblown sand depends on the hardness of a rock's surface. If a rock is the same hardness along the entire surface, the windblown sand smoothes and polishes the rock's surface. If a rock surface is made of various types of minerals with different hardnesses, the windblown sand causes abrasion at different rates. The surface of the rock becomes rippled rather than smooth, as shown in Figure 12.15.

The abrasion of rock by wind erosion can sometimes result in unusual landforms. For example, the forces of abrasion may eventually cut through rock layers, forming arches. Tall towers may be left standing after the wind carries away the soft material that surrounded hard inner layers. However, it takes many years for windblown sand to

Figure 12.16 ▲
Desert pavement is a hard, stony surface. How did this desert pavement in Arizona form?

erode large rock surfaces. Most erosion of large rocks is due to running water.

Deflation   The process of wind carrying away loose sediment is called **deflation**. Deflation comes from the Latin word meaning "to blow away." Deflation occurs primarily in desert regions. As the wind blows along the ground, it scoops up and carries away the loose sediment, such as dust and sand. The larger pebbles left behind form a hard, stony surface called *desert pavement*. Look for the rocks in the desert pavement in Figure 12.16.

In areas where the sediment is mostly fine-grained dust, deflation can cause serious problems. Turbulent winds can create dust storms. Unlike heavier sand grains, winds lift dust particles high into the air and move them long distances. Recall the area in the United States that became known as the Dust Bowl in the 1930s. The Dust Bowl disaster was caused by deflation. Deflation removed most of the fertile soil in the Great Plains after several years of severe drought.

Figure 12.15 ▲
Abrasion causes the wearing away of rock. How can you tell that this rock is composed of several different types of minerals?

Wind Deposits

When wind slows down, it drops the sediments it is carrying. The type of landform produced by the deposited sediments depends on the size and amount of particles, the wind direction, and the amount of wind from a single direction. Deposits formed by windblown sand are called *dunes*. Deposits formed by windblown dust are called *loess*.

Dunes form when an obstacle, such as a rock or a plant, causes wind to slow. The sand piles up and blocks the wind, causing more sand to deposit. Dunes have a gentle slope facing the wind and a steep slope away from the wind. As the wind blows, it pushes the sand up and over the top of a dune. This constant motion causes the dune to move forward.

◀ One type of sand dune is a crescent, or horn-shaped, dune. These dunes have horns that point in the direction of the wind. They occur where land is very flat and hard, and there is little sediment and few plants.

Transverse dunes are long, ▶ continuous sand ridges. They form at right angles to the wind direction in areas with a large supply of sediment. Transverse dunes are commonly found at the beach or in large deserts.

◀ Longitudinal dunes form in areas with strong winds and little sediment. These dunes run parallel to the wind direction. Longitudinal dunes form in desert areas with moderate amounts of sand.

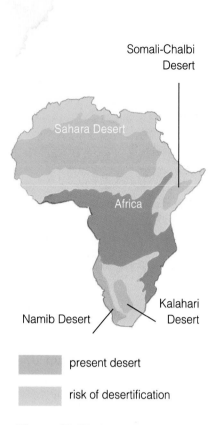

Somali-Chalbi Desert

Sahara Desert

Africa

Namib Desert

Kalahari Desert

present desert

risk of desertification

Figure 12.17 ▲
The increasing deserts in Africa have caused food shortages and climatic changes.

Science and Society *The Moving Desert*

About one-third of the earth's land surface is covered by deserts. Although some of these deserts occur because of warm temperatures and a lack of rain, many deserts have been formed or expanded by human activity. As shown in Figure 12.17, Africa has been severely affected by desert expansion. The spreading Sahara Desert removes about 100 000 hectares of useful land every year. Many human activities contribute to the spreading of deserts, a process known as desertification. These include overgrazing, poor farming practices, and overpopulation.

The primary activity responsible for increasing the size of deserts is farming. In many areas of the world, such as parts of Africa, China, and the United States, farmers cut down trees and remove the grasses to create more fields for farming. The trees and grasses help hold the soil in place. Without plants, the soil is left open to the attack of the wind. If a drought occurs or if the water in an area is used up, the soil dries out. Much of the soil blows away.

In many areas of the world, the balance between the vegetation and the climate is quite delicate. If the balance is upset, the area cannot recover, and a desert forms. Fortunately, scientists are recognizing this situation and are studying ways to avoid the problem. Proper water use and crop planting could help make these areas productive again.

Check and Explain

1. Place the following in order as examples of areas with the most to the least erosion: a grass-covered field, a bare field of damp earth, a dry desert sand dune, a sand dune covered with some beach grass.

2. Describe how sand particles move.

3. **Compare and Contrast** How are deflation and abrasion alike? How are they different?

4. **Make Models** Create a separate drawing for each type of sand dune. Include in each drawing the type of surrounding area in which the sand dune would form.

Chapter 12 Review

Concept Summary

12.1 Gravity and Erosion

▶ Weathered materials are eroded by the action of water, wind, ice, and gravity. Deposition piles these materials elsewhere.

▶ Gravity causes mass movement. Types of mass movement are landslides, mudflows, slump, and creep.

12.2 Water Erosion

▶ Rivers are classified as young, mature, or old depending on how much they erode an area.

▶ When a river slows down, it deposits sediments to form deltas, levees, floodplains, and alluvial fans.

▶ Wave erosion forms sea cliffs, sea caves, sea stacks, and sea arches. Wave deposits form beaches, spits, and bars.

12.3 Ice Erosion

▶ Great amounts of snow form valley glaciers and continental glaciers.

▶ Ice wedging, scraping, and scratching are glacial processes. Glacial erosion forms a variety of land features.

▶ Melting glaciers leave behind till and outwash deposits. Formations from these deposits include outwash plains, moraines, and kettle lakes.

12.4 Wind Erosion

▶ The wind picks up and carries particles in the air, or causes deflation. These particles may abrade rock surfaces.

▶ Particle movement by wind follows a leap-frog path.

▶ The most common wind deposits are dunes and loess.

Chapter Vocabulary

erosion (12.1)	rill (12.2)	levee (12.2)	outwash (12.3)
deposition (12.1)	meander (12.2)	glacier (12.3)	moraine (12.3)
mass movement (12.1)	alluvial fan (12.2)	till (12.3)	deflation (12.4)

Check Your Vocabulary

Use the vocabulary words above to complete the following sentences correctly.

1. An old river has many curves, or ____ .

2. Sediments deposited along the sides of rivers are called ____ .

3. Glacial deposits that contain an assortment of sediment sizes are called ____ .

4. A thick wedge of sediment that sometimes forms at a mountain base is called ____ .

5. Glacial deposits that result in sorted and layered sediment are called ____ .

6. The moving of materials by wind, water, ice, or gravity is ____ .

7. The process by which wind carries away loose sediment is called ____ .

8. The movement of rocks or soil by gravity down a slope is ____ .

9. Small channels in the dirt that are formed by rainwater flowing down a slope are called ____ .

10. A glacial deposit of till formed at the head of an outwash plain is a ____ .

11. The dropping of weathered materials in a new place is called ____ .

12. A large mass of moving ice and snow is a ____ .

Chapter 12 Review

Check Your Knowledge

Answer the following in complete sentences.

1. List the three types of dunes.

2 What is a gully?

3. Why is mass movement more common on a steep slope than on a flat field?

4. List the three stages of river erosion.

5. What is a glacier?

6. Name the two different types of glaciers.

7. Describe three ways that rocks are broken up by wave action.

8. List the factors that affect the amount of erosion in an area.

9. What are the different types of mass movement?

10. List the agents of erosion.

11. What is desert pavement?

12. What factors determine the type of wind deposit that will form?

Choose the answer that best completes each sentence.

13. An alluvial fan is an example of (water, wind, wave, glacial) deposition.

14. Greenland is a (valley, continental, retreating, advancing) glacier.

15. Smooth and polished rocks are a result of wind (deflation, differential erosion, abrasion, deposits).

16. When water slows down, the first sediments to drop out are (silt, clay, fine material, coarse material).

17. Spits, beaches, and bars are examples of (stream erosion, stream deposition, wave erosion, wave deposition).

Check Your Understanding

Apply the concepts you have learned to answer each question.

1. Describe how farmers can protect their farms from the effects of wind erosion.

2. Explain how glaciers move.

3. Describe the effects of differential wind erosion on rocks.

4. Which wind and water formations are similar in appearance? Discuss why these formations look similar although they were formed by different types of erosion.

5. Compare how a mountain lake and a kettle lake form.

6. What two agents of erosion are necessary to form loess deposits?

7. Describe two ways that river deposition is controlled by humans.

8. **Classify** Using all the agents of erosion, make a list of the different types of depositions that form only in arid regions.

9. **Find Causes** Many valleys in the mountains of Scotland are very wide and have steep sides. Explain how they were formed.

10. **Application** Farmers plow in circles around a hill instead of up and down. Explain this in terms of soil erosion.

11. **Mystery Photo** The photograph on page 262 is a closeup of the rocks in Antelope Canyon in Arizona. What agents of erosion shaped this canyon? How can you tell?

Develop Your Skills

Use the skills you have developed in this chapter to complete each activity.

1. **Interpret Data** The graph below shows the effect of stream speed on the type of sediments carried.

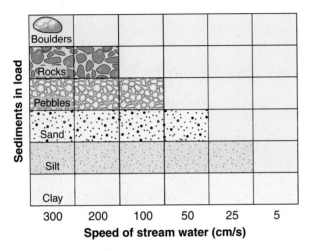

a. At which speed does a stream carry the largest load?

b. At which speed does a stream carry the smallest load?

c. Name the sediments that drop from the load first. Why?

d. Name the sediments that drop from the load last. Why?

e. At what speed do pebbles drop from the load? Sand?

2. **Data Bank** Use the information on page 612 to answer the following questions.

a. Where is the largest silt deposit located?

b. Where is the largest silt load deposit in North America?

c. **Infer** What formation would you expect to find at the mouth of each river?

3. **Design an Experiment** The sand on a beach is constantly in motion. Map the path of sand moving along a beach.

Make Connections

1. **Link the Concepts** Below is a concept map showing how some of the main concepts in this chapter link together. Only parts of the map are filled in. Complete the map, using words and ideas from the chapter.

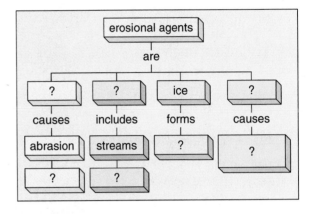

2. **Science and Society** During the late 1960s, desertification in Africa resulted in the deaths of 250,000 people. Conduct research to find out how famine relief is administered throughout the world. List organizations that are involved in famine relief.

3. **Science and Art** Use magazines or travel brochures to find pictures of the results of all types of erosion. Cut out the pictures and glue them on a sheet of paper, making an erosion collage.

4. **Science and Social Studies** The Dust Bowl of the 1930s affected the lives of many people in the United States. Find out how the Dust Bowl began. How could the Dust Bowl have been prevented?

5. **Science and You** Take an erosion walk around your school or a local park. Record and describe each agent of erosion that you find.

Chapter 13 History of Life on Earth

What do you see?

"I believe this is a prehistoric fossil of a seashell. It died and sank into mud and the mud dried, turning the seashell into a fossil."

Hector Rivera
Fleming Junior High
Lomita, California

To find out more about the photograph, look on page 310. As you read this chapter, you will learn about the information found in rocks that tells the history of the earth.

13.1 Evolution of Life

Objectives

▶ **Explain** how fossils provide evidence for evolution.

▶ **State** the theory of evolution.

▶ **Describe** how organisms are classified.

▶ **Classify** groups of organisms according to the five-kingdom classification system.

You set the dial of your time machine to 320 million years before the present and press the transport button. A moment later, you're standing in a swampy forest of strange-looking trees. You trudge through the muck to the edge of a lake and look around. Fish are swimming in the water. An animal that looks like a salamander sits by the water's edge. A flying insect buzzes overhead. There's no sign of any birds, furry animals, or flowers.

You can't actually visit the past in this way, but earth scientists can tell you what the past was like. Their information about the past comes from the study of fossils. Fossils help scientists learn about the history of the earth and the organisms living on its surface.

Earth's Changing Organisms

What types of organisms left the fossils shown in Figure 13.1? Fossils tell scientists what kinds of organisms lived during each period in geologic time. For example, in rocks 280 million years old, there are fossils of reptiles. Rocks more than 40 million years older than these, however, contain no reptile fossils. Based on this evidence, scientists hypothesize that if you traveled back more than 320 million years you would not find any reptiles. But you would find many kinds of plants and animals that do not exist today.

Similarly, if you traveled back in time 500 million years, the organisms you'd see would be different from those of any other period. Fossil evidence shows that the kinds of organisms inhabiting the earth's surface have changed over time.

Figure 13.1 ▲
The organisms that left these fossils have been extinct for millions of years.

Theory of Evolution

Each kind of organism is called a **species** (SPEE sheez). All the members of a species have nearly the same traits, and they reproduce to make more organisms like themselves. Scientists identify species that lived in the past by studying their fossil remains.

If different species lived on the earth at different periods of time, then species must change. Charles Darwin reached this conclusion over 100 years ago. He worked out a theory of **evolution**. In biology, evolution is the process by which species change over time.

Darwin hypothesized that slight differences in traits make some individuals in a species better able to survive than others. These individuals are better *adapted* to their environment. More of their offspring tend to survive compared to other individuals. Their special traits are passed on to the next generation. Darwin called his hypothesis *natural selection*.

Natural selection is the process by which the traits of the species as a whole change over time, as shown in Figure 13.2.

Changes in the earth's environment affect evolution. Environmental changes may cause the **extinction**, or dying out, of species that can't adapt to the changes. Changes in climate and sea level have resulted in the origin of new species and the extinction of others.

The movement of the earth's tectonic plates also had an important role in evolution. The breakup of Pangaea created separate continents. The environments of the continents eventually became different. Organisms on each continent, therefore, evolved differently.

The theory of evolution states that all living things are related. Scientists hypothesize that all species now alive came from one or a few simple life forms. Look at Figure 13.3. It is a simplified evolutionary tree showing how the many kinds of organisms alive today may have evolved from the first cells.

Figure 13.2 ▼
The modern horse evolved from a small mammal that lived during the early Tertiary period.

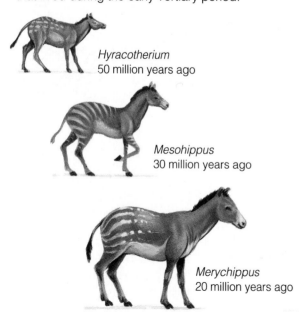

Hyracotherium
50 million years ago

Mesohippus
30 million years ago

Merychippus
20 million years ago

Equus
Present

Pliohippus
5 million years ago

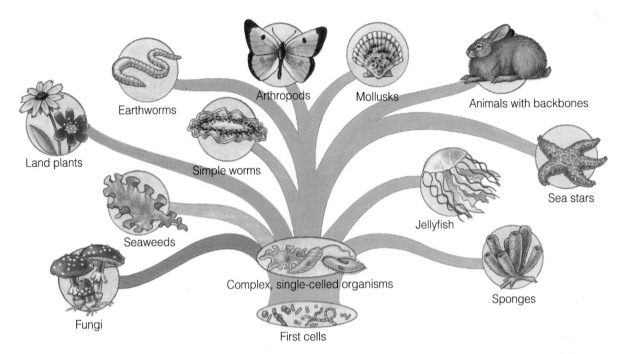

Land plants
Earthworms
Arthropods
Mollusks
Animals with backbones
Simple worms
Seaweeds
Sea stars
Jellyfish
Complex, single-celled organisms
Fungi
Sponges
First cells

Classification of Organisms

Many very different groups of organisms have evolved on the earth. Look at Figure 13.3. Notice that each branch of the evolutionary tree contains organisms more closely related to each other than to organisms on other branches. The major branches of the evolutionary tree in Figure 13.3 are the basis for a system of classification.

The system most widely used today to classify organisms divides them into five large groups called **kingdoms**. Each kingdom is made up of species with a similar body organization and method of nutrition, or way of getting food. The five kingdoms are described in Table 13.1. What kingdom do you belong in?

The monerans (MOHN ehr uhnz) are distinguished by the simple structure of their cells. This structure is similar to that of the first cells. Members of the other four kingdoms have cells with specialized parts surrounded by membranes.

Figure 13.3 ▲
This tree diagram shows the ancestry of some major groups of modern organisms.

Table 13.1 The Five Kingdoms

Kingdom	Major Characteristics	Groups
Monerans	Simple cells	Bacteria, blue-green algae
Protists	Complex cells; one-celled or many-celled organisms	Protozoa, seaweeds
Fungi	Absorb nutrients from other organisms	Mushrooms, yeasts, molds
Plants	Many-celled; use photosynthesis for energy and growth	Ferns, mosses, cone-bearing and flowering plants
Animals	Many-celled; eat food	Sponges, worms, insects, fishes, reptiles, birds, mammals, and many others

Books in Order

1. Go to your library and find out how books are classified.

2. Make a chart or diagram that shows the library's classification system.

Where can you find books about dinosaurs? About jewelry? Sports?

SKILLS WORKOUT

Science and You *Everyday Classification*

Classification systems help scientists explain the relationships among organisms. But classification is not only used by scientists. In fact, you use some type of classification system nearly every day. You use them in stores, at school, at home, and many other places.

How do you use classification systems in stores? Think, for example, what it would be like finding apples in the store if there were not a produce section. You'd have to travel throughout the store before you could locate the apples. They could be anywhere! The grocery store would be more like a flea market, where items can be found in almost any location.

How do you use classification systems in school? The library is one obvious place. Your school may have its own classification system for grouping books. They may be grouped by author, title, or subject. Many school libraries use the Dewey Decimal Classification System. This system divides books into ten main groups. Each main group is broken into more specific fields.

How do you use classification systems at home? You may have your music or video collection classified. Maybe you arrange your collection by type, such as jazz or comedy, just like most music and video stores do. Maybe your collection is arranged alphabetically. You can probably find a number of classification systems in your bedroom. Your shoes may be placed in a certain part of your closet. Your summer clothes are probably separated from your winter clothes. What other examples of everyday classification systems can you name?

Check and Explain

1. What is the theory of evolution?

2. How do fossils provide evidence for evolution?

3. **Observe** Study Figure 13.3. Are animals with backbones more closely related to arthropods or to starfish? Why?

4. **Classify** Copy the evolutionary tree in Figure 13.3. Then use the five-kingdom classification system to divide the tree into five sections, each corresponding to a kingdom.

Activity 13   How do you classify a group of items?

Skills   Observe; Classify; Model; Communicate

Task 1   Prelab Prep
Collect the following items: container of assorted washers and nuts, piece of butcher paper, pencil.

Task 2   Data Record
1. At the top of the piece of butcher paper, copy the chart shown in Figure 13.4. Leave room to make the chart larger.
2. Show all your groupings of objects in the chart.

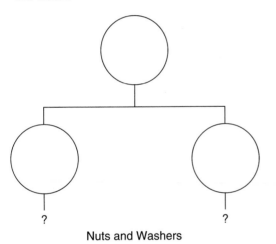

Nuts and Washers

Figure 13.4 ▲

Task 3   Procedure
1. Pour the contents of the container onto a table. Divide the contents into two groups based on similar characteristics.
2. Record the name and characteristics of each group on your chart.
3. Divide each of the two groups into two or three smaller groups. The items in each group must share at least one common characteristic. Give a name to each group based on the group's characteristics.

4. Record the characteristics of each group on your chart.
5. Continue to separate the items into smaller groups until each group contains only one type of item. Remember that items in a group must have characteristics that make them different from the items in the other groups.
6. Record the characteristics for each of the groups that you make on your chart.
7. Share your chart with your classmates. Communicate what characteristics you chose to distinguish each group.

Task 4   Analysis
1. How is your chart different from those of your classmates?
2. Which groups were the easiest to distinguish between? The most difficult?
3. **Observe**   Choose one item. Using the chart, record all the characteristics for that item based on all the different groups it belongs to. How does the name you chose for that item reflect its characteristics?
4. If someone picked an item from the group at random, how would you describe to that person how to classify it the same way you did? Write a set of step-by-step directions that someone could use to classify any item from the group.
5. How does your chart model the classification of organisms in an evolutionary tree?

Task 5   Conclusion
Imagine that your washers and nuts are organisms and that they have evolved to reach their present forms. Describe all the steps in the evolutionary process you recorded on your chart.

Extension

Make a classification chart for other items, such as nails and screws, beads, or items in a desk.

Hints of Life

1. Place a sheet of paper over a flat object that has a rough surface.

2. Rub a pencil or crayon over the paper.

3. Repeat with two or three other objects.

4. Trade your rubbings with someone else's and try to identify the rubbings you receive.

What are some benefits to finding the slightest remains of a once-living organism?

SKILLS WARMUP

13.2 The Fossil Record

Objectives

▶ **Describe** the conditions under which fossils may form.

▶ **Distinguish** among the different types of fossils.

▶ **Explain** how molds and casts differ.

▶ **Infer** geologic history from the fossil record.

Millions of years ago, organisms related to today's sea stars, crabs, and clams lived on a muddy ocean floor beside a giant reef wall. One day, a huge landslide buried these animals in thick layers of mud. Millions of years later in Siberia, a woolly mammoth wandered the icy plains in search of food. Suddenly the ground gave way, and the animal fell into a deep crack in the frozen ground.

Both the ocean-floor organisms and the mammoth became fossils. The fossils of the ocean-floor organisms were found in shale 2,400 m above sea level in the Canadian Rocky Mountains. When scientists found the mammoth, it was still frozen and perfectly preserved. Fossils such as these make up the *fossil record*—the record of the history of life on the earth.

Formation of Fossils

The ocean-floor organisms and the woolly mammoth were both unusual. Most organisms that lived on the earth did not leave any fossil remains. Usually an organism is destroyed when it dies. Another organism may eat it, or it decays. If it has hard parts, such as bones or shells, they are often broken, crushed, or scattered about.

For an organism to become a fossil, it must be protected from destructive forces and decay. This usually happens when sediments bury an organism that is alive or recently dead. When the sediments become rock, the organism may be preserved as a fossil. For this reason, most fossils are found in sedimentary rock. Why do you think metamorphic and igneous rocks contain few fossils?

Figure 13.5

How do you think these fish became fossilized? ▼

Types of Fossils

Fossils are classified according to how they formed and what is preserved. A fossil may be all or part of an organism. Some fossils are not parts of organisms at all, but traces, such as footprints or burrows.

Petrified Fossils   Most of the dinosaur bones that scientists have found are not the organisms' actual bones. They are mineralized copies of the original bones, called **petrified** (PEHT ruh fyd) fossils.

The process of petrification begins when bones, wood, shells, or other parts of living things are covered by sediment. The matter making up these parts is dissolved by seeping water. Minerals in the water slowly replace the original matter. As a result, the parts turned to stone. Even though their matter changed, the parts still have the shape and details of the original part. Can you see the growth rings in the petrified wood shown in Figure 13.6?

Figure 13.6 ▲
The wood in these petrified trees was completely replaced by stone.

Molds, Casts, and Imprints   Have you ever made a handprint in plaster of Paris? The same type of process formed many fossils. In this process, the remains of an organism buried by sediment slowly become rock. Water seeps through the rock and dissolves the hard parts of the organism, leaving a hole, or cavity, in the rock. This cavity in the shape of an organism is a fossil. This type of fossil is called a **mold**. Later, minerals may seep into and fill the cavity to form a **cast**. Look at the cast and mold in Figure 13.7.

Molds of thin objects are called imprints. A leaf pressed into sediment makes a pattern. This pattern is preserved when the sediment turns to rock.

Figure 13.7 ▲
Which is the cast of this ancient trilobite?

Trace Fossils   Footprints, tracks, trails, and burrows left by animals can be preserved as **trace fossils**. These fossils provide evidence about the size, shape, and habits of an animal. For example, the trace fossil footprints of early humans are evidence that they walked upright.

Coprolites   Waste materials from animals may be petrified, forming a fossil called a coprolite (KAHP ruh lyt). Particles of food, such as plant parts, are often preserved in the coprolite. They give information about what the animal ate and the organisms living at that time.

Figure 13.8 ▲
Why is this insect classified as an unchanged fossil?

Unchanged Fossils In petrified fossils, molds, and casts, little or none of the matter from the original organism remains. In some fossils, however, matter from the organism was not changed or removed. Such a fossil is called an unchanged or unaltered fossil.

The woolly mammoth preserved in frozen ground is an unchanged fossil. Another type of unchanged fossil is shown in Figure 13.8. It was formed when an insect got trapped in sticky plant sap. The sap hardened over time, becoming a substance called amber. Inside the amber is the insect's perfectly preserved body.

In the most common type of unchanged fossil, the soft parts of the body decayed, but the bones or other hard parts remained unchanged. This commonly occurred when an animal was trapped and buried in a tar pit. The unchanged fossil bones of wolves, sabertooth cats, bison, horses, sloths, and camels were found in the La Brea tar pits in Los Angeles, California.

SkillBuilder Inferring

ACTIVITY ACTIVITY

Case Study of a Fossil Site

Interpreting information obtained from fossils is like detective work. Numerous fossil bones have been found in limestone caves at Swartkrans in South Africa. Use clues from the fossil evidence below to determine how the fossils might have accumulated in the cave.

▶ The fossils are embedded in breccia, a sedimentary rock made of rock particles cemented together with limestone.

▶ The fossils include the skull of an early human child with two puncture wounds, a leopard jaw with a few teeth, and large bones from many types of mammals.

▶ Fossils from small bones such as ribs and vertebrae are not present.

▶ Trees grow near the opening of the cave. The trees protect the cave opening.

▶ The cave entrance is a hole in the ground that continues as a vertical shaft.

▶ Leopards are known to eat their prey in trees.

1. Why might the location of trees near the cave entrance be important?

2. How might the early human child have received its wounds?

3. Why might small animal bones be absent from the cave?

4. Is it possible to know for certain how the fossils accumulated in the cave? Why?

Write a story about how the fossil bones got into the cave over a million years ago. Make sure your explanation fits all the pieces of evidence given above. You may want to include a drawing or diagram.

The Incomplete Fossil Record

The record of past life and events is not complete. Many organisms, especially those with soft bodies, did not leave fossils. Many fossils remain covered in undisturbed layers of rock. Many fossils and rocks were destroyed by metamorphism and other forces. Other fossils and evidence of environmental change have been found, but remain unexplained.

Science and Society
What's Your State Fossil?

Does your state have a state fossil? The state fossil of Nebraska is the mammoth. All four species of extinct mammoths once lived in Nebraska. Mammoth skeletons are displayed in a museum in Lincoln, Nebraska.

Nevada's state fossil is the ichthyosaur, a reptile that lived in the ocean during the Mesozoic Era. A 15 m-long ichthyosaur was found in Nevada. *Stegosaurus*, a short-legged, plant-eating dinosaur weighing over 4 metric tons, is Colorado's state fossil. *Stegosaurus* is famous for the plates on its back. Arizona selected petrified wood as its state fossil. The largest collection of petrified wood in the world is found in Arizona in the Petrified Forest National Park.

Other state fossils include Alaska's woolly mammoth, Ohio's trilobite, and California's saber-toothed cat. If your state does not have a state fossil, what do you think would be a good choice?

Figure 13.9 ▲
Crinoids, or sea lilies, are common fossils from the Paleozoic and Mesozoic Eras. The crinoid is the state fossil of Missouri.

Check and Explain

1. Why did most organisms that lived on earth leave no fossil remains?

2. How is a mold different from a cast?

3. **Find Causes** Fossils of ocean organisms are much more common than fossils of organisms that lived on land. How do you explain this fact?

4. **Infer** In the center of North America, there are sedimentary rocks containing the fossils of ocean organisms. Based on this evidence, what can you infer about the geologic history of North America?

13.3 Interpreting Fossils

Objectives

▶ **Explain** the principle of superposition.

▶ **Determine** the relative age of fossils.

▶ **Describe** the process of radiometric dating.

▶ **Measure** the absolute age of a rock using the concept of half-life.

Age Before Beauty

Select five items in the classroom and rank them from oldest to youngest. What evidence did you use to make your ranking?

SKILLS WARMUP

I f dinosaurs lived tens of millions of years ago, how do scientists know so much about them? All knowledge about dinosaur size, appearance, diet, and behavior comes from fossils. For example, the distance between dinosaur footprints was used to estimate how fast the animals walked or ran.

One very important kind of information provided by fossils is when different species lived on the earth. By knowing the order in which species appeared, scientists can infer evolutionary relationships. To determine the age of different fossils, earth scientists use methods of relative and absolute age dating.

Relative Age Dating

On a trip to the Grand Canyon, you find a fossil in sedimentary rock near the rim of the canyon. Will this fossil be older or younger than a fossil you find near the canyon bottom? Since you know that layers of sedimentary rock get older as you move down, you can infer that the fossil near the rim is younger. By making this inference, you have described the *relative age* of the fossil.

You may not realize it, but your inference was based on the **principle of superposition**. The principle of superposition states that younger rock layers are formed on top of older rock layers. This principle is the basis for most relative age dating of fossils.

Figure 13.10

The deeper a rock layer, the older the fossils it contains. ▼

Disruptions of Rock Layers

Layers of sedimentary rock do not always stay where they form. Recall that rocks in the earth's crust may deform by folding or faulting. Folding can turn rock layers upside down or sideways. Faulting can make rock layers of different ages line up next to each other.

Erosion by water, wind, and ice removes layers of rock and creates gaps within layers. Sedimentary rock layers may also be disrupted by molten igneous rock moving into cracks and hardening to form an igneous dike.

The disruptions of sedimentary rock layers make relative age dating more difficult. But even the most deformed or eroded rock layers can be interpreted if you remember a few simple rules:

▶ Rock layers are horizontal before they deform.

▶ A fault or igneous dike did not exist when the layers formed, and is younger than the layers it cuts across.

Look at Figure 13.11. Study the rock layers and then answer the questions.

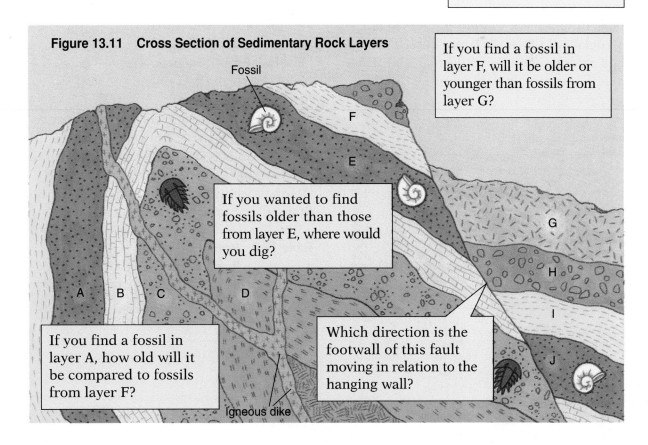

Figure 13.11   Cross Section of Sedimentary Rock Layers

Fossil

F

E

G

H

I

J

If you find a fossil in layer F, will it be older or younger than fossils from layer G?

If you wanted to find fossils older than those from layer E, where would you dig?

If you find a fossil in layer A, how old will it be compared to fossils from layer F?

Which direction is the footwall of this fault moving in relation to the hanging wall?

A   B   C   D

Igneous dike

Absolute Age Dating

The relative age of a fossil from the bottom of the Grand Canyon is older than one from the rim. But how can you determine the age in years of these fossils? You use absolute age dating. Absolute dating is based on a "clock" that accurately measures the passage of time.

Radioactive Isotopes The most accurate clock for absolute age dating is the decay of the radioactive isotopes of certain elements. An atom of a radioactive isotope contains an unstable ratio of neutrons to protons in its nucleus. It will *decay*, or release some matter and energy from the nucleus. Radioactive decay forms a new, more stable element called a decay product.

Half-Life Look at Figure 13.12. When many atoms of a radioactive isotope are present in a piece of matter, they do not all decay at the same time. Each atom has an equal chance of decaying. But over a certain amount of time, only some will decay.

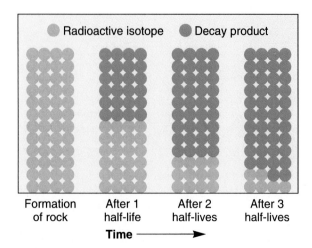

| Formation of rock | After 1 half-life | After 2 half-lives | After 3 half-lives |

Time ——————→

Figure 13.12 ▲
How many atoms decay during a half-life?

Scientists describe the rate of an isotope's decay by how long it takes for *half* of the atoms in a sample to decay. This measure of decay is called the isotope's **half-life**. The half-lives of isotopes vary from fractions of a second to billions of years. Radioactive decay makes a good clock for absolute age dating because half-lives are unchanging.

Radiometric Dating How do scientists use radioactive decay to date rocks and fossils? Many rocks contain small amounts of radioactive isotopes when they first form. And all organisms collect radioactive isotopes during their lives. After a rock forms or an organism dies, these isotopes start to decay at a regular rate. Each radioactive atom turns into an atom of another element.

Scientists measure the amount of the radioactive isotope present in the rock or fossil. They compare this amount to the amount of the decay product present. The ratio of the two amounts is used to calculate the amount of time that has passed since the formation of the rock or the death of the organism.

Look at Table 13.2. Different radioactive isotopes are used for dating different kinds of objects. Isotopes with long half-lives are best for dating old rocks. The isotope carbon-14 is used to date fossils that still contain organic material.

Table 13.2 Isotopes Used for Radiometric Dating

Isotope	Half-Life (Years)	Used to Date
Thorium-232	14 billion	Very old rocks
Potassium-40	1,300 million	Old rocks and fossils in them
Carbon-14	5,730	Fossils less than 50,000 years old

Science and Technology
Probing Fossils with New Tools

Could dinosaurs see color? How well could they smell? How smart were they? Modern technology is helping scientists find answers to these and other questions.

Fossil bones can hold a lot of information. Unfortunately much of that information must remain hidden. To learn everything a fossil has to tell, scientists must break it apart to look inside. But scientists usually do not want to destroy a fossil.

A new technology, called computed axial tomography, or CAT, helps scientists "see" inside a fossil without destroying it. CAT scans give scientists three-dimensional images of a fossil and its interior. A CAT scan is made by placing the fossil inside a doughnut-shaped ring. The ring rotates and takes top-to-bottom X-ray scans. A computer puts all the scans into one three-dimensional image, such as the one in Figure 13.13. This picture can be rotated on the computer screen.

CAT scans of fossils from the meat-eating dinosaur *Nanotyrannus* show that it had a brain twice as large as first predicted. The spaces filled by the parts of the brain used for smell and sight suggest that this dinosaur could see colors and had an excellent sense of smell. Using these techniques to learn more about fossils helps scientists get a much better picture of what dinosaurs were really like.

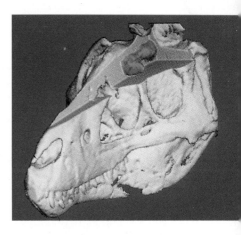

Figure 13.13 ▲
Using CAT technology, a scientist can "slice" open a fossil without actually touching it.

Check and Explain

1. How is the principle of superposition used to find the relative age of fossils?

2. What does it mean if the half-life of a radioactive isotope is 13,000 years?

3. **Infer** Fossil A is the youngest of three fossils, and fossil C is oldest. When you find that the absolute age of fossil B is 140 million years, what can you infer about fossils A and C?

4. **Measure** A rock sample contains 0.05 g of potassium-40 and 0.05 g of its decay product. Using Table 13.2, determine the age of a fossil contained in the sample.

ACTIVITY

13.4 Life Through Geologic Time

Objectives

▶ **Name** some common types of organisms from each era of geologic time.

▶ **Explain** why the Precambrian Era has a poor fossil record.

▶ **Describe** human evolution.

▶ **Organize data** that shows the major events in the history of life on the earth.

**Figure 13.14
The Eras and Periods
of Geologic Time** ▼

I f you could travel back in time, what point in the earth's history would you go to? Would you choose to go back about 10 million years, when mastodons and other large mammals lived in North America? Or would you want to travel back 150 million years to see *Seismosaurus*, a dinosaur that was over 40 m long and weighed 60 to 80 metric tons? What about going back 250 million years to explore the supercontinent Pangaea?

You will now take a short tour through the earth's history. You will learn what kinds of organisms lived in each of the four eras of geologic time, and when new types of organisms appeared on the earth. Study the "road map" of geologic time in Figure 13.14 before you begin your tour. You may also want to review the charts of geologic time on page 85, which show the relative lengths of the eras and periods.

Era		Paleozoic							Mesozoic			Cenozoic	
Period	Precambrian	Cambrian	Ordovician	Silurian	Devonian	Mississippian	Pennsylvanian	Permian	Triassic	Jurassic	Cretaceous	Tertiary	Quaternary
Millions of years ago	545	505	438	408	360	320	286	245	208	144	66	1.6	

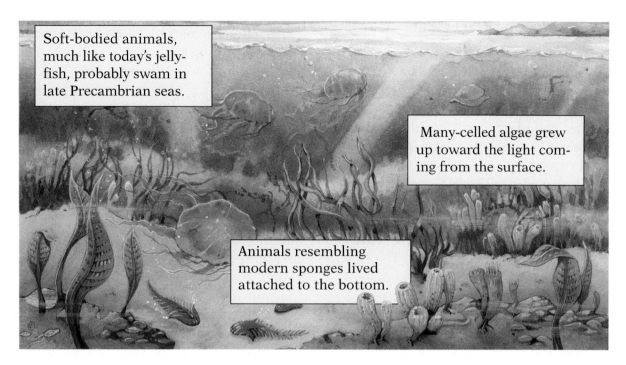

Figure 13.15
Life Near the End of the Precambrian Era ▲

Precambrian Era

For about the first 1,000 million years of the earth's history, no life existed. During this time, the atmosphere formed. Heavy rains fell, and an ocean eventually covered all the land. The first living things appeared in this ancient ocean. They were simple cells without any specialized parts. But they were able to reproduce.

Scientists do not know when these first cells appeared. The oldest known fossils are about 3,500 million years old. These fossils, called *stromatolites* (stroh MAT uh lyts), were formed by colonies of ancient monerans trapped by layers of sediment. Over hundreds of millions of years, monerans and others like them released oxygen as part of their life processes. The oxygen accumulated in the atmosphere. By about 2,500 million years ago, the atmosphere had a significant amount of this vital gas.

Monerans were the only life forms on the earth until about 1,900 million years ago. At this time, the first complex cells evolved. They contained specialized parts, or organelles. They are classified in the protist kingdom.

The first many-celled organisms probably appeared a little over 1,000 million years ago. Scientists found a fossil of a red alga that is at least 2 billion years old. By the end of the Precambrian Era, 545 million years ago, numerous many-celled organisms lived in the ocean. These included animals that resembled modern sponges and jellyfish.

There were also organisms in the fungi and plant kingdoms. However, scientists do not know very much about these organisms because few left any fossils. They all had soft bodies that decayed rapidly when they died. Look at Figure 13.15 to see how a shallow sea may have appeared near the end of the Precambrian Era.

Paleozoic Era

The appearance of animals with hard parts, such as shells, marks the beginning of the Paleozoic Era. These animals left the first abundant fossils. Unlike the Precambrian Era, the Paleozoic has a rich fossil record.

Fossil evidence shows that the oceans in the early Paleozoic Era contained diverse organisms. All the animals of the early Paleozoic Era were **invertebrates**, or animals without backbones. The first **vertebrates**, animals with backbones, were fishlike organisms. They appeared in the Ordovician period. During the Silurian period, the first organisms left the ocean to live on land. These were simple plants, which had evolved from many-celled algae.

Figure 13.16
Life at the Beginning of the Mississippian Period ▼

The first animals to live on land, about 400 million years ago, were arthropods similar to today's millipedes. The first air-breathing vertebrates were amphibians, which evolved from fish during the Devonian period. They lived partly on land and partly in water.

The Mississippian period began about 360 million years ago. Huge swamp forests covered much of the land. These forests were made up of seedless, fernlike plants and the first primitive seed plants. The first reptiles appeared during the Pennsylvanian period.

Near the end of the Paleozoic Era, the earth's landmasses came together to form Pangaea. Many places where life flourished, such as the shallow seas, disappeared. Most of Pangaea became very dry. As a result of these changes, many organisms became extinct around 245 million years ago. These mass extinctions mark the end of the Paleozoic Era.

Seedless plants similar to modern ferns and horsetails grew as high as trees.

Winged insects buzzed through the humid air of the swamp forests.

The seas were filled with invertebrates, representing every major group alive today.

Amphibians were the first vertebrates to live on land.

Mesozoic Era

About 250 million years ago, certain reptiles evolved into the first dinosaurs. Over the next 160 million years, dinosaurs continued to evolve a variety of shapes, sizes, habits, and diets. During this time, the Mesozoic Era, dinosaurs dominated the earth.

From the study of fossil evidence, scientists learned that many dinosaurs were probably warm-blooded. They were active animals, and some could run much faster than you. Some dinosaurs probably lived in groups and took care of their young.

Many of the groups of organisms common today first appeared during the Mesozoic Era. The first mammals evolved about the same time as the dinosaurs. They were small and active at night. The first birds appeared a little later, probably during the Jurassic period.

Toward the end of the Mesozoic Era, the first flowering plants evolved from seed plants. Flowering plants adapted to a variety of environments, from dry to wet and from cold to hot. Flowering plants now greatly outnumber all other kinds of plants.

The earth's landmasses changed greatly during the Mesozoic Era. At the beginning of the era, there was only the supercontinent Pangaea. By the end of the era, Pangaea had broken into the major continents present today.

The Mesozoic Era ended about 66 million years ago, when many species, including most of the dinosaurs, died out. These mass extinctions were the result of major changes in the earth's environment and climate. Some of the changes may have been triggered by the impact of a large meteorite.

Figure 13.17 Life in the Jurassic Period ▼

Many dinosaurs depended on the palmlike cycads for food.

The first birds probably evolved from a type of dinosaur.

The first mammals were small and shy.

Flowering plants appeared during the Mesozoic Era.

Cenozoic Era

The era in which you now live, the Cenozoic Era, began 66 million years ago. If the Mesozoic Era can be called the Age of Dinosaurs, then the Cenozoic Era is the Age of Mammals. The small mammals present in the Mesozoic Era evolved rapidly during the early Cenozoic Era. Some became plant-eaters, evolving hooves and a larger body size. They grazed on the increasing numbers of flowering plants. Others became meat-eaters, specializing in the hunting of plant-eaters.

By about 30 million years ago in the Tertiary period, the ancestors of most modern mammals had evolved. On land, there were horses, rhinoceroses, monkeys, mastodons, camels, antelopes, tigers, and lions. In the ocean, there were whales and dolphins.

The climate during most of the Cenozoic Era has been relatively cool and dry. Advances of glaciers shaped the land. An ice age with several periods of glaciation occurred during the last 2 million years. The human species, *Homo sapiens*, evolved during this time of repeated glaciation and warming.

**Figure 13.18
Life in the
Tertiary Period** ▼

Many plant-eating mammals grazed on the grassy plains that covered much of the land.

Meat-eating mammals, such as the ancestors of today's tigers, lions, and dogs, fed on the herds of grazing animals.

Flowering plants evolved many different forms.

Human Evolution

The first humanlike organisms, or hominids (HAHM uh nihdz), appeared about 4.4 million years ago. They lived on the ground and walked upright on two legs. Hominids evolved into several different species. Most early hominid species eventually became extinct. But one species survived to evolve further.

Scientists have found the fossils of many hominid species, but they are not sure which ones are direct human ancestors. About 1.6 million years ago, a hominid called *Homo erectus* existed. Scientists hypothesize that it is an ancestor of modern humans.

Homo erectus evolved into *Homo sapiens* sometime between 500,000 and 300,000 years ago. The first modern-looking humans appeared about 100,000 years ago, probably in Africa. They are called the Cro-Magnons (KROH MAG nuhnz). Cro-Magnons had spread to most continents by about 30,000 years ago.

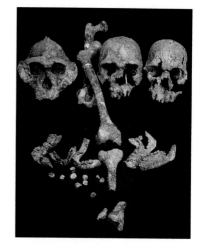

Figure 13.19 ▲
These are fossils of hominids that lived about 1.5 million years ago.

Career Corner   *Paleontologist*

Who Finds and Studies Fossils?

How would you like to discover a new kind of dinosaur? If you become a paleontologist (PAY lee uhn TAHL uh jihst), such a discovery is possible. A paleontologist studies the organisms of the past. Much of the study focuses on fossils, as they provide evidence about ancient life.

Paleontologists use fossils to trace the evolution of life. Pollen in ice, ripple marks in sandstone, the oxygen content in minerals, and other findings are used by paleontologists to describe ancient environments. Paleontologists date fossils using methods you learned about, as well as others.

Most paleontologists spend some of their time in the field. They hunt for fossils and take great care in removing and preserving them. They also work in laboratories, where fossils are studied and dated.

Paleontologists use knowledge of anatomy, geology, biology, physics, chemistry, and mathematics in their work. To prepare for a career as a paleontologist, you should take a variety of science courses in high school. You can also start fossil collecting as a hobby.

Most paleontology jobs require an advanced degree. However, with some experience or college training, you can work in the field or a laboratory assisting paleontologists.

▼ ACTIVITY

Observing

Absolute Age

Select five items in the classroom that can be given an absolute age. How can you tell the absolute age of each item?

SKILLS WORKOUT

Science and You *Going on a Dig*

In many places, fossils are more common than you may think. Many fossil beds are open to amateur fossil collectors. Do you have fossil beds near where you live? If you do, you may be able to start a collection of traces of plants and animals that lived millions of years ago.

The best place to find fossils in your area is where sedimentary rocks are at the surface. A deep road cut or a canyon wall may expose layers of sedimentary rock representing millions of years of geologic time. Coastlines where the ocean erodes tall cliffs often have visible fossil layers. Gravel and sand pits and limestone quarries are also good sites for finding fossils. The sedimentary rocks that are often used to make buildings, fences, and sidewalks may contain fossils! Look closely at structures made from rocks.

If you find fossils that you want to collect, you may need a rock hammer to break free the chunks of rock containing the fossils. Be careful not to break the fossils. A field guide to fossils will help you identify what you've found. A field guide may also help you find fossils by showing you what unfamiliar ones may look like.

Most fossils in national and state parks are protected and shouldn't be removed. These fossils may be valuable for scientific study. Before removing fossils from private land, be sure to get permission from the owner.

Check and Explain

1. What group of organisms was dominant on the earth during the Mesozoic Era? The Cenozoic Era? The Paleozoic Era?

2. Why are fossils from the Precambrian Era rare? What happened at the beginning of the Paleozoic Era to make fossils more common?

3. **Find Causes** Why did mammals begin to evolve rapidly right after the dinosaurs died out? Explain your reasoning.

4. **Organize Data** Make a timeline that dates the appearance and extinction of important groups of organisms.

Chapter 13 Review

Concept Summary

13.1 Evolution of Life
▶ Fossils help scientists reconstruct the history of life on earth.
▶ Darwin's theory of evolution explains how species change over time.
▶ Organisms are classified into five kingdoms according to similarities in body organization and method of nutrition.
▶ The organisms in each kingdom share an evolutionary history. They are more related to each other than to organisms in other kingdoms.

13.2 The Fossil Record
▶ If an organism is protected from decay and destruction when it dies, it may become a fossil.
▶ Fossils are classified into groups depending on how they form.

13.3 Interpreting Fossils
▶ The relative ages of rocks and fossils are determined by using the principle of superposition.
▶ Radiometric dating is a way of finding the absolute age of a rock or fossil. It is based on the constant rate of decay of radioactive isotopes.

13.4 Life Through Geologic Time
▶ Life first appeared during the Precambrian Era.
▶ Organisms with hard parts evolved during the Paleozoic Era.
▶ Mammals, birds, and flowering plants appeared during the Mesozoic Era, while dinosaurs dominated the earth.
▶ Modern types of mammals evolved during the Cenozoic Era.

Chapter Vocabulary

species (13.1)   petrified (13.2)   principle of superposition (13.3)
evolution (13.1)   mold (13.2)   half-life (13.3)
extinction (13.1)   cast (13.2)   invertebrate (13.4)
kingdom (13.1)   trace fossil (13.2)   vertebrate (13.4)

Check Your Vocabulary

Use the vocabulary words above to complete the following sentences correctly.

1. All organisms belong to one of five ＿＿＿.
2. When mineral-containing water seeps into a fossil mold, a ＿＿＿ may form.
3. The theory of ＿＿＿ explains how species change over time.
4. An animal with a backbone is a ＿＿＿.
5. A dinosaur footprint is an example of a ＿＿＿.
6. An impression in rock left by a shell is an example of a ＿＿＿.
7. All members of a ＿＿＿ have nearly the same basic traits.
8. Scientists use the ＿＿＿ to find the relative age of fossils.
9. Each radioactive isotope has a ＿＿＿.
10. All the organisms living in the early Paleozoic Era were ＿＿＿.
11. Environmental changes may cause the ＿＿＿ of a species.
12. A bone whose matter is slowly replaced by minerals becomes ＿＿＿.

Write Your Vocabulary

Write sentences using the vocabulary words above. Show that you know what each word means.

Chapter 13 Review

Check Your Knowledge

Answer the following in complete sentences.

1. The first organisms to live on the earth belonged to which kingdom?

2. How old is a sedimentary rock layer compared to the layer directly above it?

3. What must happen, sooner or later, to an atom of a radioactive isotope?

4. Give an example of how an unchanged fossil may form.

5. From what kind of organism did the dinosaurs evolve?

6. How do plants differ from animals?

7. How does the bone of a dead organism become petrified?

8. List three ways that layers of sedimentary rock may be disrupted.

Determine whether each statement is true or false. Write *true* if it is true. If it is false, change the underlined word(s) to make the statement true.

9. The relationships between different groups of organisms can be shown with an evolutionary bar graph.

10. The first vertebrates appeared during the Cenozoic Era.

11. A mold must form before a cast.

12. The radioactive isotopes in a rock begin to decay when the rock is formed.

13. Organisms that lived in the Paleozoic Era left few fossils.

14. A species evolves through the process of natural selection.

Check Your Understanding

Apply the concepts you have learned to answer each question.

1. Why do changes in the environment affect the evolution of a species?

2. **Critical Thinking** Both the Paleozoic and Mesozoic Eras ended at times of mass extinction. Why do you think scientists chose these times in geologic history to mark the ends of eras and the beginnings of new eras?

3. **Classify** Which of the following is a fossil? If it is not a fossil, explain why not.

   a. Bird tracks in hardened mud.

   b. A chicken in your freezer.

   c. The imprint of a leaf in a rock.

   d. A bone you dig up in your backyard.

4. New species of insects began to evolve rapidly about the same time that flowering plants appeared. Why might this be so?

5. **Critical Thinking** You find a 200-million-year-old fossil in the uppermost layer of some sedimentary rock. How is this possible?

6. Explain the relationship between the evolution of life and the classification of life into kingdoms.

7. **Compare and Contrast** How much longer did dinosaurs live on the earth than humans have lived?

8. **Mystery Photo** The photograph on page 288 shows the fossil of an ammonite, which lived during the Cretaceous period. What modern animals do you think are most closely related to ammonites? How do you think the crystals formed inside the fossil?

Develop Your Skills

Use the skills you have developed in this chapter to complete each activity.

1. **Interpret Data** The graph below shows the decay of a radioactive isotope over time.

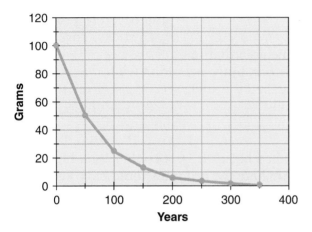

a. How much of the isotope is present after 50 years?

b. What is the half-life of this isotope? How do you know?

c. If you graphed the decay of another radioactive isotope in a similar way, how would the shape of the curve compare to the shape of this curve?

2. **Data Bank** Use the information on page 622 to answer the following questions.

a. What radioactive isotope has a half-life nearly equal to the age of the earth?

b. What is the decay product of carbon-14?

c. What radioactive isotopes could be used to date a fossil from the Paleozoic Era?

Make Connections

1. **Link the Concepts** Construct a concept map showing how the concepts from this chapter link together. Add terms to connect, or link, the concepts: unchanged fossil, evolutionary tree, trace fossil, principle of superposition, fossil, radiometric dating, fossil record, petrified fossil, mold, cast.

2. **Science and Geography** Research to find out where important fossils have been found. Make a map that shows where the fossils were discovered.

3. **Science and Writing** Choose a time in the earth's history you would like to visit in a time machine. Write a story about what you see when you get there.

4. **Science and Society** Find out if your state has a state fossil. If not, do research to find out what types of organisms have been found as fossils in your state. Write a letter to one of your state legislators explaining why a certain fossil should be adopted as the state fossil.

5. **Science and Art** Find pictures of different kinds of fossils, such as trilobites and ammonites. Use the shapes and patterns of one or more of these fossils to make a design or drawing.

6. **Science and Society** Do research on Piltdown Man, a skull and jawbone found in England in 1911. The Piltdown Man was believed to be the fossil remains of an ancient human ancestor. Find out how the bones were discovered to be a hoax.

Science and Literature Connection

Tales of a Dead King

The following excerpt is from the book Tales of a Dead King *by Walter Dean Myers.*

Ahmed grunted and began to drive. He drove for about an hour through some of the most desolate land I had ever seen. Finally he stopped and pointed toward a small dune.

"There," he said.

He pulled the jeep to a stop. The wind had picked up and the sand cut into our faces. Ahmed lowered his hood and produced a scarf from somewhere which he handed to Karen. We walked slowly over to the dune, up to our shoe tops in the loose sand.

We looked around the site. There were no signs of digging at all. I went to the crest of the dune, or as near to it as I could, to see if there was anything under it. Nothing. I looked off in the distance. The Nile was a half mile away. It was the part of the river that had overflowed when the Aswan dam was built, and that had engulfed what little greenery there was. I could see a few patches of grass growing out of the silt deposits along the water's edge, and the remains of a Nubian village.

I got back to the jeep at the same time Ahmed and Karen returned from the other side of the dune.

"You see anything?" she said.

"Nothing," I said.

The next site was a good half hour's drive away. This time Ahmed stopped at a rock formation very close to the Nile. He showed us what he said was the exact spot in which Dr. Leonhardt had been digging. We drew a large circle around the spot, about twelve feet in diameter, and began to probe with sticks. There was one area that might have been dug up before, but we couldn't tell for sure. We pushed the sticks into the soft earth carefully, so as not to break anything we might find under the earth's surface.

"I don't think this is the place," Karen called back. "If Dr. Leonhardt had really dug here the ground should have been looser."

"Ahmed, why isn't the ground looser here if Dr. Leonhardt dug here as you say?" I asked.

"He don't dig," Ahmed said. "He never dig. He just push a stick into the ground, like you."

"In that case," Karen said, rubbing her nose. "He wasn't serious about digging here. Anything that he would have been interested in wouldn't be anywhere near enough to the surface to find with a probe. You would have to dig at least six to fourteen feet, depending on the amount of erosion in the area, before you could even think about using a probe."

"I don't think that Ahmed understands that," I said. "Better explain it to him carefully."

"Dr. Leonhardt's an Egyptologist," Karen said. "Anything he would be looking for would be either above the ground, like a pyramid, or many feet below the ground, covered by years of dirt blowing over it. You understand?"

"I understand," Ahmed said. "But that's what he did. Like I say."

We went around to two more sites where Ahmed said that Dr. Leonhardt had been digging. We didn't see any signs of digging at all.

"I think," Karen said as we got back into the jeep, "that we are being had by Mr. Ahmed. You, of course, noticed that we are traveling in a direction for which there is a constant equidistant point?"

"Huh?"

"We're traveling in a circle!" she said.

I asked Ahmed to stop the jeep and I got out. I couldn't see very much where I was, so I walked up to the base of a small hill and began climbing. When I had gone up about thirty feet, I looked around. Sure enough, there was the same deserted Nubian village I had seen before, but now I was looking at it from the other side. Either Ahmed was taking us for a ride or Dr. Leonhardt was taking everybody for a ride.

Skills in Science

Reading Skills in Science

1. **Accurate Observations** Where does this story take place? What are Karen and the narrator trying to do?

2. **Infer** In what ways would the forces of erosion and deposition slow the efforts to find the location where Dr. Leonhardt was digging? Explain.

Writing Skills in Science

1. **Find Causes** Explain how silt was deposited along the edge of the Nile. Why are the silt deposits one of the only places where grass grows?

2. **Generalize** Explain why Dr. Leonhardt would have to dig at least six to fourteen feet if he were trying to find ancient Egyptian artifacts. Is this true for every place he might dig? What factors influence how deep he must dig?

Activities

Collect Data Gather information on the Aswan High Dam. How has the dam's construction affected the areas downriver from the dam? Explain how the building of the dam has affected farming in nearby areas.

Communicate Make a diagram or draw a picture of what the Egyptian Nubian village in this story might look like. Use reference materials at a library to collect information about the Nubians.

Where to Read More

Going on a Dig by Velma Ford Morrison. New York: Dodd, Mead & Co. An excellent introduction to the hands-on science of archaeology; explains why artifacts are buried and describes the procedure of a dig, giving many examples along the way.

Unit 5

Earth's Waters

Data Bank

Use the information on pages 612 to 625 to answer the following questions about topics explored in this unit.

Calculating

Approximately how much deeper is the Atlantic Ocean than the Arctic Ocean?

Making a Graph

Construct a line graph that shows the heights of the day tides. The x-axis should show the times; the y-axis should show the tide heights in meters. Be sure to label your graph.

Reading a Map

Locate and name at least three rivers in the United States that run through the Great Plains.

The photograph to the left was taken in Olympic National Park in Washington state. Is the water shown running through a creek or a river? How can you tell?

Chapter 14 Fresh Water

What do you see?

"I see a stream running along rocks. The stream is running out of a lake or river, carrying particles of the soil and rocks. It is the fall, because there are leaves on the ground. The stream is very clear, because it has not rained there in a long time. I wonder if there are any fish in the water."

Brent Leopard
Riverside Middle School
Saluda, South Carolina

To find out more about the photograph, look on page 336. As you read this chapter, you will learn about the earth's fresh water.

14.1 Water and Its Properties

Objectives

▶ **Describe** the amount of fresh water on the earth.

▶ **Relate** the structure of water molecules to the physical and chemical properties of water.

▶ **Explain** why living things need water.

▶ **Generalize** about the role of energy in the water cycle.

▶ **Make a model** tracing the path of a water molecule through the water cycle.

Think about the many ways you use water every day. You drink it, bathe in it, and water plants with it. When you turn on the tap, fresh water comes out. Where does the fresh water come from? Your home's supply of fresh water may come from a river, a lake, or an underground well.

When the weather is warm, you may use water for sports or recreation. You may go swimming, fishing, or boating. If you swam in the ocean, you would notice that ocean water is different from fresh water. Ocean water is salty because it has a large amount of minerals and salts dissolved in it. Fresh water isn't salty.

The Earth's Fresh Water

Earth is sometimes known as the water planet. Almost 75 percent of the earth's surface is covered by water. Notice in Figure 14.1 that most of the earth's water is salty ocean water. About 2 percent of the earth's fresh water is frozen in glaciers and ice caps. Another 0.6 percent lies deep underground. The atmosphere contains 0.001 percent of Earth's water. The rest of the earth's fresh water exists on the surface or in soil moisture.

To think about the amount of fresh water on the earth, you can use a mental model. For example, imagine fifty 2-L bottles filled with water. These bottles represent all the earth's waters. The amount of usable fresh water would only be enough to fill one 354-mL can!

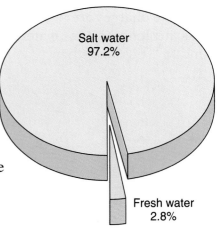

Salt water
97.2%

Fresh water
2.8%

Figure 14.1 ▲
How much of the total water on earth is fresh water? How much of it is salt water?

Properties of Water

Water is the only compound that occurs in all three phases at normal earth temperatures. Think about an ice-covered lake. Ice is water's solid phase. Beneath the ice is liquid water. Water vapor forms in the air above the ice.

Water has other unique properties. It gains and loses heat energy slowly compared to other compounds. Also, water's solid phase is less dense than its liquid phase. Ice floats on top of liquid water. In addition, liquid water dissolves many different substances.

Water's physical and chemical properties are due to the structure of its molecules. Look at Figure 14.2. Each water molecule has two hydrogen atoms and one oxygen atom.

Water is a **polar molecule.** The parts of a polar molecule have slight electric charges. A water molecule's hydrogen atoms have a slight positive charge. The oxygen atom has a slight negative charge.

Recall that opposite charges attract and like charges repel. In liquid water and ice, water molecules align so that opposite charges are next to each other. This attraction makes water molecules tend to "stick" together.

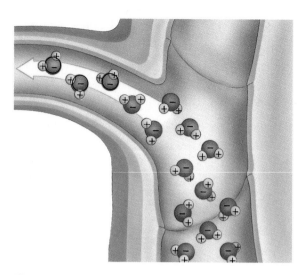

Figure 14.3 ▲
Water molecules follow one another.

Physical Properties When you heat a pan of water on a stove, which heats faster, the metal pan or the water? Water gains heat energy slowly. Recall that heat is the energy of moving molecules. It takes a large amount of heat energy to separate polar water molecules and get them moving. Water also retains heat.

Water forms a skinlike layer on its surface due to surface tension. Surface tension gives water droplets a rounded shape. Surface tension occurs because water molecules attract each other. The attraction between water molecules also makes them act like beads on a string. When a force pulls one molecule, others follow, as shown in Figure 14.3.

Ice is less dense than liquid water. Water is densest at 4°C. Usually, the molecules in a solid are closer together than those in a liquid. But, like charges repel, so polar water molecules can't get very close together. In ice, water molecules form large, open structures called crystals.

Water isn't easily compressed. If you try to push an object down into it, the water pushes back. The upward pressure on the object can cause it to float.

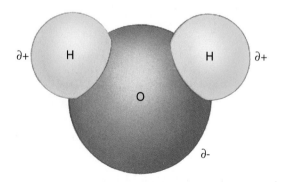

Figure 14.2 ▲
A polar molecule has electric charges. Locate the charges in this water molecule.

Chemical Properties   Water has another unique property. It can dissolve many other substances. Think of all the liquids you drink: milk, lemonade, juice, and so on. These liquids are actually mixtures of water with other substances such as sugar, fruit pulp, butterfat, and milk protein.

Water is called the **universal solvent** because it can dissolve more substances than any other liquid. Due to their polar nature, water molecules attract ions or polar molecules that make up other substances. Water molecules hold the ions or polar molecules in solution, as shown in Figure 14.4.

Water can't dissolve substances such as oils. Oils are made of nonpolar molecules. Nonpolar molecules are insoluble in water.

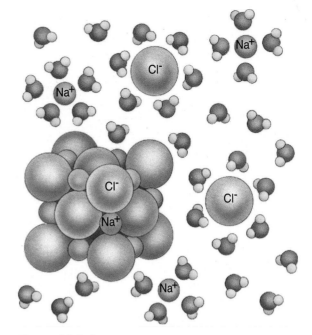

Figure 14.4 ▲
Ions form when salt dissolves in water.

SkillBuilder *Predicting*

Surface Tension

Surface tension is one of the properties of water. Use these questions to make predictions about the effects of surface tension:

▶ Are water droplets always round?

▶ Can you float a needle on the surface of a glass of water?

Write down your predictions. Then try the following activities to test your predictions. Drop some beads of water onto a tray or your desktop. Make the following observations.

1. What shape are the beads of water?

2. Does their shape change as you make them larger by adding more water?

Next, fill a glass to the top with water. Carefully lay a needle on the surface and observe what happens. Answer the following questions.

3. If metal is heavier than water, why does the metallic needle float?

4. Try to make the needle sink. Can you do it?

Write a brief report explaining how these activities demonstrate surface tension.

The Water Cycle

Water moves continuously from one place to another on the earth because of the water cycle. Water that falls on you as rain may have come from a distant ocean. Water that flows out of your tap may have once been part of the Amazon River! Study the water cycle in Figure 14.5.

Radiant energy from the sun drives the water cycle. Heat energy makes liquid water change phase to water vapor. This phase change is called *evaporation*. Water doesn't have to reach its boiling temperature (100°C) to evaporate. Even at lower temperatures, some water molecules escape a liquid to form vapor. When water evaporates, dissolved minerals or salts are left behind.

As the water vapor rises into the air, it cools. At cooler temperatures, a phase change called *condensation* occurs. Water vapor condenses into liquid droplets that form clouds. Clouds can move water over long distances. Eventually, the water falls to the earth as rain, sleet, hail, or snow. All forms of water that fall from the atmosphere are called *precipitation*.

Figure 14.5
The Earth's Water Cycle ▼

Condensation
In the atmosphere, water vapor condenses on dust particles forming clouds. Under some conditions, water droplets form rain or snow and then fall as precipitation.

Evaporation
The heat energy of the sun evaporates water from oceans, lakes, rivers, puddles and dew. Plants move water to their leaves where it evaporates.

After precipitation reaches the earth's surface, several things can happen. In cold areas, snow and ice remain on the ground. Rainwater soaks into the ground or runs along the surface in rivers and streams. Lakes and ponds of standing water form. As water moves across the land surface, it dissolves minerals and wears away rock. Most of the water eventually flows into the oceans. At any point, the water may evaporate into the atmosphere.

Water Resources

Fresh water is constantly being made in the water cycle. Precipitation is the source of the earth's fresh water. But each year, 75 percent of the precipitation falls into the oceans. Only 25 percent of the precipitation falls on the earth's land surfaces. Humans, animals, and land plants rely on this limited amount for their water needs. Therefore, it's important not to waste fresh water or pollute freshwater lakes, rivers, and streams.

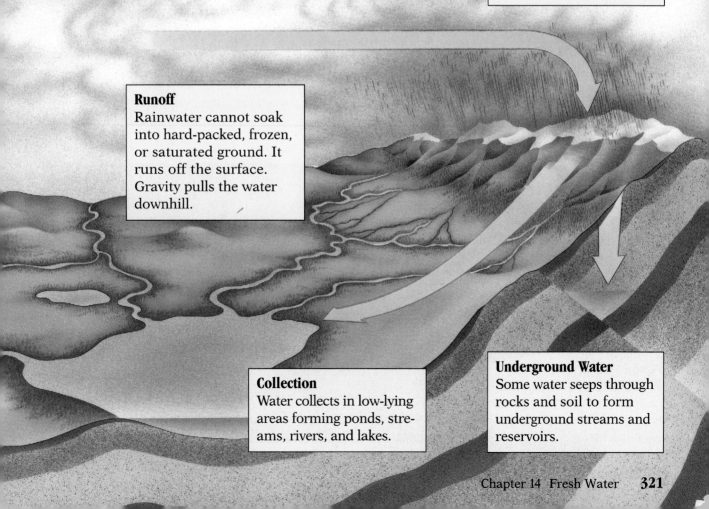

Precipitation
Water falls as rain, snow, hail, or sleet. It soaks into the ground, runs off into streams and rivers, or remains frozen.

Runoff
Rainwater cannot soak into hard-packed, frozen, or saturated ground. It runs off the surface. Gravity pulls the water downhill.

Collection
Water collects in low-lying areas forming ponds, streams, rivers, and lakes.

Underground Water
Some water seeps through rocks and soil to form underground streams and reservoirs.

Life Science

L I N K

Collect the following items: a potted plant with large leaves, a non-seal sandwich bag, and string or tape.

1. Cover one leaf of the plant with the sandwich bag. Tie or tape the bag closed around the stem of the leaf.

2. Place the plant in a sunny area for a couple of hours.

3. Remove the bag and examine it. Describe your observations and explain what happened.

A C T I V I T Y

Water and Living Things

Water is essential for all living things on the earth. Some living things spend their entire lives in water. Humans and other land animals carry water in their bodies. In fact, about 68 percent of your total body weight is from water. Most living things can survive longer without food than without water.

Animals and humans cycle water through their bodies. They take in water by drinking or eating. They release liquid water in body wastes and perspiration. They release water vapor as they exhale. For example, in Figure 14.6 you can see the "cloud" that forms when you exhale on a cold day. Water keeps your body cool in hot weather. Heat energy from your hot skin evaporates watery sweat, cooling off your skin.

Plants also need water to survive. They use light from the sun, water, and carbon dioxide to make sugars. This process is called **photosynthesis**. Plants need these sugars for their own growth. Plants bring up large amounts of water from the soil through their roots. Water carries nutrients from the soil and helps the plant stay upright and rigid, as shown in Figure 14.6.

Water moves upward through a plant, eventually exiting into the air through tiny holes in the leaves. This process is called **transpiration** (TRAN spuh RAY shun). Large amounts of water return to the atmosphere by transpiration. Most of the water that evaporates from the earth's land surfaces does so through transpiration.

Figure 14.6 ▲
What effect does adding water have on this plant? (top) What happens when you exhale on cold days? (right)

Science and You *Your Water Use*

On average, each person in the United States uses about 240 L of water each day. Study Table 14.1. How does your water use compare? The average daily water use of 240 L doesn't include indirect water uses.

The manufacturing of products uses large amounts of water. For example, it takes about 200 000 L of water to produce a car and 800 L to produce a Sunday newspaper. Agriculture also uses huge amounts of water. It takes about 500 L of water to produce one egg and 4,000 L to produce one quart of milk. Including indirect uses, the average person uses over 6,000 L per day.

The fresh water used in homes, schools, and businesses comes from one of several sources. These water sources are underground wells, lakes, reservoirs, or rivers and streams. All these sources receive their fresh water from precipitation. People also make some fresh water directly from ocean water by desalting it.

All the water people use is part of the larger water cycle. Water used for crops and other plants moves directly into the air through transpiration. Waste water from homes and businesses goes through a cleaning process before it flows back into a river or the ocean. If you live in a rural area, the waste water may go into a septic tank or a large underground hole. Wastes stay in the tank or hole, and the cleaned water seeps into the ground. If you live in a city, a system of underground pipes carries your waste water to a sewage-treatment plant. At the treatment plant, the water is filtered and cleaned. Treated water enters a nearby river or ocean.

Table 14.1
Household Water Uses

Activity	Amount of Water Used (L)
Shower	50–77
Tub bath	96–116
Washing hands	4–8
Flushing toilet	19–27
Brushing teeth	19–39
Washing dishes	20–77
Using automatic dishwasher	27–58

Check and Explain

1. Describe in your own words what fresh water is. How much of the earth's water is fresh water?

2. Explain how the structure of a water molecule relates to three properties of water.

3. **Generalize** Write a general statement describing the role of the sun's energy in the water cycle.

4. **Make a Model** Draw and label a diagram that traces the path of a water molecule through the water cycle. Be sure to label the diagram.

Rain Tracks

Based on your experience and observations, what happens to rainwater that falls on buildings where you live? Write down your observations. What could happen that might change the path of the rainwater?

14.2 Surface Water

Objectives

▶ **Describe** three ways in which fresh water exists on the surface of the earth.

▶ **Describe** a watershed and its drainage systems.

▶ **Predict** what life on earth might be like if fresh water didn't accumulate on the surface.

▶ **Organize data** about rivers and glaciers.

Think about a natural landscape that exists in your part of the country. You might think of a leafy forest with many lakes, rivers, or streams. Or you may think of a grassland or a desert with very little surface water. Why are these landscapes so different? Landscapes are different because fresh water isn't distributed equally over the earth's surface.

You can find fresh water on the surface as running water, standing water, or frozen water. The amount of surface water in an area depends on the amount of precipitation it receives. Some areas suffer severe droughts. Areas like the one in Figure 14.7 have frequent rainstorms and floods. Other areas are covered in snow and ice for most of the year.

Figure 14.7 ▲
Heavy rain can cause flooding.

Running Water

Recall that water from rain or melted snow may soak into the ground, evaporate, or flow over the surface as runoff. Recall that runoff forms rills and gullies, and flows into rivers and streams. Running water is water in rivers and streams that flows downhill because of gravity. As running water flows, it carves the landscape, forming streambeds and deep river valleys.

Running water plays an important role in the water cycle by carrying water back to the oceans. Besides returning to the ocean, the water in rivers and streams can also evaporate into the air or soak into the ground. Depending on the amount of rain or snow, a river or stream may flow just for a few months, or all year.

Figure 14.8 ▲
How many tributaries can you see flowing into this river?

Streams and Rivers

Streams flow into larger streams that flow into rivers. Rivers flow into the ocean. Together, the streams and rivers form a pattern called a *drainage system*.

On a map or satellite photograph, a drainage system often forms a treelike pattern. A drainage system can also look like a pattern of rectangles, a trellis, or the spokes of a wheel. The pattern depends on the type of landforms and rocks in an area.

A small stream that flows into a larger one is called a **tributary** (TRIB yoo TAIR ee). A complex drainage system has many tributaries. Notice the tributaries in the satellite photograph in Figure 14.8.

Rivers serve as a source of fresh water for drinking by humans and animals. They can also transport goods and people over long distances. Most of the world's major cities developed along rivers. Land along river banks is important for agriculture. Plenty of water is available for crops, and the soils are usually rich in plant nutrients.

Watersheds

The surrounding land area that supplies runoff to the streams of a drainage system is called a **watershed**. Watersheds vary in size from less than one square kilometer to thousands of square kilometers.

Watersheds that supply runoff to different drainage systems are usually separated by a ridge of land. The ridge separating the drainage systems is called a **divide**. Gravity makes water flow downhill. Therefore, a divide prevents water from getting from one drainage system to another.

Like watersheds, divides can be small or large. Look at Figure 14.9. In North America, the Rocky Mountains and the Sierra Madre Occidental make up the ridge that forms the Continental Divide. Streams to the east of the Continental Divide drain into the Atlantic Ocean or the Gulf of Mexico. Streams to the west of the Continental Divide drain into the Pacific Ocean.

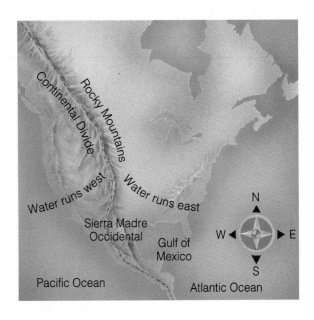

Figure 14.9 ▲
Into which ocean does the water drain from the area where you live?

Standing Water

When running water reaches a low area in a drainage system, the water stops flowing. Over time, the low area fills with standing water. A body of standing water, called a lake or pond, forms. Some water evaporates, but water added from precipitation, streams, and runoff keeps the lake or pond full.

Lakes ▶

Lakes form in large, deep depressions in the earth's crust. Lakes are usually so deep that sunlight doesn't penetrate to the bottom. The Great Lakes on the United States–Canadian border are so large that they have waves and tides like an ocean.

◀ Ponds

Ponds form in small depressions. Usually, ponds are shallow enough for sunlight to reach the bottom. Therefore, ponds tend to support lush plant growth and animal life. Ponds may be seasonal, occasionally drying up.

Reservoirs ▶

Artificial lakes, called reservoirs, form when a dam stops the flow of a river. People build reservoirs to store fresh water and control flooding. People aren't the only ones who dam rivers. Beavers build dams to form deep ponds that won't freeze solid in winter.

Frozen Water

Most of the world's fresh water is frozen. Near the poles or in very high mountains, all the snow doesn't melt each summer. Permanent snowfields form. Snow accumulates year after year. Eventually, the weight of the new snow presses the old snow together, forming ice.

A snowfield turns into a sheet of ice called a glacier. You can model this process by packing a snowball together with gloved hands. Pressure from your hands turns the snow into ice. Recall that valley glaciers form in high mountain valleys. Continental glaciers cover areas such as Greenland or Antarctica and move by the pull of gravity.

When a continental glacier reaches the ocean, large pieces break off and float away. These pieces are called icebergs. Icebergs are dangerous to ships. Only a small part of an iceberg is visible above the water's surface.

Glaciers and snowfields play an important role in the water cycle through melting and evaporation. During the short summers, some of the ice melts. Meltwater streams form, supplying fresh water to many areas.

▼ ACTIVITY

Classifying

Glaciers on the Move

1. Study the map of glacial areas on this page.

2. Compare it to a relief map of the world found in an atlas.

3. Using the information from the relief map, classify each of the glacial areas as a valley glacier or a continental glacer.

SKILLS WORKOUT

Figure 14.10

Locate the places on the earth where glaciers currently exist. ▼

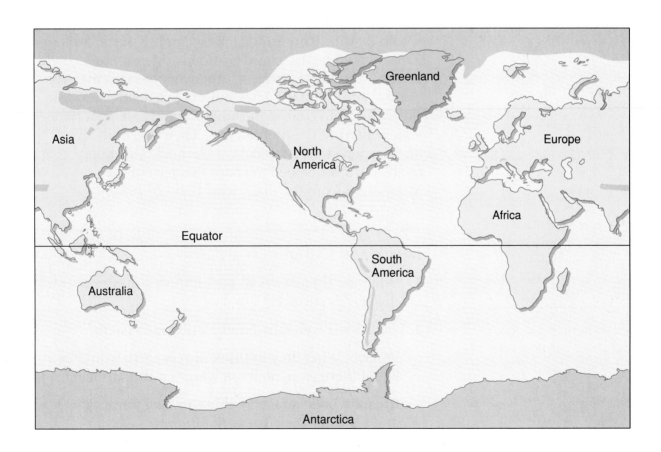

Science and Technology
The Wandering River

The Mississippi River is the third longest river in the world. It has more than 200 tributaries, and has the fourth-largest watershed in the world. The river affects more than 100 million people in 31 states and parts of Canada. Many cities and towns use the river for drinking water and for farming. The river is also a very important water highway. Barges move constantly along the river carrying cargo. At the river's end is the port of New Orleans, an international shipping center on the Gulf of Mexico. The Mississippi River hasn't always been in the same place. About every 1,000 years, it changes its course, cutting a new riverbed and abandoning its old one. The worst flood in the recorded history of the Upper Mississippi River basin occurred in the summer of 1993. Towns and farmland in many midwestern states were covered in river water. Crops and homes were destroyed.

In Louisiana, the Mississippi river has been trying to change its course westward to the Atchafalaya River. If the Mississippi changed course, the port of New Orleans would dry up. Morgan City, at the mouth of the Atchafalaya, would be destroyed by floods. After a major flood in 1927, the Army Corps of Engineers began a massive flood-control project. They built the structure shown in Figure 14.11 to control the amount of Mississippi river water entering the Atchafalaya. They also built levees and deepened the Atchafalaya channel. This flood-control project helped to spare this part of the Mississippi from the disastrous flood of 1993.

Figure 14.11 ▲
By monitoring the water that flows from the Mississippi River, flooding is controlled.

Check and Explain

1. What are three ways in which fresh water exists on the earth's surface?

2. Describe a watershed and a drainage system.

3. **Predict** What do you think life on earth would be like if there were no fresh water on the surface?

4. **Organize Data** Make a table showing how a river and a glacier are alike and different.

14.3 Water Beneath the Surface

Objectives

▶ **Explain** what forms groundwater and **describe** groundwater zones.

▶ **Describe** the movements and activities of groundwater.

▶ **Predict** changes in the groundwater.

▶ **Classify** earth materials by permeability.

Think about what happens when you water a garden or a potted plant. Where does the water go? The water soaks into the ground or soil. On a global scale, a huge amount of water from precipitation soaks into the ground. The amount of water in the ground is more than all the water in the world's rivers and lakes combined. Some underground water comes to the surface in springs and as part of rivers, streams, and lakes.

Groundwater

The water that soaks into the ground from rain or melted snow is called *groundwater*. Recall that soils and some rocks have pore spaces between the dirt or rock particles. Groundwater fills in these pore spaces. The amount of groundwater a rock or soil holds depends on how much pore space exists between the grains of the material.

The percentage of a material's volume that is pore space is called **porosity**. High-porosity rocks and soil can hold more water than those with low porosity. Look at Figure 14.12. Notice that the porosity of sandstone is high.

If the pore spaces are well connected, water flows easily through the rock. Such a rock has high **permeability**. For example, sand, gravel, and sedimentary rocks, such as sandstone, have high permeability. Shale and clay have low permeability. Rocks with low permeability are called *impermeable*. Water does not flow through them.

Figure 14.12 ▲
Sandstone has high porosity and high permeability.

Groundwater Zones

As water from rain or melted snow soaks into the ground, gravity pulls the water downward. When the water reaches an impermeable layer, such as shale, the water spreads out. When the water can't spread out further, the water level rises. To make a mental model of this, think of filling a glass of crushed ice with water. The bottom of the glass is impermeable. As you add water, it fills in the spaces between the ice particles. The water level in the glass rises.

Groundwater creates two distinct underground zones. These zones are shown on the left in Figure 14.13. In the lower zone, called the zone of saturation, all the pore spaces contain water. In the upper zone, called the zone of aeration

(AIR AY shun), the pore spaces are filled with air. The boundary line between the two zones is called the **water table.** Below the water table, the rocks and soil are saturated with water. Above the water table, the pore spaces are filled with air.

The water table isn't always at the same depth. The water table can change depths at different times of the year, depending on the amount of rainfall. When it rains more, the water table is higher. After a long dry spell, the water table is lower.

The type of rock or soil beneath the surface also affects the water table. In areas where an impermeable layer is close to the surface, the water table is higher. If the impermeable layer is deeper, the water table is lower.

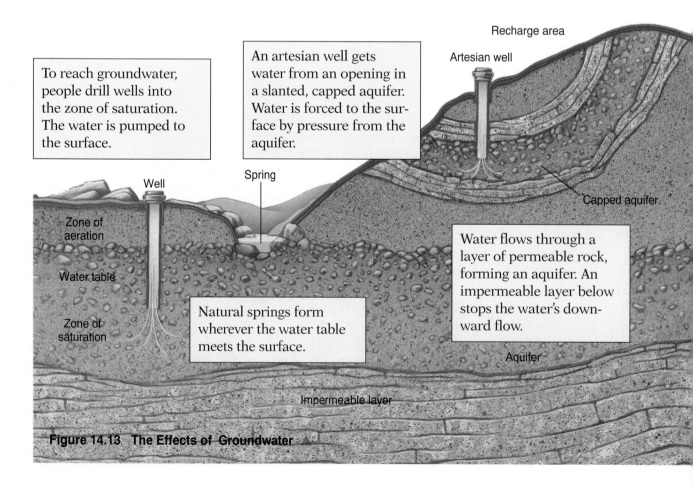

To reach groundwater, people drill wells into the zone of saturation. The water is pumped to the surface.

An artesian well gets water from an opening in a slanted, capped aquifer. Water is forced to the surface by pressure from the aquifer.

Recharge area

Artesian well

Capped aquifer

Well

Spring

Zone of aeration

Water table

Zone of saturation

Natural springs form wherever the water table meets the surface.

Water flows through a layer of permeable rock, forming an aquifer. An impermeable layer below stops the water's downward flow.

Aquifer

Impermeable layer

Figure 14.13 The Effects of Groundwater

Moving Groundwater

Groundwater can travel through layers of rock or sediments that act like pipelines. Groundwater can dissolve rocks, forming underground caverns. Hot springs and geysers are groundwater returning to the surface.

Aquifers   A layer of permeable rock or sediment containing groundwater is called an **aquifer** (AH kwih fur). Aquifers usually form in sandstone, sand, or gravel, above or between layers of impermeable rock.

Aquifers are important sources of fresh water. People drill wells into an aquifer and pump water out. The largest aquifer in the United States is the sand and gravel Ogallala Aquifer. It stretches from South Dakota to Texas.

Caverns and Sinkholes   Recall that carbon dioxide in the air combines with rainwater to form carbonic acid. As the acidic rainwater moves down through the ground, it chemically reacts with some rocks. Limestone easily dissolves away, forming caves and caverns.

Water drips into the cavern from the rock layers above, carrying dissolved minerals. When the water evaporates, the minerals are left behind. Look at Figure 14.13. If the water evaporates on the cavern ceiling, an icicle-like *stalactite* forms. If the water evaporates on the floor, it forms a pillar of minerals called a *stalagmite*.

If a layer of limestone weakens from being dissolved, it can suddenly collapse. The resulting hole is called a *sinkhole*. Areas of the southern and central United States have many sinkholes.

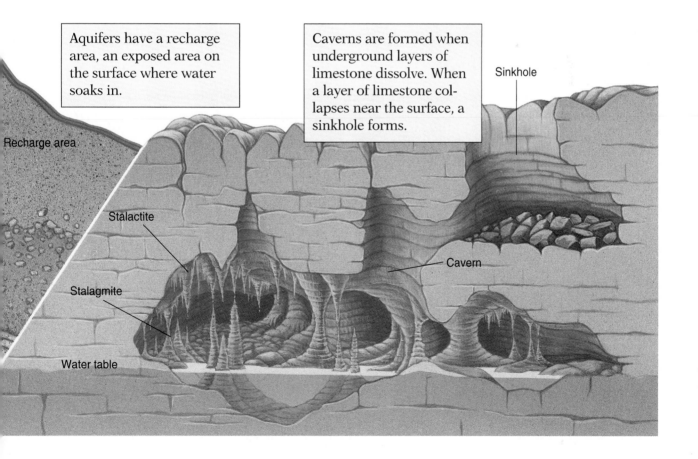

Aquifers have a recharge area, an exposed area on the surface where water soaks in.

Caverns are formed when underground layers of limestone dissolve. When a layer of limestone collapses near the surface, a sinkhole forms.

Sinkhole

Recharge area

Stalactite

Stalagmite

Water table

Cavern

Hot Springs and Geysers Some groundwater rises to the surface as hot water, in hot springs or geysers. A hot spring is any body of water with a temperature higher than the human body's. A geyser is a fountain of hot water ejected from the ground. Geysers can rise 30–60 m. They are caused by the periodic release of superheated steam that forms in underground chambers.

Groundwater can be heated either by contact with igneous rock from volcanism or by contact with warm rock deep in the earth. In the western United States, most hot springs and geysers result from water heated by igneous rock from volcanism. In the eastern United States, the water in hot springs, such as at Warm Springs, Georgia, is heated in deep regions.

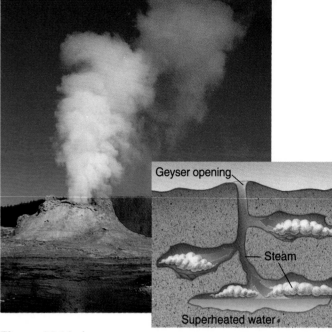

Figure 14.14 ▲
After pressure builds, this geyser erupts in Yellowstone National Park, Wyoming.

Consider This

Who Pays for the Cleanup?

Cleaning up groundwater pollution can be a difficult and costly job. Polluted groundwater moves slowly through aquifers, spreading the pollution over many kilometers. Natural processes can remove some pollutants. The aquifer itself can filter out dirt. Certain bacteria help clean up water by digesting some kinds of pollutants. However, some industrial pollutants cannot be easily removed from water.

Industries, such as agriculture and electronics, use toxic chemicals. Toxic chemicals can enter an aquifer

when farmers apply pesticides to the soil. Aquifers are polluted when industrial solvents are dumped or accidentally spilled. In the past,

many toxic chemicals entered aquifers before anyone realized the danger.

Think About It Who is responsible for cleaning up the aquifers? Who should pay for it? Should the companies pay for this, possibly putting small companies out of business? Or should the costs be passed on to the consumers?

Debate It Have a class debate on the issue of who should pay for the cleanup of aquifers. Half the class can take the side of the company owners and the other half the side of consumers.

Science and Society
Protecting Groundwater

Did you know that pollutants in one place can end up in someone's drinking water hundreds of kilometers away? Recall that water is the universal solvent. As rainwater travels through materials above the ground, it dissolves many substances. The rainwater soaks into the ground, carrying the dissolved substances into the groundwater. If the dissolved substances are harmful, the groundwater becomes polluted. Polluted groundwater can enter aquifers that supply drinking water to people many kilometers away.

Old landfills and dumps pose a major hazard to groundwater because of the chemicals in paints, cleansers, and household or industrial wastes. When rainwater moves down through a landfill or dump, the water dissolves some of the chemicals. The rainwater can soak into the ground and reach the water table, polluting the groundwater.

One way that groundwater can be protected is by using the principle of impermeability. Just as impermeable layers keep water in an aquifer, they can also help keep polluted water out. New landfills, such as the one in Figure 14.15, have a lining of impermeable clay, asphalt, or plastic. Water containing dissolved materials from the landfill can't soak into the ground. After a landfill is full, it can be capped with another impermeable layer. The impermeable cap prevents rainwater from entering the landfill and dissolving any chemicals. The groundwater is then further protected from pollution.

Figure 14.15 ▲
The landfill shown here is considered a sanitary legal landfill because it has a clay lining.

Check and Explain

1. What is groundwater? Describe two distinct groundwater zones.

2. Describe three movements and activities of groundwater.

3. **Predict** What will happen to the water table in an area during a prolonged drought? What else could affect the water table the same way?

4. **Classify** Order the following from least to most permeable: gravel, sand, clay, sandstone.

Activity 14 *How are a siphon and an artesian well similar?*

Skills Observe; Hypothesize; Model

Task 1 Prelab Prep

1. Collect the following items: 2 jars of approximately the same size, a marker and masking tape, a 50- to 75-cm long piece of clear plastic tubing.
2. Using the marker and masking tape, label one jar *A* and the other one *B*.

Task 2 Procedure

1. Fill jar *A* half full of water. Mark the level of the water on the outside of the jar with the marker. Set the jar on the desk.
2. Look at Figure 14.16. Place the empty jar *B* on a chair or the floor so that it is lower than jar *A*. Be sure that the plastic tube can reach both jars.
3. Your teacher will have prepared a bucket or sink half-filled with water. Hold the plastic tube in both hands. Dunk the entire tube into the bucket or sink. After the tube fills completely with water, tightly cover both ends with your thumbs. Now lift the tube out of the water.
4. Look at Figure 14.16. Covering both ends of the tube tightly, carry the water-filled tube back to your jar setup. Place one end of the tube, still covered, into each jar. Be sure that the end in jar *A* is underwater.
5. Without letting go of the tube, release both of your thumbs at the same time and observe what happens. This system is called a siphon.
6. When the water stops moving through the tube, mark the water levels on both jars. Compare the changes in the water level in each jar.

Task 3 Analysis

1. What caused water to move through the tube?

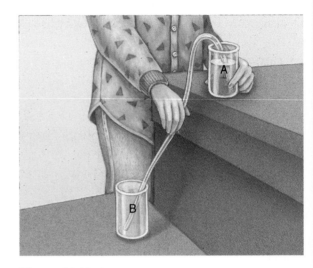

Figure 14.16 ▲

2. What caused the water to stop moving?
3. How did the water levels compare before the activity? How did the levels compare after the activity?
4. How is your siphon like an artesian well? Compare your setup to the aquifer in Figure 14.13. Is your siphon like an aquifer? Explain.

Task 4 Conclusion

Write a short paragraph explaining how the flow of water in a natural spring compares to the flow of water in a siphon.

Everyday Application

Have you ever seen someone empty a swimming pool or an aquarium? Explain how a siphon system might be used to empty a swimming pool or an aquarium.

Extension

Do you think this system would work if the jars were at the same level? What if jar *B* were higher than jar *A*? Try lifting jar *B*, when it is about 1/4 full of water, higher than jar *A*. Explain what happens. Why?

Chapter 14 Review

Concept Summary

14.1 Water and Its Properties
▶ Only about 3 percent of all the water on the earth is fresh water.
▶ Water is a polar molecule. The polar nature of the water molecule gives water many unique properties, such as gaining and losing heat slowly and the ability to dissolve many different substances.
▶ Water moves continuously from one place to another on the earth because of the water cycle. The driving force is energy from the sun.
▶ Precipitation is the source of fresh water on the earth.

14.2 Surface Water
▶ Fresh water exists on the earth's surface as running water in rivers and streams, standing water in lakes and ponds, and frozen water in glaciers.

▶ A watershed is a land area that supplies runoff to streams and rivers.
▶ Glaciers move slowly downhill because of gravity.

14.3 Water Beneath the Surface
▶ Water that soaks into the ground is called groundwater. The amount of water that soaks in depends on the ground's porosity and permeability.
▶ Groundwater forms distinct underground zones: the zone of saturation, the zone of aeration, the boundary between them, and the water table.
▶ Groundwater travels through aquifers, layers of permeable rock or sediment. Groundwater can return to the surface in springs, geysers, artesian wells, rivers, streams, and lakes.

Chapter Vocabulary

polar molecule (14.1)   transpiration (14.1)   divide (14.2)   water table (14.3)
universal solvent (14.1)   tributary (14.2)   porosity (14.3)   aquifer (14.3)
photosynthesis (14.1)   watershed (14.2)   permeability (14.3)

Check Your Vocabulary

Use the vocabulary words above to complete the following sentences correctly.

1. Surface runoff from a _____ enters streams and rivers.

2. The atoms in a water molecule carry a slight electric charge because water is a _____ .

3. Underground, the boundary between the zone of saturation and the zone of aeration is the _____ .

4. The _____ of a rock or soil is a measure of the amount of water that can pass through.

5. Plants need water to make sugar in a process called _____ .

6. Water passes easily through a rock or soil that has high _____ .

7. So many different substances dissolve in water that it is called the _____ .

8. A high ridge that separates one watershed from another is a _____ .

9. A layer of permeable rock that contains moving groundwater is an _____ .

10. Water evaporates from leaf surfaces in the process of _____ .

11. A stream that flows into a larger river is a _____ of that river.

Chapter 14 Review

Check Your Knowledge

Answer the following in complete sentences.

1. Why is the earth sometimes called the water planet?

2. What is a polar molecule?

3. Where does the earth's fresh water come from?

4. Describe the water cycle. What is its driving force?

5. How do plants and animals participate in the water cycle?

6. Why can the North American continent be described as having two large watersheds?

7. What are four ways in which fresh water exists on the earth?

8. Why can water soak into the ground?

9. How does groundwater travel long distances underground? Give an example.

Choose the answer that best completes each sentence.

10. Water moves continuously from one place to another on the earth because of the (water table, water cycle, aquifers, watersheds).

11. The physical and chemical properties of water are due to its (surface tension, solid phase, boiling temperature, molecular structure).

12. The earth's fresh water comes from (lakes, rivers, glaciers, precipitation).

13. When water (condenses, evaporates, collects, flows), dissolved salts and minerals are left behind.

14. The amount of water a rock or soil can hold depends on its (permeability, density, porosity, mass).

Check Your Understanding

Apply the concepts you have learned to answer each question.

1. How does ocean water compare with fresh water? Discuss the abundance of each on the earth.

2. Explain how a glacier forms. What role do glaciers play in the global water cycle?

3. How does the structure of a water molecule affect water's physical and chemical properties? Discuss two examples.

4. **Critical Thinking** Explain how water molecules from the Amazon River could end up coming out of the water tap in your home.

5. **Extension** Devise a way to produce fresh water from salt water.

6. **Critical Thinking** Why do different places on the earth's surface have different amounts of surface water? What effect does the amount of surface water have on a land area?

7. **Application** Sometimes, a well that has been used for many years will suddenly run dry. Explain why this happens. What could the well owners do to get water to come out of the well again?

8. **Mystery Photo** The photograph on page 316 shows a creek in California on the eastern side of the Sierra Nevada Mountains.

   a. Where did the water in the creek come from?

   b. Where is the creek water going?

   c. Why does the creek water flow in one direction only?

   d. Explain the role of the creek in the water cycle.

Develop Your Skills

Use the skills you have developed in this chapter to complete each activity.

1. Interpret Data The drawings below show magnified cross sections through three different samples of rock or soil.

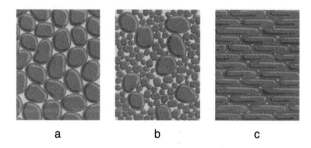

a   b   c

   a. Which one has the highest porosity? The lowest porosity?

   b. Which one has the highest permeability? The lowest permeability?

   c. Which one will hold the most water?

2. Make a Model Draw three patterns that drainage systems can take. Label the tributaries on each of the model drainage systems.

3. Predict What will happen to an aquifer if the surface of its recharge area undergoes a long drought?

4. Infer What might happen to the land in areas where large amounts of water are pumped from aquifers?

5. Data Bank Use the information on pages 620–621 to answer the following questions.

   a. Into which bay does the Sacramento River drain?

   b. How many tributaries can you see flowing into the Mississippi River? Identify two of them by name.

Make Connections

1. Link the Concepts Below is a concept map showing how some of the main concepts in this chapter link together. Only part of the map is filled in. Complete the map, using words and ideas from the chapter.

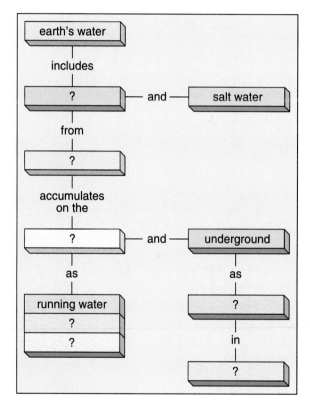

2. Science and Social Studies Do library research, and write a report on the history of a major city that developed along a river.

3. Science and You Find out where your community's supply of fresh water comes from. Write a report on the water's source and its quality.

4. Science and Society Do library research on modern sewage-treatment methods. Create a poster or bulletin board illustrating and comparing the different methods.

Chapter 15   Ocean Water

Chapter Sections

What do you see?

66This picture looks like the inside of a wave. The wave was formed by either the wind or the water's current. The water is moving in a tunnel-like way. In the next few seconds it will probably come crashing down near the shore and another will form further out and do the same.99

Sylvia Lucero
Park Junior High School
Antioch, California

To find out more about the photograph, look on page 362. As you read this chapter, you will learn about the earth's ocean water.

Figure 15.5
The Yuma Desalting Plant in Arizona uses the reverse osmosis method to desalt water. The plant can desalt nearly 275 million liters of water per day.

In the most common method of desalination, ocean water is pumped into a chamber and then heated. The water turns to steam. The steam rises into another chamber, where it cools and condenses. Salt is too heavy to be carried in the steam and is left behind. Water from condensed steam is fresh and drinkable. Most desalination plants that use this process must burn fossil fuels to heat the water.

Another desalination method uses a membrane through which water, but not salt, can pass. Water is forced through the membrane in a process called reverse osmosis. Usually the process is powered by fossil fuels, but one design uses power from ocean waves.

Check and Explain

1. What substances are dissolved in ocean water?

2. What is a thermocline? Explain how it forms.

3. **Compare and Contrast**   Compare the following properties of ocean water: composition, temperature, salinity, and density. Explain the relationships among these properties.

4. **Predict**   Imagine you have a glass of water at room temperature. You mix salt into the water until no more will dissolve. Then you put the glass in the refrigerator. Predict what will happen to the salt in the water.

Activity 15   *How do temperature and salinity affect density?*

Skills   Interpret Data; Observe; Model;
Hypothesize

Task 1 Prelab Prep

1. Collect the following items: 2 large drinking
    glasses, 2 small drinking glasses, labels,
    pen, warm and cold tap water, blue food col-
    oring, dropper, salt, plastic spoon, stir stick.
2. Number the labels *1, 2, 3,* and *4*. Label the
    large drinking glasses *1* and *2*. Label the
    small drinking glasses *3* and *4*.

Task 2 Data Record

1. On a separate sheet of paper, copy
    Table 15.2.
2. Use the data table to record all of your
    observations.

Table 15.2   Density Comparisons

Glass Number	Water Type	Observations

Task 3 Procedure

1. Add warm tap water to glass *1* until half full.
2. Add cold tap water to glass *3* until it is
    nearly full. Add three drops of food color-
    ing and stir.
3. As shown in Figure 15.6, slowly pour the
    water in glass *3* down the inside of glass *1*.
    Record your observations in the data table.
4. Add warm tap water to glass *4* until it is
    nearly full. Add three drops of food coloring
    and 5 spoonfuls of salt. Stir well.
5. Add warm tap water to glass *2* until it is half
    full. Add 2 spoonfuls of salt. Stir well.

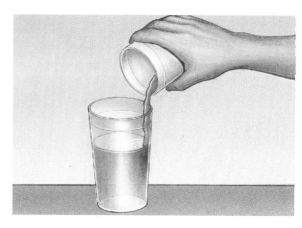

Figure 15.6 ▲

6. As shown in Figure 15.6, slowly pour the
    water in glass *4* down the inside of glass *2*.
    Record your observations in the data table.

Task 4 Analysis

1. Which was more dense, the water in glass *1*
    or the water in glass *3*? Explain.
2. Why did the water in glass *1* have a different
    density than the water in glass *3*?
3. Which was denser, the water in glass *2* or the
    water in glass *4*? Explain how you know.
4. Why did the water in glass *2* have a different
    density than the water in glass *4*?

Task 5 Conclusion

Write a short paragraph explaining the relationship between temperature and density. Then
write another paragraph explaining the relationship between salinity and density. Relate your
conclusions to the movement of deep currents
in the ocean.

Extension

Imagine you had another small glass with 8
spoonfuls of salt dissolved in it. Suppose you
poured this solution into glass *2* after completing
step 6 of the procedure. Make a hypothesis
about what would happen. Test your hypothesis.

15.2 Ocean Currents

Objectives

▶ **Describe** the major ocean current patterns in the Pacific and Atlantic oceans.

▶ **Identify** two factors that drive ocean currents.

▶ **Compare** and **contrast** surface currents and deep currents.

▶ **Predict** the effects of the Coriolis force.

▼ **ACTIVITY**

Modeling

At the Edge

Imagine you are riding at the center of a merry-go-round. You want to throw a ball to a friend at the edge of the merry-go-round. Where would your friend have to sit to be able to catch the ball? Draw a picture showing what would happen.

SKILLS WARMUP

Imagine a boat adrift in the ocean near the continent of Antarctica. Which way do you think the boat would move? The boat would travel in a clockwise direction. The boat would be carried along in a flow of water called a current. A **current** is a flow of water moving through the ocean. A strong ocean current flows in a clockwise direction around Antarctica.

Currents flow through all parts of the ocean. Surface currents flow horizontally on or near the top of the ocean. Deep currents flow horizontally far beneath the surface. Ocean water also flows vertically. Water can flow down toward the ocean floor or up toward the surface.

Surface Currents

Think about what happens when you blow on hot cocoa to cool it off. The surface of the hot cocoa moves in the direction that you blow. Wind moves ocean water in a similar way, creating surface currents.

Surface currents are driven by winds that blow for long distances over the ocean surface. The winds blow in a curved path because of the **Coriolis** (KOHR ee OH liss) **effect**. The Coriolis effect, caused by the earth's rotation, bends the earth's winds and ocean currents.

To understand how the Coriolis effect works, look at Figure 15.7. A person tries to draw a straight line on a rotating turntable. Although the line is being drawn straight, the surface on which it is drawn is moving. The motion of the surface produces a curved line.

Figure 15.7
What happens as this person tries to draw a straight line on the rotating turntable? ▼

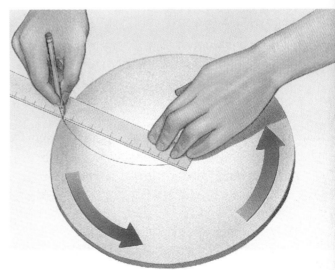

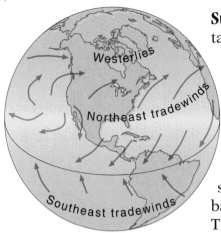

Surface Currents and Wind Patterns The earth rotates in an easterly direction. The earth's motion makes winds blowing toward the equator curve westward. In a similar way, winds blowing toward the poles curve eastward. Notice in Figure 15.8 that the winds form roughly circular patterns north of the equator. They also form circular patterns south of the equator.

Surface currents in the ocean form similar patterns. Imagine a windblown surface current traveling south toward the equator. At the same time, the ocean basin moves eastward because the earth is rotating. Therefore, the current curves slightly to the west.

If winds change direction, so do the surface currents. In summer, winds blow from the northern Indian Ocean toward Asia. The winds cause a surface current that moves in a clockwise circle. In winter, winds blow from Asia toward the ocean. The surface current changes direction, moving in a counterclockwise circle.

Figure 15.8 ▲
The prevailing winds in the northern and southern hemispheres push the ocean's surface waters in circular currents.

SkillBuilder *Interpreting Data*

Ocean Currents

The waters of the world ocean are constantly moving. In every ocean basin, there are surface currents and deep currents. All these currents exist at the same time. Therefore, in any part of the world ocean, surface water may move in a completely different direction than the deep water in the same area. For example, surface water in the North Atlantic Ocean moves in a clockwise circular motion. Meanwhile, a deep current in the same ocean carries dense water from Greenland toward the equator along the ocean bottom.

Study the map of surface currents on page 347. Place a sheet of tracing paper over the map. Using a pencil, trace the outlines of all the continents. Using a colored pencil, carefully trace all the surface currents. Be sure to include the arrows so you know in which direction the currents are moving.

Place your map of surface currents over the map of deep currents on page 348. Line up the continents so that the outlines on the two maps match exactly. Using a different colored pencil, trace the deep currents. You now have a map that shows how surface currents move in relation to deep currents. Use the combined information on your map to answer the following questions.

1. Compare the locations of the surface currents and deep currents in each ocean.

2. What differences do you see in the directions that surface currents flow and the directions that deep currents flow?

3. How are the currents similar?

Write a short report summarizing the movements of surface currents and deep currents in the world ocean.

Surface Currents in the World Ocean Study the major surface currents in the world ocean shown in Figure 15.9. Notice that warm currents flow from the equator and cold currents flow from the poles. Surface currents form a circular pattern called a **gyre** (JY ur). Gyres in the Northern Hemisphere flow clockwise. In the Southern Hemisphere, gyres flow counterclockwise.

Along the equator in the Pacific, Atlantic, and Indian oceans, warm currents flow west. In the Pacific and Indian oceans, a weak countercurrent flows east between the northern and southern currents. Around the continent of Antarctica, a current flows east.

In the North Atlantic Ocean, the North Equatorial Current flows into the Gulf Stream. The Gulf Stream flows north, meets the Labrador Current, and turns east to form the North Atlantic Drift Current. As the North Atlantic Drift Current approaches Europe, it splits in two. The northern branch moves toward the North Pole. The southern branch becomes the Canary Current that rejoins the North Equatorial Current.

In the North Pacific Ocean, the North Equatorial Current flows into the Kuroshio Current. The Kuroshio Current moves north along the coast of Asia, then joins the eastward-flowing North Pacific Current. Eventually it turns south and becomes the California Current.

Physical Science
L I N K

Collect the following materials: a small plastic ball (about 15 cm in diameter), string, a ruler, food coloring, water, and a clear container.
1. Add water to the container.
2. Using the ruler and string, suspend the ball in the water.
3. Spin the ball and slowly add drops of food coloring to the top of the ball.
Describe the flow of the food coloring around the ball. How is this flow related to ocean currents?

A C T I V I T Y

Figure 15.9

How do the currents differ north and south of the equator? ▼

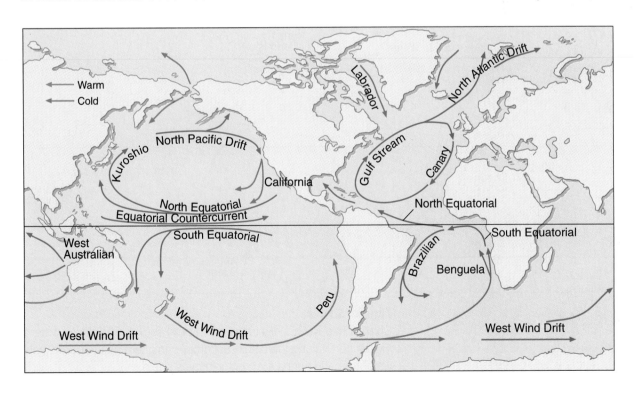

Deep Currents

Recall that density differences between warm surface waters and cold deep waters keep them from mixing. Because the waters don't mix, the movement of surface currents usually has little effect on colder deep water. In fact, while surface currents move in gyres, deep ocean currents flow from the poles toward the equator.

Deep currents are kept in motion by density differences. The densest water in the ocean forms at the North and South poles. There, the surface water is very cold. As ice forms, salts concentrate in the remaining water. The result is very dense cold water with high salinity. The dense polar water sinks downward to the deep ocean. The water continues to flow as a deep current toward the equator.

Besides density, the Coriolis effect also affects deep currents. Look at the map in Figure 15.10. Notice that deep currents tend to flow either northward or southward. But as the currents flow, the Coriolis effect bends them toward the western side of the ocean basins.

Where winds blow in a constant direction parallel to the coast, surface currents and deep currents can mix. For example, along the Pacific coast of Chile, the wind blows northward. The wind pushes the warm surface waters away from the coast. Cold, deep water moves upward to take the place of the surface water. The upward movement of deep water is called *upwelling*. Where upwelling occurs, the water is rich with nutrients that it brings up from the ocean floor. Marine animals are plentiful in these nutrient-rich waters.

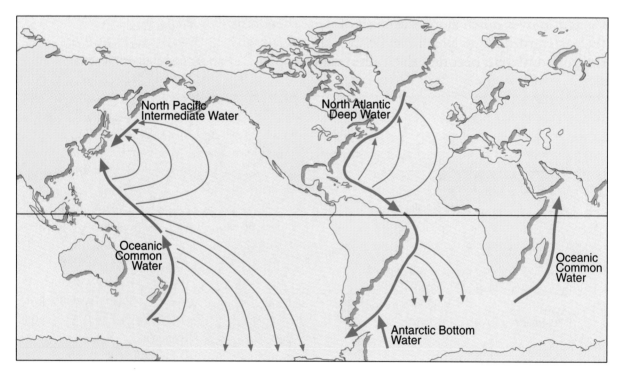

Figure 15.10 ▲
Cold, dense water sinks in the south polar region. The dense water moves north along the ocean bottom. At an intermediate depth, cold water from the north polar region moves south.

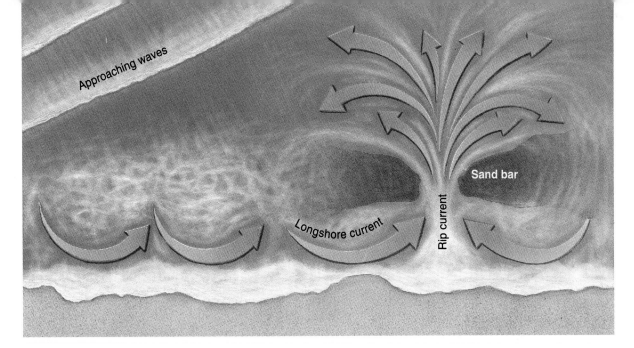

Figure 15.11 ▲

Small, localized currents form as waves break on a shoreline.

Shoreline Currents

Near the shoreline, local currents form that travel only short distances, such as a few kilometers or a few hundred meters. The distances these currents travel are like a trip across town or across the schoolyard. In contrast, surface currents and deep currents travel thousands of kilometers.

One type of shoreline current forms where waves approach a shore at an angle. After ocean waves hit the shore, the water flows back toward the ocean. The continuous back-and-forth motion of the waves forms a zigzag current parallel to the shore. Look at the zigzag current, called a *longshore current*, in Figure 15.11.

Along some shores are parallel ridges of rock or sand. Longshore currents can become trapped between the shore and the ridge. If there is an opening in the ridge, the longshore current can break through forcefully. The water in the longshore current is pulled out toward the open ocean. A narrow, powerful stream of water flows away at a right angle to the shore. This narrow stream is called a *rip current*.

Rip currents can be dangerous to swimmers. Swimmers are sometimes caught in a fast-moving rip current and pulled out to deeper water. Look at Figure 15.11. How do you think a swimmer can escape a rip current? Because a rip current is rather narrow, a swimmer can escape by swimming parallel to the shore.

A rip current is sometimes confused with an *undertow*. An undertow forms when water carried to shore in waves pulls back toward the ocean. If you stand on a beach and let small waves wash up around your ankles, the undertow drags the sand out from under your feet. An undertow isn't usually strong enough to be dangerous, unless the wave action is very strong or the ocean bottom drops away sharply. Public beaches with dangerous undertow conditions are often marked with warning signs.

ACTIVITY

Researching

Current Disasters

Use library references to research the El Niño that occurred in 1982 and 1983. Find out how it caused storms, floods, and droughts around the world. Also find out how it affected the fishing industry. Report your findings to the class.

SKILLS WORKOUT

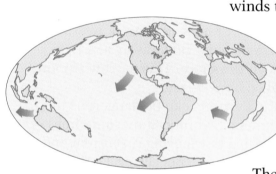

Figure 15.12 ▲
In areas of upwelling, winds blow warm surface water away from the coast. Cold, deep water moves up to fill the space.

Science and Society
Upwelling and Fisheries

Did you know that most of the world's supply of seafood comes from just a few places? Places where upwelling occurs, shown in Figure 15.12, are the world's most productive fishing grounds. Cold, deep water contains large amounts of plant nutrients, such as nitrogen and phosphates. Upwelling brings the cold, nutrient-rich water back to the ocean surface. The nutrients support the growth of diatoms and other plantlike organisms that serve as food for fishes.

The upwelling area off the western coast of South America is usually one of the world's most productive fisheries. Sometimes, however, the upwelling stops. A series of events called El Niño keeps the cold, nutrient-rich water from rising to the surface.

El Niño is a disturbance of ocean currents and winds that occurs every three to eight years. It begins when the westward trade winds weaken. These winds normally push warm surface water away from the coast of South America, allowing upwelling to occur. When the trade winds weaken, the warm equatorial current flows eastward toward the coast. The warm surface waters block upwelling along the coast.

The warming of the coastal waters and the lack of nutrients kill many microscopic organisms. Fishes and birds that feed on these organisms die of starvation or migrate elsewhere. The people who depend on fishing can't make a living during El Niño years.

Check and Explain

1. Describe surface currents in the North Pacific Ocean and the North Atlantic Ocean.

2. What two factors cause ocean currents to form?

3. **Compare and Contrast** How do surface currents and deep currents differ? How are they similar?

4. **Predict** What direction would a plane have to travel to reach a city directly south of its starting point if the winds were blowing to the east? Explain why.

15.3 Ocean Waves

Objectives

▶ **Explain** how waves form.

▶ **Identify** the parts of an ocean wave.

▶ **Explain** how to measure wave motion.

▶ **Define operationally** how a water particle moves as a wave passes.

▼ **ACTIVITY**

Observing

Wave Motion

Watch while part of the class performs the "wave" as done at sporting events. Describe how the people and the wave moved.

SKILLS WARMUP

How can you make waves in a tub of water? When you push down on the water with your hand, the water starts moving. An up-and-down movement travels the length of the tub. The periodic up-and-down movement of water is a *wave*.

Ocean waves form when wind pushes against the ocean's surface. Friction from the wind pushing against the water makes ripples form. The wind pushes against a ripple in much the same way that it would push against a sail. As the wind pushes against the surface of the ripple, energy is transferred from the wind to the water. The increasing energy makes the ripple grow into a wave. The larger a wave surface becomes, the more energy it can absorb from the wind.

Mechanics of Wave Motion

When you watch a wave move, the water appears to move forward. Actually, the water itself barely moves. It is wave energy that moves forward through the water, not the water particles. As the wave energy pulses forward, the water particles move in a circular, up-and-down motion. A cork placed in the water would bob up and down with the same motion. Look at Figure 15.13. Notice that each water particle returns to the point from which it started.

When a wave moves through water, not all of the energy transfers forward. Some energy transfers downward. However, the motion of the water particles decreases as the depth increases, as shown in Figure 15.13. Below a certain depth, there is no wave motion at all and the water particles stop moving.

Figure 15.13
How does wave motion compare to the water particle motion? ▼

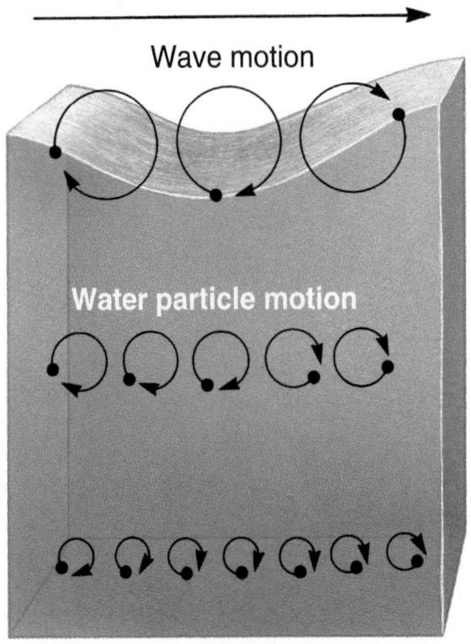

Wave motion

Water particle motion

Characteristics of Waves

If you watch the surface of the ocean over a period of time, you will see many waves of different sizes. The waves move in many directions. As the wind blows across the water's surface, it transfers energy to the water. When the wind is stronger, more energy is transferred. When the direction of the wind changes, it produces waves that move in a different direction.

Ocean waves begin to form far from land, in deep water. The wind blows over long distances of open ocean, causing unevenly spaced, ragged ridges of water to form. As the wave energy begins to travel through deeper water, the shape of the waves change. The waves form an even series of smooth, low hills of water called *swells*. No matter what its size or shape, an ocean wave always has certain characteristics. Study the characteristics of a wave in Figure 15.14.

Wavelengths of an ocean wave may vary from several meters up to several kilometers. The wavelength of an average swell is about 1,000 m. The time it takes one wavelength to pass a given point is called the *period* of the wave. The periods of most ocean waves range from 1 to 25 seconds.

**Figure 15.14
Ocean Waves** ▼

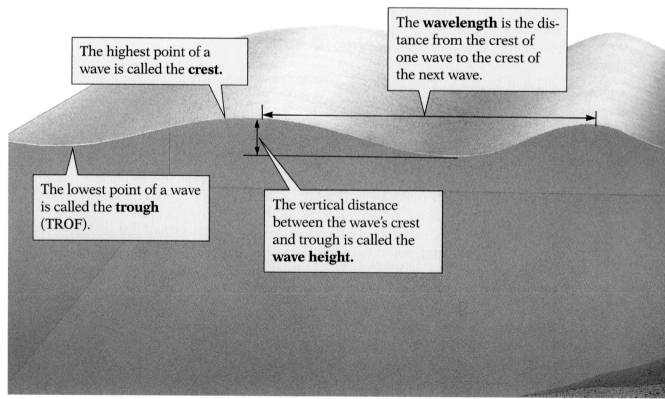

The highest point of a wave is called the **crest.**

The **wavelength** is the distance from the crest of one wave to the crest of the next wave.

The lowest point of a wave is called the **trough** (TROF).

The vertical distance between the wave's crest and trough is called the **wave height.**

Wave Action and Energy

A wave that forms a series of low swells in the open ocean changes when it gets closer to shore. Study how the wave changes in Figure 15.14. Notice that the wave height increases and the wavelength decreases. These changes start when the wave reaches shallow water. When the water depth is less than one-half the wavelength, the wave energy reaches its lowest point. As the wave contacts the ocean floor, some of the wave energy transfers upward, increasing the wave height.

As the wave contacts the ocean floor, friction gradually slows down the deeper part of the wave. However, the crest of the wave keeps moving. Eventually the crest of the wave gets so far ahead that the water topples forward. The wave breaks and washes onto the shore as swirling, foaming water.

Waves carry a large amount of energy. When a wave breaks, all the energy is released against the shore. The wave energy can destroy property along a shore and disrupt boating and shipping activities. For this reason, some communities build breakwaters to slow the waves. A breakwater is a high, sloping wall built at an angle to the shore.

A breakwater forces the waves to break away from shore. Behind the breakwater, the water near the shore stays calm. The shore is protected from the destructive force of the waves. However, sand tends to build up on the side of the breakwater that faces the ocean, while the shore behind it gets narrower. Behind the breakwater, longshore currents carry sand away from the shore. The sand can't be replaced because the longshore currents can't carry sand from one side of the breakwater to the other.

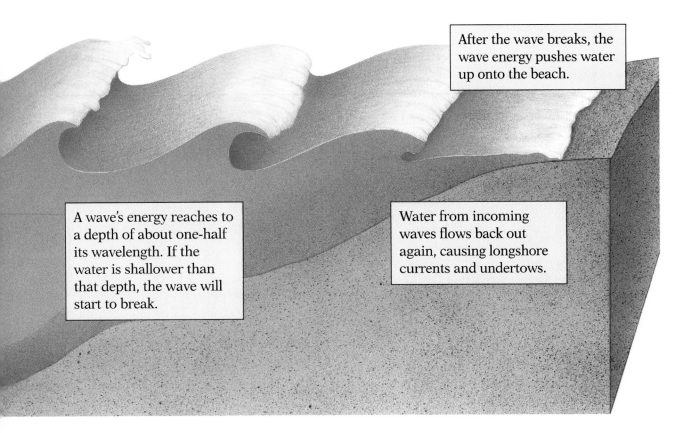

After the wave breaks, the wave energy pushes water up onto the beach.

A wave's energy reaches to a depth of about one-half its wavelength. If the water is shallower than that depth, the wave will start to break.

Water from incoming waves flows back out again, causing longshore currents and undertows.

Earthquakes and Ocean Waves

The most dramatic and destructive ocean waves are not caused by the wind, but by earthquakes. An earthquake deep underground may cause part of the ocean floor to shift upward suddenly. Notice in Figure 15.15 that the motion pushes the overlying waters upward, forming a bulge of water. As the bulge of water settles back down, it sets off a series of giant waves. The giant earthquake-generated wave, called a *tsunami* (soo NAH mee), travels at speeds of over 700 km/hr.

In the open ocean, the swells of a tsunami are low, only about 0.5 m high on the surface. They can pass unnoticed under ships. Although the swells don't look very large, they carry an enormous amount of energy. A tsunami can have a wavelength of about 250 km. Recall that the energy of a wave reaches a depth of about one-half its wavelength. Therefore, the energy of a tsunami can reach 125 km beneath the ocean surface.

As tsunamis approach the shore, all the energy stored in the deep waves transfers upward. The wave heights increase dramatically, up to 30 m. Huge breakers come crashing onto shore, one after another. Tsunamis are very destructive, destroying beaches, homes, and anything else along the shore.

Predicting tsunamis is difficult. They often can't be detected until they reach shore. Monitoring earthquakes beneath the ocean floor is the only way to find out if tsunamis may be coming.

Figure 15.15

Earthquakes on the ocean floor set tsunamis in motion. In deep water, the waves travel easily, but when they near the shore, they rise to great heights. As they crash on shore, they can destroy property and kill people nearby. ▼

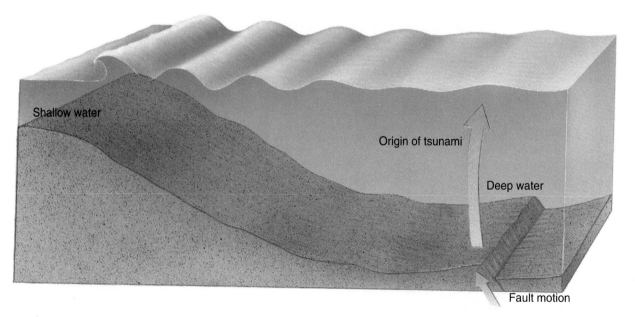

Shallow water

Origin of tsunami

Deep water

Fault motion

Science and Society *Rogue Waves*

Imagine sailing a boat through a storm. The water is choppy, the waves are high, but you are still in control of the boat. Suddenly a huge gust of wind tips the boat to one side. Then, even more suddenly, an immense wave towers above the boat and comes crashing down. The wave pushes the boat farther over. Before you can set the boat upright, a second huge wave sinks it!

This terrifying set of events actually happened to the crew of the sailing ship *Marques*. The 35-m sailing ship was sunk on June 3, 1984, with the loss of 19 of its 28 crew members. The cause of this maritime disaster wasn't just the storm winds, but a rogue wave. Rogue waves are immense waves, sometimes as large as 20 m high. They are called rogue waves because they seem to come out of nowhere, then disappear quickly.

Rogue waves can occur when two ordinary waves collide. Usually when waves collide, their crests and troughs don't "match up." What this means is that the trough of one wave meets with the crest of the other wave. The two waves partially cancel each other out, forming a smaller wave, as shown in Figure 15.16a. Occasionally, the waves do match up. The crest of one wave meets with the crest of the other. The two waves add their energy together as shown in Fig. 15.16b. A crest forms that is much higher than either of the two smaller crests. That high crest is the rogue wave. As the two waves continue to move off in different directions, the rogue wave disappears.

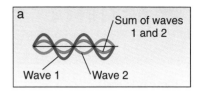

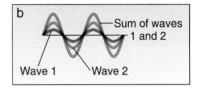

Figure 15.16 ▲
When two waves arrive at the same point, they may combine in two different ways.

Check and Explain

1. How do ocean waves form?

2. Name the parts of an ocean wave.

3. **Reason and Conclude**   Imagine you are on the deck of a boat on a calm day. How can you determine the period of the waves passing under the boat?

4. **Define Operationally**   Imagine a small piece of driftwood floating in the ocean. Describe its motion as a wave passes under it. What does this tell you about how a water particle moves as a wave passes?

Gravity's Pull

Draw a picture showing the gravitational attraction between two objects.

15.4 Tides

Objectives

▶ **Describe** the effect of gravity on the earth's water.

▶ **Explain** why tides change.

▶ **Compare** and **contrast** the different types of daily tide patterns.

▶ **Predict** the effects of tides on fishing.

What happens when you jump up in the air? You come back down, of course. You come down because of the gravitational attraction between you and the earth. All matter exerts a gravitational pull on all other matter. The gravitational pull is stronger when the objects are large or close together.

Gravity and Ocean Water

The sun and the moon are large objects that exert a gravitational pull on the earth. They exert the same amount of pull on the earth's land and water surfaces. However, liquid water shows the effects of the gravitational pull more than the solid earth. Every day, the level of the ocean surface rises and falls because of the gravitational pull of the moon and the sun. The daily changes in water level are called **tides.**

The gravitational pull of the moon on the ocean is strongest on the side of the earth nearest the moon. The ocean bulges on that side, as shown in Figure 15.17. On the opposite side from the moon, the solid earth is closer to the moon than it is to the ocean. The moon's gravity pulls the solid earth toward the moon and away from the ocean, causing a bulge. Therefore, on the opposite side of the earth, another bulge forms in the ocean. The sun's gravity also causes a bulge. But the bulge is smaller because the sun is farther away than the moon.

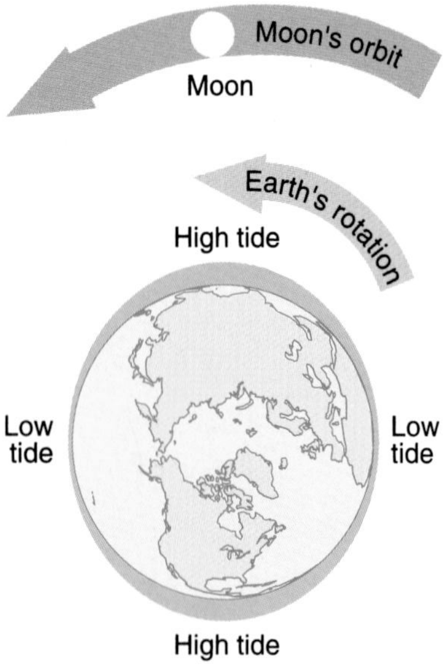

As the earth rotates, high tides occur in areas of the earth's surface beneath the bulges. *High tide* is the highest level that ocean water reaches on the shore. Low tides occur in areas between the bulges. *Low tide* is the lowest level that ocean water reaches on the shore.

Figure 15.17 ▲
All areas of the world ocean pass under the moon every 24 hours and 50 minutes. The moon's gravity produces a high tide in the places directly under and opposite it.

Figure 15.18 ▲
In the Bay of Fundy in Canada the water level varies 15 meters between high and low tide.

Daily Tide Patterns

Every coastal area has at least one high tide and one low tide every day. An example of extreme high and low tides occurs at the Bay of Fundy in Nova Scotia, Canada. The water level there changes drastically, as you can see in Figure 15.18.

Many factors influence daily tide patterns. The location on the earth's surface, the shape of the ocean floor and the coastline, and the Coriolis effect are some of the important factors. Tide patterns repeat every 24 hours and 50 minutes. Because a complete cycle actually takes slightly more than one day, tides occur at different times each day.

Semidiurnal Tides Some areas experience two high tides and two low tides each day. This pattern is known as a **semidiurnal** (SEH mee dye UR nuhl) tide pattern. The Atlantic coast of the eastern United States has a semidiurnal tide pattern.

Diurnal Tides Other areas have only one high tide and one low tide each day. This pattern is called a diurnal (daily) tide pattern. Diurnal tide patterns occur in the southeastern United States along the Gulf of Mexico.

Mixed Tides Areas such as the Pacific coast of the western United States have a mix of diurnal and semidiurnal tide patterns. Compare the daily tide patterns in the graphs in Figure 15.19. Which one is the daily tide pattern in the ocean nearest you?

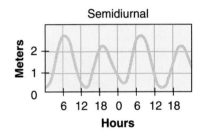

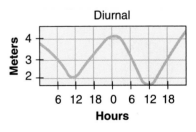

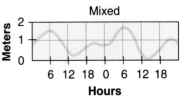

Figure 15.19 ▲
Compare the line graphs of daily tide patterns. Which tide pattern involves the most water movement?

Monthly Tide Cycles

The graph in Figure 15.20 shows how the tide heights vary during one month. The daily tides cycles with the greatest difference between high and low tides are called *spring tides*. The daily tides cycles with the least difference between high and low tides are called *neap tides*. Periods of spring tides and neap tides occur twice each month. The differences in tide heights are caused by the changing positions of the sun and moon.

Figure 15.20
Monthly Tide Cycle ▼

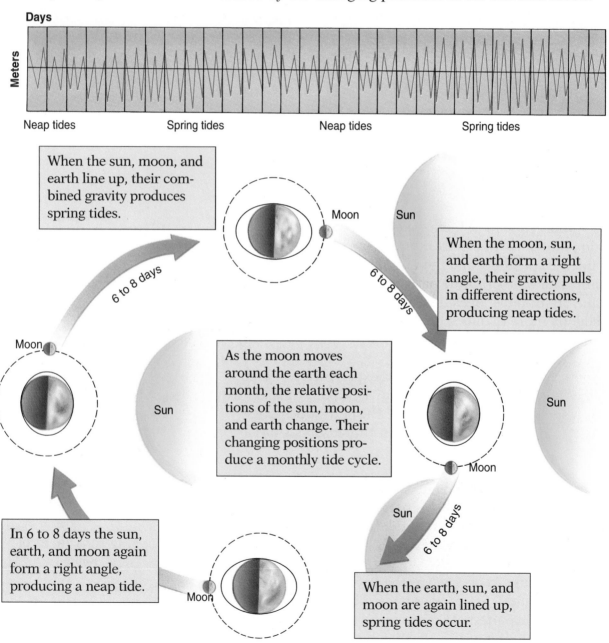

When the sun, moon, and earth line up, their combined gravity produces spring tides.

When the moon, sun, and earth form a right angle, their gravity pulls in different directions, producing neap tides.

As the moon moves around the earth each month, the relative positions of the sun, moon, and earth change. Their changing positions produce a monthly tide cycle.

In 6 to 8 days the sun, earth, and moon again form a right angle, producing a neap tide.

When the earth, sun, and moon are again lined up, spring tides occur.

Tides and Living Things

Some organisms live on the shore between the level of the highest high tides and the lowest low tides. If you walk along a beach at low tide, you might see sand dollars, hermit crabs, seaweed, and other organisms. As the tides change, these organisms may be covered with ocean water or exposed to the air and sun. Some burrow in the wet sand or hide under rocks or seaweed to escape drying out.

Fishes living near shore are also affected by tides. At high tide, many fishes come closer to the shore. They feed on algae and other organisms that can't be reached at low tide. The life cycle of the grunion depends on tide cycles. Grunion swim onto the beach to spawn during the highest spring tides. They bury their eggs in the sand. The eggs develop until the next spring tide. The rising waters stimulate the eggs to hatch, and the young grunion swim out to the ocean.

Figure 15.21 ▲
Grunions live and spawn in the warm waters off of Southern California and Baja Mexico.

Career Corner *Merchant Mariner*

Who Moves Goods Across the Oceans?

Every time you visit a mall or supermarket, you see goods from faraway places. Clothes may come from Hong Kong, Korea, Europe, or Sri Lanka. Bananas from Costa Rica and coffee from Kenya are in many markets. How do these goods get to your hometown? Merchant ships carry all kinds of goods across the oceans. The people who operate these ships are called merchant mariners.

Some merchant mariners serve as captains and deck officers. The captain is in charge of all the ship's operations. Officers supervise navigation and ship maneuvers. Navigators estimate the ship's position and plan the route using electronic and celestial, or star, navigation. A meteorologist monitors weather conditions. Engineers, machinists, and pipe fitters maintain and repair the ship's engines and all shipboard systems. Skilled workers operate the engines and perform maintenance and repair work.

To become a merchant mariner, you need practical seagoing skills, such as boat handling and navigation. Officers and engineers need college courses in physics,

chemistry, oceanography, and electronics. Specialized maritime colleges offer further training. If you think you would like a career as a merchant mariner, you can write to the California Maritime Academy in Vallejo, California.

Figure 15.22 ▶

On the Rance River in France, vehicles drive on the roadway above while the tides generate electricity below.

Science and Technology *Tidal Power*

Did you know that the ocean can be an energy source? There are vast amounts of energy in ocean waves and currents. However, the most promising ocean-linked power plants use energy from tides. One such tidal power plant is located at the mouth of the Rance River in France.

At the tidal power plant, there is a huge dam across the river, as shown in Figure 15.22. Along the dam, below the water's surface, are tunnels for the water to flow through. Inside the tunnels are large spinning blades called turbines. As the tide flows in and out, the moving water turns the turbines. The spinning turbines operate generators that produce electricity. The electricity then travels to distribution stations.

The amount of electricity generated at a tidal plant varies with the amount of water that moves through the dam. The energy is available only when the turbines are turning. However, tidal power plants can help reduce the need to burn fossil fuels for generating electricity.

▼ **ACTIVITY**

Interpreting Data

The Moon and the Tides

1. Every day for two weeks, look at a daily tide table in a newspaper.

2. Each day, record the time and height of the highest tide. When was the highest tide?

3. Using a calendar or almanac, find out if that day had a new moon or a full moon.

SKILLS WORKOUT

Check and Explain

1. How does gravity cause tides?

2. Why do tides change over the course of a month?

3. **Compare and Contrast** What is the difference between a semidiurnal tide pattern and a diurnal tide pattern?

4. **Predict** When would a person going fishing on a beach have the best chance of catching a fish? Explain your answer.

Chapter 15 Review

Concept Summary

15.1 Properties of Ocean Water
▶ Ocean water contains dissolved gases, salts, and traces of different elements.
▶ The boundary between warm surface water and colder water below is a thermocline.
▶ The density of ocean water varies with temperature and salinity. Water pressure increases with depth.
▶ Organisms extract substances, like silica, from ocean water.

15.2 Ocean Currents
▶ The Coriolis effect bends winds and ocean currents.
▶ Wind-driven surface currents form clockwise gyres in the Northern Hemisphere and counterclockwise gyres in the Southern Hemisphere.

▶ Deep currents flow from the poles to the equator.
▶ The interaction between waves and the shoreline causes longshore currents, rip currents, and undertows.

15.3 Ocean Waves
▶ Wind friction produces surface waves.
▶ Ocean waves have a crest, trough, wave height, and wavelength.
▶ Earthquakes on the ocean floor cause giant waves called tsunamis.

15.4 Tides
▶ The gravitational pull of the sun and moon causes tides.
▶ The changing positions of the earth, sun, and moon result in a monthly cycle of spring tides and neap tides.

Chapter Vocabulary

salinity (15.1)	current (15.2)	crest (15.3)	wavelength (15.3)
estuary (15.1)	Coriolis effect (15.2)	trough (15.3)	tide (15.4)
thermocline (15.1)	gyre (15.2)	wave height (15.3)	semidiurnal (15.4)

Check Your Vocabulary

Use the vocabulary words above to complete the following sentences correctly.

1. Daily changes in water level caused by gravitational pull are called _____ .
2. The highest part of a wave is its _____ .
3. The lowest part of a wave is its _____ .
4. The number of grams of salts per kilogram of ocean water is _____ .
5. As you move deeper in the water column, a _____ , or zone of rapid temperature change, occurs.
6. A flow of water moving through the ocean is a(n) _____ .
7. A bay or inlet where a river enters the ocean is a(n) _____ .

8. The clockwise or counterclockwise flow of surface currents forms a _____ .
9. The bending of ocean currents by the earth's rotation is called the _____ .
10. The distance between the highest and lowest points of a wave is the _____ .
11. The horizontal distance from one wave crest to the next is the wave's _____ .
12. A _____ tide pattern has two low tides and two high tides each day.

Write Your Vocabulary

Write sentences using the vocabulary words above. Show that you know what each word means.

Check Your Knowledge

Answer the following in complete sentences.

1. How did the oceans form?

2. Why is ocean water salty?

3. How does a thermocline form?

4. What are three physical properties of ocean water?

5. Which is denser, cold water or warm water? High-salinity water or low-salinity water? Explain.

6. What happens to water pressure as you go deeper into the water column?

7. What is the Coriolis force? How does it affect the ocean's surface currents?

8. How do deep ocean currents differ from surface currents?

9. What is a rip current? How is it different from an undertow?

10. What causes tides?

Determine whether each statement is true or false. Write *true* if it is true. If it is false, change the underlined word to make the statement true.

11. The water pressure at a depth of 600 m is <u>less</u> than at a depth of 60 m.

12. The water in an estuary has <u>lower</u> salinity than most ocean water.

13. A tsunami forms <u>high</u> wave crests as it travels across the open ocean.

14. In the Northern Hemisphere, surface currents form <u>clockwise</u> gyres.

15. Warm water is more dense than cold water.

16. In areas of upwelling, <u>cold</u> water rises to the surface.

Check Your Understanding

Apply the concepts you have learned to answer each question.

1. Why do some parts of the world ocean have higher salinity than other parts?

2. Explain how an ocean wave forms and travels.

3. **Application**   What should a swimmer who is caught in a rip current do to get back to the shore? Explain.

4. **Critical Thinking**   In some beach communities with large breakwaters, the beach has virtually disappeared. Why?

5. **Extension**   What type of daily tide pattern occurs in the coastal areas nearest your home? Describe what happens to the water level there during one day.

6. **Mystery Photo**   The photograph on page 338 shows a breaking ocean wave. Study the photograph, and answer the following questions.

   a. What do you think the water depth is like where the picture was taken? Explain.

   b. Why does the water move the way it does?

   c. What kinds of currents can be caused by the wave?

7. **Application**   Some people think sea salt from evaporating ocean water is more healthy than salt from chemical means. Why might they think this?

8. **Application**   Why are the world's most productive fishing areas in upwelling zones?

9. **Extension**   Imagine you are scuba diving 20 m beneath the ocean surface. How would the ocean's wave action affect you?

Develop Your Skills

Use the skills you have developed in this chapter to complete each activity.

1. **Interpret Data** The graph below shows the tidal cycle in one U.S. location for the month of November.

   a. On which days of the month did spring tides occur? On which days did neap tides occur?

   b. What type of daily tide pattern does the place have? Where is it likely to be located?

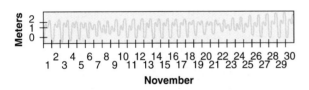

November

2. **Infer** Thermoclines form more often in summer than in winter. Why?

3. **Hypothesize** Think about conditions near the ocean surface and deep underwater. Where do you think a fish living in the ocean would be able to find more food? Describe a possible experiment to test your hypothesis.

4. **Make a Model** Describe how to use a basketball, globe, or other spherical object to demonstrate the Coriolis effect.

5. **Data Bank** Use the information on page 616 to answer the following questions.

   a. At what times do high tides occur each day?

   b. At what times do low tides occur each day?

   c. Why are the times different each day?

Make Connections

1. **Link the Concepts** Below is a concept map showing how some of the main concepts in this chapter link together. Only part of the map is filled in. Complete the map, using words and ideas from the chapter.

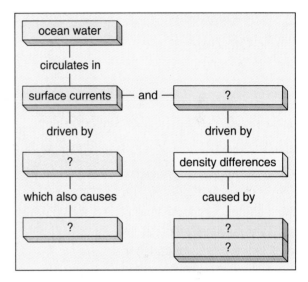

2. **Science and Social Studies** Ocean currents were very important in determining trade routes and ports of call for sailing ships. Do library research on sailing ships and the routes they traveled. Make a poster comparing the trade routes and ocean surface currents.

3. **Science and Math** Look up the tide times and heights from newspaper listings for the past month. Construct a bar graph showing the high-tide and low-tide heights for each day. Describe the patterns you find.

4. **Science and Technology** Do library research on methods of desalinating ocean water. Write a report comparing the different methods.

Chapter 16 Ocean Basins

What do you see?

"I see an organism that is transparent and is outlined by a white zipper-like line. I think it might be some kind of squid or jellyfish. I think it lives in the ocean because it looks like it is surrounded by some seaweed. It is clear so it can hide from predators."

Peter Wu
Parkhill Jr. High School
Dallas, Texas

To find out more about the photograph, look on page 386.
As you read this chapter, you will learn about the ocean basins and the kinds of organisms that live in oceans.

16.1 Ocean Exploration

Objectives

▶ **Give examples** of two oceanic research vessels.

▶ **Describe** five tools and methods used to study the oceans and the ocean floor.

▶ **Infer** how to make a bathymetric map.

Imagine trying to figure out what's at the bottom of a sealed box. How can you find out what's there if you can't see inside the box? About 70 percent of the earth's surface is somewhat like the sealed box. That part of the earth's surface is covered by a deep layer of ocean water. For hundreds of years, scientists have searched for ways to learn more about the part of the earth's surface beneath the oceans.

Oceanic Research Vessels

Until about 120 years ago, most information about the oceans came from people involved in fishing or trade. Their knowledge was mostly practical, having to do with navigation. Then, in 1872, the research vessel HMS *Challenger* began a 127 500-km voyage to study the world ocean. The voyage lasted three years. Scientists measured the depths of the ocean with long, weighted ropes. They observed currents, measured ocean temperatures, and collected samples of sediments and living organisms. The *Challenger's* data filled 50 large books!

Later, other research vessels were launched. In 1925, the *Meteor* began a two-year voyage to study currents in the Atlantic Ocean. Scientists measured water temperature and salinity. They also used sound waves to measure ocean depths. In 1968, the *Glomar Challenger* began a series of very successful voyages over a 15-year period. *Glomar Challenger* carried drilling equipment to collect samples of ocean-floor crust and sediments. The *JOIDES Resolution*, launched in 1985, continues the work today. Scientists use many other research vessels to learn about ocean life.

Figure 16.1 ▲
What can scientists learn by studying the ocean?

Tools and Methods of Ocean Research

As tools and methods have improved, people have learned more about the oceans. For example, you can measure ocean depth more accurately with sound waves than with a weighted rope. One older way of studying the ocean floor, called scraping, is still used today. Scraping involves dragging a heavy object, called a dredge, along the ocean floor. The dredge picks up loose rocks, sediments, and bottom-dwelling organisms. The samples are raised to the surface for study. Some modern tools and methods used to gather data about the deep ocean and the ocean floor are described here.

Coring

In coring, a ship uses a drilling rig to drive long metal tubes down into the ocean floor. The tubes fill up with layers of sediment and rock. Aboard ship, the layers are removed as a long cylindrical sample called a core. Cores as long as 1,500 m have been obtained. A core sample provides data about the age and composition of the ocean floor. Core samples have been collected from all parts of the ocean floor, even the deepest trenches. ▼

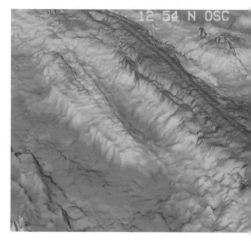

Sonar ▲

Sonar uses sound waves to map the ocean floor. A transmitter on a ship sends a sound wave toward the ocean floor. The sound wave reflects off the ocean bottom back to a receiver on the ship. Scientists know how fast sound travels through ocean water. By measuring the time it takes the sound wave to make one round trip, they can determine the depth of the ocean.

With modern tools and methods, the type and amount of data that can be collected have increased greatly. Satellites make it possible to survey conditions over the entire ocean surface several times each day. In a submersible (suhb MUR suh buhl), scientists can travel to the deep ocean bottom and make direct observations. Remote-controlled submersibles collect data even more efficiently and at less cost.

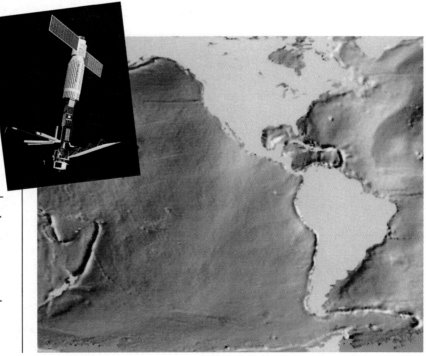

Submersibles

◀ Submersibles are underwater research vessels. All submersibles are designed to withstand the tremendous pressure of ocean water deep below the surface. Submersibles carry cameras and scientific instruments. One type of submersible is shown in the photograph. It is operated by remote control from the surface. Others are piloted by people who make direct observations.

Satellites

In 1978, a satellite ▶ named *Seasat* was launched to study the oceans from space. *Seasat* orbited the earth for about three months. *Seasat* used electronic instruments to collect data about water temperatures, currents, surface heights, and ocean life. The data were transmitted to receiving stations on the earth's surface. Computers translated the data into photographs and very accurate maps.

ACTIVITY

Hypothesizing

Can't See a Thing

1. Place pebbles in a pattern in the bottom of a pan.

2. Cover the pebbles with an opaque liquid, such as tempera paint or dark-colored water.

3. Hypothesize about how someone could determine the pattern of the pebbles without draining the pan.

4. Test your hypothesis.

SKILLS WORKOUT

Figure 16.2

How does this bathymetric map compare to a topographic map?

▼

Mapping the Ocean Floor

Although the ocean floor is more than 70 percent of the earth's surface, it has been the last part to be mapped. For a long time, the overlying water made mapping extremely difficult. Some of the ocean floor is covered by a layer of water more than 10 000 m deep!

One of the first maps of the ocean floor was made by Matthew Fontaine Maury, a United States naval officer. He gathered data about winds, tides, currents, and ocean depths from mariners in different parts of the world. In 1855, he used this information to construct a simple topographic map of the floor of the North Atlantic Ocean. Recall that a topographic map uses contour lines to show surface shapes and elevations. A topographic map of the ocean floor is called a *bathymetric* (BATH uh MEHT trihk) map. Study the bathymetric map in Figure 16.2. Each contour line on a bathymetric map is called an *isobath* (EYE soh bath).

To determine the shape of the ocean floor, mapmakers needed depth measurements from many different locations. The weighted-rope method of measuring depth, called depth sounding, was not very good for mapmaking. Depth sounding was only effective in somewhat shallow waters. Also, depth sounding was slow. It took several months to measure just a small area of the ocean floor.

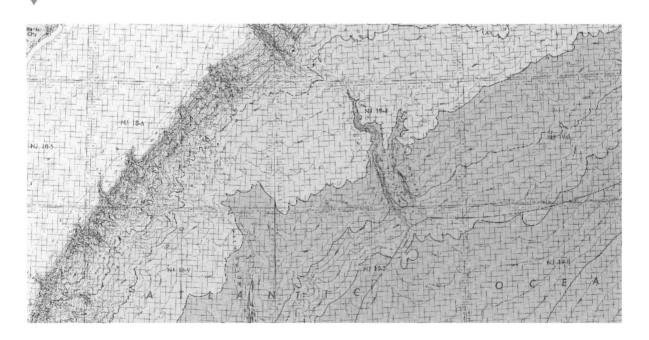

In 1925, scientists aboard the research vessel *Meteor* measured the depth of the ocean with sonar. Sonar enabled them to measure the ocean's depth continuously as the ship moved. They made a detailed record of how the depth changed as the ship moved over a wide area. They used the depth records to make a map of the shape of the ocean floor.

The launching of *Seasat* in 1978 introduced an even more efficient mapping technique. *Seasat* carried a device called a radar altimeter. The radar altimeter measured the distance between the satellite and the ocean surface within 10 cm. The data showed that the height of the ocean surface varied with the shape of the ocean floor beneath it. The surface height above an ocean trench was lower than the surface height above an underwater mountain. The differences in ocean surface height provided new information for more complete maps of the ocean floor.

Life Science
L I N K

Obtain a blindfold and a large sheet of cardboard.

1. Have a partner blindfold you.

2. Your partner then holds the cardboard at head level some distance in front of you.

3. Slowly, move forward making sounds in the direction of your partner.

Depending on your echo, determine when to stop before touching the cardboard.

How would a heightened sense of hearing help you in a darkened room?

A C T I V I T Y

Historical Notebook

Life on the Ocean Floor

For many years, people thought the bottom of the deep ocean was a barren and lifeless desert. It was thought to be lifeless because of the lack of sunlight. However, this hypothesis turned out to be incorrect. In 1977, scientists discovered life on the Pacific Ocean floor at a depth of 2,500 m. In 1985, life was discovered at depths below 3,600 m on the Atlantic Ocean floor. These organisms were found along the mid-Atlantic Ridge by cameras lowered from vessels on the ocean surface.

Organisms on the deep ocean floor do not use energy from sunlight to survive. Instead, they use chemical energy from sulfur-rich water. The sulfur-rich water streams from vents in the ocean floor. Water temperatures near some Pacific Ocean vents ranged between 8° and 12°C. The normal bottom water temperature at these depths is about 2°C.

Living near the vents on the Atlantic Ocean floor were worms, anemones, fast-moving shrimps,

crabs, and fishes up to 25 cm long. One vent was named the Snake Pit. This vent supported organisms like those listed above, as well as snakelike swimming animals that were about 30 to 60 cm long. Near the Pacific Ocean vents, scientists found tube worms over 1 m long, large mussels, white crabs, and some giant clams up to 25 cm long.

1. Why did scientists think that life couldn't exist on the ocean floor?

2. How do ocean-floor organisms stay alive without sunlight?

3. **Research** Do library research to find out what organisms live on the Pacific Ocean floor. Compare them to the organisms on the Atlantic Ocean floor. How are they the same? How do they differ?

Science and Technology
Alvin, Jason, and ABE

Imagine you had never seen any of the earth's land surfaces. Could you describe them using only topographic maps, satellite images, rocks, and soil samples? For many years, descriptions of the ocean floor were based on such indirect observations.

Submersibles make it possible for scientists to directly observe the deep ocean floor. Submersibles called *bathyscaphs* (BATH ih skafs) are like small submarines. The bathyscaph *Alvin* has made more than 1,600 dives. While exploring the East Pacific Rise, scientists aboard *Alvin* discovered geyserlike vents in the ocean floor. Streams of hot, mineral-rich water flowed from the vents. The earth's mantle heated the water to more than 350°C.

The most promising tools for exploring the deep sea are robotic submersibles. For example, *Jason* is an underwater robot equipped with video cameras, computers, and manipulator arms. Another robot, *ABE*, can be programmed to explore an area on its own. *ABE*, also called the *Autonomous Benthic Explorer*, can collect data more than 6 km under the water for up to one year.

Figure 16.3 ▲
Alvin returns from one of its many dives.

Check and Explain

1. Describe the voyages of two oceanic research vessels.

2. What are five tools and methods used to study the oceans and the ocean floor? Describe the kind of information each tool or method provides.

3. **Evaluate Sources** Which would you consider more accurate and reliable, a bathymetric map drawn from information gathered by HMS *Challenger*, or one drawn from information gathered by the ship *Meteor*? Give reasons for your answer.

4. **Infer** The earth's gravitational force is slightly stronger in the region of an ocean trench than it is near an oceanic mountain. How might such gravity differences be used to make a bathymetric map?

Activity 16 *What can you learn from a core sample?*

Skills Model; Infer; Generalize

Task 1 Prelab Prep

1. Collect the following items: 3 different-colored pieces of modeling clay (each piece about the size of a golf ball), square of waxed paper, butter knife, 3 plastic drinking straws, small scissors.
2. Soften each piece of clay by squeezing it in your hands.
3. Flatten each piece of clay into a slab. Vary the width and length of the slabs. Let the thickness vary between 0.5 and 1 cm. Each slab should be somewhat uneven.
4. Stack the clay slabs on top of each other to form a block. Place the clay block on the waxed paper. Compact the layers by pushing down on the clay block. Using the butter knife, trim the edges.

Task 2 Data Record

On a separate sheet of paper draw a block and three cylinders, as shown in Figure 16.4. You will use this data sheet to record your observations.

Figure 16.4 ▼

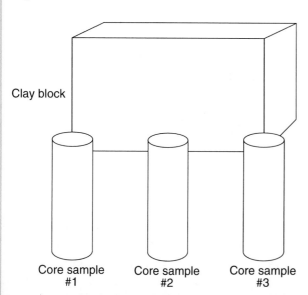

Clay block

Core sample #1   Core sample #2   Core sample #3

Task 3 Procedure

1. Refer to the block you have drawn on your data sheet. Then draw a view of two sides of your clay block.
2. Push the straw through the layers of clay. Pull the straw out of the clay. On the block on your data sheet, record the location of your first core sample.
3. Use the scissors to cut open the straw lengthwise. Remove the clay plug, and place it on the waxed paper.
4. Draw the layers of core sample #1 on one of the cylinders on your data sheet.
5. Repeat steps 2 to 4 to create and examine core samples #2 and #3.

Task 4 Analysis

1. **Observe** Compare your three core samples. How were they alike? How were they different? What was the cause of the differences between the core samples?
2. Could you tell what each core sample would look like by first observing the sides of the clay block? Why?
3. Which layer of the core sample was the oldest? How could you tell?
4. Which layer of the core sample was the youngest? How could you tell?
5. **Infer** How might your core samples differ from another group in the class?

Task 5 Conclusion

How are the data from your model core sample similar to data from an actual core sample of the ocean bottom? How are they different?

Extension

Attach the sides of all the clay blocks in the class together to form a model ocean floor. Take ten samples from the large clay block. Infer the geologic history of the model ocean floor from the core samples.

ACTIVITY

Inferring

The Ocean Floor

Make a list of the different types of landforms that exist on the earth's continents. Review each land formation. Place an "O" next to each formation that you think may also exist on the bottom of the ocean.

SKILLS WARMUP

16.2 Ocean-Floor Topography

Objectives

▶ **Describe** three features of the continental margin.

▶ **Identify** the major features of the ocean floor.

▶ **Compare** and **contrast** ocean trenches and ridges.

▶ **Predict** motion along underwater plate boundaries.

Imagine what the earth's surface would look like if all the water drained from the ocean basins. What do you think the newly uncovered ocean floor would look like? For many years, people thought that most of the ocean floor was flat. They also thought a thick layer of sediments covered the entire ocean floor.

Modern oceanographic research shows that those early ideas about the ocean floor were incorrect. For example, the ocean floor has a variety of landforms similar to those on land. The ocean floor is dotted with volcanic peaks, many higher than any volcano on land. A system of underwater mountain ranges, called ridges, crosses each ocean basin. Other features of the ocean floor include canyons and vast, flat, featureless plains. The canyons are deeper than the Grand Canyon, and the plains are larger than any desert.

Continental Margins

Have you ever gone to the shore at low tide and waded out into the water? Perhaps you thought you were walking on part of the ocean floor. However, the continent does not end right at the water's edge. The continent extends for some distance into the ocean. The part of a continent that extends out into the ocean is called the *continental margin*. The continental margin slopes downward toward the ocean floor. Three distinct regions make up the continental margin. Study the parts of the continental margin shown in Figure 16.6 on page 373. At some places, deep submarine canyons cut across the continental margin.

Figure 16.5 ▲
These mountains in Iceland are part of the mid-Atlantic Ridge. The same mountains run thousands of kilometers along the floor of the Atlantic Ocean.

Continental Shelf   A gently sloping surface, called the **continental shelf**, extends under the water from the shoreline. Sediments transported by rivers form most of the continental shelf.

The average width of a continental shelf is about 65 km. But the width may be much wider or narrower. Continental shelves are generally narrower in coastal areas, such as California, that are near tectonic plate boundaries.

Continental Slope   At the edge of the continental shelf, the **continental slope** drops off rather steeply toward the ocean floor. The continental slope is made up of the same materials as the continental shelf. The boundary between continental crust and oceanic crust occurs along the continental slope.

In some areas, almost no continental slope exists. One example is the Pacific coast of South America, where there are deep ocean trenches very close to the edge of the continental shelf.

Continental Rise   Look at Figure 16.6. The area from the continental slope to the deep ocean floor is called the **continental rise**. The continental rise is much less steep than the continental slope.

The continental rise is made of sediments. The sediments are carried from the continents and washed down the continental slopes. Continental rises vary in width from a few kilometers to hundreds of kilometers.

Submarine Canyon   In many places, continental margins are cut by deep submarine canyons. Rivers flowing to the ocean cut some of the canyons during the ice ages, when sea levels were lower. Moving masses of water and sediments, called turbidity currents, formed other submarine canyons. Turbidity currents are not related to other ocean currents. Because of the heavy load of sediments they carry, turbidity currents are very dense. They flow swiftly down the steep canyons in the continental slopes.

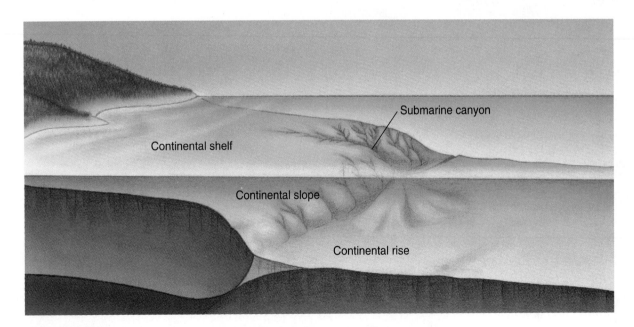

Figure 16.6 ▲
Continental margins usually have three separate regions.

Ocean-Floor Features

The ocean floor has many features similar to those on land. Look at Figure 16.7. Volcanoes, sediments, and moving crustal plates shape the ocean floor.

Abyssal Plains Flat areas of the deep ocean floor are called **abyssal** (uh BIHS uhl) **plains**. Core samples from abyssal plains show layers of sediment deposited over thousands of years. The sediments fill in rough spots on the ocean floor, forming a smooth, flat surface.

Sediments vary in different parts of an abyssal plain. Near the continental margin are fine rock particles from land areas. Deep ocean sediments contain the remains of microscopic organisms. After the organisms die, they sink to the ocean floor, forming a sediment called ooze. The largest abyssal plains are in the Atlantic and Indian oceans, where large rivers deposit more sediments.

Figure 16.7
Features of the Ocean Floor

▼

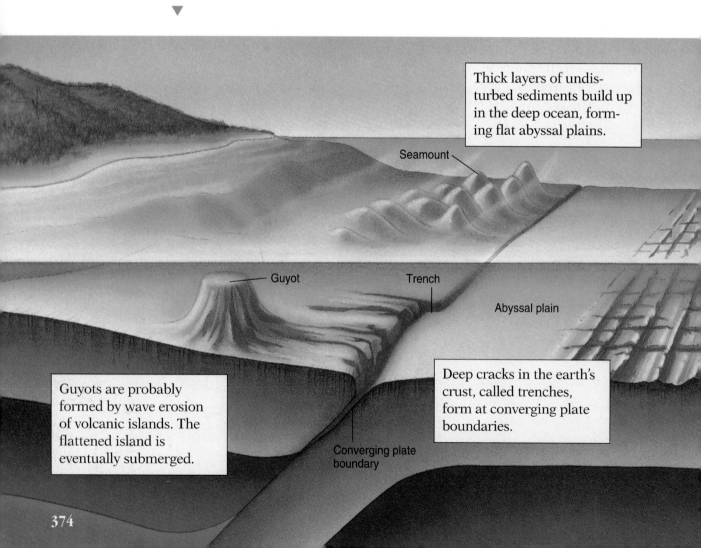

Thick layers of undisturbed sediments build up in the deep ocean, forming flat abyssal plains.

Seamount

Guyot

Trench

Abyssal plain

Guyots are probably formed by wave erosion of volcanic islands. The flattened island is eventually submerged.

Deep cracks in the earth's crust, called trenches, form at converging plate boundaries.

Converging plate boundary

Ridges Each ocean basin has mountain ranges that form a ridge. For example, the mid-Atlantic Ridge runs through the Atlantic Ocean basin. Ridges form at diverging plate boundaries.

Seamounts and Guyots Volcanic mountains rising more than 1,000 m above the ocean floor are called **seamounts**. Seamounts form near mid-ocean ridges, or at volcanic "hot spots." Seamounts grow until plate movement carries them away from the plate boundary or hot spot. Some seamounts grow tall enough to form volcanic islands. When a volcanic island stops growing, wave action can flatten it, forming a *guyot* (GHEE oh).

Reefs and Atolls Coral reefs form in shallow water on continental shelves or along the shorelines of volcanic islands. If the volcanic island later sinks below the surface of the water, the ring of coral reefs is left behind. Such a formation is called an *atoll* (A tohl).

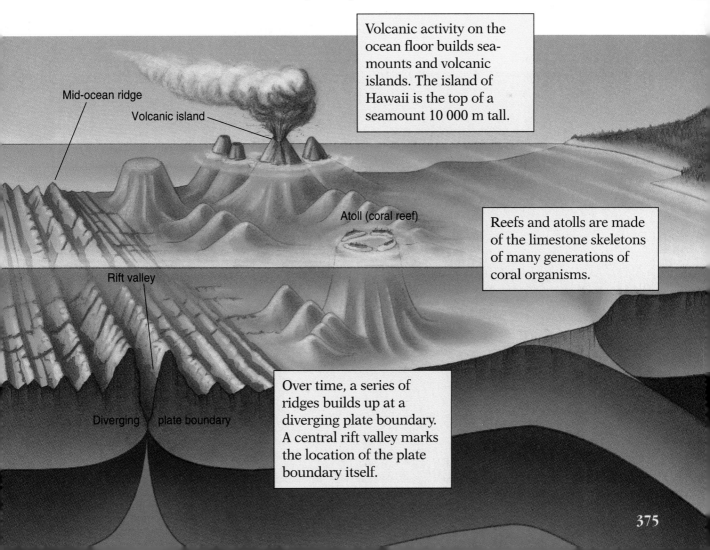

Volcanic activity on the ocean floor builds seamounts and volcanic islands. The island of Hawaii is the top of a seamount 10 000 m tall.

Mid-ocean ridge

Volcanic island

Atoll (coral reef)

Reefs and atolls are made of the limestone skeletons of many generations of coral organisms.

Rift valley

Diverging plate boundary

Over time, a series of ridges builds up at a diverging plate boundary. A central rift valley marks the location of the plate boundary itself.

Plate Boundaries and Trenches Plate boundaries are geologically active areas. Volcanic eruptions, earthquakes, and mountain building occur at and near plate boundaries. Recall that at a plate boundary, the plates can interact in different ways. The plates may spread apart, slide alongside one another, or one plate may sink underneath the other.

Ocean trenches form where oceanic plates sink beneath continental plates or other oceanic plates. Recall that these areas are subduction zones. As the oceanic crust continues to sink, it eventually melts and becomes part of the mantle.

Look at the map in Figure 16.8. Notice the series of subduction zones along the western edge of the Pacific Ocean. The deepest trenches in the world ocean are in this part of the Pacific basin. There are five trenches more than 10 km deep. The deepest is the Marianas (MAIR ee AN uhs) Trench, located north of New Guinea. The Marianas Trench is more than 11 km deep and 70 km wide. The tallest mountain on land, Mt. Everest, would easily fit inside this deep trench.

Figure 16.8
Both land elevations and ocean depths are shown on this computer-generated map of the world. ▼

Because of the large number of volcanoes around the Pacific Ocean basin, the area is called the Ring of Fire. Volcanoes in this area form in subduction zones. One plate sinks, triggering melting in the mantle rock above it. Some of the molten material forms pockets of magma along the subduction zone. The magma can erupt to the surface, forming volcanoes. If the subduction zone is under the water, eruptions there may form a chain of volcanic islands. In Figure 16.8, notice the chains of volcanic islands alongside the trenches in the western Pacific. A chain of volcanic islands that forms along a subduction zone is known as an *island arc*.

On a global scale, the process of subduction balances the plate spreading that occurs at the mid-ocean ridges. In the subduction zones, material from the edge of one plate sinks down and melts. Some of the melted material is recycled into the mantle. At the ridges, material from the mantle wells up to form mountains.

▼ ACTIVITY

Making a Model

Paper Boundaries

Obtain two paper towels.
1. Moisten the paper towels with water.
2. Place the towels side by side on a table. Position each hand on the outer edge of each towel.
3. Slowly push the towel together until your hands meet.

How are the towels like plate boundaries?

SKILLS WORKOUT

SkillBuilder *Making a Graph*

Ocean Trenches

To understand how deep the Marianas Trench is, you need to compare it with other objects. Make a bar graph to compare each object listed in the table. Label the *y*–axis *Size (km).* Label the horizontal *x*–axis *Object.* Record the name of each object under the correct bar on the graph. Use the graph to answer the questions.

Object	Depth or Height (km)
Marianas Trench	11.0
Mt. Everest (China)	9.0
Mt. McKinley (Alaska)	6.0
Grand Canyon (Arizona)	1.6
Sears Tower (Illinois)	0.5
Tallest tree (California)	0.1

1. How tall is the tallest mountain? The tallest building?

2. How tall is the tallest mountain in the United States?

3. Which object is the largest?

4. How many mountains the size of Mt. McKinley could fit into the Marianas Trench?

5. How many buildings the size of the Sears Tower could fit into the Marianas Trench?

6. How many times deeper is the Marianas Trench than the Grand Canyon?

Write a paragraph explaining how the depth of the Marianas Trench compares to the height or depth of other objects, such as the tallest tree, you, or the Grand Canyon.

Science and Society
Great Barrier Reef Park

The Great Barrier Reef of Australia is one of the most unique environments in the world. It extends for a distance of more than 2,000 km. Inside the main reef, islands have been set aside as national parks. The islands teem with tropical birds and other wildlife.

The Great Barrier Reef is almost 30 million years old. During its lifetime, the reef has grown and shrunk as the water level changed. After the last ice age, about 15,000 years ago, the water rose to its present level and the reef began to grow. The new growth took place on the eroded remains of older reefs.

The reef itself is made up of the limestone skeletons of coral organisms. In addition to the corals, the reef is home to many other organisms. There are more than 500 species of algae, or seaweed. Approximately 1,500 species of fish, 4,000 species of mollusks, and thousands of other animals live on or near the reef.

The Great Barrier Reef Marine Park Authority manages the reef. The Park Authority supervises commercial and sport fishing, research, reef preservation, and tourism. The reef is already a major tourist attraction. New hotels and an aquarium are being added to the area. The number of tourists may increase dramatically. The Park Authority's job will be to preserve the unique reef environment and manage the increased activity near the reef.

Figure 16.9 ▲
Living corals coat the surface of the Great Barrier Reef.

Check and Explain

1. Name and describe three features of the continental margin.

2. What are the major features of the ocean floor?

3. **Compare and Contrast** What do ocean trenches have in common with mid-ocean ridges? In what ways are the two regions different?

4. **Predict** Two volcanoes form on opposite sides of the mid-Atlantic Ridge. How will the size and location of these volcanoes change in 10,000 years?

16.3 Life Zones in the Ocean

Objectives

▶ **Describe** vertical and horizontal ocean life zones.

▶ **Identify** ocean resources.

▶ **Find causes** for the differences between various ocean life zones.

▶ **Make a model** of an ocean food web.

Imagine what it would be like to be an organism living in the ocean. How could you survive in that watery environment? Although it may seem difficult or even impossible, every part of the ocean has some kind of organism living there.

All living organisms are adapted to survive in the environments where they live. The place where an organism lives is called its **habitat** (HAB uh tat). Every organism lives where it can obtain necessities such as food, proper temperature, and protection.

Factors Affecting Ocean Life

Many different environmental factors affect ocean organisms. One major factor is the amount of available sunlight. Sunlight only penetrates part of the way down into the water column. Sunlight affects the second factor, water temperature. A third important factor is water pressure. Recall that as you move deeper in the water column, the water pressure increases. Other environmental factors include salinity, distance from shore, water depth, and wave action. The type of material on the ocean bottom is also important. The ocean bottom may be sandy, muddy, or rocky.

Environmental factors make conditions vary from one part of the ocean to another. For example, organisms near the ocean surface experience more sunlight and warmer temperatures than those near the ocean floor. Organisms living on a rocky shore face different conditions than those living on a sandy beach. The differing conditions produce many different habitats for organisms in the ocean.

Figure 16.10 ▲
In what part of the ocean do you think this Portuguese man-o'-war lives?

Major Ocean Life Zones

The ocean can be divided into horizontal and vertical life zones. Study the life zones shown in Figure 16.11. How do conditions in each zone compare?

Littoral Zone The shallow-water area between the low-tide line and the high-tide line is the **littoral** (LIHT uh ruhl) **zone**. Conditions there can be very harsh, with strong sunlight, wave action, and changing water levels. Organisms in the littoral zone include crabs, clams, mussels, and algae.

Neritic Zone The zone extending from the low-tide line to the edge of the continental shelf is called the **neritic** (nuh RIHT ihk) **zone**. The water is usually no more than 200 m deep, so there is plenty of sunlight, except in the very deep areas. Seaweeds and plantlike microorganisms, called phytoplankton, use the sunlight to grow. Water temperature stays fairly constant, and the water pressure is not very high. Under these conditions, fishes, squids, seals, whales, lobsters, shrimps, and other organisms thrive. Most of the seafood that people eat is harvested from the neritic zone.

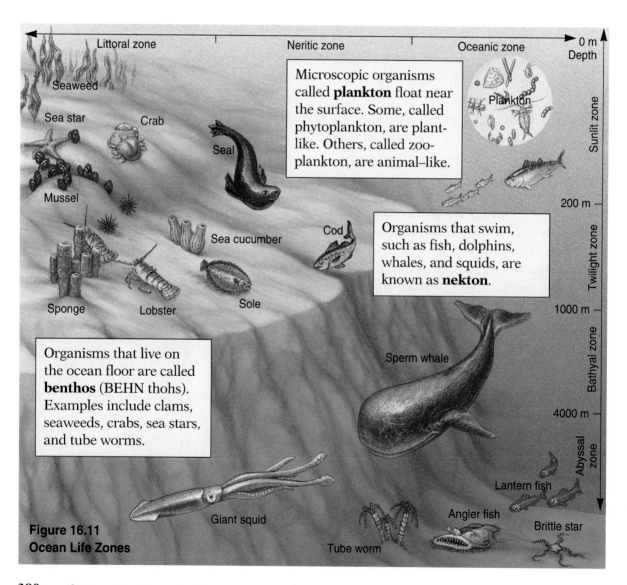

Figure 16.11
Ocean Life Zones

Oceanic Zone The oceanic zone is the deep ocean beyond the continental shelf. Look at the right edge of Figure 16.11. Notice the four vertical zones of the oceanic zone. Sunlight goes through the *sunlit zone* and into the *twilight zone*. The *bathyal zone* and *abyssal zones* are in complete darkness.

In each life zone, many interactions take place. An area in which organisms interact with each other and their environment is called an **ecosystem** (EEK oh SIHS tuhm). Look at Figure 16.12. Energy transfer in an ecosystem takes the form of a *food chain*. A network of food chains forms a food web.

Estuaries and Wetlands In many places where rivers flow into the ocean, estuaries and tidal wetlands form. Many ocean organisms spend part or all of their life cycle in these habitats. Recall that an estuary is a bay or inlet where fresh river water mixes with ocean water. Salinity is low. Clams, oysters, shrimps, fishes, and other organisms living there are adapted to low salinity.

Tidal wetlands form in low-lying areas around estuaries and in other areas protected from the open ocean. Tidal wetland areas are periodically covered by ocean water. There may be mangrove swamps, salt marshes, or mud flats.

Figure 16.12
Oceanic Food Chain ▼

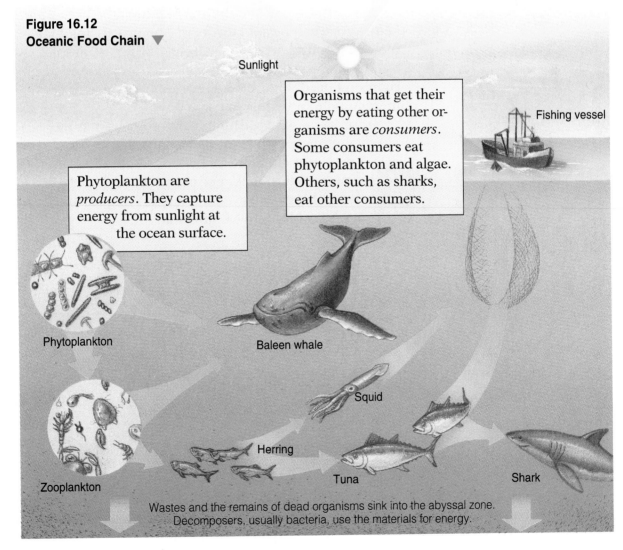

Sunlight

Organisms that get their energy by eating other organisms are *consumers*. Some consumers eat phytoplankton and algae. Others, such as sharks, eat other consumers.

Fishing vessel

Phytoplankton are *producers*. They capture energy from sunlight at the ocean surface.

Phytoplankton

Baleen whale

Squid

Zooplankton

Herring

Tuna

Shark

Wastes and the remains of dead organisms sink into the abyssal zone. Decomposers, usually bacteria, use the materials for energy.

Seafood for Thought

What are your favorite types of seafood? List two or three kinds that you especially like. Share your list with the class. Then make a bar graph that shows everyone's choices. What is the most popular seafood?

Ocean Resources

All over the world, people depend on the ocean as an important source of food. But food is not the only resource that people get from the ocean. Today people obtain minerals, oil, fresh water, and many other resources from the ocean.

Fisheries Each year, the fishing industry takes more than 75 million metric tons of food from the ocean. Most of this food comes from such fish as tuna, cod, herring, and salmon. About 10 percent of the food comes from other animals such as lobsters, clams, oysters, and shrimps. Recall that many of the world's most important fisheries are in areas of upwelling.

Modern fishing vessels equipped with sonar can locate and catch large schools of tuna, cod, or other species. After being caught, the fish must be processed before they can be sold for food. The processing may include canning, freezing, salting, drying, or simple cleaning. Large "factory" vessels can process the catch right on board. Figure 16.13 shows two kinds of commercial fishing vessels in use today.

Improvements in fishing technology lead to the removal of more fish from the oceans. If too many are taken, not enough will be left to reproduce and replenish the stock. For example, in the 1940s, overfishing destroyed a once-thriving sardine fishery near Monterey, California.

Figure 16.13 ▲
Deckhands sort fish on a small fishing boat (above). Fish may be canned on board large ships (right).

Minerals Ocean water contains many dissolved minerals. Recall that many organisms remove minerals from ocean water as part of their life processes. Shellfish use calcium to make their shells. Some organisms remove iodine from ocean water. Seafood is an important source of iodine in the human diet.

Salt is an important mineral resource found in ocean water. The salt can be removed by the desalination process. People evaporate the water and collect the solid salt. Salt evaporation ponds are shown in Figure 16.14. The desalination process can also be used to collect fresh water from the ocean.

Small, rocklike deposits known as manganese nodules cover some parts of the ocean floor. Look at Figure 16.14. The nodules contain manganese, iron, copper, and nickel. At present, it costs more to collect these nodules than the minerals are worth. But in the future, the nodules may be a valuable resource.

Oil Large deposits of oil, or petroleum, and natural gas occur beneath the continental shelves. In North America, the largest offshore oil deposits are in the Gulf of Mexico. Oil-drilling platforms have been built offshore.

People depend greatly on oil to meet their energy needs. But oil is also a major source of ocean pollution. Oil spills and leaks from oil wells kill fishes, birds, and marine mammals, and damage beaches. Today governments in many parts of the world are taking steps to reduce the pollution of ocean water.

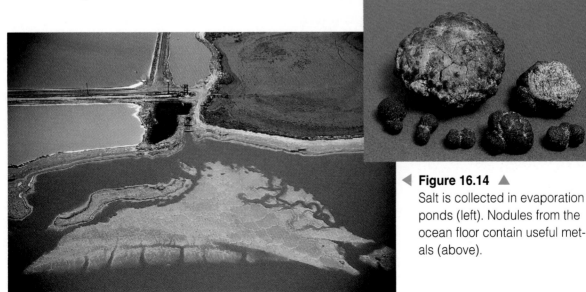

◀ **Figure 16.14** ▲
Salt is collected in evaporation ponds (left). Nodules from the ocean floor contain useful metals (above).

How do some water filters clean the water? If you could take a small sample of the filter material and rub it between your thumb and forefinger, it would feel gritty. If you could examine it with a hand lens, you might see tiny particles of silica (SIL ih kuh). Silica is the compound that makes up most sand.

These filters contain a powdery material called diatomaceous (DY uh tuh MAY shuhs) earth. Diatomaceous earth is made up of the glasslike skeletons of diatoms. Diatoms are single-celled plantlike organisms with a silica skeleton.

Diatoms live in great numbers in ocean water. After the diatoms die, their skeletons sink. They accumulate on the ocean bottom, forming a deposit of diatomaceous earth, also called diatomite.

Large diatomite beds built up near the continental margins and in places where shallow inland seas once existed. Large diatomite deposits are in California. One of these diatomite deposits covers an area of 10 km^2 and is more than 200 m deep.

In addition to its use as an abrasive, diatomite is used to make many other items. More than half of all the diatomite mined every year is used in filters for beverages and other liquids. The porous silica shells trap impurities while allowing liquid to pass through. Silica is also resistant to many chemicals. This property makes diatomite a useful filler in paints, paper, and other chemical products.

Figure 16.15 ▲
Diatomite is made up of the skeletons of diatoms. The diatom shown above is greatly enlarged.

Check and Explain

1. Name and describe the horizontal and vertical life zones of the ocean.

2. What resources do people get from the oceans?

3. **Find Causes** As you go deeper in the ocean, the types and numbers of organisms change. What causes these changes?

4. **Make a Model** Use references to make a drawing or diagram of a possible food web in the neritic zone. Present your model to the class.

Chapter 16 Review

Concept Summary

16.1 Ocean Exploration
▶ Oceanic research vessels, such as *HMS Challenger* and *Glomar Challenger* made voyages to study the world ocean.
▶ Some tools and methods of ocean research include scraping, coring, sonar, submersibles, and satellites.
▶ Mapmakers determined the shape of the ocean floor from depth measurements taken at different locations.

16.2 Ocean-Floor Topography
▶ The continental margin extends into the ocean. It has three regions called the continental shelf, the continental slope, and the continental rise. Submarine canyons cross the continental margin.

▶ Some features of the ocean floor include abyssal plains, ridges, seamounts, guyots, reefs, and atolls.
▶ At subduction zones, ocean trenches and volcanos form.

16.3 Life Zones in the Ocean
▶ Many environmental factors, such as sunlight, temperature, and pressure, affect ocean habitats.
▶ Life zones in the ocean are divided horizontally and vertically.
▶ An ecosystem is an area in which organisms interact with each other and with their environment. Energy in an ecosystem is transferred in a food chain.
▶ People depend on the ocean for such resources as food, minerals, salt, oil, and fresh water.

Chapter Vocabulary

continental shelf (16.2)	seamount (16.2)	benthos (16.3)
continental slope (16.2)	habitat (16.3)	plankton (16.3)
continental rise (16.2)	littoral zone (16.3)	nekton (16.3)
abyssal plains (16.2)	neritic zone (16.3)	ecosystem (16.3)

Check Your Vocabulary

Use the vocabulary words above to complete the following sentences correctly.

1. The boundary between the continental crust and the oceanic crust is the ____ .
2. Large, flat areas of the deep ocean floor are called ____ .
3. Swimming organisms, such as whales and squid, are known as ____ .
4. The sloping surface that extends from the shoreline of a continent is the ____ .
5. The area of shallow water between the high- and the low-tide line is the ____ .
6. In an ____ , organisms interact with each other and with the environment.

7. The area in the ocean between the continental slope and the ocean floor is the ____ .
8. A volcanic mountain that rises from the ocean floor is a ____ .
9. Microscopic organisms that float near the ocean surface are ____ .
10. The area from the low-tide line to the edge of the continental shelf is the ____ .
11. Organisms that live on the ocean floor are called ____ .
12. The place where an organism lives is called its ____ .

Chapter 16 Review

Check Your Knowledge

Answer the following in complete sentences.

1. List three tools or methods that are used to study the ocean.

2. What is a bathymetric map?

3. What is a guyot?

4. Explain how reefs and atolls form.

5. List two environmental factors that affect ocean life.

6. Name an organism that lives in the littoral zone.

7. Why are estuaries important?

8. List two resources that people get from the ocean.

9. What are zooplankton? Phytoplankton?

10. What forms the ridges that are found in the major ocean basins?

11. What are submarine canyons? Where are they found?

12. Name four ocean vertical life zones.

Choose the answer that best completes each sentence.

13. The name of the deepest life zone in the ocean is the (sunlit, twilight, bathyl, abyssal) zone.

14. The areas where oceanic plates collide with and sink under continental or oceanic plates are called (atolls, subduction zones, mid-ocean ridges, guyots).

15. Vertical samples of ocean floor crust are called (scrapes, sonar, cores, submersibles).

16. Dead organisms that settle to the ocean floor form a sediment called (ooze, magma, limestone, coral).

Check Your Understanding

Apply the concepts you have learned to answer each question.

1. **Critical Thinking** How could collecting manganese nodules or building more offshore oil platforms affect life in the ocean?

2. Compare conditions in the neritic zone to conditions in the littoral zone.

3. Describe how each of the following are related: continental rise, continental shelf, continental slope.

4. Describe how the ocean floor was first mapped. Compare this early technique to tools and methods used to map the ocean floor today.

5. **Application** Make a list of some different resources that come from the ocean. Which of these resources do you use? Which did you use today?

6. **Extension** Dolphins emit high-pitched sounds and listen for the echoes. Why do you think they do this?

7. Name the horizontal ocean life zone for each of the following: plankton, seaweed, lantern fish, crab.

8. Name the tools or methods that you would use to conduct the following studies: map the ocean floor, obtain a sample of the ocean floor, observe life on the ocean floor.

9. Discuss the history of ocean floor exploration.

10. **Mystery Photo** The photo on page 364 shows a closeup of a comb jelly. A comb jelly is part of the nekton in the sunlit zone. Infer how the comb jelly may adjust to changes in water pressure, salinity, and water temperature.

Develop Your Skills

Use the skills you have developed in this chapter to complete each activity.

1. Interpret Data The drawing below shows three types of coral reefs.

a   b   c

a. Which drawing shows an atoll?

b. Which drawing do you think shows a fringing reef? Why?

c. Which drawing do think shows a barrier reef? Why?

d. Place the drawings in a sequence that would show the formation of an atoll.

2. Data Bank Use the information on page 622 to answer the following questions.

a. Which ocean is the largest?

b. Which ocean is the smallest?

c. Which ocean has the deepest average depth?

d. What is the average depth of the Arctic Ocean?

3. Compare Compare the height of the seamount that forms the island of Hawaii to the height of mountains on the surface of the earth. Use a map of North America and of the Pacific Ocean floor to compare the size of the Great Plains to the size of the abyssal plain.

4. Make a Model Draw a food chain using the following terms: sunlight, squid, phytoplankton, fish, shark.

Make Connections

1. Link the Concepts Draw a concept map showing how the following concepts from the chapter link together. Add terms to connect, or link, the concepts.

ocean basins   seamounts
trenches   submarine canyons
ridges   continental slope
ocean floor   continental shelf
abyssal plain   continental rise
guyots

2. Science and Literature The book *20,000 Leagues Under the Sea,* by Jules Verne, is a story about the adventures of a crew aboard an incredible underwater ship. Read this story. What parts of the story are scientifically possible? What parts are pure fantasy?

3. Science and Physical Education Scuba diving is a strenuous sport. In the United States, scuba divers must complete certain requirements before they can get a license to dive. Find out the requirements that must be completed before applying for a scuba license. Why do you think these requirements exist?

4. Science and Society For many years dumping wastes into the ocean was common. Currently, stricter controls are being placed on ocean dumping. How do you think ocean dumping affects life in the ocean? Infer how ocean dumping could be completely eliminated.

Science and Literature Connection

From the time [our buffalo, Tank, helped catch the giant white catfish], I had considered the idea of catching golden eels with Tank's help. There were two kinds of golden eels living in our area—one kind had bulging eyes, the other had beady eyes. Both were much sought after because their meat was excellent. These eels, when matured, reached two meters in length and weighed about five kilos.

The eels lived in muddy ditches that brought water to the fruit gardens, the banana groves, and the coconut groves when the level of the water in the river in front of our hamlet was high. They hid in deep holes that they dug in the hard clay soil beneath the mud of the ditch, usually near a tree planted on the border of the ditch. The roots of the tree were a natural barrier against intruders, and when an eel coiled its body around the root of a tree, it was almost impossible to pull it out.

One could lure an eel with almost any kind of bait, but we used earthworms because they were easy to find. We would dangle the worm at the nest's entrance, and sooner or later the eel would come out and bite the bait. We allowed the eel to swallow the bait far down into its stomach, instead of pulling the line right away, for if we pulled the line too soon we would only succeed in tearing off the eel's jaw during the struggle to pull it out of its nest. But with a hook in its stomach,

The Land I Lost

The following excerpt is from the book The Land I Lost *by Huynh Quang Nhuong.*

it could not get away—no matter how hard it tried. Sooner or later, unless the fishing line broke, we would drag the eel out of its nest, dead or alive.

But a live eel got a better price than a dead one in the market, and since Tank had easily succeeded in pulling the white catfish out of the river for our old friend, I came up with the idea of letting him drag eels out of their nests for me. If he could pull an eel out quickly, I had a better chance to get the eel alive instead of dead.

First I had to find an eel's nest, but this was not difficult. One can know roughly the location of a nest by listening carefully to the sound an eel makes when it snaps at a victim. The sound made by its closing jaws is similar to that of a loud click and can be heard clearly from thirty or forty meters away, especially at night.

After finding the general area of a nest, I pinpointed the exact location by examining the mud. The mud around the main entrance of the nest is always more disturbed than the rest. Then I tied the end of a fishing line to Tank's horns and made the bait jump up and down on the mud covering the hole. The eel stuck its head out of the mud first, saw the bait clearly, snapped it up, and returned to its nest below. I loosened the line to let the eel swallow the bait into its stomach, then I signaled Tank to pull. Despite his tremendous strength, Tank needed quite a bit of effort to pull the eel out of its nest. But it was the most exciting sight to see the wagging head of the eel stick out of the mud first, and then its big, trembling, golden body come slowly out of the hole. When the eel was on dry ground, it yanked, turned, and squirmed like an earthworm attacked by a swarm of fire ants.

Using this method, I caught several big eels; none of them could resist Tank more than fifty counts. When Tank started pulling, I counted, "One, two, three . . . "

Some strong eels reached forty-five, but the weaker ones were already on dry ground, wriggling, when I had not yet reached twenty. Often, when an eel had taken the bait, I yelled to my friends to come see Tank's work. When everybody arrived, I signaled Tank to pull. Some of my friends counted with me while the others yelled, clapped their hands, or cheered loudly for Tank.

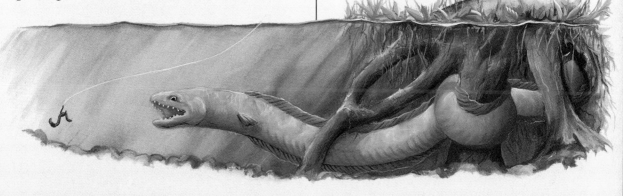

Skills in Science

Reading Skills in Science

1. **Infer** Why do you think a live eel was worth more at the market than a dead eel?

2. **Find Context Clues** The first sentence of the second paragraph infers that the people in the hamlet used water from the river to water their gardens and trees. Why do you think they must use river water? Explain.

Writing Skills in Science

1. **Reason and Conclude** What do you think life was like for the narrator in this remote village in Vietnam? Why was the river so important to the people? Identify four ways the people relied on the river. Explain your choices.

2. **Infer** Describe what might happen in the hamlet if a drought caused the water level in the river to become very low.

Activities

Communicate In a library, research the food chains commonly found in a river ecosystem. Make a diagram of a food web that illustrates the relationships among these food chains.

Collect Data Gather information about eels. Where do most types of eels live? What are some differences between freshwater eels and saltwater eels? Try to identify the species of eel in this story.

Where to Read More

This is a River by Lawrence Pringle. New York: MacMillan Company, 1972. This text explores the workings of a running-water ecosystem and describes how the actions of humans interferes with such a system.

Unit **6**
Earth's Atmosphere

Chapters

Data Bank

Use the information on pages 612 to 625 to answer the following questions about topics explored in this unit.

Interpreting a Map

Where are the high pressure systems located on the weather map? Where are the low pressure systems located?

Making a Graph

Make a bar graph that shows the maximum daily temperatures in January of all the cities listed in the table. Which cities have similar climates in January?

Reading a Table

What are three major air pollutants? What are some causes of these pollutants?

The photograph to the left is of lightning over San Francisco, California. What kind of weather did San Francisco have that evening? During what season do you think the photograph was taken?

Chapter 17 The Atmosphere

What do you see?

66In this picture, I see a large cloud of colors. I think it's called an aurora borealis. I think the best place to see this would be the mountains, forests, or maybe even the North Pole. I mention these places because they do not have very much pollution, and the sky can be seen more clearly.99

Leticia Cruz
Belvedere Junior High
School
Los Angeles, California

To find out more about the photograph, look on page 412.
As you read this chapter, you will learn about the composition and structure of the earth's atmosphere.

17.1 A Blanket of Air

Objectives

▶ **Describe** the ways that heat is transferred in air.

▶ **Explain** what happens to the sun's radiation as it passes to the earth.

▶ **Explain** how the density of air is related to air pressure.

▶ **Infer** how changes in the nitrogen cycle and oxygen–carbon dioxide cycle would affect the composition of air.

▼ **ACTIVITY**

Observing

Potato Physics

Place a potato on a table. Quickly thrust the end of a plastic drinking straw into the potato. What happens? Hold your thumb over the end of another straw and quickly thrust it into the potato. What happens? Why?

SKILLS WARMUP

T ake a deep breath. You may not know it, but you will probably breathe about 26 000 times today alone. Your lungs will take in almost 11 000 L of air during a day. Without air, you could only live for several minutes. Almost all organisms need air to survive. Even though you probably don't think about it, air is very important to life on the earth.

Composition of Air

Look at the composition of air shown in Figure 17.1. Notice that about 78 percent of air is nitrogen. Although most organisms can't use nitrogen directly, nitrogen reacts with other elements to form many compounds that are necessary for life. Oxygen is the next most plentiful gas. Plants and animals use oxygen directly from air to release their food energy during respiration. Plants also produce oxygen during the process of photosynthesis.

Although the amount of carbon dioxide present in air is very small, carbon dioxide is also essential for plant life. During photosynthesis, plants use carbon dioxide, sunlight, water, and materials from air to produce glucose. Glucose is a simple sugar used by plants for energy and growth.

Water vapor, argon, and trace gases, such as neon and helium, make up the rest of the gases contained in air. Water vapor is especially important because it absorbs heat energy from the sun and forms clouds and rain. The amount of water vapor contained in air can vary from 0 to 4 percent.

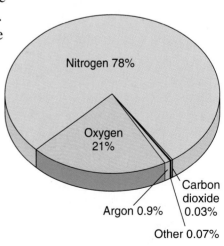

Figure 17.1 ▲

Air is composed of many different chemicals.

The Oxygen–Carbon Dioxide Cycle

The **oxygen–carbon dioxide cycle** is a closed cycle in which the total amount of carbon and oxygen is kept constant. Look at Figure 17.2. Carbon moves between the atmosphere, inside the earth as fossil fuels, the soil, and the oceans. Carbon dioxide is essential for plants, algae, and some bacteria. Oxygen is released into the air by plants and algae, which absorb carbon dioxide.

**Figure 17.2
Cycles in Nature** ▼

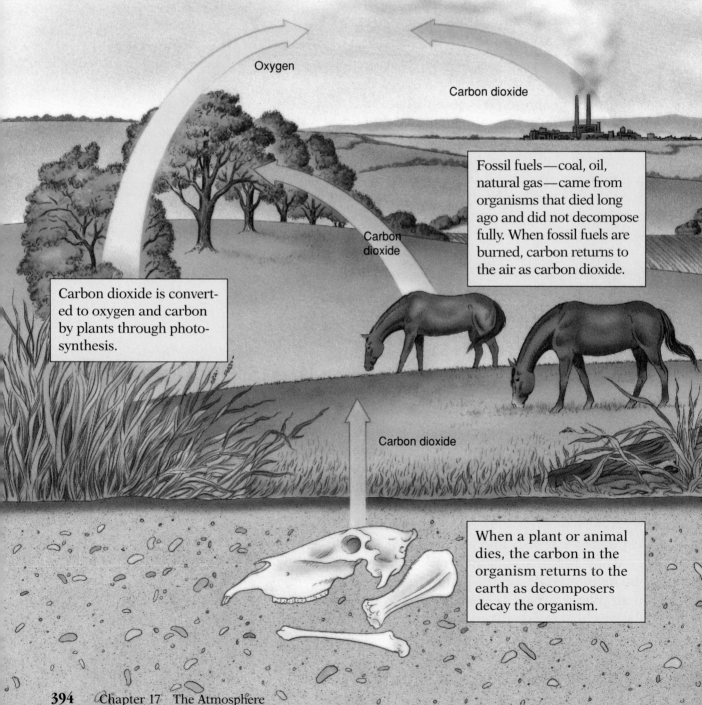

Oxygen

Carbon dioxide

Fossil fuels—coal, oil, natural gas—came from organisms that died long ago and did not decompose fully. When fossil fuels are burned, carbon returns to the air as carbon dioxide.

Carbon dioxide

Carbon dioxide is converted to oxygen and carbon by plants through photosynthesis.

Carbon dioxide

When a plant or animal dies, the carbon in the organism returns to the earth as decomposers decay the organism.

The Nitrogen Cycle

The **nitrogen cycle** is a closed cycle in which the total amount of nitrogen on the earth is kept constant. Nitrogen helps support life by building proteins and other body chemicals. Nitrogen in the air can't be used directly by most organisms. To be useful, nitrogen is removed from the air and combined with other elements to form nitrogen compounds. This process is called *nitrogen fixation*.

After nitrogen is converted to compounds by lightning, it is washed out of the air by rain and deposited into the soil.

Nitrogen compounds

Nitrogen compounds

When coal or gasoline is burned, nitrogen is released in the form of nitric oxides.

Soil bacteria produce nitrogen compounds from decaying organisms and animal wastes. Denitrifying bacteria break down these compounds to form nitrogen gas.

During nitrogen fixation, bacteria that live on root nodules remove pure nitrogen from the air and release it into the soil.

Nitrogen

Nitrogen compounds

Decomposers

Air Density

Recall that density is a measurement of how much matter is packed into a certain volume. Since air is composed of gas molecules, air has density. Gravity affects the density of air. Gravity decreases as you move away from the surface of the earth. Therefore, farther from the surface, the air density decreases as well.

Where would you find more dense air? At a mountaintop, or at sea level? Since a mountaintop is farther from the surface of the earth, it would usually have less dense air than sea level. However, air density is affected by temperature as well as by gravity. In some instances, the temperature offsets the effect of gravity.

Cold air is more dense than warm air. When air is heated, the molecules gain energy and move apart from one another. The air becomes less dense. When air is cooled, the molecules lose energy and move closer together. The density of the air increases.

SkillBuilder Observing

Temperature and the Density of Air

Temperature causes the molecules in air to move closer together or farther apart. The distance between the molecules determines the density of the air. Trapped air inside a balloon can show how temperature affects the density of air.

Blow up a round balloon and tie the end. Using a measuring tape, carefully measure the circumference of the balloon as shown. Record the circumference. Place the balloon in hot water for 10 minutes. Remove the balloon, measure the circumference, and record. Now place the balloon in ice water for 10 minutes. Remove the balloon, measure the circumference, and record.

1. Which circumference was the largest? The smallest?

2. What happened to the air molecules to make the circumference increase? To make it decrease?

3. In which balloon were the air molecules the most dense? The least dense ? How could you tell?

Write a short report explaining how temperature affects the density of air.

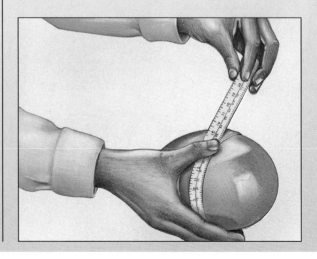

Air Pressure

Recall that gas is matter. Since all matter has mass, gas also has mass. Gases in the air push against each other and push down on the surface of the earth. When you blow up a balloon or inflate a bicycle tire, you probably notice an increase in pressure as the air pushes against the sides. The force that air exerts in an area is called **air pressure**. The standard used for measuring air pressure is the air pressure at sea level, or atmosphere.

Every day your whole body is being pushed on by many kilograms of gas above you. You don't even notice this tremendous pressure. The air in your body pushes out with a pressure equal to the pressure of the surrounding air.

The density of air and air pressure are directly related. Figure 17.3 shows what happens to air pressure at different heights.

Air becomes less dense as it is heated. In the atmosphere, heated air rises, exerting less pressure on the earth's surface. If air is cooled, the density increases. In the atmosphere, cooler air sinks down, exerting more pressure on the earth's surface.

The amount of water in air can change the air pressure. Water vapor molecules are smaller and lighter than many gas molecules. When water molecules take the place of larger, heavier molecules, the air pressure decreases.

Figure 17.3

How are the density of air and the air pressure related to the height above the surface of the earth? ▶

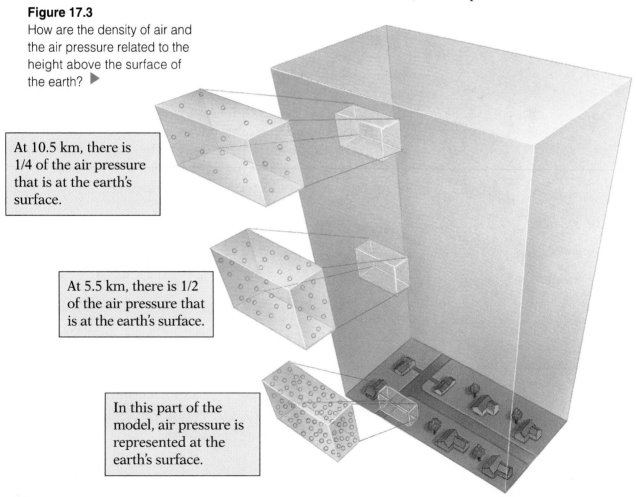

At 10.5 km, there is 1/4 of the air pressure that is at the earth's surface.

At 5.5 km, there is 1/2 of the air pressure that is at the earth's surface.

In this part of the model, air pressure is represented at the earth's surface.

Pre-heated Oven

Obtain two cake pans.

1. Cover the inside of one pan with black construction paper and the other with white construction paper.

2. Put both pans in bright sunlight.

3. Measure the temperature after one hour. Which temperature was higher? Why?

SKILLS WORKOUT

Energy in the Air

The movement of gas molecules in air does more than change the air pressure. The energy of the gas molecules also determines the temperature of the air. When air molecules gain energy, they move faster and the air temperature rises. When air molecules lose energy, they slow down and the air temperature drops. The energy of the molecules in air can change through three processes: conduction, convection, and radiation.

Heat Transfer   Several processes work to reduce the difference between temperatures at the earth's surface and temperatures higher in the atmosphere. One of the processes that moves heat away from the surface is **conduction.** Conduction is the direct transfer of heat from particle to particle. Air touching the surface of the earth is heated by conduction. The movement of heat from the surface to the air transfers heat away from the earth.

Another process that moves heat away from the earth's surface is convection. Convection is the transfer of heat in gas or liquid. Recall that heat in the earth's mantle moves by convection. Convection in the air is similar to convection in the mantle. Heated air rises and cools to form a convection cell. Convection cells move heated air to warm a room, as shown in Figure 17.4. Convection cells are also present in the atmospheric air that surrounds the earth. The uneven heating of the earth between the equator and the poles sets up large convection currents in the earth's atmosphere.

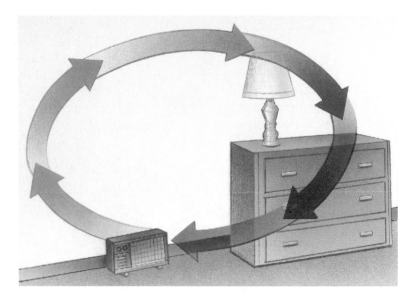

Figure 17.4 ▶
Convection cells form in air to warm a room. Where else might you find convection cells in your home?

Radiation Energy that can travel through empty space is called radiant energy or radiation. The earth receives energy from the sun by radiation. This radiant energy is in the form of visible light, ultraviolet radiation, and infrared radiation.

Look at Figure 17.5. What happens to the sun's radiation as it passes to the earth? Over 50 percent of the solar radiation is absorbed or reflected by the atmosphere before reaching the surface of the earth. Almost all of the harmful ultraviolet radiation is absorbed. Clouds reflect 25 percent of the visible light that travels toward the earth back into space.

Of the radiation that reaches the surface of the earth, some is absorbed and some is reflected. The solar energy reaching the surface that is reflected varies from as high as 95 percent for fresh white snow to only 5 percent for a black asphalt road. About 70 percent of the solar energy that reaches the earth's surface is absorbed. This high percentage of absorption causes very high temperatures in areas near the equator where the sun shines for many hours.

Life Science

L I N K

Research the labels of sunscreen and sunblock products. Draw a graph showing the relationship between sun protection factor (SPF) numbers and the length of time you are protected from the sun.

Which SPF number would you require for an average summer day? Which would you need for a day in winter?

A C T I V I T Y

Figure 17.5
What might happen to radiant energy passing to the earth? ▼

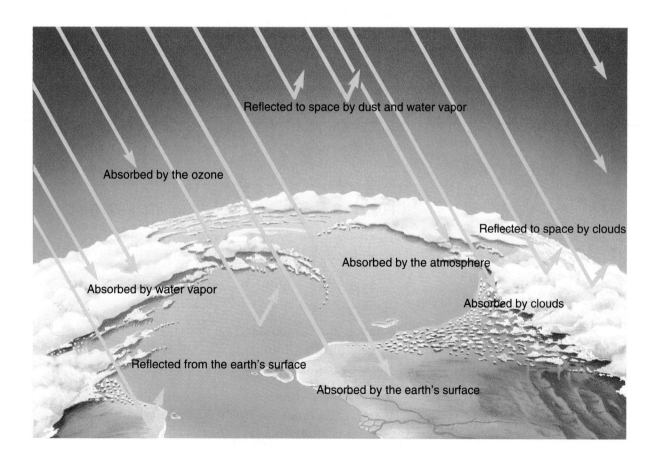

Reflected to space by dust and water vapor

Absorbed by the ozone

Reflected to space by clouds

Absorbed by the atmosphere

Absorbed by water vapor

Absorbed by clouds

Reflected from the earth's surface

Absorbed by the earth's surface

On a sunny, warm day, you may spend the day outdoors at the park, the beach, or in your yard. The sunshine heats your clothes and skin. After staying in the sun for a while, you may notice that your skin becomes darker, or tanned, where it was exposed to the sun. Or maybe your skin becomes red, or burned, from sun exposure.

All skin types are affected by radiation from the sun. Some ultraviolet, or UV, radiation is necessary for the formation of vitamin D. Vitamin D helps your bones develop. However, too much UV radiation is dangerous for anyone. Overexposure to UV radiation can cause sunburn, skin cancer, snow blindness, eye cataracts, and skin aging. UV exposure can lower your body's defenses against diseases that enter through the skin.

To avoid exposing your skin to large amounts of UV radiation, there are several things you can do. Between the hours of 10:00 a.m. and 3:00 p.m., the sun's radiation is strongest, even on cloudy days. During the middle of the day, stay out of the sun, wear protective clothing, or put on a sunscreen.

When buying a sunscreen, look for the sun protection factor, or SPF, on the bottle. This number tells you how well the sunscreen blocks UV radiation. Use a sunscreen with an SPF of 15 or greater. A 15 SPF means that it takes 15 hours to receive the same amount of UV radiation that you would get in 1 hour without the sunscreen.

▼ ACTIVITY

Communicating

Melting in the Sun

Take a survey of ten people to see how they protect themselves from the sun. Questions should be the same as those asked by your classmates. Combine the results of your survey with the rest of the class. What percentage of the people surveyed use sunscreen? Avoid the sun? Wear protective clothing?

SKILLS WORKOUT

Check and Explain

1. Describe the movement of air molecules during the transfer of heat by conduction and convection.

2. Describe what happens to visible light as it travels from the sun to the surface of the earth.

3. **Reason and Conclude** The density of air decreases as you climb a mountain. What happens to the air pressure as you climb higher? Why?

4. **Infer** How would air composition change if there were no plants? No nitrogen-fixing bacteria? No denitrifying bacteria?

Activity 17   *How can you observe the pressure of air?*

Skills   Observe; Infer

Task 1   Prelab Prep

1. Collect the following items: water, food coloring, empty 0.5 L soda bottle, clear plastic drinking straw, marking pen, metric ruler, dropper, clay, funnel.

2. Add several drops of food coloring to the water.

3. Using the marking pen, draw marks on the drinking straw that are 1 cm apart.

Task 2   Data Record

1. On a separate sheet of paper, copy Table 17.1.

2. Record all your observations in the data table.

Table 17.1   Water Levels

	Day 1	Day 2	Day 3
Weather			
Height of water			

Task 3   Procedure

1. Pour colored water into the empty soda bottle until the bottle is about 1/3 full.

2. Hold the straw in the water until it is just below the surface of the water. Seal the straw securely in place with the clay.

3. Use the dropper to drop water into the straw until it is about halfway up the straw. Your air-pressure bottle should look like the one shown in Figure 17.7.

4. Place your air-pressure bottle in a place where the temperature will remain fairly constant.

5. Measure the height of the water in the straw, starting from the marks at the bottom. Record your measurement in the data table.

6. Measure the height of the water in the drinking straw for several days. Record your measurements in the data table.

Task 4   Analysis

1. What happened to the water in the drinking straw?

2. Did the weather affect the height of the water in the drinking straw? How do you know? Explain your observations.

3. If the air pressure outside of the bottle decreases, how will the water level inside the straw change? Why?

Task 5   Conclusion

Write a short paragraph explaining how air pressure can be observed.

Everyday Application

Instruments that measure air pressure are called barometers. Barometers help predict the weather. When the air pressure drops, it often means rainy weather. High air pressure readings mean fair weather. Over the period of several days, use a barometer. Record your observations. Can the barometer predict the weather? Explain your conclusions.

Figure 17.7 ▲

In the Sky

Make a list of everything you have ever seen in the sky. Combine your list with those of your classmates. What objects were most commonly listed?

17.2 Structure of the Atmosphere

Objectives

▶ **Name** the layers of the atmosphere, from the closest to the farthest layer from the surface of the earth.

▶ **Explain** how the atmosphere affects life on the earth.

▶ **Compare** and **contrast** the magnetosphere and the ionosphere.

▶ **Predict** the changes that would occur on the earth if the atmospheric layers did not exist.

When you look up at the sky on a sunny day, you may see many fluffy clouds or an airplane moving across the blue sky. It seems like you can see forever. On a clear night, you view the light from the many stars that penetrate the sky. Now you *can* almost see forever.

Atmospheric Layers

Air that surrounds a planet is called the **atmosphere**. The atmosphere of the earth extends from the surface to about 1,000 km. The earth's atmosphere is composed of several layers of air with different characteristics.

The atmosphere is important to the earth. The layers affect climate, photosynthesis, and even the height of thunderstorms. Meteorites traveling toward the earth burn up from the friction of passing through the atmospheric layers. The atmosphere provides a method for redistributing heat. The layer of atmosphere closest to the surface supports life.

Nineteenth-century meteorologists investigated the first several thousand meters of the atmosphere by using hot-air balloons. Early in this century, scientists made measurements using aircraft and hydrogen-filled balloons. In the last 50 years, sophisticated ways to measure the atmosphere included balloons that radio data back to the earth, rockets, high-flying aircraft, and satellites. This technology helped uncover an atmosphere with distinct layers.

Figure 17.8 ▲
This weather balloon released in Australia will travel high into the atmosphere.

Exosphere The *exosphere* is the outermost layer of the atmosphere. The exosphere extends to the outer edges of space, several thousand kilometers from the earth. Light gases escape from the exosphere to outer space.

Thermosphere Below the exosphere is the *thermosphere*. Thermosphere temperatures increase rapidly with height, reaching 1,200°C. The air in the thermosphere is not very dense. The thermosphere is greatly affected by the sun's radiation.

Mesosphere The *mesosphere* extends from the stratosphere to the thermosphere. Mesosphere temperatures decrease with height.

Stratosphere The *stratosphere* contains the gas **ozone** (OH zohn). Ozone protects the earth from excessive ultraviolet radiation. Little air exchange occurs between the troposphere and the stratosphere. Gases released during violent volcanic eruptions remain in the stratosphere for years before settling into the troposphere. Very high clouds and large thunderstorms penetrate this layer, but weather generally does not occur here.

Troposphere The **troposphere** (TROH puh sfihr) is the layer of air closest to the surface of the earth. It contains over half of all the air in the atmosphere. The height varies from about 20 km at the equator to 8 km at the poles. Temperature in the troposphere decreases with height, which is why mountaintops are much colder than valleys. Almost all weather occurs in the troposphere. Most pollution also remains in the troposphere.

Figure 17.9
Atmospheric Layers ▶

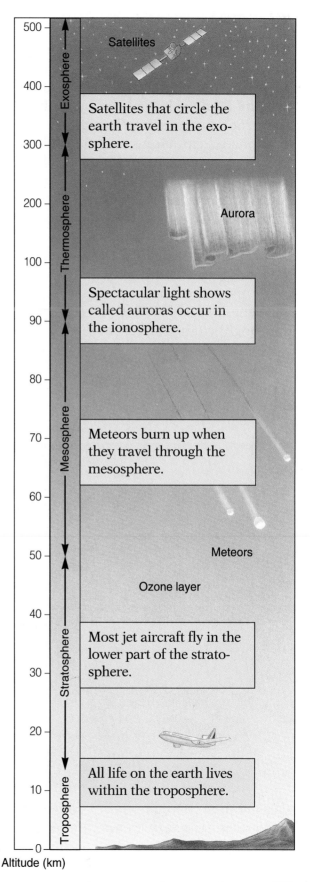

Altitude (km)

Ionosphere

The *ionosphere* (eye AHN oh sfihr) is a layer of air within the upper mesosphere and the thermosphere. It is not a distinct atmospheric layer by itself. Solar radiation passing through the ionosphere strips atoms and molecules of their electrons. The atoms and molecules become charged particles called ions. These ions reflect radio waves like a mirror reflects light. The ionosphere allows radio signals to travel by bouncing between the surface of the earth and the ionosphere.

At night, the ionosphere increases in height. Look at Figure 17.10. How does this height change affect radio signals? Notice that radio waves can travel farther at night than during the day. As a result, the signals can travel farther on the earth's surface.

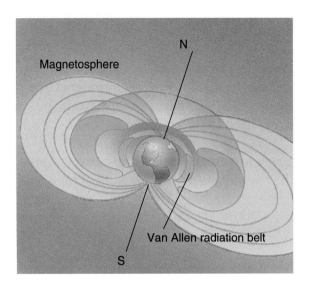

Figure 17.11 ▲
Locate the magnetosphere. Where is the Van Allen radiation belt?

Magnetosphere

The outermost region of the atmosphere is called the *magnetosphere*. The magnetosphere is created by the earth's magnetic field and the sun. The sun continuously emits electrically-charged particles called ions. The fast-moving stream of ions, or solar wind, becomes trapped in the earth's magnetic field. The trapped ions make up the magnetosphere.

Solar wind travels at speeds between 250 and 800 km per second. The solar wind causes the magnetosphere to compress on the side toward the sun and stretch out on the side away from the sun.

The magnetosphere contains a doughnut-shaped belt of charged particles that surrounds the earth. This band is shown in Figure 17.11. It is called the Van Allen radiation belt.

Solar wind also changes the ionosphere. When the solar wind enters the ionosphere, an aurora may occur. An aurora looks like sheets of blue-green light in the sky. The lights occur because the solar wind causes ions to emit energy in the form of light.

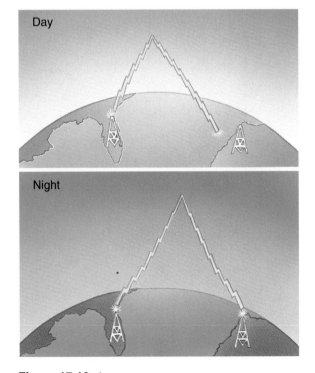

Figure 17.10 ▲
The ionosphere reflects radio waves, allowing for worldwide communication.

Science and Technology
Loud and Clear?

When you tune in a radio station to listen to your favorite music, you probably don't think about how far the signal has traveled to reach your radio. On AM radio, the signals have probably traveled from the broadcast antenna to the ionosphere and then bounced back to your radio antenna. AM and other shortwave radio signals bounce back and forth between the ionosphere and the earth. They may travel thousands of kilometers. FM radio signals are not reflected by the ionosphere, so they don't travel long distances.

Although the ionosphere allows shortwave signals to travel great distances, it can create noise in the signals. During solar flares the sun releases great amounts of charged particles. The charged particles enter the ionosphere where they produce magnetic storms. These magnetic storms may cause radio fade-outs that can last for several hours, or they may cause noise in the radio signal known as static.

Radio signals are important for communication between astronauts and scientists on the earth. However, when a spacecraft begins to enter the atmosphere, there is a disruption of signals that lasts for 10 to 15 minutes. This area is called the blackout zone. The blackout zone occurs when air friction on the craft reaches such high temperatures that the air molecules ionize. The spacecraft is surrounded by ions that prohibit any radio communication between the earth and the spacecraft.

Figure 17.12 ▲
Besides music and a clear voice, disc jockeys also need the atmosphere.

Check and Explain

1. Starting at the surface of the earth, list each layer of the atmosphere by increasing altitude.

2. Why is the atmosphere important to life on the earth? Explain your reasoning.

3. **Compare and Contrast** How are the ionosphere and the magnetosphere the same? How do they differ?

4. **Predict** For each layer of the atmosphere, predict how the earth would change if the layer suddenly disappeared.

17.3 The Changing Atmosphere

Objectives

▶ **Describe** the early atmosphere of the earth.

▶ **Explain** how the atmosphere has changed through time.

▶ **Compare** the early atmosphere and the current atmosphere.

▶ **Predict** the effects of pollution on the atmosphere.

The atmosphere around you constantly changes. As you read this book, oxygen converts to carbon dioxide each time you breathe. Oxygen is also changed into various different chemicals by cars, trucks, and factories burning fuel. If the atmosphere constantly changes, what was it like a thousand years ago? A million years ago?

Origin of the Atmosphere

The atmosphere 4.6 billion years ago was probably made of hydrogen and helium gases. Most of the ancient atmosphere escaped the gravity of the earth.

Volcanic activity probably formed the early atmosphere. Volcanoes spew large amounts of carbon dioxide, water vapor, and nitrogen. Because carbon dioxide warms the atmosphere by absorbing outgoing heat, it was probably very warm then, compared to today.

Figure 17.13
The early atmosphere was probably created by volcanic eruptions. ▼

As the earth's inner core cooled, volcanic activity subsided. Water vapor condensed to form clouds, rivers, and lakes. As primitive marine plants photosynthesized, they produced oxygen. The conversion of carbon dioxide to oxygen decreased the carbon dioxide level, allowing the earth to cool.

The Current Atmosphere

Today the atmosphere is very different from that of the ancient earth. Look at Table 17.2. How does the early atmosphere compare to the atmosphere now? Currently, nitrogen and oxygen make up 99 percent of the atmosphere. But there are small amounts of many other gases. Despite their low concentrations, several of these gases are very important.

▶ Plants need carbon dioxide to carry on life processes. Carbon dioxide also absorbs outgoing radiation from the earth's surface, making the air temperature comfortable. Without carbon dioxide, the temperature on the earth would be about −10°C.

▶ Ozone is an essential gas for organisms. It protects organisms from harmful ultraviolet radiation by absorbing the radiation before it reaches the earth's surface.

▶ Water vapor is also necessary for life. All plants and animals rely on water to sustain life. Water vapor also forms clouds. Clouds help control air temperature.

▼ **ACTIVITY**

Predicting

Atmospheric Conditions

The atmosphere is always changing. Predict how the atmosphere will be different 100 years from now. What might cause the changes?

SKILLS WORKOUT

Table 17.2 Gases in the Early and Present Atmosphere

Type of Gas	Early Atmosphere	Present Atmosphere
Carbon dioxide	92.2%	0.03%
Nitrogen	5.1	78.1
Sulfur dioxide	2.3	Trace
Hydrogen sulfide	0.2	Trace
Ammonia	0.1	Trace
Methane	0.1	Trace
Oxygen	0.0	20.9
Argon	0.0	0.9

Smog What do you notice about the atmosphere over the city shown in Figure 17.14? The haze over the city is the result of human activity. It is a type of air pollution, called **smog**, that forms from the burning of fossil fuels, such as gasoline and coal. Depending on the climate and the type of air pollution in an area, two different types of smog can form: gray air and brown air.

Gray air occurs in colder, moist climates. Here the pollution combines with moisture in the air to form a grayish haze.

Brown air is typical in warm, dry, sunny climates. The pollution in the air reacts with sunlight to form brown smog. Brown air is referred to as photochemical smog, since it requires photo, or light, to form.

Both smog and photochemical smog have negative effects on human health. They cause burning eyes, headaches, and respiratory problems.

Greenhouse Effect Several gases in the atmosphere help control Earth's temperature. Carbon dioxide and some other gases absorb infrared radiation that reflects from the earth's surface. This traps some of the sunlight's energy that would be lost back to space. So, carbon dioxide and other gases help to keep the atmosphere warm. When heat is trapped by gases in the atmosphere, the result is called the **greenhouse effect.** Without the greenhouse effect, Earth's surface would freeze.

However, the amount of carbon dioxide in the atmosphere has been increasing for the last two centuries. With more carbon dioxide in the air, the atmosphere absorbs more heat and the temperature rises. This rise in the temperature of the atmosphere is called *global warming.* People are concerned that global warming may change the climate of the world. Some scientists predict that the air temperature might rise 2° to 4°C in the next 50 years. Many scientists are trying to analyze how these changes could affect life on Earth.

Figure 17.14 ▲
Industry and automobiles create smog over Frankfurt, Germany. From the color, determine the type of smog you see over Frankfurt.

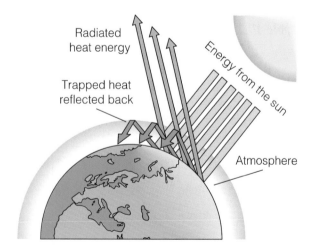

Radiated heat energy

Energy from the sun

Trapped heat reflected back

Atmosphere

Figure 17.15 ▲
The greenhouse effect traps energy from the sun to warm the atmosphere. An increase in this effect could lead to worldwide global warming.

Ozone Depletion Recall that ozone in the stratosphere protects organisms from harmful ultraviolet radiation released by the sun. Ultraviolet radiation is necessary for forming vitamin D in humans. But overexposure can cause sunburn, cataracts, and skin cancer. Too much UV radiation also harms plants and animals.

Chemicals called chlorofluorocarbons, or CFCs, are released from air conditioners, styrofoam, aerosol cans, and other sources. These chemicals rise into the stratosphere and destroy the ozone. The depletion of the ozone layer by chlorofluorocarbons is shown in Figure 17.16. This ozone thinning is allowing more harmful UV radiation to reach the surface of the earth.

Efforts are under way throughout the world to control and reduce the release of CFCs so that the ozone shield can be preserved. CFCs are being replaced by ozone-safe chemicals. In many countries, there is a ban on the use of CFCs.

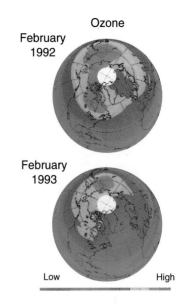

Ozone
February 1992

February 1993

Low   High

Figure 17.16 ▲
Map of Ozone Depletion

Historical Notebook

Searching for the Hole in the Ozone

"This is one of the most challenging things that we've ever come across in atmospheric chemistry. Whatever the source is, we need to understand it because this is a change in the ozone that's of absolutely unprecedented proportions."

These are the words of Susan Solomon, the leader of the scientific team that determined what was destroying the ozone layer. This expedition, called NOZE for National Ozone Experiment, took place in Antarctica during 1986. Earlier measurements had shown a drastic decrease in the ozone layer over Antarctica. The NOZE experiments revealed that CFCs are responsible for reducing the amount of ozone in the stratosphere.

Ever since NOZE, scientists have continued monitoring the ozone levels over the Antarctic. They found that the ozone level varies from year to year. However, drastic ozone loss is still occurring and is spreading to lower latitudes.

1. Why did NOZE study the atmosphere over Antarctica? What did NOZE find out?

2. **Research** The photograph shows current atmospheric studies being conducted in Antarctica. Using scientific magazines, find out the ozone levels over the Antarctic for the last several years. How are organisms in Antarctica being affected?

Science and Society
Solutions to Air Pollution

How do you think air pollution will affect the people who live on the earth in the future? You may imagine people wearing gas masks to filter out the dirty air, or full body coverings to protect their skin from UV radiation. Hopefully, this disturbing image will not become reality. Today many steps are being taken to control the release of air pollutants.

In the United States, the Clean Air Act set standards for the amount of pollutants that can be released into the air. It requires that automobiles and factories reduce the amount of pollution released into the air. As a result of the standards set by the Clean Air Act, the amount of air pollutants released into the air in the United States from 1970 to 1980 decreased by 25 percent.

Ozone depletion is a global pollution problem, not a local one. To help save the ozone layer, 112 nations united. The countries that attended the International Convention for the Protection of the Ozone Layer agreed to stop using chlorofluorocarbons by the year 2000. They also set controls on other ozone-depleting substances.

Solving the problems of air pollution is not just the responsibility of governments. The citizens of all countries must take part as well. You can help reduce air pollution by recycling your cans and bottles instead of throwing them away. You can conserve energy at home and at school by turning off unused appliances and lights. You can also help save the ozone by using ozone-safe products. For example, use paper products instead of styrofoam.

▼ ACTIVITY

Collecting Data

Chlorofluorocarbons

1. Write a list of CFC sources from page 409.

2. Conduct a CFC search for one day.

3. Record every potential CFC source you observe on a piece of paper.

How many sources did you get after one day? Does your data show any trends of areas with higher concentrations of CFC sources?

SKILLS WORKOUT

Check and Explain

1. Describe the ancient atmosphere of the earth.

2. What was the source of nitrogen, carbon dioxide, and oxygen in the early atmosphere?

3. **Compare** Make a bar graph comparing the gases in the early atmosphere to the gases in the current atmosphere.

4. **Predict** How may life be affected by the greenhouse effect? By increasing ozone depletion?

Chapter 17 Review

Concept Summary

17.1 A Blanket of Air
▶ The most common gases in air are nitrogen and oxygen.
▶ The oxygen–carbon dioxide cycle keeps carbon levels constant. Nitrogen fixation and deposition in the nitrogen cycle keep nitrogen levels constant.
▶ Air density is the number of molecules in a certain volume of air.
▶ The force that air exerts on an area is air pressure.
▶ Conduction and convection transfer heat energy through air.

17.2 Structure of the Atmosphere
▶ The atmospheric layers are the troposphere, stratosphere, mesosphere, thermosphere, and exosphere.
▶ All life is contained in the troposphere.
▶ The magnetosphere collects charged particles in its magnetic field.

17.3 The Changing Atmosphere
▶ Hydrogen and helium made up the ancient atmosphere.
▶ Volcanic gases and oxygen released by primitive marine plants formed the early atmosphere.
▶ Important components of the atmosphere today are carbon dioxide, ozone, water vapor, and aerosols.
▶ Smog, certain pollutants, and possibly global warming are affecting atmospheric layers today.

Chapter Vocabulary

oxygen–carbon dioxide cycle (17.1)
nitrogen cycle (17.1)
air pressure (17.1)
conduction (17.1)
atmosphere (17.2)
ozone (17.2)
troposphere (17.2)
smog (17.3)
greenhouse effect (17.3)

Check Your Vocabulary

Use the vocabulary words above to complete the following sentences correctly.

1. The name for types of air pollution called brown air and gray air is _____ .

2. Air that surrounds a planet is called the _____ .

3. The recurring events in which the amount of carbon is kept constant by moving between locations is called the _____ .

4. The gas in the stratosphere that absorbs ultraviolet radiation is _____ .

5. Fixation and deposition are part of the _____ .

6. The layer of the atmosphere that supports all life is the _____ .

7. The force that air exerts in an area is called _____ .

8. The transfer of heat directly from one particle to another is called _____ .

9. The warming of the atmosphere by gases that trap heat is called _____ .

Identify the word or term in each group that does not belong, and explain why.

10. troposphere, stratosphere, ozone
11. denitrifying bacteria, nitrogen fixation, photosynthesis
12. convection, air pressure, conduction

Write Your Vocabulary

Write sentences using the vocabulary words above. Show that you know what each word means.

Chapter 17 Review

Check Your Knowledge

Answer the following in complete sentences.

1. What was the likely source of water vapor in the early atmosphere?

2. Which atmospheric layer is farthest from the surface of the earth?

3. What causes smog?

4. In which layer of the atmosphere is the magnetosphere contained?

5. How much of the energy released by the sun reaches the surface of the earth? What happens to the rest?

6. Explain how convection affects air.

7. What chemicals made up the ancient atmosphere of the earth?

8. How could ozone depletion affect living things on the earth?

9. Name the most common gas in the atmosphere.

10. Which is more dense, cold air or warm air? Why?

11. Give an example of an aerosol.

12. What is an aurora?

Determine whether each statement is true or false. Write *true* if it is true. If it is false, change the underlined word to make the statement true.

13. The Van Allen radiation belt is located in the <u>magnetosphere</u>.

14. The formation of carbon dioxide is part of the <u>nitrogen cycle</u>.

15. Air is <u>more</u> dense at the top of a mountain than at sea level.

16. The greenhouse effect is related to <u>global warming</u>.

Check Your Understanding

Apply the concepts you have learned to answer each question.

1. Explain why knowing the daily air pressure could be important to you.

2. Compare the transfer of heat in air by conduction and convection.

3. **Infer** Contained in the name for every atmospheric layer is the word "sphere." Explain why this word relates to each layer of the atmosphere.

4. How would the air in a classroom full of students be different from the air outside the school?

5. Discuss how the sun has a direct effect on the magnetosphere.

6. Explain how global warming relates to the greenhouse effect.

7. **Critical Thinking** Discuss how the world would be different if the present atmosphere were still like the ancient atmosphere.

8. **Extension** Conduction occurs in solids and liquids, as well as in the air. Give an example of conduction in a solid.

9. **Application** Air pollution and ozone depletion are still problems that affect the earth. What could you do to help reduce the amount of pollutants released into the atmosphere?

10. **Mystery Photo** The photograph on page 392 shows the aurora borealis, or the northern lights. This aurora occurs over the North Pole. The aurora australis, or southern lights, occurs over the South Pole. Why do you think this phenomenon occurs only at the poles?

Develop Your Skills

Use the skills you have developed in this chapter to complete each activity.

1. **Interpret Data** The graph below shows the varying temperatures for some layers of the atmosphere.

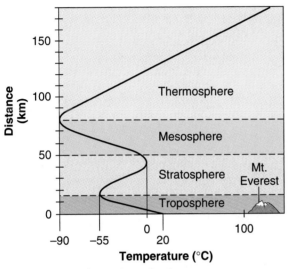

a. Which layer has the hottest temperature? The coldest?

b. What is the temperature range for the troposphere?

c. Which layer has the greatest temperature difference?

2. **Data Bank** Use the information on page 623 to answer the following questions.

a. What are some short-term effects of carbon monoxide on people's health? What are some long-term effects?

b. What are some causes of nitrogen oxide pollutants? How are people affected by them?

3. **If...Then** Carbon is stored in wood and plants. Trees remove carbon dioxide from the air. If trees are cut down, how might this affect the oxygen–carbon dioxide cycle? How might the burning of trees affect the cycle?

Make Connections

1. **Link the Concepts** Below is a concept map showing how some of the main concepts in this chapter link together. Only part of the map is filled in. Copy the map. Complete the map using words and ideas from the chapter.

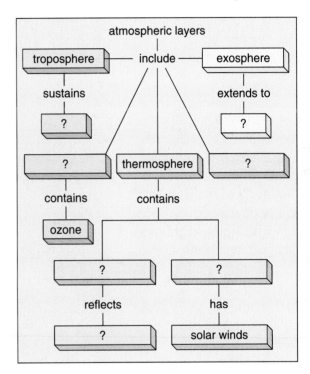

2. **Science and Writing** Imagine you are a wave of ultraviolet radiation. Write a story about your travels as you and your friends journey from the sun to the surface of the earth. Remember to explain what happens to your friends.

3. **Science and You** Find reports of air quality in your newspaper. Graph the reports for one week. Also record the weather for each day. When was the air quality worse, on weekdays or weekends? Why? Did the weather affect the air quality?

Chapter 18

Water in the Atmosphere

What do you see?

❝I see berries on a frosty morning with cold dew on them. The berries are just budding. The white stuff is dew that was frozen in little icicles on the berries. Dew forms during the night while it is cold, and in the morning you can see it while the sun rises, before it melts. For this to occur during the night, the temperature has to go below freezing for a period of time.❞

David Rich
Burney Harris Lyons
Middle School
Athens, Georgia

To find out more about the photograph, look on page 436. As you read this chapter, you will learn about the effects of water in the earth's atmosphere.

18.1 Humidity

Objectives

▶ **Explain** relative humidity.

▶ **Describe** how humidity affects life.

▶ **Explain** the formation of dew and frost.

▶ **Interpret data** contained in a relative humidity table.

Water exists in three phases: as a solid in ice, as a liquid in water, and as a gas in water vapor. The amount of water in each phase in nature is affected by many things, such as the depth of the oceans, the amount of clouds, the moisture content of soil, and the amount of water in aquifers. Understanding how water moves between phases is important to understanding the earth and its climate.

Water Vapor in the Air

   Recall that water moves in a continuous cycle on the earth. Part of this water cycle is shown in Figure 18.1. Water vapor enters air when liquid water evaporates from such places as bodies of water, grass, or water boiling on your stove. Water vapor is invisible. But the effects of invisible water vapor molecules are seen everywhere. When air contains a lot of water vapor, water particles in the air become large. Water condenses to form droplets when air is cooled. For example, the steam from a hot shower contains tiny water droplets.

   The amount of water vapor in the air is called **humidity**. The humidity depends on the temperature of the air. Much more water can evaporate into warm air than cold air. When the air temperature is 40°C, air can hold 10 times more water vapor than at 5°C.

   When air can hold no more water, it is saturated. Saturated air contains all the water vapor it can hold at a certain temperature. The relative humidity that is given in weather reports is the percentage of water vapor saturation of the air. A relative humidity of 50 percent means that the air contains 50 percent, or half, of the water vapor it can hold at that temperature.

Figure 18.1 ▲
During one part of the water cycle, moisture is added to the air.

Figure 18.2 ▶

The amount of water vapor that
a cubic meter of air can hold
changes with the temperature.

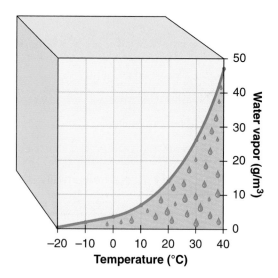

Figure 18.3 ▲

The lowering of temperature to
the dew point forms both dew
(top) and frost (bottom).

Relative humidity changes with the temperature
and pressure. The warmer the temperature, the more
water vapor the air can contain, and the higher the relative humidity. Look at Figure 18.2. How many grams of
water can a meter of air contain at 40°C before it
becomes saturated? How many grams of water can air
contain at –20°C before saturation?

Imagine that in the early morning on an autumn
day, the air temperature is 10°C and the relative humidity is 100 percent. The air is saturated. It contains all
the water vapor possible. If the air cools even further,
the water vapor will change into a liquid, or condense.
The temperature at which air is saturated is called
the **dew point**. At temperatures lower than the dew
point, tiny water droplets, or dew, condense on cold
surfaces.

You may have seen or felt dew, or condensation, on
grass or cars on cool early mornings. Figure 18.3 shows
condensation on the outside of a pitcher. The condensation formed when ice was added to cool the beverage.
The air temperature around the glass is lowered below
the dew point. At this temperature, condensation forms
on the glass.

When the dew-point temperature is below freezing,
tiny ice crystals, or frost, can form. If you live in an area
where the temperature gets below freezing, you may
have seen frost form on windows, as the bottom photograph in Figure 18.3 shows. Frost isn't frozen dew. Frost
forms as water vapor condenses on surfaces as a solid.
As you can see in Figure 18.3, the ice crystals in frost
can form beautiful patterns.

Effects of Humidity on Life

Some regions of the earth are very dry. As a result, there is little humidity. Other regions, such as the tropical rain forests in South America, are very humid. Plants and animals that live in these areas have adapted to the humidity differently.

Very low humidity is potentially harmful to plants because moisture in the plant evaporates. Certain plants, such as this Saguaro cactus, have waxy coverings on their spines and stems. These coverings help prevent water loss from plant tissues. ▼

▲ In the humid air of tropical rain forests, orchids grow high off the ground on the limbs and trunks of trees. These flowering plants don't collect moisture from the soil. Instead, they collect moisture directly from their surroundings by dangling their roots in the humid, tropical air.

Many animals develop ▶ the ability to conserve water in their bodies. The gerbil, a small desert mouse, conserves moisture effectively by staying in its burrow during the day. The underground burrow protects the animal from the sun, and the humidity is several times higher here than it is above the ground.

▲ Like the orchid, bromeliads (broh MEE lee ads) are air plants. Notice the leaves of the bromeliad shown in the top photograph. They grow so closely together that they form a bowl in the center that fills with water. A miniature frog, shown above, carries its young tadpole on its back to the small plant pond. The tadpole lives in this pool of water until it develops into a mature frog.

Measuring Humidity

You may have noticed that humidity sometimes makes your hair frizzy or wavy. Hair length changes in proportion to relative humidity. Hair lengthens as humidity increases, and shrinks as humidity decreases.

A device called a *hygrometer* measures humidity using human hair. A hair hygrometer works by stretching many strands of human hair between two points. As the humidity rises, the hairs swell and lengthen. If the humidity decreases, the hair shrinks back to a shorter length. The change in length of the hair strands is recorded mechanically by a pen on a chart. Over the range of 0 percent to 100 percent humidity, 10 cm of hair will shorten by about 0.25 cm.

A more precise instrument to measure humidity is the sling **psychrometer** (sy KRAHM ih tur) shown in Figure 18.4. The psychrometer uses two thermometers.

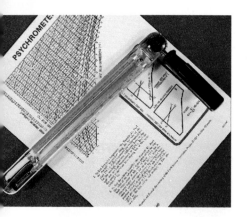

Figure 18.4 ▲
How does a psychrometer measure the relative humidity of air?

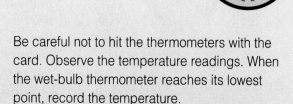

SkillBuilder Measuring

Determining Relative Humidity

To make a psychrometer for finding the relative humidity of your classroom, obtain two thermometers, cotton gauze, a notecard, and some water.

To make a wet-bulb thermometer, wet the cotton gauze and wrap it around the bulb of one thermometer. For the dry-bulb thermometer, leave the bulb dry and uncovered. Use a book to suspend the two thermometers in the air, as shown. Fan the two thermometers with a notecard.

Be careful not to hit the thermometers with the card. Observe the temperature readings. When the wet-bulb thermometer reaches its lowest point, record the temperature.

1. What was the lowest temperature of the wet-bulb thermometer?

2. What was the temperature of the dry-bulb thermometer?

3. Subtract the wet-bulb temperature from the dry-bulb temperature. What is the difference? Record this number.

4. Use Table 18.1 to find the relative humidity. What is it?

5. Do you think the relative humidity would be the same if you took a reading outdoors? Why? Explain your reasoning.

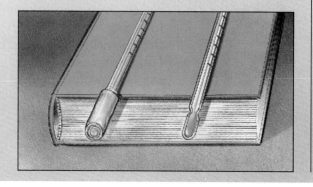

Table 18.1   Relative Humidity in Air

	Difference between dry-bulb and wet-bulb temperature (C°)															
	1	2	3	4	5	6	7	8	9	10	11	12	13	14	15	16
0	81	64	46	29	13											
2	84	68	52	37	22	7										
4	85	71	57	43	29	16										
6	86	73	60	48	35	24	11									
8	87	75	63	51	40	29	19	8								
10	88	77	66	55	44	34	24	15	6							
12	89	78	68	58	48	39	29	21	12							
14	90	79	70	60	51	42	34	26	18	10						
16	90	81	71	63	54	46	38	30	23	15	8					
18	91	82	73	65	57	49	41	34	27	20	14	7				
20	91	83	74	66	59	51	44	37	31	24	18	12	6			
22	92	83	76	68	61	54	47	40	34	28	22	17	11	6		
24	92	84	77	69	62	56	49	43	37	31	26	20	15	10	5	
26	92	85	78	71	64	58	51	46	40	34	29	24	19	14	10	5

Dry-bulb temperature (C°) is the left-hand axis label.

One thermometer has a cloth attached over the bulb, while the other is uncovered. The cloth on the covered thermometer bulb is dipped in water. The two thermometers are then twirled. As the air passes over both thermometers, the thermometer with the wet cloth cools to the wet-bulb temperature. The dry thermometer measures the air temperature, or the dry-bulb temperature.

Relative humidity is determined by using a relative humidity table, like the one in Table 18.1. To determine relative humidity, you calculate the difference between the dry-bulb temperature and wet-bulb temperature. Using this difference and the dry-bulb temperature, the relative humidity can be located in the table. For example, if the difference between the two temperatures is 4°C and the dry-bulb temperature is 14°C, the relative humidity is 60 percent. What is the relative humidity if the temperature difference is 6°C and the dry-bulb temperature is 20°C?

Cooled Down

Obtain two cotton balls, rubbing alcohol, and water.

1. Soak one cotton ball in rubbing alcohol and another cotton ball in water.

2. Wipe each cotton ball along the inside of your arm.

3. Blow on the wet area of your arm.

Which area gets cooler faster? Why?

Science and You
It's Not the Heat; It's the Humidity

When water evaporates, heat is absorbed. Maybe you've noticed that when you get out of a swimming pool or a lake on a hot summer day, you sometimes feel chilled. If the humidity is low, the air is dry. Dry air allows evaporation. When the water evaporates from your skin, it removes heat and makes you feel cool. But what happens if it is hot outside and the humidity is high? Very little evaporation occurs. You don't feel chilled even though you are wet.

Your body regulates your skin temperature in a similar manner. When the weather is warm, your body produces perspiration, or sweat. Perspiration covers your body with a thin layer of water. As the perspiration evaporates, your skin is cooled.

In a hot, tropical climate, you would sweat more than in a hot, desert climate. If the weather is dry and hot, your body can keep its temperature steady by producing a small amount of perspiration. Since the air is dry, the perspiration quickly evaporates into the air, and your skin is cooled.

When the humidity is high and it is hot, your body still produces perspiration. However, very little evaporation occurs because the air is already nearly saturated with water vapor. Your skin does not cool significantly. So your body reacts by producing more perspiration.

Check and Explain

1. What is relative humidity? How do you determine the relative humidity in an area?

2. Describe an organism that has adapted to living in an area with low humidity and one that has adapted to an area with high humidity. Explain how each organism has adapted differently.

3. **Find Causes** What conditions cause dew to form? What conditions cause frost to form?

4. **Interpret Data** Using Table 18.1 determine the relative humidity if a wet bulb thermometer outside reads 14°C and the temperature inside your house is 21°C.

Activity 18 *How can you determine the dew point?*

Skills Measure; Observe; Compare

Task 1 Prelab Prep

Collect the following items: small or medium-sized metal can, warm water, crushed ice, spoon, thermometer.

Task 2 Data Record

1. On a separate sheet of paper, copy Table 18.2.
2. Record your observations from each location in the table.

Table 18.2 Dew Points

Location	Dew Point
Classroom	
Outdoors	

Task 3 Procedure

1. Fill the can about half full with warm water.
2. Place the thermometer in the water. Position the thermometer so it doesn't touch the sides or bottom of the can, as shown in Figure 18.5.
3. Add a spoonful of ice. Watch the sides of the can for condensation as you stir the water.
   CAUTION! Stir with the spoon, not the thermometer.
4. Continue adding spoonfuls of ice, and continue stirring until condensation, or dew, forms on the outside of the can. Record this temperature as the dew point in the data table.
5. Remove the contents from the can.
6. Repeat steps 1 to 4 outdoors.

Task 4 Analysis

1. What is the dew point of the air in your classroom?
2. What is the dew point outdoors?
3. Compare the dew point of the air in your classroom to the dew point of the air outdoors.
4. List the variables in this activity.

5. List one reason why your dew point may not be the same as the dew point for other groups in your classroom.

Task 5 Conclusion

Write a short paragraph defining dew point, based on the activity you just completed.

Everyday Application

Find out the predicted low temperatures for your area over the next seven days. Will the temperature reach the dew point on each day? What will happen if it does? Make a line graph that plots the dew points for each day.

Extension

Set up a station outdoors on the school grounds to measure relative humidity and dew point. For measuring relative humidity, use wet and dry bulb thermometers. For dew point testing, set out a metal container. Check the container each morning to see if the dew point was reached the night before. Then test to find the relative humidity.

Figure 18.5 ▼

18.2 Clouds

Objectives

▶ **Explain** two ways that clouds can form.

▶ **Describe** the three types of clouds.

▶ **Predict** the type of fog that forms in different conditions.

▶ **Classify** clouds by altitude.

You probably know a lot about clouds without even realizing it. If you notice that it's a gray, cloudy morning, you may bring an umbrella to school. If you see a large, dark cloud, you may cancel the picnic or ball game you planned. You may have admired the puffy clouds floating across a blue sky on a warm summer day. How did these puffy clouds form? Why are there so many different types of clouds?

Cloud Formation

Clouds can form at any altitude in the troposphere. One way that clouds form, by surface heating and convection, is shown in Figure 18.6. It begins when the sun heats an area of the ground rapidly. The ground heats the air above it, reducing the air density. The warm air rises in a column. As the air column rises, it cools until it reaches its dew point. At dew point, the water vapor condenses and forms a cloud.

Figure 18.6

Convection clouds form when moist air rises high enough to cool and condense. ▼

Warm, moist air

As air rises in the air column, it cools and becomes saturated. At the saturation point, the relative humidity of the air is 100 percent. When the relative humidity reaches 100 percent, water in the atmosphere condenses around small particles called *condensation nuclei*. Condensation nuclei are tiny particles that float in the atmosphere. These small particles enter the atmosphere from windblown dust, volcanoes, factory smoke, forest fires, and even salt from ocean spray. Because so many condensation nuclei are present in the lower atmosphere, the relative humidity is rarely more than 100 percent before condensation begins.

Water vapor molecules stick to the condensation nuclei. As more water molecules attach to the nuclei, a water droplet forms. These droplets are so small that they float in the air. Even a slight air current will keep the droplets suspended. However, when a large number of droplets collect, they form clouds.

You may have noticed that mountains are often covered by clouds, like those in Figure 18.7. Mountain clouds typically are formed by a second cloud-forming process. The process depends on air being affected by the elevation of the land. Clouds can form when warm, moist air is lifted and cools as it passes over higher areas of land. In many regions of the world, the wind carries warm, moist air toward mountains. As the air rises up the sides of the mountains, it cools. When the air reaches its dew point, the water vapor in the air condenses to form clouds.

Figure 18.7
Some mountains are usually covered by clouds due to the continuous upwelling of warm, moist air.

Warm, moist air

Types of Clouds

Clouds are classified by their appearance. Three main types of clouds are **stratus**, **cumulus** (KYOO myuh luhs), and **cirrus** (SYR ruhs).

Stratus

◄ "Stratus" comes from the Latin word meaning "to spread out." Stratus clouds are flat and dull gray in appearance and cover the entire sky in widespread sheets. Stratus clouds often produce rain or drizzle. In this photograph, you can see stratus clouds above the New York City skyline.

Cumulus ▶

"Cumulus" comes from the Latin word for "heap." These clouds are the type often drawn in pictures. Cumulus clouds are puffy in appearance. On a warm summer day, you may see cumulus clouds become larger or evaporate entirely throughout the day.

Cirrus

◄ "Cirrus" is the Latin word for curl. Cirrus clouds appear thin and wispy and are located at high altitudes. Cirrus clouds are made of ice crystals. Long streaks of cirrus clouds high in the sky often indicate a change in weather.

Clouds are also classified by their height or altitude. The prefixes *cirro-*, *alto-*, and *strato-* help identify a cloud's altitude. *Cirro-* refers to high, *alto-* to middle, and *strato-* to low-altitude clouds.

High-Altitude Clouds ▲

These are clouds above 6 km that have very low temperatures. The high clouds seen at these altitudes are thin, curling cirrus clouds. High, puffy clouds are called cirrocumulus. Extensive flat, high clouds, called cirrostratus, occur when cirrus clouds spread into thin sheets. Cirrostratus clouds sometimes create halos around the sun or the moon.

Low-Altitude Clouds ▶

These clouds have bottoms below 2 km, and they form at warm temperatures. All low-altitude clouds forecast rain or snow. Stratus is a thick, gray cloud that extends over a wide area. Stratocumulus are small, puffy summer clouds. Some clouds start near the ground and extend to very high altitudes. The term *nimbus* is used to identify some rain-bearing clouds. A tall, dark rain cloud is called a **cumulonimbus**. It can produce lightning and strong winds. Cumulonimbus clouds can begin 1,000 m above the ground and extend up to 18,000 m.

Middle-Altitude Clouds

◀ These are clouds with bottoms in the altitude range of 2 to 6 km. The temperatures generally vary between –25°C and 0°C. Altostratus, or broad, gray clouds, occur frequently. A thin veil of altostratus clouds means light rain will soon arrive. Altocumulus clouds are white to gray and may have dark, shadowed sides that can mean rain or snow. However, these types of clouds most often occur in the summer.

In a Fog

Fog is part of the settings of many stories and movies. Make a list of examples. Determine why fog was chosen for each movie or story scene on your list. Based on how fog is used in stories and movies, how do you think most people feel about fog? Explain.

Fog

Look at Figure 18.8. What would you call this type of cloud? The photograph shows a landscape covered in **fog**. Actually, fog is a cloud that forms on the earth's surface. But fog develops differently from the way in which clouds form. Fog can form in several ways. The type of fog that forms depends on the location, temperature, and the movement of the air.

Radiation fog forms when warm air cools. At night when the earth's surface cools, the dew point is reached quickly. This process produces millions of tiny water droplets that stay in the air and form fog. You may have seen radiation fog early in the morning before the temperature rises enough to evaporate the water droplets.

Fog also forms where water and land meet. Land cools more quickly than water. The warm air over the water is more moist than the cool air over the land. If the warm, moist air from the water moves across the cooler land, fog forms. This type of fog, called advection fog, is common in the San Francisco Bay Area. You can see advection fog in Figure 18.8.

The reverse process may form a different type of fog. Steam fog occurs when cold air moves over warm water. In this case, the relative humidity of the cold air is very low. As water evaporates from the surface, the cold air becomes saturated. As more water vapor meets the cooler air, it condenses and forms fog. You may have seen this type of fog form over rivers and lakes.

Figure 18.8 ▶
The Golden Gate Bridge in San Francisco is often blanketed in advection fog.

Science and Technology
Flight Navigation and Clouds

If you have ever been flying in an airplane on a cloudy day, you may have wondered how the pilot knew where to find the airport runway. Most of the time, pilots can see the countryside they fly over. This type of weather condition is called VFR (visual flight rules). However, when low-altitude clouds form or the weather at the airport makes seeing the runway difficult, the weather conditions are called IFR (instrument flight rules).

Pilots used to navigate during IFR by using sensors that pointed to commercial radio station towers. Now they use transmitters located all over the country called VHF OmniRange (VOR) radio beacons. This system of beacons tells pilots the direction and distance of a station on the ground. In the cockpit, the pilot has a display of this information. At the destination airport, another special radio beacon leads the airplane to the beginning of the runway. If the runway is not visible at that point, it is too dangerous to land. The pilot will then land at another airport.

On-board computers can also use VORs to plot a route anywhere in the United States. This system is used, for example, if a cumulonimbus cloud is spotted that could cause heavy rain, turbulence, or hail.

In the next few years, most aircraft will use satellites for navigation. These satellites are so accurate that a pilot can tell if the airplane is on the left side, the right side, or the middle of the runway.

Figure 18.9 ▲
On-board computers display cloud patterns in the flight path of an airplane.

Check and Explain

1. What are the two ways that clouds can form?

2. Describe a stratus cloud, a cumulus cloud, and a nimbus cloud.

3. **Predict** What type of fog would form on a cool night after rain? Over a lake during the fall? During a cold winter night?

4. **Classify** Make a table to classify each cloud according to whether it is a high-, middle-, or low-altitude cloud: cirrostratus, cumulonimbus, altocumulus, stratocumulus, cirrocumulus, altostratus.

Waiting for the Rain

The total amount of rain and the rate at which rain falls are both important. On a rainy day, conduct the following activity:

1. Use a container to measure the rainfall every 30 minutes.

2. Use a line graph to plot both the rain increase for each 30 minute period and the total rainfall.

3. Compare your graph to a classmate's. How do they compare?

18.3 Precipitation

Objectives

▶ **Explain** how raindrops and snowflakes form.

▶ **Describe** how hail increases in size.

▶ **Classify** instruments used for measuring precipitation.

▶ **Compare** and **contrast** sleet and freezing rain.

I f you live in an area that receives a lot of snow in the winter, you probably know that the amount of precipitation that falls influences the outcome. What would be the effect on your community if 20 cm of snow fell in 3 hours? Many activities would probably be cancelled.

Precipitation affects people and the earth in many ways. It can be hazardous, such as freezing rain on busy highways. Precipitation is also very beneficial, such as rain for watering crops.

Causes of Precipitation

Any form of moisture that falls from a cloud to the ground is called **precipitation**. The most common forms of precipitation are rain and snow. Table 18.3 shows that the cloud type and the temperature of the air below the cloud determine the form of precipitation.

Table 18.3 Precipitation, Cloud Type, and Temperature

Cloud Type	Temperature	Precipitation
Altocumulus	Above freezing	Rain
Altostratus	Above freezing	Rain
Stratocumulus	Above freezing	Rain
Cumulonimbus	Above freezing	Rain
Nimbostratus	Above freezing	Rain
Altostratus	Below freezing	Snow
Stratocumulus	Below freezing	Snow
Nimbostratus	Below freezing	Snow

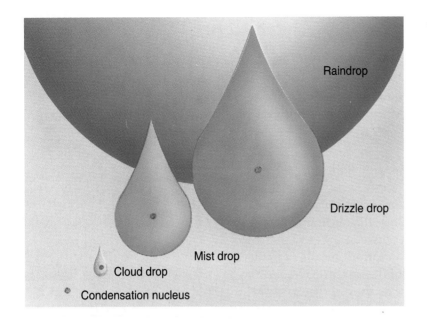

Figure 18.10
Compare the relative sizes of
different water drops that form
in a cloud.

Raindrop

Drizzle drop

Mist drop

Cloud drop

Condensation nucleus

Recall that when water vapor in a cloud condenses onto condensation nuclei, a cloud droplet forms. Air currents move the tiny droplet. The droplet lifts higher in the atmosphere where the temperature is below freezing. As the droplet travels, it collects water and grows larger.

A few droplets, with their nuclei of ice, freeze. Water surrounding the supercooled droplets evaporates and deposits on the frozen droplets as ice crystals. Eventually, the ice crystals become a small snowflake. As the snowflake falls through the cloud, it may collide with other ice crystals and become larger. If the air below the cloud is cold, the snowflake will fall to the ground as snow.

If ice crystals fall into air that is warmer than freezing, they melt and become raindrops. As raindrops fall, they sometimes collide with other raindrops. The raindrops combine to form bigger drops. The bigger raindrops fall faster and collide with more drops. Compare the relative sizes of raindrops in Figure 18.10.

In warm climates, clouds are rarely high enough to reach temperatures below freezing. So a different process forms precipitation. After water vapor condenses on condensation nuclei, the liquid droplets begin to fall very slowly. If one droplet collides with another, they either bounce off each other, or they merge. Droplets that merge get bigger and begin to fall faster. Eventually, the drops reach the ground as large raindrops.

▼ ACTIVITY

Making a Model

Rainmaker

Spray a fine mist of water from a spray bottle onto a window or mirror. Observe the droplets. Spray more water onto the surface. What happens to the drops? How is this similar to the formation of raindrops?

SKILLS WORKOUT

Rain ▲

In the United States, rain can fall at a rate from almost 0 cm/h to 4 cm/h. Extremely high rainfall rates approaching 10 cm/h can occur in thunderstorms or other severe weather. Such heavy rain, however, rarely lasts for long. As shown above in Calcutta, India, heavy rains can cause severe flooding.

Snow ▶

When the temperature above the ground is near freezing, precipitation may fall as snow. About 10 cm of snow equals 1 cm of rain. Snow is common in areas at middle to high latitudes and at high altitudes.

Snowflakes usually fall more slowly than large rain-drops. As snow hits the ground, it accumulates loosely with a great deal of air trapped between flakes. Snowflakes vary greatly in diameter, from several milli-meters to several centimeters.

Forms of Precipitation

When precipitation hits the ground, it can be in many different forms. The most common forms, rain and snow, both begin as ice crystals or water droplets in clouds. Other forms of precipitation are freezing rain, sleet, and hail.

Freezing Rain ▶

Besides snow, freezing rain occurs during winter. When the air temperature is between 0°C and 3°C, precipitation falls as rain. But the raindrops freeze into ice as they hit the ground or other objects. The rain forms a thick layer of sheet ice, or glaze ice. Glaze ice occurs during ice storms.

Freezing rain produces beautiful effects, but it is also dangerous. Roads be-come slippery, and branches or power lines can fall from the weight of the ice.

Sleet

Partially melted grains of ice are called *sleet*. Sleet forms when raindrops or snowflakes fall through air layers of different tempera-tures. A mixture of rain and snow hit the ground. If the temperature near the sur-face is below –3°C, sleet forms as frozen raindrops.
▼

Hail Balls of ice that form in thunderstorms with upward-rising air are known as hail. Hailstones begin as small snow pellets or frozen raindrops. As they fall, they collide with supercooled water droplets in the cloud. The droplets freeze onto the hailstone, making it grow. As strong winds toss the ice crystals up and down in the cloud, more droplets of water freeze around the ice crystals. This process makes the hailstone layered, a little like the layers of an onion. Look at the hailstones in Figure 18.11. What evidence shows the effects of the up and down motion of the ice crystals within the cloud?

Most hailstones are the size of a pea, but they can get as large as a golf ball. The largest hailstone ever collected was at Coffeyville, Kansas, in 1970. It weighed 758 g and had a diameter of 14 cm. Hailstorms can be very damaging to crops and buildings. A hailstorm in Denver, Colorado, in July 1990, caused damage to cars and houses that totaled nearly $600 million.

Figure 18.11 ▲
Hail can fall during any season. What do you think was the season during this hailstorm?

Consider This

Is Cloud Seeding Helpful or Harmful?

In regions that receive little rainfall, a method called cloud seeding is sometimes used to increase the rainfall. In one method, cloud-seeding planes inject crystals of silver iodide into certain clouds. The crystals create huge numbers of ice crystals, increasing the amount of cloud formation and the chance of precipitation.

Cloud seeding can increase rainfall in dry areas by as much as 30 percent. The process is very helpful to farm communities when water reservoirs are low. It can also disperse fog at airports, allowing planes to land. Cloud seeding can also reduce the size of large hailstones that damage crops and structures.

Cloud seeding is also controversial. It often shifts the location of rainfall from one place to another. This means that one region's water increase causes water loss in another region. Some people think that cloud seeding has not proven to be effective. Other people think that the use of silver iodide may have a harmful effect on the environment.

Think About It What are the benefits of cloud seeding? What are some of the problems? How might cloud seeding create conflicts between communities in a region?

Debate It Imagine that you are on a state water resources board and your state is in a severe drought. A group of citizens comes to your board asking for money to fund a cloud-seeding program. Write which way you would vote on the issue. Include reasons for your decision. With several classmates, have a mock board meeting in which two sides with opposing views debate the issue of cloud seeding.

Measuring Rainfall

Rainfall is usually measured with a simple rain gauge like the one shown in Figure 18.12. The rain gauge contains a funnel that collects and directs rain into a small cylinder. The area of the funnel is ten times larger than the area of the cylinder. So 1 cm of rain will appear as 10 cm of water in the cylinder.

Other methods provide rainfall rates, as well as total rainfall. For example, the tipping-bucket gauge has a small bucket at each end of a lever. When one bucket fills to about 1 mm, it tips over and the other bucket begins to fill. The tipping-bucket rain gauge counts the number of tips over a certain time, which tells the rate of rainfall.

Sophisticated radar devices can also measure rainfall. They measure rainfall over a large area without even making a measurement on the ground.

Figure 18.12 ▲
Estimate the amount of rain collected by this rain gauge.

Measuring Snowfall

Snowfall is difficult to measure because wind blows the snow around unevenly. At most weather stations, such as the one in Figure 18.13, snow accumulates in the funnel of a rain gauge. It is then melted to determine the amount of water. Snowfall rates can also be measured with the tipping-bucket gauge. The gauge is modified so the funnel that collects the snow also heats and melts it. The melted snow drains into the gauge, which then measures it like rain.

Snowpack, or the amount of snow that will melt and flow into rivers, is measured by a different device. This device extracts a vertical column of snow. The snow in the column is weighed to indicate the water content.

Figure 18.13 ▲
Snowfall is measured in this automated radio-reporting snow gauge in California.

Precipitation and People

People must get water from some source. Since people need water for many purposes, its availability often determines where they live. Look at the maps in Figure 18.14. The map on the left shows average amounts of rainfall in South America. The map on the right shows population density. How has the availability of water affected where people have settled in South America?

Around the world, populations have grown large where water is abundant. Populations are usually fairly small where water is scarce. However, technology has changed population distribution in some countries. In the United States, construction of massive water projects, such as dams and irrigation canals, has enabled people to settle in areas where water resources are very limited.

Southern California is a location where the population has grown dramatically despite limited water resources. Southern California is a desert region. Water is brought into the region from the Colorado River and the Sierra Nevada Mountains. The imported water has enabled farmers to grow a variety of crops. The availability of water made industry growth possible. It has also provided many recreational opportunities on reservoirs.

▼ **ACTIVITY**

Collecting Data

City of Rain

Select five cities that represent a variety of climates. Using data from a newspaper, keep a record of the daily precipitation in each city for five days. Which city received the most precipitation? The least?

SKILLS WORKOUT

Figure 18.14

How is the amount of rainfall in an area related to the area's population? ▼

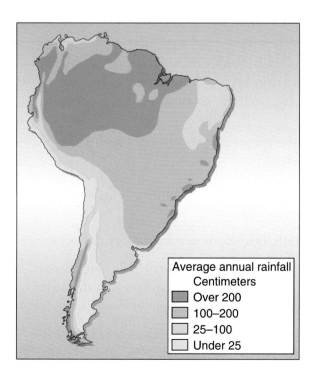

Average annual rainfall
Centimeters
- Over 200
- 100–200
- 25–100
- Under 25

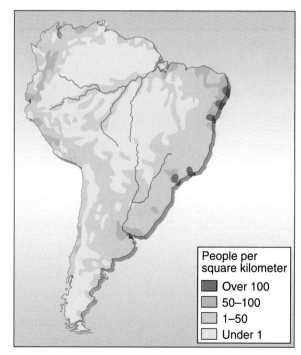

People per
square kilometer
- Over 100
- 50–100
- 1–50
- Under 1

Science and Society *Acid Rain*

As raindrops fall through the air, gases dissolve into the droplets. Some gases, such as carbon dioxide, cause rain to become a weak acid. Over a long period of time, weak acids from rain can cause rocks to weather, and can change the acidity of lakes.

In some areas, however, the acidity of the rain is much higher than normal. This increase in acidity is caused by pollutants from industrial factories, power plants, and cars. Raindrops that dissolve these pollutants cause much stronger acids to fall to the ground. This type of precipitation is called acid rain.

Acid rain can damage a forest ecosystem. Acid rain falling in a forest can kill trees. If acid rain drains into a lake or pond, water animals die. Sometimes these animals are not affected directly by acid rain, but their breeding cycle may be interrupted. This interruption can cause an entire population to die off. Food webs may be disrupted, which in turn affects land animals.

The amount of damage in a forest depends a lot on the type of soil. Some lakes don't contain natural chemicals that counteract acids. Therefore, many lakes are very acidic, and they have lost their fish population. Other areas have soil with natural buffers that neutralize the acid rain.

The best way to reduce acid rain is by reducing the air pollutants that cause acid rain. However, reducing air pollution is a complex task. Finding acceptable ways to do it will involve politics, technology, and economics.

Figure 18.15 ▲
Acid rain killed many of the trees in Mount Mitchell, North Carolina.

Check and Explain

1. How does precipitation form before it falls to the surface of the earth?

2. How can a hailstone form several layers of ice?

3. **Classify** State whether each of the following instruments is used to measure rain, snow, or both: rain gauge, tipping-bucket rain gauge, snowpack device.

4. **Compare and Contrast** How are sleet and freezing rain alike? How are they different?

Chapter 18 Review

Concept Summary

18.1 Humidity
▶ Humidity is the amount of water vapor in air. Relative humidity is the percent of water vapor in the air compared to what air can hold.
▶ Plants and animals have adapted differently to living in areas with low or high humidity.
▶ Humidity can be measured by using a sling psychrometer and a relative humidity table.

18.2 Clouds
▶ At the correct temperature and altitude, water vapor condenses to form clouds.
▶ Water vapor must collect on condensation nuclei for cloud droplets to form.
▶ Clouds classified by their appearance are stratus, cumulus, or cirrus.

▶ Clouds are classified according to their height in the atmosphere by the prefixes cirro- (high), alto- (middle), and strato- (low).
▶ Fog is a cloud near the ground. The different types of fog are radiation fog, advection fog, and steam fog.

18.3 Precipitation
▶ Any form of moisture that falls from a cloud to the ground is precipitation.
▶ The forms of precipitation are rain, snow, freezing rain, sleet, and hail.
▶ Precipitation-measuring instruments include the rain gauge, the tipping-bucket rain gauge, and radar devices.
▶ People used to settle mostly in areas with abundant rainfall. But water is now transported to arid regions, making them livable.

Chapter Vocabulary

humidity (18.1)
dew point (18.1)
psychrometer (18.1)

stratus (18.2)
cumulus (18.2)
cumulonimbus(18.2)

cirrus (18.2)
fog (18.2)
precipitation (18.3)

Check Your Vocabulary

Use the vocabulary words above to complete the following sentences correctly.

1. The amount of water vapor contained in air is the ____.

2. A precise instrument used for measuring humidity is a ____.

3. Clouds flat in appearance that often produce drizzle are ____.

4. A cloud that forms on the ground is called ____.

5. Thin, wispy clouds that occur at high altitudes are ____.

6. Puffy clouds that appear on summer days are ____.

7. The temperature at which air becomes saturated is called the ____.

8. Any form of moisture that falls from a cloud is ____.

Explain the difference between the words in each pair.

9. cumulus, cumulonimbus

10. humidity, dew point

11. hair hygrometer, psychrometer

12. cloud, fog

13. snow, precipitation

14. relative humidity, humidity

15. strato-, stratus

Chapter 18 Review

Check Your Knowledge

Answer the following in complete sentences.

1. List three names used to classify clouds by their appearance.

2. How does a cactus prevent water from evaporating from its surface?

3. Describe a cumulonimbus cloud.

4. List the different types of precipitation.

5. Explain how snowpack is measured.

6. Why can people now settle in areas where water is not readily available?

7. Explain how an orchid and a bromeliad are similar.

8. Discuss how a hair hygrometer works.

9. What is advection fog?

10. What are condensation nuclei?

11. List the types of clouds that produce rain.

12. Explain one way that a raindrop can form.

Choose the answer that best completes each sentence.

13. An instrument used for measuring rainfall that consists of a funnel and a cylinder is called a (rain gauge, tipping bucket, psychrometer, hygrometer).

14. High, puffy clouds that are common on a summer day are (cumulonimbus, cirrocumulus, stratocumulus, altocumulus).

15. When the dew point is below freezing, tiny ice crystals called (dew, snow, sleet, frost) form on objects.

16. Partially melted grains of ice are called (ice crystals, hail, sleet, freezing rain).

Check Your Understanding

Apply the concepts you have learned to answer each question.

1. Compare the formation of snow and the formation of rain.

2. **Application** Describe how you could measure the relative humidity in your kitchen.

3. Discuss how animals that live in arid climates have adapted differently from animals that live in humid climates.

4. Explain what the name "cirrostratus" tells you about this type of cloud.

5. Discuss the conditions necessary to develop each form of precipitation: sleet, freezing rain, rain, snow.

6. **Critical Thinking** Explain why the amount of rainfall in an area would determine the number of people that can live in an area.

7. Discuss how the effect of humidity on hair was applied to make an instrument that measures humidity.

8. Explain how pollution could cause an increase in precipitation in an area.

9. **Extension** Ask a young child to draw you a picture that includes clouds. Identify the type of cloud the child draws.

10. **Application** Watch or listen to your local weather report for three days. Write down what is reported about the humidity for each day.

11. **Mystery Photo** The photograph on page 414 shows frost on the berries and the leaves of the bittersweet plant. Why are farmers concerned about frost? What can farmers do to prevent frost from affecting crops?

Develop Your Skills

Use the skills you have developed in this chapter to complete each activity.

1. **Interpret Data** The drawing below shows the altitudes for different types of clouds.

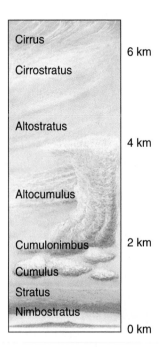

a. What type of clouds form at the highest altitudes?

b. At what altitude do altocumulus clouds form?

c. What type of clouds form at the lowest altitudes?

d. **Predict** What is the altitude for altostratus clouds? Look up your prediction in the drawing. Explain how you could predict the relative height.

2. **Data Bank** Use the information on page 617 to answer the following questions.

a. Which city has the lowest average precipitation?

b. What is the average annual precipitation in Shanghai, China?

Make Connections

1. **Link the Concepts** Below is a concept map showing how some of the main concepts in this chapter link together. Only parts of the map are filled in. Complete the map, using words and ideas from the chapter.

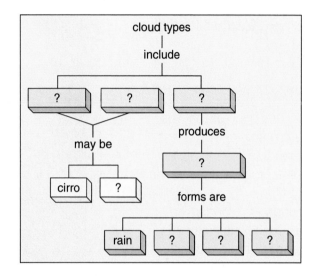

2. **Science and Literature** There are many poems written about different forms of precipitation, such as rain or snow. Find a poem written about a form of precipitation. Share the poem with your class. Write your own poem about a form of precipitation.

3. **Science and Society** Acid rain can affect buildings and statues in a community by dissolving the rock. Observe the rock structures in your area to see if there is any evidence of the effects of acid rain.

4. **Science and Social Studies** Conduct library research to find out where snowfall is greatest on the earth, where there is the least amount of rainfall, and where it rains the most.

Chapter 19 Weather

Chapter Sections

What do you see?

"This photograph was taken from space. It was probably from a satellite. I see Europe and the top part of Africa. The swirly white things are clouds. The clouds in this picture are swirly-shaped probably because it's a cold front blowing in from Greenland or Canada."

Anna Mauser Martinez
Stivers Middle School
Dayton, Ohio

To find out more about the photograph, look on page 460.
As you read this chapter, you will learn about weather.

438

19.1 Air in Motion

Objectives

▶ **Identify** the six types of air masses.

▶ **Explain** how winds occur.

▶ **Compare** and **contrast** the four kinds of fronts that occur when air masses meet.

▶ **Infer** about the differences in barometric pressure.

Every time you go out, you are exposed to the outside air. Is the outside air the same every day, or different? Conditions in the outside air change often. The air may be warm or cold. It may be moving or still. It may be moist, dry, or wet with rain. The general condition of the outside air at a given time and place is called the weather. Weather includes air temperature, cloud cover, precipitation, humidity, air pressure, and air movement.

Air Masses

Why does the weather around you change? You are always in an **air mass** that extends into the atmosphere above you. The air mass around you changes several times during a typical month. The characteristics of an air mass, where it came from, and how it moves all affect the weather.

All weather occurs in the layer of air directly above the earth's surface. This layer, the *troposphere*, is warmed or cooled by direct contact with the earth and by convection. Look at Figure 19.1. As the sun heats the earth's surface, the heat energy warms the air above it.

When a very large amount of air sits over one location for several days, an air mass with certain characteristics forms. The air mass takes on the location's temperature and humidity. For example, a cold air mass forms over cold land areas. A moist air mass forms where water is able to evaporate into the air. A dry air mass forms over a surface without much water.

Figure 19.1
Air masses absorb heat and moisture from the earth's land and water surfaces. ▼

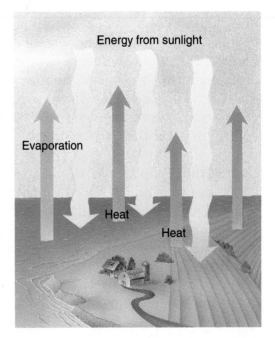

Energy from sunlight

Evaporation

Heat

Heat

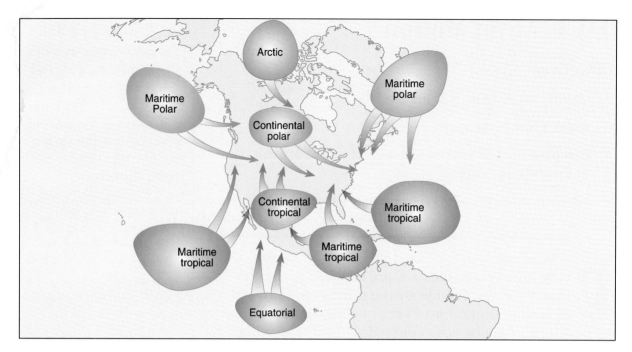

Figure 19.2 ▲
Study the air masses that affect the weather in North America. Which one do you think is influencing the weather you are experiencing now?

Types of Air Masses

Air masses differ in their origin and temperature. Study the six types of air masses shown in Figure 19.2.

Continental Polar A continental polar air mass forms over a very cold, dry land surface. During the winter, a continental polar air mass forms over Canada. After many days or weeks, the air mass may move south. It produces cool, dry air conditions over the United States.

Continental Tropical When the weather becomes warm and dry, a continental tropical air mass may be the cause. This type of air mass forms over hot, dry land areas, such as desert regions in the southwestern United States.

Maritime Polar A maritime (MAIR uh tym) polar air mass forms as air over

cold polar oceans cools and takes on moisture. When a maritime polar air mass moves over land areas, the weather there usually becomes cold and wet.

Maritime Tropical A maritime tropical air mass is warm and moist. This type of air mass forms over a warm body of water, such as the Gulf of Mexico. Maritime tropical air masses often cause warm, humid weather with rain and occasional thunderstorms.

Equatorial An equatorial air mass forms near the earth's equator. This type of air mass is hot. Equatorial air masses influence weather in Florida and Texas.

Arctic An arctic air mass forms near the North Pole. This type of air mass is extremely cold. Arctic air masses sometimes move into the northern United States, causing very low temperatures.

Fronts

Have you ever been caught in an unexpected storm? The wind suddenly changes direction and starts to blow very hard. Dark rain clouds replace fluffy white clouds. These kinds of sudden weather changes can occur when two different air masses meet. The boundary where the two different air masses come together is called a *front*.

Collisions between different types of air masses produce different conditions at fronts. Dramatic changes in weather occur at fronts between air masses with very different temperatures. If the air masses have similar temperatures but different humidities, the changes in weather are less dramatic. The way the air masses move also affects the weather conditions at fronts.

Cold Fronts At a **cold front**, a cold, dry air mass displaces a warm, moist air mass. As the air masses collide, the cold air mass forces its way beneath the warm air mass. Cold fronts move quickly. Strong gusts of wind and rain often occur. After the rain, the weather turns fair and cool. Study the movement of air masses at a cold front in Figure 19.3.

Huge cumulonimbus clouds often form at cold fronts. As the dense, cold air mass slides under the warm, less dense air mass, the warm air is pushed upward. The warm air cools as it rises. The moisture the warm air carries condenses into clouds.

A series of thunderstorms often lines up along a cold front. Cold fronts are shown on a weather map as a line with triangles on one side. The triangles point in the direction of the warmer air mass.

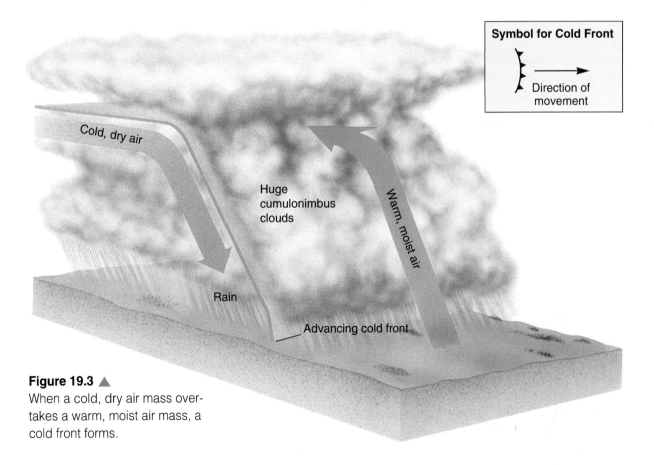

Symbol for Cold Front

Direction of movement

Cold, dry air

Huge cumulonimbus clouds

Warm, moist air

Rain

Advancing cold front

Figure 19.3 ▲
When a cold, dry air mass overtakes a warm, moist air mass, a cold front forms.

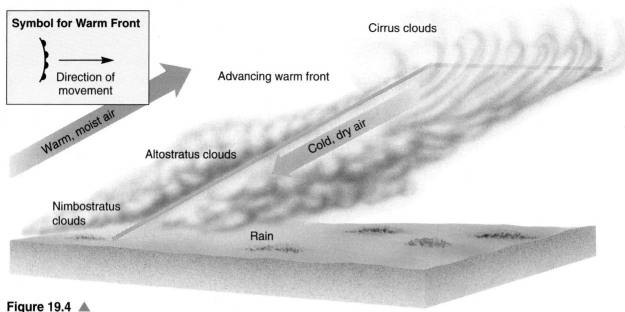

Symbol for Warm Front

Direction of movement

Warm, moist air

Advancing warm front

Cirrus clouds

Cold, dry air

Altostratus clouds

Nimbostratus clouds

Rain

Figure 19.4 ▲
When a warm, moist air mass overtakes a cold, dry air mass, a warm front forms.

Warm Fronts

A **warm front** forms when a warm, less dense air mass overtakes a cold, dense air mass. The warm air creeps over the cold air. Moisture in the warm air condenses, producing cloudy skies and rain or snow. Study the warm front in Figure 19.4. How does it differ from a cold front?

Warm fronts move slowly. As a warm front approaches a location, high cirrus clouds arrive first. The next clouds to arrive are thicker and closer to the ground. The rain or snow intensifies. Eventually, the skies clear and the air temperature rises. A warm front is shown on weather maps as a line with half-circles on one side. The half-circles face in the direction of the colder air mass.

Stationary Fronts

The boundary between two nonmoving air masses is called a **stationary front**. Sometimes a warmer air mass slightly overlaps a colder one, causing a gentle rain. On weather maps, a stationary front is shown as a line with triangles on one side and half-circles on the other side.

Occluded Fronts

Where a cold front overtakes a warm front, an **occluded** (uh KLOOD uhd) **front** forms. Look at Figure 19.5. Warm air behind the warm front rises over the cooler air ahead of it. The advancing cold front also lifts it. As the warm air rises, it produces light to moderate rain. On weather maps, an occluded front is a line with triangles and half-circles facing the same way.

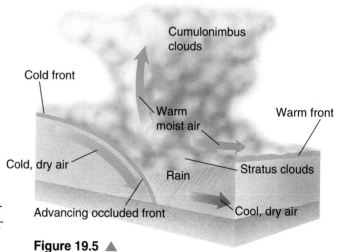

Cumulonimbus clouds

Cold front

Warm moist air

Warm front

Cold, dry air

Rain

Stratus clouds

Advancing occluded front

Cool, dry air

Figure 19.5 ▲
When a warm front and a cold front collide, an occluded front forms.

Air Pressure and Movement

Air exerts pressure on everything at the earth's surface. Air pressure at sea level is about equal to the pressure exerted by a column of water 10 m high. Because pressure inside your body pushes out with an equal force, you do not feel normal air pressure.

Air pressure is measured with a barometer (buh RAHM uh tur). A barometer is like a tall drinking glass upside down in a sink filled with water. With the rim of the glass under the water, the column of water inside the glass acts like a barometer. As air pressure on the sinkful of water changes, the water column moves up or down.

Physical Science
L I N K

Observe and compare the flow of smoke rising from a blown out candle when held next to a closed window and then next to an open window.
Should the smoke behave differently at different times of the day? Explain.

A C T I V I T Y

A mercury barometer is ▶ a glass tube 1 m long. It is sealed at one end and filled with mercury. The open end sits in a container of mercury. As the air pressure on the mercury in the container changes, the mercury in the tube moves up or down. At sea level and 0°C, normal barometric pressure is 760 mm of mercury. Barometric pressure is also expressed in millibars, the actual weight of air pressing on a 1 cm² area.

▼ An aneroid (AN ur oyd) barometer contains a sealed, flexible cylinder of air. The cylinder expands when the atmospheric pressure is decreasing. The cylinder gets smaller when the atmospheric pressure is increasing. A mechanism measures changes in the size of the cylinder.

◀ Barometer readings taken in different places at the same time can be shown on a map. Lines called **isobars** connect places with the same barometric pressure. Notice the isobars on the map at left. Isobars forming closed circles show areas of low pressure and high pressure. Air moves from high-pressure areas to low-pressure areas.

Figure 19.6 ▶
Study the earth's wind patterns.
Why do they move in different
directions at different latitudes?

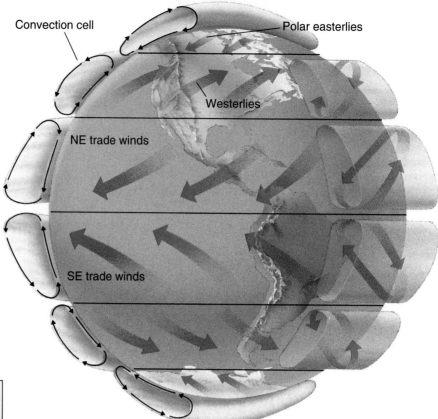

Convection cell

Polar easterlies

Westerlies

NE trade winds

SE trade winds

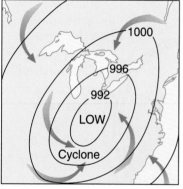

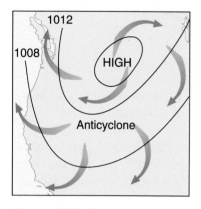

Figure 19.7 ▲
Cyclonic winds move in a
counterclockwise direction (top).
Anticyclonic winds move in a
clockwise direction (bottom).

Winds

Differences in air pressure produce winds. The pressure difference between a high-pressure area and a low-pressure area determines the strength of the wind. Larger pressure differences produce stronger winds.

Differences in air temperature also lead to pressure differences that cause winds. Temperature differences occur because the sun heats the earth unevenly. The warmer air is less dense, so it rises. The rising air creates a low-pressure area. For example, the sun's heat is most intense at the earth's equator. The air there heats up and rises. Air rushes in along the earth's surface to replace the hot air. The moving air becomes a surface wind.

The Coriolis effect influences Earth's wind patterns. Study the global wind map in Figure 19.6. Recall that the Coriolis effect is caused by the earth's rotation. The Coriolis effect pushes winds to the right in the Northern Hemisphere and to the left in the Southern Hemisphere.

Two kinds of smaller wind patterns can form as air moves from a high-pressure area to a low-pressure area. Look at Figure 19.7. At a low-pressure area, the air moves in toward the low-pressure center.

In the Northern Hemisphere, the Coriolis force turns the moving air to the right. The result is a counterclockwise **cyclonic** (sy CLAH nihk) **wind pattern** that surrounds the low-pressure area.

Cyclonic wind patterns can produce hurricanes and major winter storms. Air rushing away from a high-pressure center also turns to the right in the Northern Hemisphere. Therefore, a clockwise **anticyclonic wind pattern** forms around the high-pressure area. Anticyclonic wind patterns often produce warm and sunny weather. Compare the cyclonic and anticyclonic wind patterns shown in Figure 19.7.

Winds also blow far above the earth's surface. The *jet stream* is a narrow ribbon of moving air located 8,000 to 12 000 m above the earth's surface. Look at the North American jet stream patterns in Figure 19.8. The jet stream is caused by temperature differences between the earth's equator and the poles.

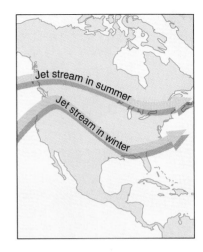

Figure 19.8 ▲

High above the earth's surface, the jet stream winds blow. Compare the position of the jet stream above North America in winter and in summer.

Career Corner   *Weather Forecaster*

Who Forecasts the Weather?

A weather forecast of "Cloudy, chance of showers in late afternoon and turning colder" told you that you might need a jacket at the baseball game. Who predicted the weather? A weather forecaster did. A weather forecaster is usually a meteorologist. A meteorologist studies the atmosphere and how it changes.

To predict what the weather will be like tomorrow, weather forecasters use data that describe current weather. They also use special computer forecasts of air movements. Often, they use weather satellites and weather radar to track storms. Weather forecasters are alerted to severe weather so they can warn others who may be in the path of the storm. Weather forecasters also do research on weather. They sometimes fly in airplanes or use research ships to collect data. The data helps forecasters improve the accuracy of their weather forecasts.

Weather forecasters take college courses in mathematics, physics, chemistry, and computer science before they study about the atmosphere. If you would like to learn how to forecast the weather, you can prepare by taking mathemat-

ics and physics in high school. You might also want to practice your weather observation and data-recording skills at home. In a public library or school library, you can find information on how to build a home weather station.

Science and Technology *Wind Energy*

In some places on the earth's surface, the wind seems to blow all the time. Since 1970, engineers have developed ways to use these persistent winds to generate electricity. Look at the wind turbine in Figure 19.9. Wind turbines like this one are much more efficient than the windmills that were used in the past to pump water. A modern wind turbine can harness about 35 percent of the energy in the wind. Twenty wind turbines can generate enough electricity to supply a neighborhood with electric power. Scientists estimate that about 20 percent of all United States electrical needs could be met by the use of wind energy.

The most difficult part of producing wind energy is finding a suitable site with strong, consistent winds. A wind turbine generally needs a consistent wind of at least 20 km/h to work efficiently. Meteorologists and engineers spend years researching a site before placing an installation of wind turbines. Since 1982, more than 13,000 wind turbines were installed in the state of California alone. These wind turbines helped save more than a million barrels of oil that would have burned in power plants.

The use of wind energy can help reduce air pollution and save supplies of fossil fuels. But despite the advantages, wind energy cannot completely replace fossil-fuel-burning electrical power plants. There must be a fuel-burning backup system to produce electricity when the wind isn't blowing. Also, many locations are not suitable because they are too close to cities and towns.

Figure 19.9 ▲
Using a wind turbine to pump water saves energy compared to an electric pump.

Check and Explain

1. What are the six types of air masses? What is each one like?

2. What is the main cause of winds? What other factors are important?

3. **Compare and Contrast** Describe the four kinds of fronts that occur. How are they similar? How are they different?

4. **Infer** Do you think a barometer would give a low or high reading on a hot day? Explain why.

Activity 19 *How do pressure changes affect the wind?*

Skills Measure; Observe; Interpret Data

Task 1 Prelab Prep

Collect the following items: barometer, compass, stick with a 30-cm string attached at one end.

Task 2 Data Record

1. On a separate piece of paper, copy Table 19.1.
2. Record barometric pressure in the units marked on the barometer. The units are usually millibars or millimeters of mercury. Record the pressure as accurately as you can.
3. Record wind direction as one of the following: North, Northeast, East, Southeast, South, Southwest, West, or Northwest.

Table 19.1 Weather Data

Date	Time	Pressure	Wind Direction

Task 3 Procedure

1. Choose an outdoor spot near your home or school to make measurements of pressure and wind direction. Choose a convenient spot, because you will need to make two sets of observations each day: one in the morning and one in the evening.
2. Use the barometer to measure the pressure. Record the time and the pressure measurement in the data table.
3. Shove the stick into the ground, string-end up. Move around the stick until the string is being blown toward you by the wind.
4. Move the compass so the magnetic needle points north. Look down at the compass and the string and estimate the direction the wind is blowing from. Record the wind direction in the data table.
5. Repeat this procedure twice each day, morning and evening, every day for one week. Try to make your observations at about the same time each day.

Task 4 Analysis

1. Describe how the barometric pressure changed each day.
2. Describe how the wind direction changed each day.
3. Did the wind direction change more on days when the barometric pressure was changing or when the barometric pressure was relatively constant?

Task 5 Conclusion

Write a short paragraph explaining what you learned about the relationship between pressure, pressure change, and wind direction. How could the principles you discovered be used every day?

Everyday Application

Farmers and mariners traditionally watch the barometer closely to see when pressure starts to change rapidly. Although rapid pressure change does not predict a specific type of weather, it almost always means a change in the weather. Explain why.

Extension

Develop a hypothesis about pressure change and weather. Does increasing pressure imply better weather and decreasing pressure stormy weather? Look in your library for information. Books about sailing or the *Farmer's Almanac* may help.

19.2 Storms

Objectives

▶ **Identify** the three major types of storms.

▶ **Describe** the air movements that produce thunderstorms.

▶ **Compare** and **contrast** hurricanes and tornadoes.

▶ **Classify** storms that occur in your region.

Think about what happens when you see a flash of lightning in the distance. You hear thunder, the wind blows, and it rains hard. You experience a storm. People all over the world experience similar storms. Scientists estimate that about 2,000 thunderstorms occur every hour somewhere on the earth!

Thunderstorms are only one type of storm. If you live on the coast, you may experience tropical hurricanes. Winter snowstorms occur in many areas. Each type of storm causes different weather. Storms may be small and localized, or they may occur over a large area. Also, each type of storm forms during different seasons of the year or in different geographical regions.

Characteristics of Storms

Storms involve rising moist air. For example, air that rises when it is forced to go over a mountain may cause a local rainstorm. Also, recall that warm air rises. Generally, warm air continues to rise until it cools or encounters a cooler air layer. As warm, moist air rises and cools, the moisture it carries condenses to form clouds. The clouds produce precipitation.

Storms also involve high winds. Recall that a cyclonic wind pattern is an area of counterclockwise rotating air around a low-pressure center. As the rotating air spirals inward toward the low-pressure center, the air moves faster. High winds result. The principle that produces the high winds is the same one a figure skater uses to perform a spin. As the spinning skater pulls her arms in close to her body, she spins faster.

Figure 19.10 ▲

Are thunderstorms common where you live?

Thunderstorms

A thunderstorm forms when masses of warm, moist air move rapidly upward. Study the thunderstorm in Figure 19.11. Air, heated by contact with the ground, rises until it reaches a height where it is no longer buoyant. The air may stop rising, or it may begin to sink. If the air cools enough, the moisture in the air will condense to form a cloud.

Above the freezing level, cloud particles grow bigger and bigger. They also grow heavier. When the particles get too heavy, rising air in the cloud can no longer keep the particles from falling toward the ground. Eventually they reach the earth as rain drops.

When the warm, moist air rises rapidly, a huge, towering, cumulonimbus cloud can form. Each surge of warm, moist air adds to the size of the cloud. The cumulonimbus cloud, sometimes called a thundercloud, can be 5 to 8 km across and more than 10 km high.

About 5 km up in the cloud, the air temperature goes below freezing. Tiny ice crystals form. As these crystals collide, positively charged and negatively charged fragments break off. The smaller positively charged fragments are carried upward with the rising air. The larger negatively charged fragments build up at the bottom of the cloud.

Lightning occurs when the charge difference is released suddenly in an electric spark. A flash of lightning produces incredible heat. The heat makes the air expand rapidly, producing a loud sound called thunder.

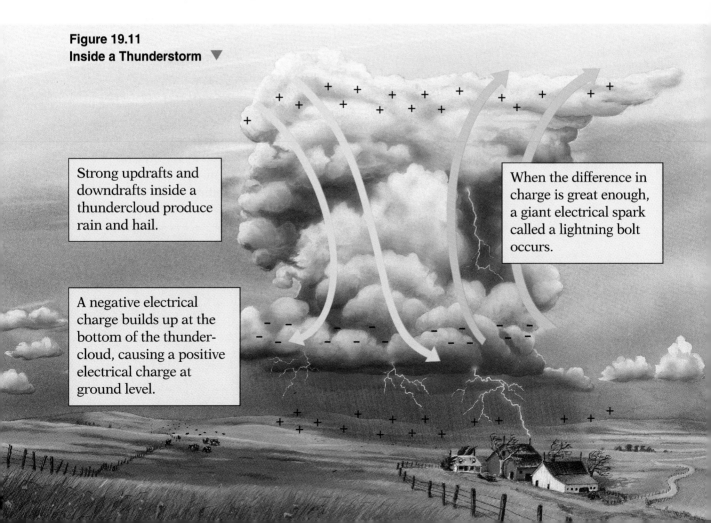

Figure 19.11
Inside a Thunderstorm ▼

Strong updrafts and downdrafts inside a thundercloud produce rain and hail.

When the difference in charge is great enough, a giant electrical spark called a lightning bolt occurs.

A negative electrical charge builds up at the bottom of the thundercloud, causing a positive electrical charge at ground level.

Hurricanes

A tropical storm with sustained winds of at least 119 km/h is a **hurricane**. The average size of a hurricane is about 600 km in diameter. The most violent storms on the earth, hurricanes have several names. In the western Pacific Ocean, they are called *typhoons*. In the Indian Ocean, they are called *cyclones*.

Hurricanes form over warm, tropical oceans near the earth's equator. Warm, moist air over the oceans rises rapidly. The rising air cools and forms clouds and rain, while releasing enormous amounts of energy. The rapid upward air movement causes a drop in pressure. A low-pressure center forms, as shown in Figure 19.12. The pressure at the hurricane's center is much lower than the pressure at its edges. Air, spinning counterclockwise, moves forcefully toward the center.

A hurricane can travel 1,000 to 3,000 km and last for 9 to 12 days over the warm ocean. After forming, a hurricane begins to move in a westerly direction, then curves toward the north. Eventually, it moves over land or colder water. There the source of warm, moist air is cut off, and the hurricane weakens.

When a hurricane reaches land, it causes violent winds, heavy rains, and flooding. Predicting hurricanes can help save lives and property. Satellite images and computer models are used to predict the path of a hurricane.

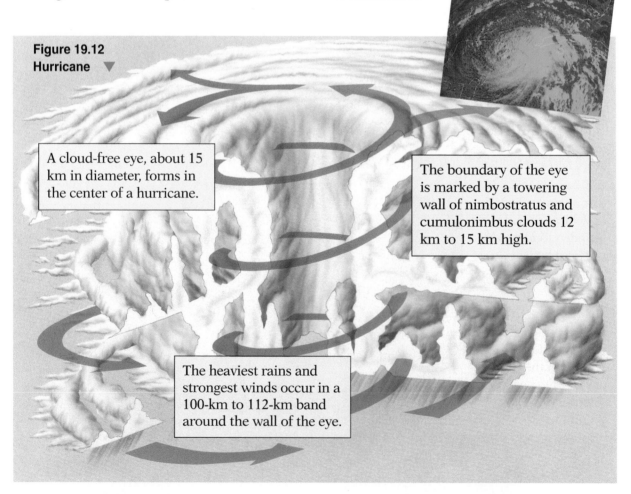

**Figure 19.12
Hurricane** ▼

A cloud-free eye, about 15 km in diameter, forms in the center of a hurricane.

The boundary of the eye is marked by a towering wall of nimbostratus and cumulonimbus clouds 12 km to 15 km high.

The heaviest rains and strongest winds occur in a 100-km to 112-km band around the wall of the eye.

Tornadoes

A **tornado** (tor NAY doh) is a whirling, funnel-shaped windstorm like the one in Figure 19.13. Tornadoes sometimes form at the southwest side of a severe thunderstorm. In the thunderstorm, warm air is forced upward rapidly, so the air pressure drops. Winds begin to rotate rapidly around the low-pressure area, forming a tornado.

The rotating winds of a tornado often move at speeds of up to 450 km/h. Air rushes into the tornado from all directions and spirals upward. A dark, funnel-shaped cloud of condensed water vapor reaches down from the thundercloud, mixing with dirt near the ground.

Tornadoes move in a narrow path along the ground. Sometimes they skip over an area. One area along a tornado's path may be destroyed, while another area is undamaged. Tornadoes occasionally form over the ocean or large lakes. Such tornadoes are called water spouts. The rotating winds can lift water high into the air.

Figure 19.13 ▲
What causes the funnel-shaped cloud of a tornado to form?

Regional Storms

Different types of storms occur in different regions. For example, tornadoes occur mostly in plains regions, such as Oklahoma, Kansas, and Texas. Hurricanes strike along coastlines in the Caribbean Sea, along the Gulf of Mexico, and along the eastern coast of the United States.

There are other examples of regional storms. Lake-effect snowstorms are common downwind of the Great Lakes. Air moving over the lakes picks up heat and moisture. When it reaches the cold shoreline, as much as 1 m of snow can fall in 24 hours. The Hawaiian island of Kauai receives more than 8 m of rain per year. Tropical trade winds blow moist air up and over the island, causing daily rain.

Regions such as southern Asia and eastern Africa have changing winds called **monsoons**. Monsoons cause seasonal storms. Look at Figure 19.14. Farmers in these areas depend on the monsoon rains each summer to water their crops. Crop failure and food shortages can result when the monsoon rains do not occur.

Figure 19.14 ▲
During certain seasons in India, monsoons cause heavy rains.

Science and Society   *Storm Warnings*

When you listen to the weather report on television, you might hear about a storm watch or storm warning. The U.S. National Weather Service issues a storm watch when the forecast shows that a big storm is coming. When the storm is about to occur, or is already occurring, a storm warning is issued.

Storm watches are issued for severe thunderstorms, floods, tornadoes, blizzards, and hurricanes. Storm watches warn people to be prepared for the storm that is on its way. When a severe storm hits suddenly and without warning, disaster can occur. For example, on July 11, 1992, hail damaged more than 100,000 cars in Denver. If the car owners had known of the storm in advance, they could have moved the cars into garages or carports. In the case of a hurricane, a storm watch gives people time to leave low-lying beach areas and gather emergency supplies. The storm watch issued for Hurricane Andrew in August of 1992 helped save many lives in south Florida.

When the National Weather Service issues a storm warning, it always includes instructions on what to do. If a storm warning is issued, you should take immediate action to protect yourself and others. In a tornado, go into a basement or a small interior room on the lowest floor of a building. Stay away from windows. In a severe thunderstorm, take shelter in a building to avoid lightning and high wind. If a flood or hurricane warning is issued, take shelter on high ground. In a blizzard, stay inside, and keep blankets and flashlights handy in case of a power failure.

Figure 19.15 ▲
With advance notice of a hurricane, people can try to protect their homes and businesses from damage.

Check and Explain

1. What are the three major types of storms? Write a short description of each one.

2. How do air movements produce a thunderstorm? Why do lightning and thunder occur?

3. **Compare and Contrast** Will a tornado cause more or less damage than a hurricane? Explain.

4. **Classify** Describe and classify two or more dramatic storms that have occurred in the area where you live.

19.3 Weather Prediction

Objectives

▶ **Describe** how different weather conditions can be shown on a weather map.

▶ **Discuss** how meteorologists forecast the weather.

▶ **Compare** and **contrast** sources of data about weather conditions.

▶ **Collect data** by observing weather conditions.

▼ **ACTIVITY**

Inferring

Looks Like Rain

When you look out your window in the morning, how do you decide what the weather will probably be like? What observations do you make? What conclusions do you draw from each observation?

SKILLS WARMUP

You look outside in the morning and decide that the weather will probably be warm and sunny. You're making your own weather forecast! You base your forecast on your observations and your past experiences. Weather forecasts are important to many people. For example, farmers need to know if the weather will be right for planting or harvesting crops.

Weather Forecasts

To make the weather forecasts you see on television or read in the newspaper, meteorologists gather data about the current weather conditions over a large area. These data on temperature, precipitation, air pressure, and wind tell meteorologists the locations of high and low pressure areas. They tell them where fronts are.

By keeping track of changes in the location of fronts and air masses, meteorologists can figure out how fast they are moving and in what direction. They can predict where fronts and air masses will be in the future. Based on their knowledge of the kind of weather produced by different air masses and fronts, they can then predict the weather for different places.

To make predictions about the weather more than a day or two ahead of time requires much guesswork. Meteorologists are improving the accuracy of their long-range forecasts, however, by using computer models. The high-speed supercomputers running the models can make predictions based on very large amounts of weather data.

Figure 19.16 ▲
When do you need to know tomorrow's weather forecast?

Sources of Weather Data

Good weather forecasting depends on data that describe conditions in the atmosphere. There are four main sources of data about the atmosphere. Study the examples on this page.

Weather Satellites

◀ Weather satellites are stationed at various points above the earth. They send images of cloud movements back to stations on the earth. The satellites also collect data on cloud temperature, moisture, and surface temperature of the land and oceans.

Weather Radar

◀ Weather radar monitors the weather around a weather station. The radar sends out radio signals that reflect off rain and snow. Radar shows where storms are located and in which direction they are moving. On the radar map, different colors show rainfall amounts.

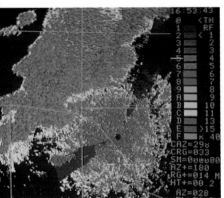

Weather Balloons ▶

Helium-filled weather balloons high in the atmosphere transmit data on temperature, pressure, and humidity. A ground station tracks the movements of the balloon to determine the winds. The atmospheric conditions at about 5,500 m are very important. The winds at this altitude, for example, influence the direction that storms will move.

Weather Stations ▲

There are weather stations, large and small, located all over the world. They provide data on temperature, humidity, winds, clouds, and precipitation. Many states transmit these data hourly. The data from the stations are plotted on weather maps and used for weather forecasting.

The National Weather Service

In the United States, the National Weather Service (NWS) issues weather forecasts to the public. There are more than 400 NWS field offices and weather stations in the United States. Every year, the NWS makes more than three million weather observations at these facilities. The NWS also receives international weather data from more than 150 countries all over the world.

Current weather information and weather forecasts issued by the NWS are used for many purposes. Weather forecasters on television use the data to prepare their own forecasts. Airlines and shipping companies carefully monitor the weather and the weather forecasts so that passengers and cargo will arrive safely. Construction companies, electrical power companies, and highway departments all closely monitor weather forecasts to plan work schedules.

▼ ACTIVITY

Comparing

Tomorrow's Forecast

Collect weather reports each day for three days. Plot the data for your location, and for two or three cities nearby. Predict the weather for the next day based on the data you have collected.

Compare how close your predictions were to official forecasts and actual weather conditions? How might you improve the accuracy of your forecasts?

SKILLS WORKOUT

SkillBuilder *Interpreting Data*

Climatological Data

During a summer day, would you expect the temperature to reach only 5°C? Because of your knowledge of climatology, you know this is very unlikely. The seasonal average temperature for a certain location is usually a good predicator of the range of temperatures you can expect for a day during that season. For this reason, meteorologists take into account climatological data when they make their forecasts.

Study the table to the right. It shows the actual maximum temperatures observed over three days in four different cities. The far right column shows the seasonal averages for those locations.

1. Which city has observed temperatures closest to its climatological average? Which city is much warmer than its climatological average?

2. Which city has the most constant observed temperatures? The most variable observed temperatures?

3. What trend do you see in the observed temperatures for Los Angeles? Based on this trend, what maximum temperature would you predict for Day 4?

Maximum Temperature (°C)

| City | Observed | | | Seasonal |
	Day 1	Day 2	Day 3	Average
Los Angeles	28	27	26	25
Denver	26	25	24	25
Chicago	28	28	28	23
New York	30	25	34	27

Weather Maps

The weather conditions over a large area are best understood when they are mapped. Weather maps have two main uses: to give an overall picture of present weather conditions, or to show a weather forecast. Weather maps of both types use symbols, numbers, and lines to represent weather conditions at different locations. The symbols that are used depend on the type of map and who is going to read it.

Official Weather Maps Weather maps made and used by meteorologists and the National Weather Service must show as much weather data as possible. For this purpose, meteorologists use the weather station model. The weather station model is a set of symbols that shows many kinds of current weather data from one observation station. The model takes up very little space on a map. The weather station model and its symbols are understood around the world.

Look at Figure 19.17. It shows an example of a weather station model. Study the model to learn what the different parts mean.

**Figure 19.17
Weather Station Model** ▼

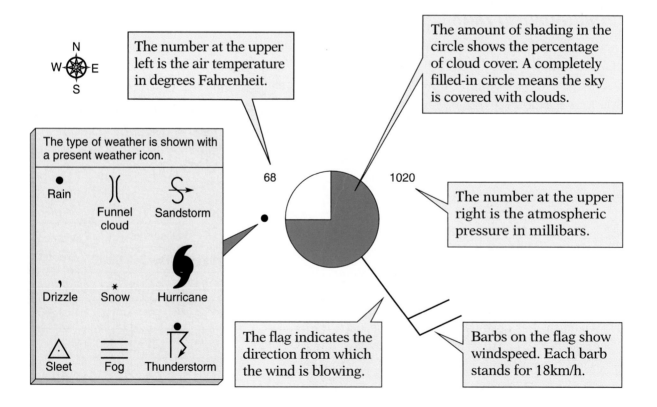

The number at the upper left is the air temperature in degrees Fahrenheit.

The amount of shading in the circle shows the percentage of cloud cover. A completely filled-in circle means the sky is covered with clouds.

The type of weather is shown with a present weather icon.

Rain

Funnel cloud

Sandstorm

Drizzle

Snow

Hurricane

Sleet

Fog

Thunderstorm

68

1020

The number at the upper right is the atmospheric pressure in millibars.

The flag indicates the direction from which the wind is blowing.

Barbs on the flag show windspeed. Each barb stands for 18km/h.

A map using the weather station model to show current weather data from many different locations is called a *synoptic chart*. Synoptic charts also have isobars to show atmospheric pressure. Meteorologists use synoptic charts to make weather forecasts.

Reading a Weather Map Most of the weather maps you'll see and read are simplified. Their symbols don't show quite as much information as those on official weather maps, but they are easier for most people to understand.

Look at the weather map in Figure 19.18. It shows a weather forecast. It is similar to the daily weather map you find in your newspaper or see on the television news. Notice the symbols used to show different kinds of pre-

dicted precipitation. What is the symbol for thunderstorms?

The curving lines you see on the map are not isobars, but **isotherms** (EYE soh thurmz). Isotherms are lines connecting locations that have, or are predicted to have, the same temperature. The isotherms are labeled in degrees Fahrenheit, not Celsius. The predicted high and low temperatures given for selected cities are also in degrees Fahrenheit.

Instead of showing atmospheric pressure with isobars, maps like these use the letters *H* and *L* to show the centers of high and low pressure systems. You'll recognize the symbols for fronts as the same ones used on official weather maps. Answer the questions as you study the weather map in Figure 19.18.

**Figure 19.18
Map of a Day's
Weather Forecast** ▼

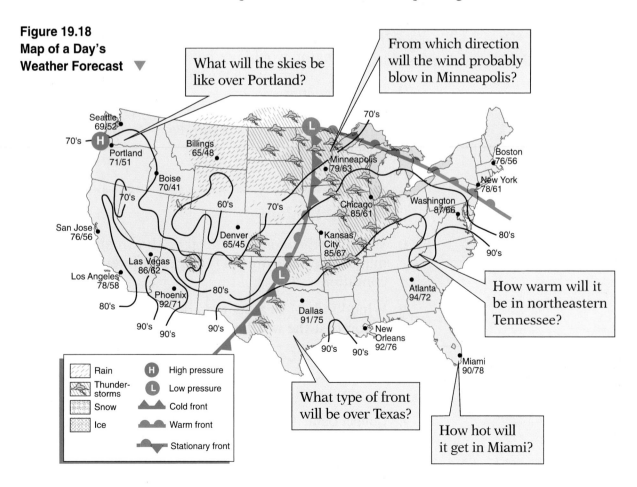

What will the skies be like over Portland?

From which direction will the wind probably blow in Minneapolis?

How warm will it be in northeastern Tennessee?

What type of front will be over Texas?

How hot will it get in Miami?

Seattle 69/52
70's
Portland 71/51
Billings 65/48
Boise 70/41
70's
60's
70's
Minneapolis 79/63
70's
Boston 76/56
New York 78/61
San Jose 76/56
Denver 65/45
Chicago 85/61
Washington 87/66
80's
Kansas City 85/67
90's
Las Vegas 86/62
Los Angeles 78/58
80's
Phoenix 92/71
Atlanta 94/72
80's
90's
90's
Dallas 91/75
New Orleans 92/76
90's
90's
Miami 90/78

Rain
Thunderstorms
Snow
Ice

H High pressure
L Low pressure
Cold front
Warm front
Stationary front

Science and Technology *Weather Satellites*

A weather report on the television news usually includes an image of the clouds as seen from a satellite. The cloud images come from a geostationary satellite 35 200 km above the earth. The satellite is called geostationary because it orbits the earth every 24 hours. Since the earth also rotates once every 24 hours, the satellite remains over the same point on the earth's surface.

There are usually five geostationary weather satellites around the earth to provide complete coverage. The satellites collect images and transmit them to the earth as often as every five minutes. During the day, a satellite collects and transmits images formed by visual light. During the day and at night, a satellite uses infrared radiation to measure the amount of heat given off by the earth's surface and clouds. Computers make weather maps using the information from satellites.

Satellites are very important in collecting weather data over the oceans, where there are few weather stations. Without satellite data, people in California, Oregon, and Washington would not have advance warning of weather moving in from the ocean. Satellites also help detect hurricanes over the ocean. If you live on the eastern coast of the United States, data from satellites can give you 24-hour advance warning of an approaching hurricane.

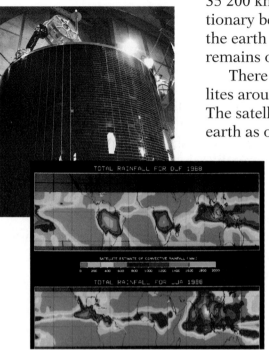

Figure 19.19 ▲

Data collected by weather satellites such as the GOES-D (top) were used to make these maps of world rainfall (bottom).

Check and Explain

1. What weather conditions can be shown on a weather map? Describe symbols for three different weather conditions.

2. What kinds of weather data do meteorologists need to forecast the weather?

3. **Compare and Contrast** What are the sources of data for weather forecasting? How do the types of data they collect differ?

4. **Collect Data** Observe the weather conditions in your region four times during one day. Draw a weather station model for each set of observations.

Chapter 19 Review

Concept Summary

19.1 Air in Motion
▶ Air masses differ in their origin and temperature.
▶ Air masses interact at fronts. There are four kinds of fronts: cold, warm, stationary, and occluded.
▶ Differences in air pressure at the earth's surface produce winds. Winds move from an area of high pressure to an area of low pressure.

19.2 Storms
▶ Storms involve high winds and rising moist air, which cause precipitation.
▶ A thunderstorm forms when masses of warm, moist air move rapidly upward.

▶ A huge, towering cumulonimbus cloud produces heavy rain and lightning.
▶ A hurricane is a tropical storm with sustained winds of at least 120 km/h.
▶ A tornado is a whirling, funnel-shaped windstorm.

19.3 Weather Prediction
▶ Weather forecasters rely on weather data from a wide area.
▶ Weather data are collected from weather stations, weather balloons, weather satellites, and weather radar.
▶ Weather maps have symbols, numbers, and lines showing weather data at different locations.

Chapter Vocabulary

air mass (19.1)	occluded front (19.1)	hurricane (19.2)
cold front (19.1)	isobar (19.1)	tornado (19.2)
warm front (19.1)	cyclonic wind pattern (19.1)	monsoon (19.2)
stationary front (19.1)	anticyclonic wind pattern (19.1)	isotherm (19.3)

Check Your Vocabulary

Use the vocabulary words above to complete the following sentences correctly.

1. When a very large amount of air sits over one location for several days, a(n) _____ forms.

2. At a(n) _____, rain occurs when a cold, dry air mass forces its way beneath a warm, moist air mass.

3. The boundary between two nonmoving air masses is called a(n) _____.

4. On a weather map, lines called _____ connect places with the same barometric pressure.

5. A clockwise wind pattern is called a(n) _____.

6. The most violent storms on the earth are _____.

7. When a warm air mass meets and creeps up over a cold air mass, a(n) _____ forms.

8. When a warm front and cold front collide, a(n) _____ can form.

9. Some weather maps have lines of constant temperature called _____.

10. Farmers in southern Asia depend on _____ as a source of water for their crops.

11. A(n) _____ moves in a narrow path along the ground or over water.

12. A counterclockwise wind pattern is called a(n) _____.

Chapter 19 *Review*

Check Your Knowledge

Answer the following in complete sentences.

1. What is an air mass? How does an air mass form?

2. How do air masses affect weather?

3. Describe a cold front. What kind of weather occurs there?

4. Describe a warm front. What kind of weather occurs there?

5. What do barometer readings tell you?

6. Describe how the Coriolis effect influences global wind patterns.

7. What is a storm?

8. What are the characteristics of a hurricane?

9. Why do lightning and thunder occur during a thunderstorm?

10. What information is needed to make a weather forecast? Explain why.

11. Describe a weather map.

Determine whether each statement is true or false. Write *true* if it is true. If it is false, change the underlined word(s) to make the statement true.

12. Hurricanes usually form over warm, tropical <u>oceans</u> near the earth's equator.

13. A continental polar air mass forms over cold polar <u>oceans</u>.

14. Air rushes toward a low-pressure center in a <u>clockwise</u> cyclonic wind pattern.

15. Two different <u>air masses</u> collide at an occluded front.

16. Wind moves rapidly <u>toward</u> a high-pressure center.

Check Your Understanding

Apply the concepts you have learned to answer each question.

1. When a maritime polar air mass moves into your area, what kind of weather should you expect? What kind of weather should you expect from a continental tropical air mass?

2. **Critical Thinking** Compare a mercury barometer to an aneroid barometer. How do they function differently?

3. Explain why each of the four main sources of weather data are needed to provide a complete picture of conditions in the atmosphere.

4. **Critical Thinking** Compare and contrast the weather in Los Angeles and Minneapolis.

5. **Application** What kind of action should you take when you hear a storm warning for a severe thunderstorm in your area?

6. **Critical Thinking** How is an isobar different from an isotherm? How are they alike?

7. **Mystery Photo** The photograph on page 438 is a computer-enhanced satellite image of cloud formations over western Europe and North Africa.

   a. Locate Spain and North Africa on the satellite image. When the image was taken, what do you think the weather was like in each place? Explain your reasoning.

   b. Locate the British Isles on the satellite image. When the image was taken, what do you think the weather was like there? Explain your reasoning.

Develop Your Skills

Use the skills you have developed in this chapter to complete each activity.

1. Interpret Data Weather symbols for two different weather stations are shown below.

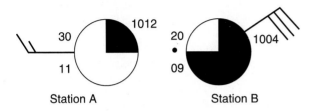

Station A   Station B

a. At which weather station is the wind blowing fastest? Explain.

b. Which weather station has more cloud cover? Explain.

c. Describe any precipitation that is occurring at either weather station.

d. Which station has the highest barometric pressure?

e. What is the temperature at each weather station?

2. Hypothesize Look at the map of global wind patterns on page 444. Notice how air rises at the earth's equator. Develop a hypothesis explaining why this occurs. How could you test your hypothesis?

3. Infer Based on the type of weather that is occurring right now, what kind of air mass do you think is present?

4. Data Bank Use the information on page 616 to answer the following questions about the weather on December 22, 1992.

a. Describe where any fronts are located. Identify the type of each front.

b. Choose three station models. Identify their locations and describe the weather condition they report.

Make Connections

1. Link the Concepts Below is a concept map showing how some of the main concepts in this chapter link together. Only parts of the map are filled in. Complete the map, using words and ideas from the chapter. Add boxes on storms.

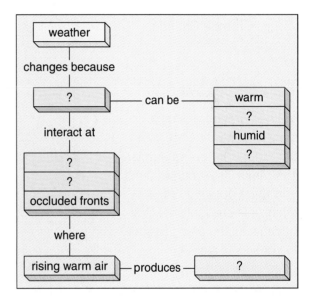

2. Science and Art Design a poster about storm safety. Show what actions to take to protect yourself and your family from a serious storm, such as a hurricane or tornado.

3. Science and Literature The book *The Hurricane*, by Nordhoff and Hall, describes the effects of a devastating hurricane on people living on a small island in the South Pacific. Locate and read this book. Write a report describing what it was like to live through the hurricane.

4. Science and Physical Education Research the sport of sailing or sailboarding. Find out how people can use wind energy to travel in any direction.

Chapter 20 Climate

What do you see?

"I see green trees on a steep slope with white lines that appear to be waterfalls. The climate is probably humid and rainy, very hot, tropical. I think it is probably like this because of the green and all the growth. It looks like a very good growing place. I think the photograph was taken in South America or even a part of Mexico with jungles."

Kelly Hinkle
Lyles Middle School
Garland, Texas

To find out more about the photograph, look on page 482.
As you read this chapter, you will learn about different climates and the factors that determine them.

462

20.1 Causes of Climate

Objectives

▶ **Distinguish** between weather and climate.

▶ **Describe** two ways that the ocean affects climate.

▶ **Compare** the temperatures of two different regions in the United States.

▶ **Infer** about the factors that influence local climate.

Imagine it is January 1, the first day of the new year. Under clear blue skies in one part of North America, a group of friends shovel snow from the local pond so they can go ice skating. At the same time, in a different part of North America, another group of friends play volleyball on a warm, sandy beach. Why is the weather so different?

Although both groups might describe their weather as "fair," at least one condition—temperature—is quite different at the two locations. The temperatures are different because each location has a different **climate**. Climate is the characteristic weather for a region over a long period of time. The two major conditions that determine climate are temperature and precipitation.

Temperature

The temperature of a region depends on a number of factors, including latitude, altitude, and distance from an ocean. These factors are dependent on the heat that the earth receives from the sun. Recall that radiant energy from the sun strikes the earth's surface, where some absorbed energy converts to heat. Some energy isn't absorbed. It is reflected from the earth's surface back into space.

Latitude A measure of distance in degrees, north and south of the equator, is called *latitude*. Latitude and the tilt of the earth's axis determine the angle at which the sun's rays strike different regions of the earth.

Figure 20.1 ▲
How do the climates in these two locations differ?

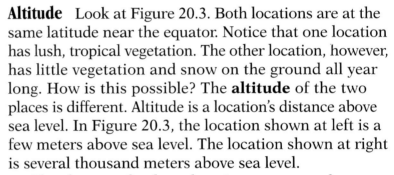

Look at Figure 20.2. Sun rays that strike the earth at almost no slant heat the earth's surface better than rays that strike at a slant. Direct rays provide more radiant energy. Notice that the most direct rays strike the areas near the equator, which is 0° latitude. Temperatures are highest in these regions. So areas near the equator have steady high temperatures, resulting in a warm climate. As latitude increases, the sun's rays strike at more of an angle and over a wider area. Why do you think the coldest places on the earth are at the poles?

Figure 20.2 ▲

The sun's rays strike more directly at low latitudes than at high latitudes. Notice how the rays seem to spread out at higher latitudes.

Altitude   Look at Figure 20.3. Both locations are at the same latitude near the equator. Notice that one location has lush, tropical vegetation. The other location, however, has little vegetation and snow on the ground all year long. How is this possible? The **altitude** of the two places is different. Altitude is a location's distance above sea level. In Figure 20.3, the location shown at left is a few meters above sea level. The location shown at right is several thousand meters above sea level.

The photographs show that air temperature decreases as altitude increases. The decrease in air temperature occurs because air pressure decreases with altitude. As altitude increases, less air presses down on the earth's surface. Therefore, the particles of air are spread farther apart, and the air is less dense. Less dense air cannot hold as much heat, so air temperature decreases.

Figure 20.3

How is climate affected by altitude in each location? ▼

Distance from an Ocean   Oceans have a noticeable effect on the temperature of nearby landmasses. Water heats up and cools down more slowly than land does. This property tends to make the temperatures of coastal areas more moderate. In summer, coastal waters warm slowly, keeping temperatures cool over the water and nearby land. In winter, coastal waters cool very slowly and air temperatures stay relatively mild. By contrast, land far from oceans heats up and cools down quickly. So inland areas usually have hot summers and cold winters. Study Table 20.1. Which city is in a coastal area? Which city is inland? Compare the temperature ranges of the two cities.

Surface ocean currents also affect the temperature of coastal areas. Surface ocean currents are broad bands of water that flow in a definite path over the surface of the ocean. Warm currents carry warm water from the equator toward the poles. Cold currents carry cold water away from the poles toward the equator. Surface currents warm or cool the air above them. Therefore, the presence of an ocean current can affect the air temperature of nearby coastal regions.

Figure 20.4 shows surface ocean currents around the United States during the summer. The Florida Current brings warm temperatures to the southern and middle states. The Labrador Current brings cool temperatures to the Northeast. The California Current brings cool temperatures to much of the West Coast.

Table 20.1 Average Temperatures

	Springfield, MO (about 37°N)	San Francisco, CA (about 38°N)
Jan.	−2°C	10°C
Jul.	26°C	15°C
Year	13°C	13°C

Figure 20.4
The map shows ocean currents near the eastern and western coasts of the United States during the summer. How do the currents affect the climates in these two regions? ▼

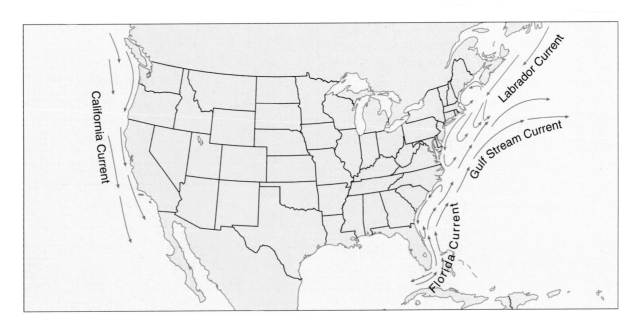

Precipitation

Does it seem to rain whenever you have plans for an outdoor activity? If so, you probably think you live in a wet climate. Precipitation, along with temperature, determines climate. Prevailing winds and topography are two factors that affect the amount of precipitation a place receives.

Prevailing Winds Winds that blow from one direction more often than any other are called **prevailing winds**. Prevailing winds blowing from the water generally carry moisture because the air over oceans and large lakes contains a lot of water vapor. So nearby land receives a great deal of precipitation.

Places where the prevailing winds blow from the land toward the water receive little precipitation. For example, the Sahara Desert is one of the driest places in the world, even though the Atlantic Ocean lies just

SkillBuilder *Finding Causes*

Worldwide City Temperatures

The temperature in an area depends on the latitude, the altitude, and the distance from an ocean. Most newspapers list the daily high and low temperatures for various cities in the world. Study the table on the right, which lists the actual temperatures for some cities on a day in March.

On a world map, locate the two warmest and coldest cities listed in the table. Determine the cause of the regional temperature for each city. Record your findings. Then answer the following questions.

1. What city had the warmest temperatures? Where is this city located?

2. What city had the coldest temperatures? Where is this city located?

3. What factor was the most common for causing warm temperatures?

4. What factor was the most common for causing cold temperatures?

Write a paragraph explaining how latitude, altitude, and distance from an ocean affect an area's temperature.

City	Temperature (°C)	
	High	**Low**
Amsterdam	6	2
Bangkok	34	24
Cairo	17	11
London	9	3
Montreal	1	−10
Moscow	−6	−13
Nairobi	26	14
Rio de Janeiro	29	19
Vienna	−1	−6

to the west. The Sahara's prevailing winds blow over dry land from the east, where there is little moisture.

Topography   The surface features of an area make up its **topography**. One topographical feature that affects precipitation patterns in an area is a mountain range. In California, the Sierra Nevada Mountains force moist air moving east from the Pacific Ocean to rise. As a result, clouds form, and rain falls on the windward side of the mountains, the side facing the wind. The air continues to move over the mountains and down the leeward side, the side facing away from the wind. This air becomes warmer and drier as it moves down, producing the very dry conditions of the Nevada desert areas. The dry region on the leeward side of a mountain is known as the **rain shadow** of the mountain. Study Figure 20.5 to see how a rain shadow is created.

In contrast to the mountainous regions, plains and prairies generally have little precipitation. There are no mountains in these locations to "catch" any moisture carried by prevailing winds. In addition, the prevailing winds over plains and prairies do not carry very much moisture because the oceans are far away.

Figure 20.5
Warm, moist air rises as it hits the windward side of mountains. Rain falls, and dry air moves down the leeward side of the mountains, forming a rain shadow. ▼

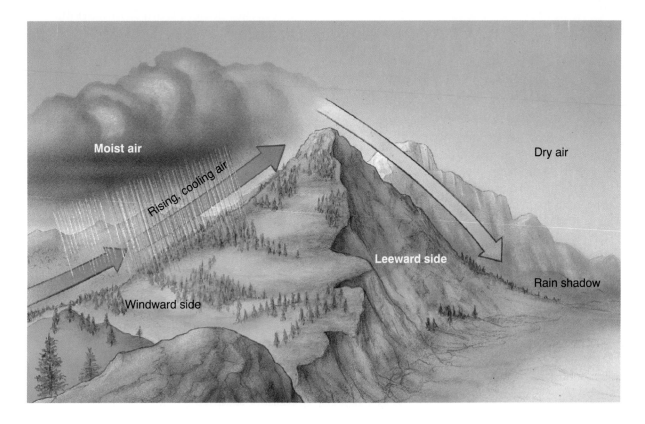

Figure 20.6 ▲
Although both of these people are dressed for cold climates, their type of warm clothing varies greatly.

Imagine you are going on a two-week vacation. One week you'll be in Minneapolis, Minnesota, a northern city in the middle of the United States. The second week you'll be in Miami, Florida, a southeastern city near the ocean. What kinds of clothes should you pack? That depends on what time of year you are traveling. In July, the temperatures for Minneapolis and Miami are about the same. You will probably be most comfortable in shorts and short-sleeved shirts.

If your vacation is in January, you'll find an entirely different situation. The average January temperature in Minneapolis is –12°C. If you're going to spend any time outdoors, you'll need warm clothing and boots. Also, you can probably expect snow. In Miami, the average January temperature is 19°C. While it might be a little chilly for swimming, you'll be comfortable in lightweight clothing. At night or on cloudy days, you might need a sweater. You should also pack some rainwear because winter is the rainy season.

Keep in mind that conditions on any given day can be far different from the average for the month. For example, the lowest temperature ever recorded in Miami was –1°C. Even vacationers from Minneapolis were shivering that day!

Check and Explain

1. How does the climate of a location differ from its weather?

2. Describe two ways in which oceans affect the climate of coastal areas.

3. **Compare** How do you think the average temperatures for January and July in a coastal city in the southeastern United States compare with the average temperatures in the central part of the country? Explain your reasoning.

4. **Infer** Describe the climate where you live. Indicate whether it is wet or dry, hot or cold, and whether it has seasonal changes in precipitation and temperature. Infer how the factors discussed in this section affect your climate.

20.2 Climate Classification

Objectives

▶ **Name** and **describe** the three main climate zones.

▶ **Compare** climate types in the United States to other parts of the world.

▶ **Compare** and **contrast** some plants and animals that live in various types of climates.

▶ **Classify** climates based on climate data.

Suppose your family is moving from Chicago, Illinois, to Los Angeles, California. It's late December, and it's windy and −3°C in Chicago. The ground is covered with snow as you set out to drive to California.

On your trip, you'll pass through several types of climate. The Great Plains states will have a climate similar to Chicago's. From central Colorado through Utah, you will find a drier, warmer climate and a cold, mountainous climate. In Nevada and southern California, you will cross a desert. When you reach Los Angeles, the temperature will be pleasantly warm, about 15°C, and rain may be falling.

You can see from this example that the climate of the United States is varied. What are the different climate types? What factors cause them?

Climate Zones

A region that has a characteristic temperature range is called a **climate zone**. Because temperature is influenced primarily by latitude, the climate zones are based on latitude.

The main climate zones are the tropical, temperate, and polar zones. The tropical zone is the warmest of the three zones. It is located between latitudes 30°N and 30°S. The temperate zone lies on both sides of the tropical zone, extending to about 60° north and south latitude. The polar zone, as you might guess, has the coldest temperatures of the three zones. It is located between 60° north and south latitude and the poles.

Figure 20.7
What type of climate zone is shown in this photograph? ▼

Table 20.2 Climate Types

Climate Type	Temperature Ranges (°C)	Precipitation (annual average)
	−20 to 30	25–150 cm
	5 to 60	under 25 cm
	−3 to 18	200–500 cm
	−30 to 30	40–125 cm
	−40 to 10	under 30 cm

Climate Types

Both the wettest place and the driest place on the earth are located in the tropical climate zone. How is it possible for two very different climates to be located in the same climate zone? The answer is that many factors other than latitude affect the climate of a particular place. Each climate zone is divided into specific climate types that share certain conditions. The most useful

Figure 20.8 World Climate Types ▼

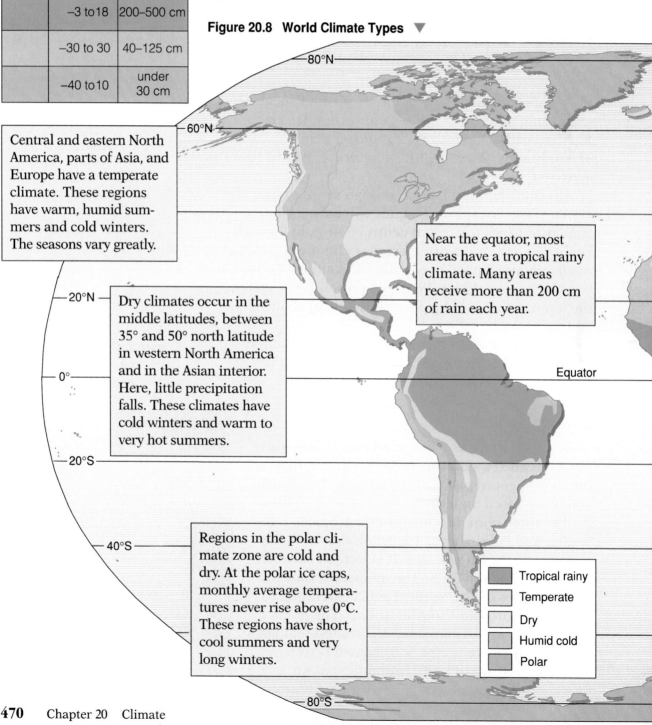

Central and eastern North America, parts of Asia, and Europe have a temperate climate. These regions have warm, humid summers and cold winters. The seasons vary greatly.

Near the equator, most areas have a tropical rainy climate. Many areas receive more than 200 cm of rain each year.

Dry climates occur in the middle latitudes, between 35° and 50° north latitude in western North America and in the Asian interior. Here, little precipitation falls. These climates have cold winters and warm to very hot summers.

Regions in the polar climate zone are cold and dry. At the polar ice caps, monthly average temperatures never rise above 0°C. These regions have short, cool summers and very long winters.

- ■ Tropical rainy
- □ Temperate
- □ Dry
- ■ Humid cold
- ■ Polar

condition for classifying climate types is the amount of precipitation an area receives. Major plant types, altitude, and seasonal variations in winds and precipitation are also considered when classifying climates.

One version of world climate types is shown in Figure 20.8. They are based on the classification system of Wladimir Köppen, a German meteorologist. This climate map is a simplified version of the one used by climatologists. Notice that the map and Table 20.2 are color-keyed.

▼ ACTIVITY

Researching

Extremes

Find out the wettest, driest, hottest, and coldest locations in your state. What type of climate does each place have?

SKILLS WORKOUT

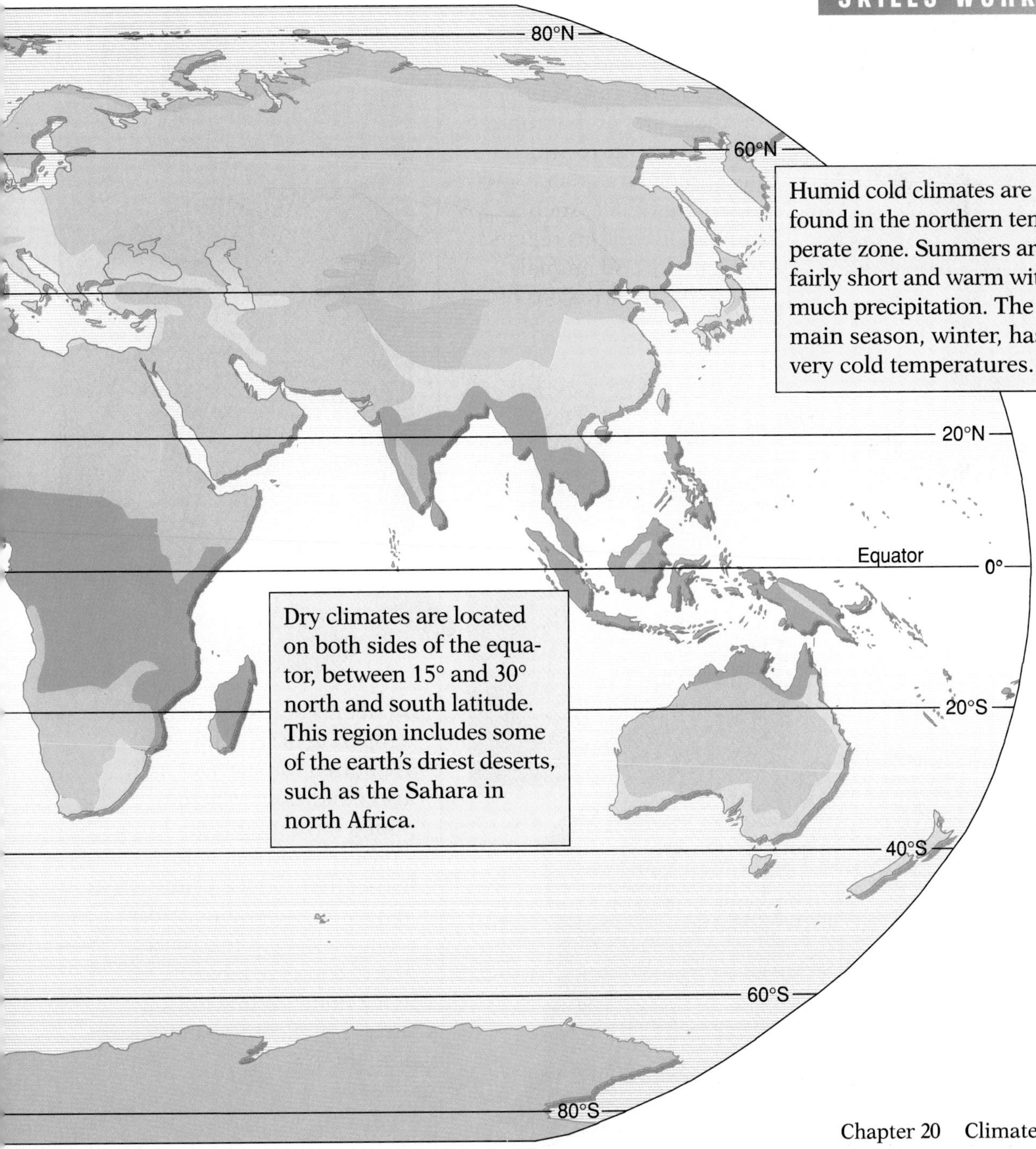

Humid cold climates are found in the northern temperate zone. Summers are fairly short and warm with much precipitation. The main season, winter, has very cold temperatures.

Dry climates are located on both sides of the equator, between 15° and 30° north and south latitude. This region includes some of the earth's driest deserts, such as the Sahara in north Africa.

80°N

60°N

20°N

Equator — 0°

20°S

40°S

60°S

80°S

Life in the Climate Zones

Each climate zone is home to a variety of living things. In order to survive, animals and plants must adapt to conditions within their climate zone. Conditions include temperature, precipitation, and the amount of sunlight, food, water, and living space. What animals have adapted to conditions in the polar climate zone? What plants have adapted to conditions in the tropical climate zone?

Grasses and drought-resistant trees are common in drier parts of the tropical zone. Many burrowing animals, such as gophers, and grazing animals, such as buffalo, live in this region. Few plants and animals live in the drier regions of this zone. ▼

▲ The heavy precipitation in tropical rainy climates ensures plentiful plant life. The vegetation of tropical climates includes a variety of trees, vines, ferns, and mosses. The animal life includes many kinds of birds, amphibians, reptiles, insects, and mammals.

▲ Plants and animals of temperate desert climates are suited for survival in arid conditions. Cactus plants have tough, thick surfaces and thin, spiny leaves that reduce water loss from evaporation. Most animals, such as this gecko lizard, conserve moisture by living underground during the day and coming out at night.

The different climate zones and types also affect humans. Unlike many plants and animals, however, humans have adapted to live in just about every climate type. Though humans don't live permanently in the driest deserts or the coldest polar regions, they are able to survive in those areas for limited amounts of time.

A forest of deciduous trees, trees that lose their leaves annually, is typical of the climate in the temperate zone. Animals include a variety of birds, small mammals, and many insects. Birds often migrate from this climate during winter. Many mammals hibernate during part of the year. ▼

No vegetation grows in the ice cap region of the polar zone. Year-round snow, ice, and cold temperatures prevent plants from growing. Penguins live year-round in the southern polar zone. Polar bears and seals may be found in some seasons. These animals feed on fishes and other marine animals. ▼

▲ The tundra is located in the northern polar zone and in high mountain regions worldwide. As shown above, vegetation in tundra regions is limited to lichens and mosses. In warmer tundra areas, shrublike trees may grow. Animals include birds, reindeer, wolves, and many mosquitoes and flies in the summer.

Have you ever heard the saying, "Everybody complains about the weather, but nobody does anything about it"? Though people have never truly controlled the weather, they have changed the climate in very small areas. The climate of a small area is called a **microclimate**.

Farming has done more to create microclimates than any other human factor. To raise crops, farmers often change conditions on their farms. Through the use of irrigation, farmers brought water to dry regions of the world, such as Israel and parts of California. This water changed barren land into rich, fertile farmland.

Farmers in rice-growing countries, such as China, also alter conditions on their land. Much of the farmland lies on steep slopes. Farmers carve out flat surfaces on these slopes to plant rice. Once planted, rice plants require much water. To keep the plants irrigated, farmers create ways of transporting large amounts of water up to the rice paddies.

Farmers sometimes try to control temperatures. In Florida, for example, a sudden frost can destroy much of the citrus crop. To prevent this, farmers use smoke or large fans to keep air temperatures in their citrus groves from falling below freezing, thus saving the fruit.

Figure 20.9 ▲
Rice paddies growing in Indonesia require flat surfaces and large amounts of water.

Check and Explain

1. Name and describe the three main climate zones.

2. Refer to Figure 20.8. List the climate types in the United States. Which one do you live in? What parts of the world have the same climate type as yours?

3. **Compare and Contrast**   How does climate influence the types of plants and animals that live in an area? Compare the types of plants and animals in a tropical rainy climate with those in a humid cold climate.

4. **Classify**   Using a world map, Figure 20.8, and the Data Bank on page 617, classify the following cities by climate zone (polar, temperate, or tropical) and climate type (tropical rainy, dry, temperate, humid cold, or polar): Moscow, Lima, Reykjavik, and Manila.

Activity 20 *How can you model climates?*

Skills Model; Observe

Task 1 Prelab Prep

1. Collect the following items: 2 small cans (such as tuna fish cans), nail, hammer, 2 jars with lids, gravel, soil, sand, spoon, several plants, water.
2. Make sure each can fits inside a jar by placing a can inside a jar lid. Place the jar upside down on the lid, and screw it closed. If the can doesn't fit, try another can or another jar.
3. Use the hammer and nail to poke three or four holes in the bottom of each can. **Caution! Be careful when using a nail and hammer.**

Task 2 Data Record

1. Copy Table 20.3 on a separate piece of paper.
2. Record your observations in the data table for several days.

Table 20.3   Observations of Bottle Climates

Bottle Climate	Elapsed Time (Days)			
	Day 1	Day 2	Day 5	Day 7
Tropical				
Desert				

Task 3 Procedure

1. Label one jar *Desert* and one jar *Tropical*.
2. For the *Desert* jar, cover the bottom of the can with gravel. Fill the rest of the can with sand.
3. Moisten the sand by sprinkling it with water. Transplant several plants by poking a hole into the sand with your finger and inserting the plant roots into the sand.
4. Place the can on the inside of the jar lid. Lift the lid and can into the *Desert* jar and screw the lid closed.

5. Place the *Desert* jar in a sunny, warm place. Observe for several days, and record your observations.
6. For the *Tropical* jar, cover the bottom of the can with gravel. Fill the rest of the can with soil.
7. Moisten the soil by sprinkling it with water. Transplant several plants by poking a hole into the soil with your finger and inserting the plant roots into the soil.
8. Place the can on the inside of the jar lid. Lift the lid and can into the *Tropical* jar and screw the lid closed.
9. Place the *Tropical* jar in a sunny, warm place. Sprinkle water on the plants every day. Observe for several days, and record your observations.

Task 4 Analysis

1. Which climate had the most moisture? How could you tell?
2. In which climate did the plants survive the best? Why?
3. How does an actual desert climate differ from your *Desert* jar?
4. How does an actual tropical climate differ from your *Tropical* jar?
5. List the variables in this activity.

Task 5 Conclusion

Write a paragraph explaining how your models show the similarities and differences between desert and tropical climates.

Extension

Make climate jars for a tundra and a temperate climate. Follow the same procedure outlined in the activity. Place the tundra jar in the refrigerator and vary the location of the temperate jar. How are tundra and temperate climate types similar? How are they different?

Forest Through the Ice

Fossils indicate that forests once grew around the Arctic Circle. Today this area is covered year-round with ice and snow. What conditions must have been different for plants to have grown in this area?

SKILLS WARMUP

20.3 Climate Change

Objectives

▶ **Explain** the effect of El Niño on climates.

▶ **Describe** the possible effects of major climate changes.

▶ **Name** three possible causes of climate change.

▶ **Predict** how a future ice age could affect an area.

Imagine you could travel back 15,000 years to what is now Illinois. You'd expect the winters to be cold and snowy, just as they are today. But you might be surprised to see the landscape in the summer. The land would be covered with ice and snow. The air temperature would be frigid. About 15,000 years ago, the climate in the midwestern United States was very different from the climate today. What could cause such a change to occur? Have other such climate changes occurred?

Scientists have accumulated evidence indicating that the world's climate has changed gradually but dramatically over time. Though they do not know the exact causes, scientists have a number of theories.

Climate Change Over Time

Major climate changes produce long-lasting shifts in temperature and precipitation patterns worldwide. Long-term changes in climate can have major effects on all living things. About 65 million years ago, many species of plants and animals, including the dinosaurs, died out. Many scientists hypothesize that these mass extinctions were caused by climate changes brought about by natural occurrences.

Although some climate changes can occur quickly, most happen slowly. For example, recall that the earth's continents were once one great landmass called Pangaea. As the landmass broke up and drifted, the distribution of land and water on the earth's surface slowly changed. Because land and water absorb heat differently, the heating of the earth's surface was affected. These changes, in turn, may have produced changes in the world's climates.

Ice Ages and Climate Glaciers covered much of the earth's surface in the past. Recall that a period when glaciers grow and advance over the land is referred to as an ice age. Scientists infer from evidence that many ice ages occurred in the past 2 million years. During these ice ages, the average temperature on the earth was about 6°C cooler than it is today, and sea levels were lower.

Each ice age was separated by a period of warming, called an *interglacial*, when the ice sheets melted and retreated. The last ice age ended about 10,000 years ago. Figure 20.10 shows how much of North America was covered by glaciers during the last ice age.

Today large land surfaces, such as Antarctica and Greenland, are still covered by sheets of ice. Some scientists hypothesize that we are now in an interglacial and that the ice sheet may advance again in the future. How would the advance affect the earth's climate?

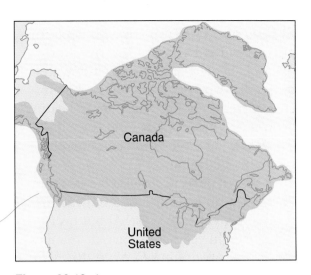

Figure 20.10 ▲
The last ice age in North America extended into the United States.

Though scientists don't know for certain the cause of the ice ages, they do know that the moving ice sheets changed the earth's surface. For example, the Great Lakes were shaped by the last glacier. Long Island, New York, is made of materials left behind by glaciers.

Figure 20.11 ▲
The kettle lakes in Wisconsin were formed by the last ice age. Kettle lakes are also common in New York and Minnesota.

Figure 20.12 ▲
Scientists in South Dakota uncover fossilized mammoth bones from the ice ages. The bones help them learn more about the ice ages.

El Niño and Climate Recall that ocean currents affect climate. Air over the ocean is heated or cooled by the water beneath. Warm currents heat the air; cold currents cool it. This uneven heating generates winds. Winds influence climate. Therefore, changes in ocean currents may affect climate.

A warm current flowing across the Pacific Ocean near the equator generally moves from east to west. About every three to eight years, this current changes direction, producing *El Niño*. Recall that El Niño is a warm ocean current that flows from west to east across the Pacific Ocean. When El Niño reaches South America, it moves down the west coast, where a cold current usually flows. El Niño eventually warms the water off the coast.

The warm water affects many living things. For example, it is a hazard to certain fishing industries in these regions. Here, fishes are adapted to a cold water environment. Coral reefs die off. Island nesting birds migrate to cool waters. Marine animals move to escape the warming.

Figure 20.14 ▲
In Ecuador, El Niño caused massive floods. Bridges, buildings, and homes washed away.

El Niño does more than raise the water temperature off the coast of South America. It disrupts other ocean currents, worldwide precipitation, and temperature patterns. In the early 1980s a very strong El Niño caused dramatic climate changes throughout the world. Parts of Africa and Australia suffered severe drought. Other regions of the world, such as Peru and Ecuador, had heavy rains and flooding. Figures 20.13 and 20.14 show some of the damage caused by El Niño.

When El Niño occurs, scientists can only observe its effects. Currently, computer models developed from past El Niño patterns may help predict how El Niño develops. For example, a computer model at the Lomont-Doherty Geological Observatory in New York forecasted in 1990 that an El Niño warming trend would occur in the central Pacific Ocean in 1992. Scientists were pleased that the model proved to be correct. Although such forecasts cannot prevent El Niño, they can possibly help save lives and property.

Figure 20.13 ▲
El Niño caused severe droughts in parts of Africa. Crops, livestock, and people suffered.

Human Causes of Climate Change

Human activities also influence climate. As human populations increase, people need new places to live. They need land to grow food. All over the world, land has been cleared for farming and construction. In many areas, the removal of trees has caused a decrease in the amount of precipitation the area receives. The result is a drier climate.

The building of a city alters the climate in an area. The paved surfaces absorb sunlight and heat up. This heat slightly raises the average temperature of a city compared to the surrounding countryside.

People affect climate through farming, industry, and driving automobiles. Smoke and dust created by farming and industry reduce the amount of radiant energy reaching the earth's surface. Industry and automobiles release carbon dioxide into the air through the burning of fossil fuels.

Ecology
L I N K

Collect the following items: a spray bottle, water, a fan, and two plates.

1. Spray a fine mist of water onto two plates.

2. Use a small fan to blow air over one of the plates.

3. Determine which plate dries faster.

Imagine the increase of open space in a dense rainforest due to deforestation. How might the process you modeled affect vegetation that requires a moist climate?

A C T I V I T Y

Consider This

What Can Be Done About Global Warming?

Recall that global warming is a worldwide increase in average temperature. Many scientists hypothesize that people contribute to global warming by adding certain gases to the atmosphere.

One major cause of global warming, some scientists say, is the burning of fossil fuels in cars and factories. These activities add large amounts of carbon dioxide to the air. In the atmosphere, carbon dioxide traps heat and prevents it from escaping into space. The result may be higher temperatures on the surface of the earth.

The effects of global warming are difficult to predict. Some scientists say the results will mean human and economic disaster. Others say that global warming may be balanced by a cooling trend, or that its effects will not be great. There may even be benefits, if global warming increases the growth of crops.

Think About It   Should people and countries reduce their use of fossil fuels in an attempt to prevent global warming?

Write About It   Pretend you are the editor of a newspaper.

Write an editorial about what kinds of actions, if any, people or countries should take to reduce the use of fossil fuels.

For years, some scientists theorized that one of the major causes of the ice ages was changes in the tilt of the earth's axis. The theory states that, as the axis slowly changes, the amount of sunlight hitting part of the earth changes. This, in turn, causes the advance and retreat of glaciers.

Recent studies in an unlikely place are making some scientists rethink this theory. Researchers studied ancient mineral deposits in Devil's Hole, Nevada, for clues to changes in the earth's temperature. Devil's Hole is a water-filled fissure, or crack, in Nevada's desert floor. The hole is more than 120 m deep but only about 210 cm wide. Over thousands of years, the water that seeped into Devil's Hole left layers of the mineral calcite on the walls. Divers used special drills to take out samples.

Study of the calcite suggested to scientists that the warming of the second-to-last ice age began about 140,000 years ago. At this time, the earth was not tilted so that maximum solar radiation reached polar regions any time during the year. However, other research sets the end of the second-to-last ice age at about 128,000 years ago. At that time, the earth's axis was tilted so that the maximum solar radiation reached the polar regions. If the Devil's Hole finding holds true, perhaps the tilt of the earth's axis was not the main reason for the end of this ice age.

The scientists who conducted the Devil's Hole studies think that ice ages come and go for a number of reasons. In addition to the changes in the tilt of the earth's axis, they hypothesize that ice ages are due to changes in the oceans, glaciers, and atmosphere.

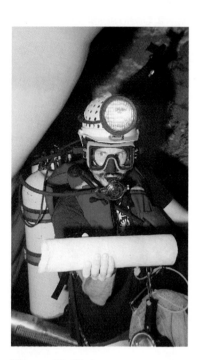

Figure 20.15 ▲
A core sample from Devil's Hole may hold some answers to the cause of ice ages.

Check and Explain

1. What is El Niño? How does it change climates?

2. Describe possible effects of major climate changes.

3. **Find Causes** Name three possible natural causes of worldwide climate change.

4. **Predict** How would the place where you live be affected by a new ice age? Explain.

Chapter 20 Review

Concept Summary

20.1 Causes of Climate
▶ Climate is the weather of a region over a long period of time. It is determined mainly by temperature and precipitation.
▶ Generally, temperature decreases as latitude increases.
▶ Air temperature tends to decrease as altitude increases. Altitude is distance above sea level.
▶ Oceans have a moderating effect on temperatures of nearby landmasses.
▶ The amount of precipitation a place receives depends on prevailing winds and topography.
▶ A rain shadow is created when moist air deposits precipitation on a mountain range's windward side.

20.2 Climate Classification
▶ The three main climate zones are the tropical, temperate, and polar zones.
▶ Within the climate zones are different climate types, which are classified by the amount of precipitation.

▶ The plants and animals in each climate zone are adapted to the conditions in that zone.
▶ A microclimate is the particular climate of a small area.

20.3 Climate Change
▶ Global climate changes can have far-reaching and dramatic effects.
▶ Ice ages are periods of worldwide climate change. Periods when the ice sheets retreated are called interglacials.
▶ El Niño is a change in the normal ocean currents off the coast of South America.
▶ Past climate changes may have been caused by continental drift, changes in the tilt of the earth's axis, and changes in the radiation given off by the sun.
▶ Human activity causes change in microclimates and may produce worldwide global warming.

Chapter Vocabulary

climate (20.1)
altitude (20.1)
prevailing winds (20.1)

topography (20.1)
rain shadow (20.1)

climate zone (20.2)
microclimate (20.2)

Check Your Vocabulary

Use the vocabulary words above to complete the following sentences correctly.

1. Many climate types are found in each of the three _____ .

2. On the leeward side of a mountain, a _____ is often located.

3. Winds that blow most often from one direction are called _____ .

4. The weather for a region that occurs over a long period of time is its _____ .

5. One influence on temperature is _____ , which is height above sea level.

6. The climate of a small area is called a(n) _____ .

7. The surface features of an area make up its _____ .

Write Your Vocabulary

Write sentences using the vocabulary words above. Show that you know what each word means.

Chapter 20 Review

Check Your Knowledge

Answer the following in complete sentences.

1. Explain the difference between climate and weather.

2. Describe how latitude is related to temperature.

3. Explain how oceans can affect the temperature of nearby landmasses.

4. List the two main influences on precipitation.

5. What are the three main climate zones, and what are their boundaries?

6. List five climate types and one location where each can be found.

7. What is a microclimate? How is one formed?

8. What are the kinds of climate change that El Niño can cause?

9. List factors that may have caused past climate changes.

Choose the answer that best completes each sentence.

10. A time when ice sheets are retreating is called (an interglacial, an ice age, El Niño, summer).

11. The (leeward, north, windward, south) side of a mountain often receives the most precipitation.

12. The sun's rays strike the earth most directly at the (poles, equator, temperate zone, oceans).

13. Few plants grow in the (temperate, tropical, polar) climate zone.

Check Your Understanding

Apply the concepts you have learned to answer each question.

1. Explain how two locations at the same latitude but different altitudes can have a very different climate.

2. Would you expect a coastal area where the prevailing winds blow from the land to the ocean to receive much or little precipitation? Explain your thinking.

3. Why are areas at greater latitudes generally cooler than areas at lower latitudes?

4. Explain how variations in the amount of radiation given off by the sun could cause climate change.

5. **Mystery Photo** The photograph on page 462 was taken from an airplane. It shows waterfalls streaming down the hills of a tropical rain forest. What is the typical climate in a tropical rain forest? Would you expect to see these green trees in the winter?

6. **Extension** Some scientists think that great amounts of volcanic dust in the atmosphere could lead to cooler average temperatures over the entire globe. Explain how this cooling might occur.

7. **Compare and Contrast** El Niño and the ice ages are two types of climate change. How are they similar? How are they different?

8. **Infer** Most trees in a humid cold climate are conifers. Why?

Develop Your Skills

Use the skills you have developed in this chapter to complete each activity.

1. **Interpret Data** The graph below shows average temperature ranges in an area over a year. Study the graph, then answer the following questions.

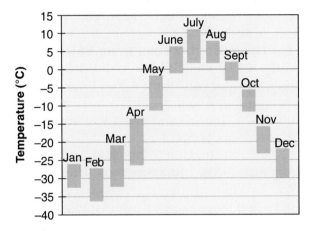

a. Which month is the warmest? The coldest?

b. What is the average temperature in April? In November?

c. What kind of climate is indicated by the graph: polar, temperate, or tropical? How do you know?

2. **Infer** Some animals excrete wastes that contain almost no water. In which type of climate might such an animal live?

3. **Data Bank** Use the information on page 617 to answer the following questions.

a. Which city has the lowest average temperature?

b. Which city has the highest average rainfall?

4. **Communicate** Make a poster that shows the five major climate types. List the temperature and precipitation characteristics of each type. Also list plants and animals in each zone.

Make Connections

1. **Link the Concepts** Draw a concept map showing how the concepts below link together. Add terms to connect, or link, the concepts.

   world climate
   temperature
   precipitation
   ocean currents
   topography
   prevailing winds
   latitude
   altitude

2. **Science and Technology** Houses are built differently in different climates. What features would you expect a house built in a desert to have? What features would you expect in a house built in a polar or near-polar climate?

3. **Science and Social Studies** Climate affects the plants that grow in a region. Use the library to find out how climate affects which types of crops are grown. Also find out about ways that farmers are able to grow a crop in an environment to which that crop is not suited.

4. **Science and Society** Groups of people called Bedouins live in the deserts of the Middle East. Do some research to find out how these people survive in the extreme heat and aridity of the desert.

Going Home

*The following excerpts are from
the novel* Going Home
by Nicholasa Mohr.

When my parents asked me and my brothers to come into the living room to discuss something important, I tried not to act too nervous. I couldn't think of anything I'd done that was bad. Maybe one of my brothers had gotten into trouble.

Papi spoke first. "Kids, we want to tell you all something—something that should make you all feel happy. You know how we've always talked about taking a trip to Puerto Rico? The whole family going there together? Well, now we are going to do it! That's right. This summer we are all gonna spend two weeks in Puerto Rico."

"That's fantastic, Papi!" said Tito. Not only was I relieved, I felt just as happy as Tito. . . .

"Okay, now wait,"—Papi paused— "there's something more. You know how we told you kids that Tio Jorge is retiring and has plans to live permanently in Puerto Rico? Well, the time has come; Tio will be staying in Puerto Rico and he's going to build a house in our village in the country-side. So—"

"That's right!" Tio Jorge interrupted Papi. "A house big enough for all of you to spend time with me."

"Correct," said Papi, "and since Tio Jorge is staying, we have decided that—" Papi turned toward me— "you, Felita, will stay the whole summer in Puerto Rico and keep Tio Jorge company." When I heard those words, I could hardly believe my own ears!

"Papi, you mean I'm going away for the whole summer? Wow!" I hugged Papi, Mami, and Tio Jorge. "Thank you, everybody!"

"The most important thing," Mami said, "is that you children will finally get to meet all of your family. You have your grandfather, Abuelo Juan; your Aunt Julia and Uncle Tomas; and many cousins that you have never met. . . ."

"Listen, children," Papi said, "you are going to eat the most delicious fruits. Mangos right off the trees—so sweet and juicy. You'll see lots of flowers and green everywhere. And the weather is great. Even in the summer you always have a breeze. And, of course, it's never cold like here where you freeze in the winter and the humidity makes your bones ache."

The first thing I did was head for the phone and call my best friend, Gigi, but there was no answer. Maybe my second best friend, Consuela, would be hanging out. Anyway, I wanted to check out my block so I could share the good news with somebody. I asked Mami if I could go out to play.

"It's cold out, Felita. What kind of games are you going to play? And besides, there's probably nobody outside now."

"Come on, Mami, you know we can play tag, hide-and-go-seek, lots of games. Or I can just hang out and talk to my friends." She always gives me a hard time about going out alone just to hang out. "Mami, please, I'd like to tell my friends about our trip. Look, if there's nobody outside, I'll come back up. I promise. Please say yes!"

"All right, but you are not to leave this

block. Understand?"

I put on my warm jacket, hat, and gloves so that I wouldn't freeze when I went outdoors. My street was pretty empty. Except for a passerby now and then, no one was about. Thick dark clouds covered the sky, making everything look gray and gloomy. It wasn't very windy, but it felt cold and humid. I sat down on my stoop and exhaled, watching my hot breath turn into white puffs of smoke as it hit cold air, and I thought about Puerto Rico. All that bright sunshine every day. I shivered, feeling the cold of the stone steps going right through me, and I wondered what it must be like to live in a place where it didn't ever snow and the leaves never left the trees. I stood up, leaning against the railing, and checked my street, hoping to see somebody I could talk to about my trip.

Skills in Science

Reading Skills in Science

1. **Find Context Clues** Use context clues contained in the passage to describe the climate of Puerto Rico.

2. **Predict** The selection is told from the point of view of Felita, who is going to spend the summer in Puerto Rico. Suppose one of her brothers was narrating the story. How might the selection differ? (Remember, her brothers will stay in Puerto Rico for only two weeks.)

Writing Skills in Science

1. **If . . . Then Arguments** The climate of the town in which you live impacts many areas of your lifestyle, such as your manner of dress and your leisure activities. Think how the climate of Puerto Rico differs from that of your home town. Write a paragraph describing how your lifestyle might be different if you lived on this island.

Activities

Collect Data One of Puerto Rico's most valuable natural resources is its climate. In a library, research the weather of this island. Use your findings to create a travel brochure that would encourage tourists to visit Puerto Rico.

Communicate Use reference tools to determine the average monthly temperature in San Juan, Puerto Rico. Make a graph to illustrate your findings.

Where to Read More

Puerto Rico in Pictures prepared by the Geography Department of Lerner Publications. Minneapolis: Lerner Publication Company, 1987. Through the use of photographs and drawings, the reader is introduced to the topography, history, society, economics, and government structure of Puerto Rico.

Unit 7
Energy and Environment

Data Bank

Use the information on pages 612 to 625 to answer the following questions about topics explored in this unit.

Reading a Graph

What percentage of the land in the United States is used for parks and wildlife? What percentage is used for cities?

Comparing

Which area of the world has more natural gas reserves, North America or Eastern Europe and Russia?

Predicting

What do you think the graph on land uses will look like in the year 2020? Predict the percentages of land use in 2020. Explain your predictions.

The photograph to the left is of solar mirrors at a power-generating facility in Mohave, California. How can solar mirrors help generate energy?

Chapter 21 Mineral and Energy Resources

What do you see?

66In this picture, crushed aluminum cans are getting ready to be recycled at a recycling center. People are getting it together by recycling aluminum cans to be reused in other aluminum products. This process is very important for the future because it does not waste valuable resources. Please recycle!99

Jill Partridge
Rockwood South Junior
High School
Fenton, Missouri

To find out more about the photograph, look on page 506. As you read this chapter, you will learn about the mineral and energy resources of the earth.

488

21.1 Mineral Resources

Objectives

▶ **Distinguish** between renewable and nonrenewable resources.

▶ **Describe** the problems associated with mining and processing ores.

▶ **Compare** and **contrast** different views on reclamation.

▶ **Make a table** showing information about three types of mining.

Did you know that most things you use each day come from natural resources? *Natural resources are materials from the environment that people* use to carry on their lives. For example, the beverage can you drink from is made from aluminum.

Aluminum, most other minerals, coal, and oil are examples of **nonrenewable resources.** Many nonrenewable resources are removed in great amounts. Once they are removed, they cannot be replaced. Other natural resources include air, water, and plants. They can be replaced as they are used. For this reason, they are called **renewable resources.**

Formation of Ores

Aluminum belongs to a group of nonrenewable resources called minerals. Recall that a mineral is an element or a compound that forms naturally in the earth. Some elements chemically combine with other elements, forming minerals. Other minerals, such as copper, are in the earth's crust in elemental form. Minerals are commonly found in deposits called ores. An **ore** is a mineral-rich rock deposit that can be removed from the earth and used to make products.

Ores may form as sedimentary, igneous, or metamorphic rocks change during the rock cycle. For example, ores containing iron may form in igneous rock when magma cools. Some ores form in metamorphic rock when minerals dissolve in hot, underground water. The minerals settle and harden, producing pure mineral veins.

Figure 21.1 ▲
Copper ore (top) is mined and made into copper wire. Copper wire is used in many different types of electrical equipment.

Mining of Ores and Useful Rocks

Once an ore is located, it is mined, or removed from the ground. The type of mining depends on how close the ore is to the earth's surface. Surface mining and open-pit mining remove ores that are close to the earth's surface. Underground mining removes ores that are deep under the earth's surface. Once an ore is removed from the ground, workers and machines separate the desired substance from the rest of the ore.

Open-Pit Mining

Some ores near the earth's surface are removed by giant earthmoving equipment. This process is called open-pit mining. When open-pit mining removes rocks, it is called quarrying. Rocks, such as granite and marble, are collected from the earth by quarrying. The photograph below shows limestone being quarried. ▼

Underground Mining

In underground mining, shafts or tunnels are dug down to ore deposits deep within the earth. The ore is dug or blasted out of the ore-containing rock. It is then transported to the surface. Salt, uranium, lead, limestone, and potash are sometimes mined in this way. ▼

Surface Mining

◄ Surface mining removes ores that are very close to the earth's surface. One type of surface mining is strip mining. During strip mining, a trench is cut and the ore is removed. A second trench is dug next to the first one. The material dug up from the second trench is pushed into the first trench. This process continues over an entire site.

Science and Society *Effects of Mining*

People benefit from the materials obtained from mining. However, mining can harm the environment. For example, open-pit and surface mining can leave the land scarred and barren. Underground mining can cause collapse or sinking of the surface above. By-products of mining and ore processing can pollute the air, land, and water. For example, uranium mining creates waste materials that give off harmful radiation. Surface mining produces the very poisonous chemical, arsenic (AR suh NIHK).

Surface mining also produces many sources of water pollution. When an area is surface-mined, rain may absorb lead, copper, or arsenic from piles of mining wastes. The polluted water then sinks into the groundwater. Mining can also pollute surface water when silt and pollutants run off into lakes and rivers.

For years, mining companies often abandoned mined areas. Recently, however, laws require operators of mines to return a mined area to a clean, useful condition. Returning a mining site to its former condition is called **reclamation**. In some reclaimed areas, no evidence of mining remains. But often, so much topsoil was lost in mining that a reclaimed area will never be the same.

Figure 21.2 ▲
The land in the foreground is the result of surface mining for coal. The land in the background was reclaimed after coal mining.

Check and Explain

1. What are the differences between renewable and nonrenewable resources?

2. What are some problems associated with mining and processing ores?

3. **Compare and Contrast** Compare and contrast the advantages and disadvantages of reclamation. Include two points of view: a resident in a mined area, and a mining company executive.

4. **Collect Data** Make a table that includes three types of mining. For each type list ores obtained, sources of pollution, and the type of area mined.

Running on Empty

How is the food you eat similar to the gasoline that powers an automobile? How is it different? Explain.

21.2 Fossil-Fuel Resources

Objectives

▶ **Name** the four stages of coal formation.

▶ **Describe** how petroleum and natural gas form.

▶ **Identify** the uses of fossil fuels and some problems associated with burning fossil fuels.

▶ **Make a graph** showing numerical data about energy sources.

C oal, oil, and natural gas are formed from the preserved remains of plants and animals. The preserved remains of once-living things are called fossils. Therefore, coal, oil, and natural gas are known as **fossil fuels.**

The energy stored in fossil fuels can be traced to the sun. Plants use energy in sunlight to produce a sugar called glucose. Animals eat plants for the energy provided by glucose. Some of the energy is stored in the bodies of animals. When animals and plants die, this energy remains stored. If conditions are right, the remains may become fossil fuels. Thus, the energy stored in fossil fuels originally came from the sun.

Figure 21.3

A teenager who lives in Ireland unloads peat. Peat serves as a fuel for fires in many countries.

Coal

Millions of years ago, swamps covered much of the land. Plant life was plentiful. After plants and other organic materials died in swamp waters, they slowly decayed. They eventually lost most of their oxygen and hydrodgen. However, most of their carbon remained. As the sediment aged and compacted, it changed into coal. Coal is an organic sedimentary rock. Different types of coal form in stages, as shown on page 493.

Coal deposits are located all over the world. In areas with coal deposits near the earth's surface, surface mining removes the coal from the ground. An example of this type of coal is peat, shown in Figure 21.3. Some coal deposits deep under the surface are mined using underground methods.

Peat Look at Figure 21.4. In the first stage of coal formation *peat* is formed. Peat is made of decaying leaves, twigs, and branches. It has a high water and carbon content. When peat burns, it releases smoke and pollutants. Many peat deposits are located in wet, marshy areas in Great Britain, Russia, and Ukraine.

Lignite As peat compresses and ages, it changes into *lignite*. Lignite is more solid than peat. It is a soft brown coal that is about 40 percent carbon. When lignite burns, it releases pollutants that are harmful to people and the environment. Most lignite is mined in eastern European countries. In the United States, lignite is mined in Texas, North Dakota, and Louisiana.

Bituminous Coal Over time, pressure and heat convert lignite into *subbituminous* (sub by TOO mihn uhs) *coal*, then into *bituminous* coal. This soft coal is about 85 percent carbon. It is the most common type of coal in the world. It is also the type of coal most mined and used in the United States. Because bituminous coal has a higher carbon content than lignite or peat, it burns cleaner and releases fewer pollutants. However, even bituminous coal releases some pollutants.

Anthracite Hard coal, or *anthracite* (AN thruh syt), forms in the fourth stage of coal formation. Great pressure and heat over millions of years change bituminous coal to anthracite. Because anthracite is about 90 percent carbon, it releases a great amount of heat and few pollutants when burned. Unfortunately, anthracite is not very common.

Figure 21.4 ▶
The Stages of Coal Formation

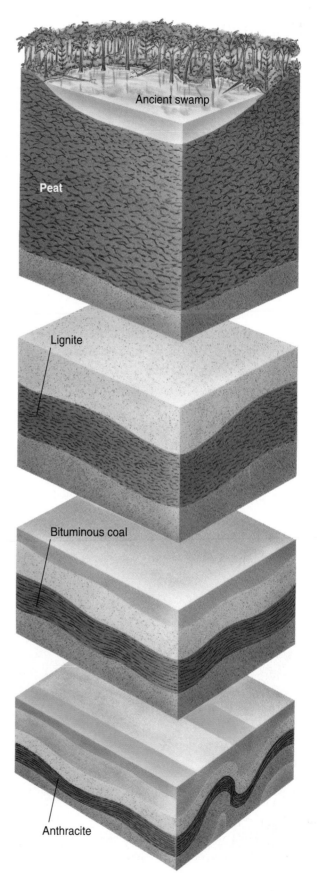

Petroleum and Natural Gas

Fossil fuels are hydrocarbons; they contain compounds of hydrogen and carbon. Crude oil, or **petroleum**, is a liquid mixture of hydrocarbons. Most petroleum deposits are found under the oceans or in areas once covered by oceans.

Most petroleum is made of the partly decayed remains of plants and animals that lived hundreds of millions of years ago in the oceans. When the plants and animals died, their remains settled to the ocean floor and were covered by sediments. Heat and pressure changed the sediments into rock, and the plant and animal remains into oil. The oil seeped through openings, or pores, in the rock. When the oil reached a lower layer of rock, such as shale, the oil could not penetrate and the oil collected in pools, as shown in Figure 21.5.

A gaseous mixture of hydrocarbons is called **natural gas**. Because natural gas is less dense than petroleum, it is usually found above oil deposits.

Drilling for Oil

Geologists use many different techniques to search for oil and natural gas. They may study rock formations at the earth's surface. They may look at patterns of seismic waves set in motion by underground explosions. They may measure the density of underground rock.

Once geologists locate an oil deposit, the oil is brought to the surface. Oil is removed from the ground by drilling a well from the surface down to the oil. As shown in Figure 21.6, a tall structure called a derrick is built to support the drilling equipment. In offshore oil drilling, a platform supports the derrick and equipment above the ocean water.

After the drill reaches the oil deposit, the oil is pumped to the surface. Pumping oil is similar to water being pumped from a groundwater well. The oil is then transported by a pipeline. If natural gas is present, it is sent through a different pipeline.

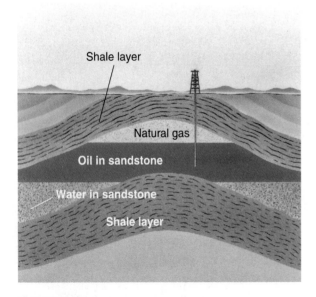

Figure 21.5 ▲
Oil and natural gas are often found in sedimentary layers located beneath a layer of shale.

Figure 21.6 ▲
Oil drilling equipment explores for oil deposits in Alaska. Which structure is the derrick?

Uses of Coal

At one time, coal was the major source of energy throughout the world. It was used to heat buildings, drive locomotives and ocean liners, and run factories.

Much of the coal used today produces electric power, or electricity. Look at Figure 21.7 to see the current uses for coal in the United States. At power plants, the heat from burning coal boils water to produce steam. The steam turns huge, fanlike devices, called turbines, in electric generators. Generators change the mechanical energy of the turbines into electrical energy.

Bituminous coal is used to make coke. Coke is important in the processing of iron ore and in steel production. Coke is a fuel that burns with intense heat and produces little smoke.

In some countries, such as Russia and Ireland, peat is an important fuel. Dried peat is used mainly for heating homes.

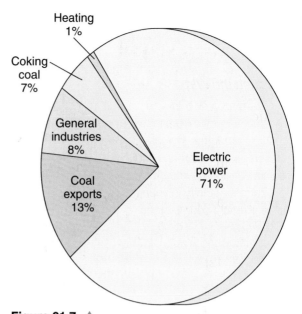

Figure 21.7 ▲

What is the most common use of coal in the United States?

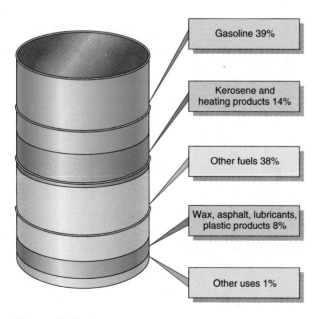

Figure 21.8 ▲

What percentage of petroleum is refined into gasoline?

Petroleum and Natural Gas Uses

Today, oil and natural gas meet most of the energy needs in the United States. For example, natural gas is commonly used to heat homes and for cooking. Natural gas has certain advantages over other fossil fuels. It burns clean, produces less pollutants, and is easy to transport.

Petroleum pumped from a well is separated, or refined, into various products, as shown in Figure 21.8. Many types of transportation use petroleum as fuel. Gasoline, diesel fuel, kerosene, and jet fuel are examples of petroleum fuels.

Many nonfuel products, such as motor oil, waxes, asphalt, and petrochemicals, also come from petroleum. Useful chemical compounds made from the raw materials of petroleum or natural gas are called **petrochemicals**. Petrochemicals are used to make plastics, fabrics, fertilizers, and medicines.

Through the Wire

Where do you think the electricity comes from that powers the lights in your classroom? Research to find out which energy sources produce electricity in your area. Present your findings to the class.

SKILLS WORKOUT

Impact of Fossil Fuels

Although people in the United States are dependent on fossil fuels, using them can harm the environment. Recall some of the effects on the environment of mining and processing ores. The mining and processing of fossil fuels affect the environment in similar ways. In addition, oil pumping and shipping can lead to oil spills. Oil spills cause major damage to plants and animals in a spill area.

The burning of fossil fuels also has harmful effects. When fossil fuels burn, a number of different substances are released into the air. Some of these substances are smoke and tiny particles of ash, which make the air unhealthy to breathe. Others are gases that dissolve in rainwater, producing a weak acid that falls to the earth as acid rain. Acid rain can damage buildings and destroy plant and animal life in lakes. Carbon dioxide produced when fossil fuels are burned may lead to global warming.

Career Corner *Natural Gas Service Person*

Who Helps People Stay Warm?

Have you ever been in a building that wasn't heated during winter? Heat is one thing you wouldn't want to be without. Home heating is important to your comfort and health.

Many homes in the United States are heated with natural gas. Also many people cook using natural gas in their stoves. Your local power company probably hires natural-gas service people to maintain furnaces and cooking equipment in homes, public buildings, and businesses.

A natural-gas service person responds when gas lines get clogged, pilot lights go out and need to be relit, and gas leaks occur. It's a responsible job involving problem solving and critical thinking.

Most jobs for a gas service person require a high school degree. To prepare for a career in this field, you should take courses in math and science. Upon completion of high school, you take tests in basic high school math to enter a training program. During training, you learn about gas lines and furnaces.

Once you finish training, you must pass more tests before becoming a qualified gas service person. If a training program is not available in your area, you can take courses in heating and air conditioning at many colleges. After two years of courses, you will be qualified to repair heating systems.

Science and Society
Pumping Oil from the Sea

Some of the richest oil deposits in the world are beneath the ocean floor near continental coasts. To drill down to these offshore deposits, oil companies often use portable drilling platforms. These platforms support the derrick, drilling equipment, and living quarters for up to 50 workers. The platforms are built on the shore and then towed to the drilling site. At the drilling site, legs are lowered until they rest on the ocean floor. Once the offshore rig is set up, the methods for drilling and removing oil and gas are similar to those used on land.

Offshore oil drilling presents a few problems that do not exist on land. The drill must be lowered through many meters of water. Also, weather conditions can affect offshore drilling operations. For example, when Hurricane Andrew struck the Gulf of Mexico in 1992, several thousand oil workers had to return to shore until the storm passed.

One of the biggest disadvantages of offshore drilling is the possibility of oil spills. Sometimes, the pressure of the oil or gas can cause blowouts. During a blowout, large amounts of oil spill into the sea. Oil spills also result from leaks in pipelines and tankers. Oil spills cause very serious pollution problems that can kill many marine organisms. When oil spills wash onshore, coastal plants and animals are killed or injured, and the land is polluted.

Figure 21.9 ▲
An accident at an oil platform (above) could cause major environmental damage (below).

Check and Explain

1. Name and describe the stages of coal formation in the order in which they occur.

2. What is petroleum, and how did it form? What is natural gas, and how did it form?

3. **Reason and Conclude** How would your life be different without fossil fuels? Explain.

4. **Make a Graph** Make a circle graph using the percentage of energy in the United States supplied by each of the following types of fossil fuels: petroleum, 43 percent; natural gas, 24 percent; coal, 22 percent; other, 11 percent.

In the Stone Ages

Fossil fuels became widely used only during the last century. What energy resources do you think people used before coal and oil were easily available? Explain.

21.3 Alternative Energy Resources

Objectives

▶ **List** reasons for the increased demand for energy.

▶ **Identify** alternative ways of generating energy.

▶ **Compare** and **contrast** direct and indirect solar power.

▶ **Predict** which factors determine the possibility of using alternative ways of generating energy.

How much oil do you use every year? You may not believe it, but you use about ten barrels of oil a year. And every year, the amount increases. In fact, the demand for energy has almost doubled every 20 years since 1900. Some reasons for higher energy demand include an increase in world population, an increased use of electricity, and the invention of energy-using devices.

As the demand for energy rises, the use of fossil fuels increases. The result is that reserves of fossil fuels are being used up. Therefore, scientists and engineers are working to develop alternative ways of generating energy that do not require the use of fossil fuels. Most alternative energy comes from renewable resources.

Wind Energy

In recent years, windmills, such as those shown in Figure 21.10, have been used to generate electricity. The blades of the windmills serve as turbines that turn the shaft of a generator to produce electricity. The amount of electricity produced by one windmill is small. However, hundreds of windmills together produce enough energy for commercial use.

Wind may seem to be the perfect energy source because it is clean and free. But at most locations the wind doesn't blow constantly. Power companies need a constant, reliable source of energy. Only a few locations can provide enough wind to meet their needs. Also, snow and freezing rain can interfere with the operation of windmills.

Figure 21.10 ▲
Windmills in California generate electricity.

Geothermal Energy

Geothermal energy is heat energy from within the earth. In some parts of the world, magma heats surrounding igneous rock. Hot igneous rock near the earth's surface heats underground water and changes it to steam. Geothermal reservoirs form when rock traps the hot water and steam underground.

Steam and hot water from geothermal wells are used to heat homes and buildings. Some electric power plants use geothermal steam to turn turbines in generators. Look at Figure 21.11. Water is pumped into wells dug into an area with very hot underground rock. As the water boils, it creates steam. The steam is brought to the surface to run a generator. The electricity produced powers homes and businesses.

Geothermal energy isn't a practical source in areas without present or past volcanic activity. But some scientists are studying how to use the ordinary heat trapped in underground rocks.

Figure 21.11 ▲
A geothermal power plant in Iceland uses steam escaping from within the earth to produce electricity.

Energy from Water

The production of electricity from water power is called **hydroelectric energy.** Look at Figure 21.12. Water moving through huge dams built across rivers turns turbines and generators that produce electricity. In the United States about 4 percent of the electricity used is produced at hydroelectric plants. Hydroelectric energy is energy efficient, and it doesn't create pollution. But the construction of dams is costly and requires the use of much energy. Also, the lake formed by damming a river changes the river and surrounding area's ecosystem.

Another form of hydroelectric energy is tidal energy. Tidal energy comes from the movement of ocean water during tidal changes. In some coastal areas, the water of an incoming tide rushes into narrow rivers or bays. When the tide changes, the water rushes with great force back to the ocean. Hydroelectric plants built in such areas use moving water to generate electricity. This type of power plant is currently used in France and eastern Canada. However, because tidal energy needs special conditions, it will never be widely used.

Figure 21.12 ▲
The Bonneville Dam, on the Columbia River at the Washington–Oregon border, generates hydroelectric energy.

Nuclear Energy

Nuclear energy is produced when the nucleus of an atom splits into smaller particles. This splitting is known as **nuclear fission** (FIHSH uhn). Study the fission reaction shown in Figure 21.14.

The element uranium is used as the fuel for nuclear energy. A certain type of uranium nucleus splits easily into lighter particles. This type of uranium is collected and put in long, metal pipes at a nuclear power plant. The pipes are lowered into a pool of water contained in a large structure, called a nuclear reactor. The reactor bombards uranium nuclei with fast-moving neutrons. When hit, the nuclei split and release particles. The released particles cause other nuclei to split. As each nucleus splits, it releases a large amount of energy in the form of heat. The heat is used to produce steam, which turns a turbine, producing electricity. A nuclear power plant is shown in Figure 21.13.

Figure 21.13 ▲
This nuclear power station in England has several nuclear reactors.

The use of nuclear energy helps save the world's oil and natural gas reserves. However, the materials for producing nuclear energy give off radiation that can harm living things. Even the mining and processing of uranium ores can be very dangerous. Also, the waste products left behind in fission reactors are radioactive and extremely dangerous. These materials release radiation for a very long time.

Figure 21.14
Nuclear Fission Reaction
▼

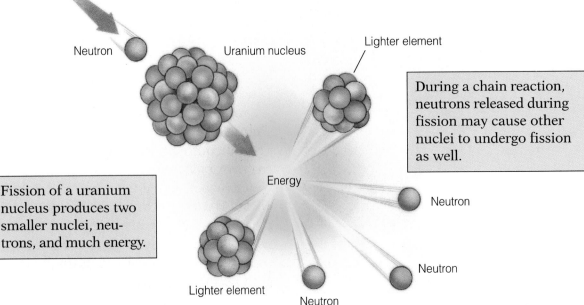

Neutron

Uranium nucleus

Lighter element

During a chain reaction, neutrons released during fission may cause other nuclei to undergo fission as well.

Fission of a uranium nucleus produces two smaller nuclei, neutrons, and much energy.

Energy

Neutron

Neutron

Lighter element

Neutron

Today, about 16 percent of the electricity in the United States is produced by nuclear energy. Other countries, such as France, rely more on nuclear energy. About 60 percent of the electricity in France is generated by nuclear power plants.

When the first nuclear power plant in the United States began operation in 1960, many people believed that one day nuclear energy would generate all the electricity in this country. Since then many people have questioned the safety of nuclear energy. In the 1980s, people became concerned about the dangers of radiation on living things. They also worried about the possibility of an accident at a nuclear power plant. As a result of these concerns, the construction of nuclear power plants stopped in the United States in 1989. Researchers all over the world are trying to solve the problems with nuclear energy and the disposal of radioactive wastes.

Consider This

Should Radioactive Wastes Be Stored?

Radioactive wastes give off harmful radiation for thousands of years. Currently, wastes are stored at nuclear power plants and in steel tanks buried in shallow trenches. Neither method is safe from natural disasters. Leakage could release radiation into the air and water. Wastes buried near the surface could be dug up during mining or construction operations.

A deep underground repository, or pit, could provide a permanent storage area. It would keep dangerous wastes far away from living things and the environment.

A deep repository would protect nuclear wastes from natural disasters. The wastes would be far away from air and groundwater. Deeply buried wastes are not likely to be accidentally uncovered.

On the other hand, locating a site and building the repository would be costly. Many organisms in the chosen area would be greatly disturbed by the construction.

Think About It What type of rock would be best for a repository? How could the choice of a storage site affect you?

Write About It Your area is being considered for the building of a nuclear waste repository. Write a letter stating your position for or against the proposal.

Figure 21.15 ▲
Both passive and active solar heating is used in this home. ▼

Solar Energy

Energy from the sun is called **solar energy**. Direct solar power produces heat directly from the sun's energy and is used to heat buildings and homes. Although the sun's energy is free and nonpolluting, it cannot yet be collected and used on a large scale.

Look at Figure 21.15. In active solar heating, a solar collector absorbs energy from sunlight to heat a liquid. The hot liquid heats a tank of water. A pump forces the heated water to flow through a system of pipes. The piped water delivers home heating and hot water.

Passive solar heating uses conduction to transfer heat. Windows and skylights trap sunlight and heat energy. The heat raises the temperature in the room.

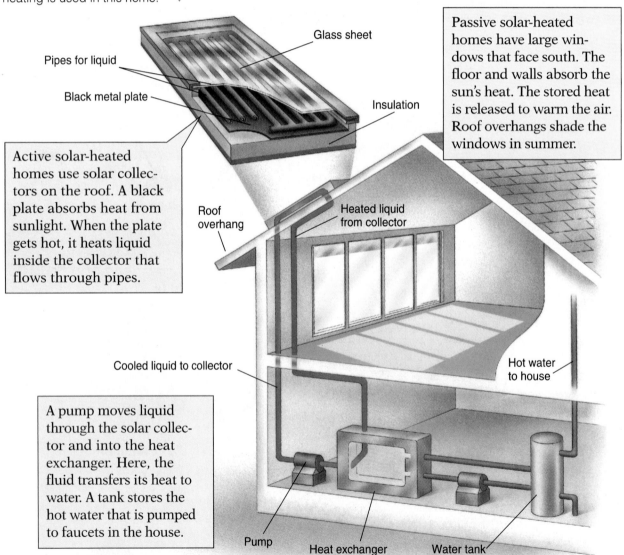

Glass sheet

Pipes for liquid

Black metal plate

Insulation

Passive solar-heated homes have large windows that face south. The floor and walls absorb the sun's heat. The stored heat is released to warm the air. Roof overhangs shade the windows in summer.

Active solar-heated homes use solar collectors on the roof. A black plate absorbs heat from sunlight. When the plate gets hot, it heats liquid inside the collector that flows through pipes.

Roof overhang

Heated liquid from collector

Cooled liquid to collector

Hot water to house

A pump moves liquid through the solar collector and into the heat exchanger. Here, the fluid transfers its heat to water. A tank stores the hot water that is pumped to faucets in the house.

Pump

Heat exchanger

Water tank

Indirect solar power produces energy for use as a power source. For example, solar cells change solar energy into electricity. The electricity is used to power appliances. A number of solar cells connected in a solar panel provides enough energy to power most machines, such as the solar panels used on spacecraft.

Science and Technology *Alternative Cars*

Imagine an automobile that runs as quietly as an electric mixer. It doesn't burn gasoline or any other fossil fuel, so it does not pollute the air. Its engine has few moving parts to wear out. Does such a vehicle sound too good to be true? It's not. The automobile described runs on electricity.

In a gasoline-powered car, the engine powers an alternator to produce electricity. The electricity is stored in a battery. The battery powers the electrical devices in the car, such as the headlights, horn, and radio. In an electric car, the "engine" is actually an electric motor, powered by storage batteries. When these batteries run down, they can be recharged using ordinary household current. One disadvantage of an electric car is that after a relatively short distance its batteries need charging. Also, the faster it goes, the more quickly its batteries run down.

Now imagine a car that uses the sun's energy, rather than electricity, to recharge the batteries. Or better yet, look at the car that uses solar panels shown in Figure 21.16. The solar panels change solar energy into electrical energy. This energy recharges the storage batteries, which power the car's motor.

Figure 21.16 ▲
Locate the solar panels in this solar-powered car.

Check and Explain

1. Why has the demand for energy increased?

2. What is an alternative energy source? Give examples.

3. **Compare and Contrast** How is direct solar power different from indirect solar power? How are they similar?

4. **Predict** What factors would determine where you would build a house that receives electricity from wind energy? Solar energy?

Activity 21 *Which color works best for solar heating?*

Skills Measure; Infer; Make a Graph

Task 1 Prelab Prep

1. Collect the following items: 4 pie tins; 4 pieces of flexible plastic, one in each of these colors: white; black, brown, and green; scissors; water; thermometer; graph paper; four pencils of different colors.
2. Cut each of the plastic pieces so that they completely cover the bottom and sides of a pie tin. Make sure to cover all of the metal.

Task 2 Data Record

1. On a separate sheet of paper, copy Table 21.1.
2. Record all your temperature measurements for the four different colors in the data table.
3. Use the data table to graph each of the four colors that you measure.

Table 21.1 Temperature Change

Water Temperature (°C)					
Color	0 min	10 min	20 min	30 min	40 min
white					
black					
brown					
green					

Task 3 Procedure

1. Place a different color of plastic into each of the pie tins.
2. Find a sunny location where all the pie tins can be placed together. Make sure that all four tins receive an equal amount of sunlight.
3. Fill each pie tin half-full with cool water.

4. Measure the water temperature in each pie tin, and record it in the table.
5. Continue to measure the water temperature for each color at 10-minute intervals for 40 minutes. Record your temperature measurements in the table.
6. Graph the measurements for each of the colors on graph paper. Use a different colored pencil to graph each color of plastic. On the *x*-axis, place the time measurements. On the *y*-axis, place the temperature measurements.

Task 4 Analysis

1. Which color caused the water to heat up the fastest?
2. Which color caused the water to heat up the slowest?
3. Which color caused the water to reach the highest temperature?
4. Which color caused the water to remain at the coolest temperature?
5. Identify the variables in this activity.

Task 5 Conclusion

How quickly does each color collect and hold heat from the sun? In a short paragraph, compare and contrast how the different colors heat up.

Everyday Application

If you wanted to heat your swimming pool using energy from the sun, what color would you paint the pool? Why? If you wanted to keep your home cooler in the summer, what color would you paint the outside? What color would you paint the inside. Why?

Extension

Test each of the four colors without using water. Does the water make a difference in how quickly the colors heat up? Explain.

Chapter 21 Review

Concept Summary

21.1 Mineral Resources
▶ Nonrenewable resources can't be replaced as they are used. Renewable resources can be replaced as they are used.
▶ Minerals are commonly found in deposits called ores. An ore is a mineral-rich rock deposit that can be removed from the earth profitably.
▶ Ores near the earth's surface are surface mined or open-pit mined. Ores deep within the earth are mined underground.
▶ Returning a mined site to its former condition is called reclamation.

21.2 Fossil-Fuel Resources
▶ Coal, oil, and natural gas are fossil fuels. Fossil fuels formed over millions of years from plant and animal remains.

▶ The stages of coal formation are peat, lignite, subbituminous coal, bituminous coal, and anthracite.
▶ Petroleum, or crude oil, is a liquid mixture of compounds of hydrogen and carbon. Natural gas is a gaseous mixture of the same two elements.
▶ Fossil fuels meet most of our energy needs. But the use of fossil fuels harms the environment.

21.3 Alternative Energy Resources
▶ Fossil fuels are being used up. Alternative ways of generating energy are being developed.
▶ Most alternative energy comes from renewable resources, such as wind, water, and the sun.

Chapter Vocabulary

nonrenewable resource (21.1)	fossil fuel (21.2)	hydroelectric energy (21.3)
renewable resource (21.1)	petroleum (21.2)	nuclear fission (21.3)
ore (21.1)	natural gas (21.2)	solar energy (21.3)
reclamation (21.1)	petrochemicals (21.2)	

Check Your Vocabulary

Use the vocabulary words above to complete the following sentences correctly.

1. Energy from the sun is a(n) _____; it can never be used up.

2. Useful chemicals made from petroleum are _____.

3. The splitting of nuclei to produce energy is called _____.

4. A fossil fuel often found with petroleum is _____.

5. A mineral deposit that can be removed from the earth profitably is a(n) _____.

6. Fuels that cannot be replaced once they are removed are called _____.

7. Returning a mined area to a clean, usable condition is called _____.

8. A type of fuel that took millions of years to form is _____.

9. Moving water is the source of power when _____ is used.

10. Kerosene and gasoline, among other products, are made from _____.

11. Homes can be heated by using passive or active _____.

Write Your Vocabulary

Write sentences using the vocabulary words above. Show that you know what each word means.

Chapter 21 Review

Check Your Knowledge

Answer the following in complete sentences.

1. What are some examples of renewable resources? What are some examples of nonrenewable resources?

2. Describe the different types of mining. In what situation is each type used?

3. Trace the energy source back for fossil fuels as far as you can.

4. List the stages of coal formation. Which type is most common? Which type is most polluting when burned?

5. Describe where petroleum and natural gas are often found.

6. List some of the uses of fossil fuels.

7. What are some alternative ways of generating energy? Why are they important?

8. Explain why wind energy and tidal energy may never be used widely.

9. Describe nuclear fission.

10. Explain the difference between direct and indirect solar power.

Choose the answer that best completes each sentence.

11. World demand for energy is (decreasing, increasing, staying the same, over).

12. The world's supply of (fossil fuels, ore deposits, copper, energy from the sun) will never run out.

13. Geothermal energy comes from heat stored in hot (water, wind, rocks, weather).

14. Coal formed over millions of years from (plant and animal remains, the mantle, fossil fuels, mineral deposits).

Check Your Understanding

Apply the concepts you have learned to answer each question.

1. Does nuclear energy come from a renewable resource or a nonrenewable resource? Explain.

2. Based on what you know about each type of mining, describe the ways an area can be harmed by mining.

3. Trace wind energy back to energy from the sun.

4. **Extension** Imagine you read a newspaper story saying that a large new oil field has been found and that people would not have to worry about running out of petroleum. How would you argue against this conclusion?

5. **Mystery Photo** The photograph on page 488 shows aluminum cans compressed for recycling. They will be processed into aluminum that can be used to make new cans and other items. Why is it important to recycle aluminum items?

6. **Extension** Nuclear fusion is a process in which hydrogen and helium nuclei are combined under high temperatures. When they combine, they release a great deal of energy. Would you classify nuclear fusion as a renewable or nonrenewable energy resource? Why?

7. **Application** How do farmers rely on natural resources? How does a manufacturing company rely on natural resources? Compare and contrast the resource needs of these two industries.

8. **Infer** Why are fossil fuels and minerals considered nonrenewable resources even though they form naturally within the earth?

Develop Your Skills

Use the skills you have developed in this chapter to complete each activity.

1. **Interpret Data** The circle graph shows the major sources of energy use in the United States in the early 1990s. Study the graph, then answer the questions.

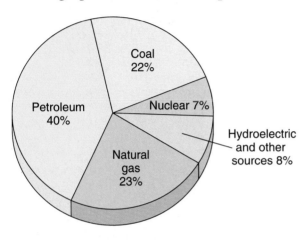

a. How much nuclear energy is consumed?

b. Which energy source is used the most?

c. **Infer** Draw a circle graph that shows the types and percentages of energy you think will be used in the United States in the year 2050.

2. **Data Bank** Use the information on page 623 to answer the following questions.

a. Where are the world's largest reserves of crude oil? Where are the smallest reserves?

b. Where are the world's largest reserves of natural gas? Where are the smallest reserves?

3. **Communicate** Write how you would explain the importance of conserving energy resources to a younger brother, sister, or friend.

Make Connections

1. **Link the Concepts** Below is a concept map showing how some of the main concepts in this chapter link together. Only part of the map is filled in. Complete the map using words and ideas from the chapter.

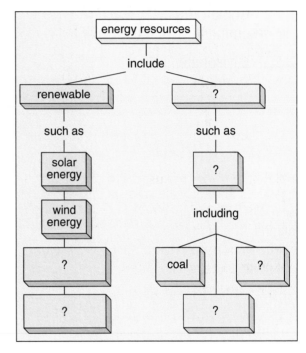

2. **Science and Technology** Some scientists are studying how to get energy from garbage and other organic sources. Using the library, find out about the use of biomass as an energy source.

3. **Science and Society** Wood is a popular resource for fuel in many areas of the world. In some places, however, wood is no longer plentiful, and people have had to meet their energy needs in other ways. Explain how a renewable resource like trees can become a nonrenewable resource.

Chapter 22 Humans and the Environment

What do you see?

❝I can see a lot of rectangle shapes of basically the same size. The shapes are pieces of land. The land is being changed by people. It probably used to be all one level. People are changing it so that they can live on it.❞

Erin Blaney
Richardson West Junior
*   School*
Richardson, Texas

To find out more about the photograph, look on page 530. As you read this chapter, you will learn more about the earth's environment and how people interact with the environment.

508

22.1 Human Ecology

Objectives

▶ **Explain** technology and give several examples.

▶ **Describe** the ways people in different societies live.

▶ **Find causes** for the rapid increase in the human population.

▶ **Make a table** that compares the differences in the three types of societies.

▼ **ACTIVITY**

Classifying

Meeting Needs and Wants

Make a list of everything you did or bought yesterday that used a resource. Classify the items on the list into two groups: Satisfying Needs and Satisfying Wants. The needs list should only include things that you must have to survive. Compare your list to a classmate's list.

SKILLS WARMUP

Think about the area where you live. What does it look like? How has it changed since you were born? Imagine what your area may have looked like 100,000 years ago. Many different types of plants grew. Mammals lived in the trees and on the ground. Humans had not yet reached the Western Hemisphere.

Now imagine what life was like in North America about 1,000 years ago. Small tribes of people lived across the land. Some groups wandered in search of food, while others lived in permanent farming communities. In parts of Mexico and Central America, the Maya built magnificent cities.

What was your area like 100 years ago? Maybe it was a town or a city. There were no cars because the gasoline engine was not yet invented. People traveled on foot, by horse, or in steam powered trains. Many urban people worked in factories powered by coal. In the past 100 years, how have people changed the land?

Societies and Culture

Humans affect the environment in different ways. The way that a group of humans, or a society, interacts with the environment is determined by their culture. Culture is the way of life of a society. It includes the ways that people interact and communicate with each other, and how they use the earth's natural resources.

Human cultures vary in their technology. Technology is the tools, skills, and knowledge a culture uses to obtain natural resources. Technology includes simple tools, such as grinding stones and spears, and more complicated tools, such as computers and satellites.

Environmental Science
L I N K

Research the history of the town or city in which you were born. Make a list of plants and animals that lived in this area about a hundred years ago. Describe what the countryside looked like then.

Use illustrations and photographs to compare what your birthplace looks like now to what it looked like 100 years ago.

What significant changes have been made? Which of these changes were natural and which were human-made?

A C T I V I T Y

Hunting-and-Gathering Societies

Fossil evidence indicates that humans have been on the earth for thousands of years. For much of this time, they lived by hunting animals and gathering fruits, nuts, seeds, and roots. Today, there are very few full-time hunting-and-gathering societies left in the world. However, some hunting-and-gathering societies still live in Australia, South America, and Africa.

Hunting and gathering is a way of life in which people travel the land in search of plants and animals. The groups must move often, as the seasons change the availability of plants and animals. Some people are hunter-gatherers for only parts of the year. They may find a plentiful food source in an area and settle there for a period of time. For the Inuit people of Canada and Alaska, fish is an important food source. ▶

Hunting-and-gathering societies have small, stable populations. However, the hunting-and-gathering way of life has had an impact on the environment. In prehistoric times, fire was often used to clear land. Land was cleared for many reasons, including the need to attract grazing herds. The use of fire, however, greatly altered the environment.

For example, in some areas of North America, fires may have prevented the spread of forests. ▼

◀ The technology used by hunter-gatherers is fairly simple. Many rely on spears and other sharp tools for cutting, clearing, carving, and digging. This Samoan (suh MOH uhn) man uses a chisel and a wood hammer to carve a bowl. Fire is also an important technology for some hunting-and-gathering societies.

Agricultural Societies

Another way of life is based on the growing of crops, or agriculture. Agricultural societies depend on certain species of plants and animals for their food supply. These plants and animals are *domesticated*—humans care for them and control their reproduction.

Many types of agricultural societies exist today. They are different sizes and use different agricultural methods. Some have kept their population stable, while others have grown in size.

▲ Technology, such as the plow and other metal tools, helps farmers grow crops with less effort. Irrigation increases food production. In the past, a few farmers produced enough food for many people. So some farmers became potters, toolmakers, and weavers. Today, it still takes only a few farmers to produce enough food for many people.

▲ An agricultural society does not depend on the local natural ecosystem for its food. The ecosystem is changed to support the growing of crops, such as rice, corn, and wheat. Food from crops may be stored for winter or in case of drought. As a result of a constant food supply, an agricultural society can stay in one place.

Throughout history, there ▶ are examples of agricultural societies that grew too fast, as shown by these ruins in Morocco. By overgrazing and overplanting, people removed too many nutrients from the soil. Because these nutrients were not replaced, the soil became poor or eroded away. The land could no longer support the people.

Industrial Societies

In an industrial society, machines transform natural resources into useful products. Agriculture still produces food, but machines till, plant, weed, and harvest the crops. Machinery also makes it possible to grow more food on a piece of land than with human labor and hand tools.

◀ Industrial societies are based on growth. Technology is constantly improved, and more products are created. What kinds of products can you see in the photograph? How have these products changed over the past ten years? Twenty years? Much of the manufacturing of these products is centered around cities.

▲ In industrial societies, food is shipped in to urban centers that are outside of agricultural areas. As in agricultural societies, machines help produce food products.

The technology of industrial societies can produce many copies of the same thing. Products made in one location are shipped and sold in many locations. Often the materials needed for production are brought in from other places, such as mining or farming areas.

▲ Industrial societies use far greater amounts of natural resources than any other type of society. Many of the resources are not reusable. The burning of fossil fuels for energy creates pollution. The collecting of natural resources from mining and the clearing of forests scars the land. Also, the building of factories and housing changes the natural habitat. Look at the photograph of Hong Kong. What might its natural habitat be like if buildings had not been constructed?

Human Population Growth

The population of a society is directly related to the available technology. Because of limited technology, hunting-and-gathering societies have small, stable populations. The number of people born every year usually equals the number of people who die.

Since the technology of an agricultural society allows for permanent settlement, its population may increase. Compared to the populations of hunting-and-gathering societies, the populations of agricultural societies are large. The population of an agricultural society may even grow large enough to support cities.

Industrial societies support the largest populations. The technology of industrial societies makes great amounts of food available to many people. The development of new medicines helps people live longer. The culture encourages growth. Together, these factors cause a rapid increase in the population. The increase is so great that it is sometimes called a *population explosion*.

Look at Figure 22.2. How would you describe the curve of human population growth? The graph shows exponential (EHKS poh NEHN shuhl) growth. When a population grows exponentially, it doubles at regular intervals. A graph of this growth produces a curve that gets more steep, as shown in Figure 22.2.

A future population size can be predicted by extending the curve to a certain point. For example, in 1950 an estimated 2.5 billion people lived on the earth. In 1990, there were about 5.3 billion people. At this rate of growth, the world population will triple by the year 2075.

Figure 22.1 ▲
Shanghai, China, was a small town in the 1800s. Today more than ten million people live in Shanghai. It is the most populated city on Asia's mainland.

Figure 22.2
When did the world's population begin to increase rapidly? ▼

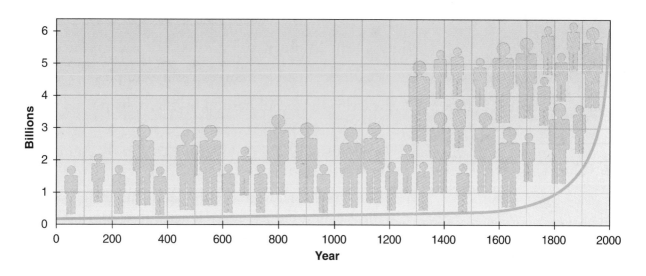

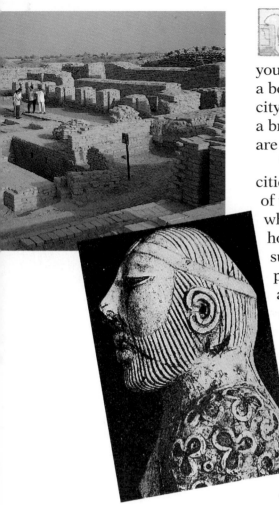

Science and Society *Ancient Cities*

As you travel toward a large city in the distance, you notice an irrigated field at the edge of the river and a boat sailing up the river. In the distance, above the city, you see a huge monument. You enter the city on a broad avenue with many crossing streets. The streets are lined with houses and shops.

The description of this city could belong to many cities in the world today. However, it is a description of the city Mohenjo-daro (moh HEHN joh DAIR oh), which existed in India about 2500 B.C. City ruins reveal houses, each one with its own bathroom and water supply. The remains of a large building include a floor plan with several courtyards, many rooms, and other compartments. This may have been an early college. The ruins also show that Mohenjo-daro had a planned drainage and sewage system.

Mohenjo-daro was part of the Indus Valley civilization. This civilization flourished near the now arid area of Pakistan by the Indus River. The Indus Valley civilization was an agricultural society. The farmers grew wheat, barley, rice, dates, and peas. They may have also grown cotton. Drawings found in the ruins also reveal that cattle and water buffalo were domesticated.

The city of Mohenjo-daro probably existed for hundreds of years. Scientists are not sure what caused people to abandon Mohenjo-daro. One theory is that a number of natural disasters, such as earthquakes, volcanic eruptions, and flooding, destroyed the city.

Figure 22.3 ▲
You can see some of the remains of Mohenjo-daro (above). This sculpture was found buried near the ruins.

Check and Explain

1. What is technology? Give several examples.

2. Describe the use of natural resources by people in industrial societies.

3. **Find Causes** What factors have caused the human population to increase rapidly?

4. **Make a Table** How do hunting-and-gathering, agricultural, and industrial societies differ? Make a table with at least three columns that shows the differences between these societies.

22.2 Human Impact on the Environment

Objectives

▶ **Explain** how humans interfere with natural earth cycles.

▶ **Explain** the importance of biodiversity.

▶ **Find causes** for species extinction.

▶ **Observe** the impact of humans on the environment in your community.

▼ **ACTIVITY**

Observing

Source of Your Worries

What are ten different sources of pollution in your community?

1. Make a list of the sources and compare it with a classmate's list.

2. From the two lists, choose what you think are the five major sources of pollution.

3. Share your list with the class.

SKILLS WARMUP

Think about the last meal you ate. What resources were required to produce the food? How did the food production change the environment? The natural environment was changed into agricultural land for growing food. The farm machinery burned fossil fuels. The burning of fuel polluted the air.

Machines that burn fossil fuels also processed the food. Trees were cut down to make the paper for the packaging. Trucks brought the food to your town or city. Energy was used to prepare the food.

Trucks also collected the wastes from the meal. The wastes were dumped on land that was changed in order to hold garbage. Fresh water piped in from lakes or streams washed the dishes. At a sewage-treatment plant, energy separated the water and the waste.

You and the Environment

How do you affect your environment? You affect it in many different ways. In fact, it is impossible for you not to affect the environment. You are an organism, and all organisms change and interact with their environment.

The environment includes everything around you: water, air, minerals, organisms, and energy. All these things are related through interactions and cycles. Even when you breathe, you affect the environment. Every day, you change substances from the biosphere, such as food, air, and water. And every day, you add substances, often called waste, to the biosphere.

Figure 22.4 ▲
What kinds of resources were needed for the dinner that this family is eating?

▼ **ACTIVITY**

| **Inferring** |

Broken Circle

Locate the nitrogen cycle in Chapter 17 on page 395. Infer how human actions interfere with the nitrogen cycle.

SKILLS WORKOUT

Human Impact on Natural Cycles

What happens when you throw a pebble into a small pond? Ripples move across its smooth surface. By altering part of the pond, you caused a change over the entire pond. Ecosystems are similar to throwing a pebble into water. A change in any part of an ecosystem affects other parts of that ecosystem.

Substances need to circulate through an ecosystem to keep it working properly. Recall that natural cycles pass many substances through an ecosystem. Some of the natural cycles on the earth are the nitrogen cycle, the oxygen-carbon dioxide cycle, and the water cycle.

As humans use the environment to meet their needs, they constantly change the natural cycles. Humans use resources, pollute the environment, and alter habitats. These changes affect the flow of substances through a natural cycle. Look at Figure 22.5. How does human interaction affect the circulation of substances in the oxygen-carbon dioxide cycle?

Figure 22.5

Humans change natural cycles in many ways. ▼

Plants change carbon dioxide into oxygen through photosynthesis. Plants are the main source of oxygen on the earth. The cutting of trees and city development reduce the number of plants.

Carbon dioxide

The burning of fossil fuels adds carbon dioxide to the atmosphere. The amount of carbon dioxide in the atmosphere has increased by more than 11 percent since 1870.

Oxygen

The bodies of dead organisms that didn't decompose fully changed into fossil fuels. Humans remove fossil fuels from the earth and burn them for energy.

Coal, oil, gas

Endangered Species

The red wolf, the California condor, the black-footed ferret, and the American crocodile all have estimated populations of less than 1,000 animals. These animals are called **endangered species** because they are in immediate danger of becoming extinct. Scientists estimate that every day, 100 species of plants and animals become extinct. Other species, such as the grizzly bear shown in Figure 22.6, are threatened. This means that they are abundant in certain areas of their natural range, but very rare in other areas of the range.

The loss of even one species affects other organisms because many different organisms make up an ecosystem. If one part of the food web is lost, other organisms are affected. For example, the southern sea otter lives among the kelp beds. In the kelp beds, one of the main food sources for the otters are sea urchins. Overhunting nearly caused the extinction of the otter. With fewer sea otters, the sea urchin population exploded, endangering the kelp beds. In recent years, however, legal protection has allowed the otter population to increase, bringing the numbers of sea urchins under control.

Scientists studying ecosystems found that a stable ecosystem has a variety of different species. The number of species making up an ecosystem is a measure of its **biodiversity** (BY oh dih VURS uh tee). The greater the biodiversity of an ecosystem, the more healthy it is. Whenever a species is removed, the biodiversity of the ecosystem is reduced.

▼ **ACTIVITY**

Researching

The List

Find out which plant or animal species is listed as endangered in your state. Choose one of the organisms to write about. In your paper, discuss reasons why the organism is endangered and steps that can be taken to save the organism.

SKILLS WORKOUT

Figure 22.6

The grizzly bear, American crocodile, and California condor are all endangered species. ▼

Habitat Loss

Every species on the earth requires a certain habitat in which to live. A major cause of lowered biodiversity is the loss of habitats. Humans change, or modify, habitats by using the natural resources. Habitats changed by humans can't support as many species as natural habitats.

Many human activities completely destroy habitats. For example, plowing the land to grow crops destroys the prairie habitat. When a habitat is destroyed or damaged, few of the organisms that live there can survive.

Deforestation   One serious method of habitat destruction is **deforestation**, the cutting down of forests. Deforestation is occurring most rapidly in the tropical rain forests. About 200 000 km² of rain forest disappear every year. Rain forests contain the greatest variety of species of any habitat on the earth. Look at Figure 22.7. When the rain forest trees are removed, many organisms die.

Water Loss   A change in the amount of water in a habitat can destroy a habitat. Wetlands, marshes, and bogs are drained to make building sites. Wetlands, or swamps, are an important habitat for migrating water birds, alligators, frogs, and other organisms. Without the water, the wetland habitats are destroyed. The organisms that depend on this habitat migrate or die.

Another effect of water loss is desertification. Overgrazing and poor agricultural practices cause desertification. The once grassy land is transformed into a lifeless desert. The area may return to its former state if it is left free from farming or grazing.

Pollution   Habitats are also damaged by pollution. Pollution of lakes, rivers, and oceans makes these habitats unsuitable for many organisms. In some places, acid rain has killed or stopped the reproduction of many of the living things in the lakes. In the world ocean, huge oil spills cause great destruction and habitat loss.

Figure 22.7 ▲
The left photograph shows a tropical rain forest that has not been cut down. Compare this environment to the rain forest at right, which has been cleared to construct farms and roads.

Pollution and Human Health

Chemicals that can damage the health of organisms are called **toxins**. Toxins may enter the human body through breathing, direct contact, or eating. They may affect human health in many ways. Some of these health effects are noticed immediately, while others result after long-term exposure.

Toxins are contained in chemical substances, such as pesticides, plastics, and detergents. Sometimes these toxins enter lakes, streams, and rivers. Table 22.1 shows some of the human health effects from toxin exposure.

The burning of fossil fuels and tobacco also produce toxins. Air pollution contains toxins that cause irritated eyes, burning throats, and headaches. Exposure to heavy air pollution over a short period of time increases colds, coughs, and nose irritations. Long-term exposure may result in permanent irritation of the respiratory system, heart disease, and cancer.

Table 22.1
Health Effects of Toxins

Toxic Chemical	Some Health Effects
DDT	Tremors, central nervous system damage
Cadmium	Headache, chest pains, hypertension, heart disease, possibly cancer
Lead	Anemia, central nervous system damage
Mercury	Kidney and liver damage, central nervous system damage, fetal abnormalities

Consider This

Should Taxes Pay for Public Transit?

For people to get from place to place, governments spend money to build roads, buy buses, and run subways. New transportation projects are very expensive, and maintaining roads and buses costs money, too. Since tax money is limited, governments and citizens must decide exactly how the money should be spent.

Consider Some Issues
Public transportation, which includes subways, buses, and trains, creates much less pollution than automobiles. And since public transportation moves many people at once, it is more energy-efficient than automobiles.

However, public transportation is not always convenient or fast. Often trains and buses don't stop at places that are close to a person's destination. Transferring to other destinations can take a long time to get somewhere.

Think About It Most people travel in cars. Do you think they should be encouraged to take public transportation to clean up the air? Should tax money be spent to build freeways for automobiles or for better public transit?

Write About It Write a letter to one of your state representatives that explains your position on where money should be spent for transportation. Be sure to include all your reasons for choosing that position.

Science and Technology
Keeping Track of Biodiversity

How large is the population of an endangered species? How much of its habitat is left? Scientists and government officials need to know the answers to questions like these if they are to preserve biodiversity.

Researchers collect large amounts of data on the populations of plant and animal species. They also map and measure the areas of important habitats. But gathering all the data together to determine which species and habitats need the most protection is difficult.

Computer technology is solving this problem. Scientists and wildlife managers all over the world are creating biodiversity databases. A *database* is a large collection of information that a computer can quickly sort through. The speed of computers makes it easy to search, find, sort, count, compare, and combine information in the database.

A biodiversity database allows scientists and wildlife managers to obtain information for making better decisions. Development projects can be designed to avoid sensitive habitats. Accurate and updated lists of endangered and protected species are possible.

Separate biodiversity databases are being connected to form information networks. A network allows the sharing of information between separate databases. With networks, scientists can keep track of biodiversity on a global scale.

Figure 22.8 ▲
A forest ranger collects information about organisms in a forest. Her information will become part of a large biodiversity database.

Check and Explain

1. Describe three ways that humans interfere with natural earth cycles.

2. Why is biodiversity important in the earth's ecosystems? Explain.

3. **Find Causes** You want to determine why a certain species is in danger of becoming extinct. What possible causes of its decline would you investigate?

4. **Observe** How have humans affected the environment in your area? Observe the landscape for evidence of past or present impacts. Make a list of what you find.

22.3 Environmental Solutions

Objectives

▶ **Describe** ways that humans are reducing their impact on the environment.

▶ **Explain** what is meant by conservation, preservation, and restoration.

▶ **Predict** what will happen to the biosphere during the next 20 years.

▶ **Communicate** steps that you can take to help protect the environment.

Many people are involved in cleaning up and protecting the environment. Maybe you have participated in a community or school litter cleanup. You may recycle much of your waste at home and at school. Members of your family may use public transportation or ride bicycles instead of driving a car. Perhaps you buy products made from recycled material. These are just a few ways that people can help reduce pollution and restore the environment. Can you think of any more?

Environmental Impact Studies

What steps can people take to help the environment before it is harmed? One way is by considering the impact on the environment before beginning a construction project. Any project, such as building a housing development, has both drawbacks and benefits. The benefits include more homes for families and more jobs. The drawbacks may include increased pollution, greater use of local resources, and damage to natural habitats.

People are recognizing that land-use decisions must be carefully made. Environmental impact studies are now required for most major construction projects. These studies are based on careful research of the possible effects of the project on the environment. Projects with major negative impacts may not be approved.

Figure 22.9 ▲
A group of people protests the effects of local deforestation in San José, Costa Rica. Why is it important that people everywhere make efforts to solve environmental problems?

Preservation

One way of preventing further damage to the earth's ecosystems is by protecting existing natural habitats. Keeping wilderness areas in their natural condition is called **preservation**. Preservation may involve creating parks, preserves, or reserves. In these areas, the human use of nature is limited or forbidden.

The largest game preserve in the world is the Etosha Reserve in Namibia, Africa. This preserve is almost 23 000 km^2, which is about the size of the state of New Hampshire. In the United States, national parks serve as animal preserves. In the parks, hunting or tampering with the wildlife is prohibited. The parks also try to maintain the natural habitats of the wildlife.

Some organizations buy land to make into wildlife preserves. People contribute money to purchase the natural habitats. These organizations include the Nature Conservancy and the World Environmental Fund.

Figure 22.10 ▲
In North Carolina, the natural habitat of this gull is being protected from human disturbances.

SkillBuilder *Evaluating Sources*

Environmental Issues

Every day, newspapers and magazines print articles about environmental problems. Sometimes it is difficult to fully understand an environmental problem because two different articles may report very different information. Although the information in both articles may be correct, each one might be written to influence readers in a certain way. Before you make a decision about how to solve an environmental problem or who is blame for it, you should evaluate several different sources.

Obtain several different articles that discuss the same environmental problem. Read each article carefully. Try to pick out the main points in each article. You may wish to list these points on a sheet of paper. Then answer the following questions for each of the articles you read.

1. What environmental problem was addressed in the article?

2. What is the source of the article's information and facts?

3. Does the writer present more than one side of the problem?

4. What evidence is used to support the conclusions of the article?

5. What do you think was the writer's reason for writing the article?

6. What do you think is the writer's opinion of the problem?

7. How did the article make you feel?

8. Make a list of questions you would like to have answered before you make a decision on the problem.

9. Did the article change your opinion about the problem? Why?

Conservation

The wise use of natural resources is called **conservation.** Conservation help to set limits so that the earth's resources will provide the greatest benefit for the longest time. Soil, water, land, plant, and wildlife conservation protect these resources for the future.

Soil conservation is important because improper farming techniques sometimes result in soil erosion and loss of fertility. Many farmers who practice soil conservation manage farm fields as ecosystems. Contour farming, shown in Figure 22.11, reduces soil erosion by slowing down the amount of runoff.

Wildlife conservation limits the amount of hunting or collecting of certain species. National and international laws now protect threatened and endangered species. Wildlife conservation also includes protecting the natural habitats of plants and animals.

Recall that less than 3 percent of the earth's water is fresh. Fresh water comes from rivers, lakes, and groundwater. To conserve fresh water, it is important for you to use only as much water as necessary.

Figure 22.11 ▲
How does contour farming help conserve soil?

Figure 22.12 ▲
In Oregon, a technician replants trees to restore a forest habitat.

Restoration

Look at Figure 22.12. Since few areas of the earth are in their natural condition, many people are restoring damaged habitats. The process by which a habitat is returned to its natural condition is called **restoration**. A restored habitat can usually support many of the same organisms it did originally.

A forest habitat is restored by planting trees. A meadow is restored by planting native plants. When the natural plants in a habitat return, the animal life often comes back as well. However, sometimes animals must be reintroduced, or brought back, to a restored habitat by environmentalists.

Habitat restoration often takes a long time. For example, if all the trees are cut down in a large area, the habitat may need more than just new trees. The lack of trees may greatly increase the rate of erosion. As a result, the streams may fill with sediment and much of the best soil may erode. For successful restoration, the stream might have to be cleared and the soil replaced before new trees can be planted.

Pollution Solutions

Many steps are being taken to reduce the amount of pollution in the environment. Governments can play an important role in this effort. Governments make and enforce laws that require people and businesses to control the amount of pollution they produce.

Plastics that disintegrate when placed in the ground reduce the build up of solid waste. The biodegradable bag shown below can be broken down by bacteria in the soil. ▼

▲ Highly poisonous chemicals, or toxic wastes, are handled, stored, and discarded properly to prevent leakage. Areas contaminated with toxic waste are also being cleaned up.

Laws require that automobiles be tested for exhaust pollutants. Limits on automobile pollutants help reduce air pollution. ▼

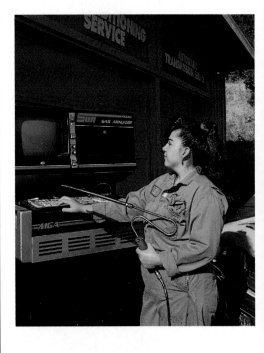

◄ The process of **recycling** cuts down on garbage and saves energy. Recycling is using the original material of an object over again. With the energy used to produce one aluminum can, 20 aluminum cans can be recycled. Imagine the amount of energy being saved at the recycling center in Tennessee shown at left!

Many people and businesses are reducing pollution without government enforcement. They may install energy-saving devices, start carpools, or recycle paper. These people and businesses know that reducing pollution takes cooperation and action at all levels.

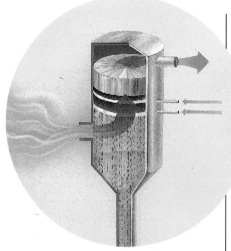

Alternative energy, such as these solar cells, creates less pollution and uses renewable resources. Name several other alternative energy resources. ▼

▲ Many factories and power plants are required to install devices called scrubbers on their smokestacks. The scrubbers remove certain pollutants by trapping solid particles and gas as they pass through a mist of water.

▲ Large fines for improper dumping and littering discourage people from polluting the land and the water. Have you seen signs like this anywhere in your town?

Farmers who practice organic agriculture balance what goes into the ecosystem with what comes out. They control pests without using chemical pesticides. They keep the soil rich by adding decayed organic matter. ▼

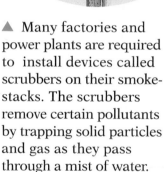

▲ Wastes from hospitals and medical clinics must be labeled to ensure proper disposal. The international biohazard symbol is shown above.

Throw Nothing Away

1. Make a list of the various ways you can reduce, reuse, and recycle products.

2. Choose several ideas from your list, and design a poster illustrating your ideas.

3. Share your poster with the class.

SKILLS WORKOUT

Figure 22.13

How are these students helping to solve some of the earth's environmental problems? What contributions can you make? ▼

Reduce, Reuse, Recycle

All the products you use are made with natural resources. Soda cans are made of aluminum, plastics come from petroleum, paper comes from trees. Also, resources are used to make the cans, plastics, and paper. If people use fewer natural resources, the impact on the environment will be reduced. You can do three things to reduce your impact on the environment: reduce, reuse, and recycle.

Reduce means to use less. By reducing, you use fewer resources and create less garbage. You can reduce by carrying your lunch in a lunch pail instead of a paper bag. You can use all of a sheet of paper before discarding it and buy products with less packaging.

Reuse means to use materials over again or for other purposes. For example, you can take plastic bags back to the grocery store to carry your food. You can save magazines, cardboard, and other materials to create art projects. What are some other ways that you can reuse?

Many types of materials today are recycled. When material such as an aluminum can is recycled, it is melted down, and the aluminum metal is turned into another object. Cardboard, newspaper, paper, aluminum, tin, steel, glass, and some types of plastic are recycled in most parts of the United States. You don't do the recycling of the material yourself, but you collect the objects for reprocessing. Many communities have curbside recycling programs. Recyclable materials are put out at the curb, where they are picked up.

Science and You *Composting*

What do you do with banana peels? Apple cores? Vegetable peelings? Most people throw these materials away in the garbage. Along with plastic packaging, dead batteries, and other trash, they end up in landfills or garbage dumps.

Materials such as banana peels and apple cores are made of organic matter. Organic matter is the source of the soil's fertility. It provides the nutrients plants need to grow. So you may ask, why not put wastes made of organic matter back into the soil?

That is exactly what many people are now doing by practicing composting. *Composting* is creating the conditions that decay organic matter naturally. The decayed matter breaks down into simple substances that can return to the soil.

The simplest way to compost is to make a compost pile. Different kinds of organic matter are layered into a mound. The layers could include salad scraps, lawn clippings, and dead leaves. Meat, dairy, and bread products should not be composted. Some soil is added to provide bacteria. The bacteria begin to break down the pile's ingredients. Often earthworms are added to the pile as well to help decompose the organic matter.

The pile is kept moist and turned occasionally. After a few weeks or months, a rich, dark, sweet-smelling natural fertilizer is left. Adding this fertilizer to garden soil helps plants grow.

ACTIVITY

Observing

A Heap of Good

1. Make a compost pile at school or at home using organic matter, such as food wastes, grass clippings, and leaves.

2. Every few days, make observations of the pile's size, smell, internal temperature, and appearance.

What changes occur? How can you make a better compost pile?

SKILLS WORKOUT

Check and Explain

1. Describe three ways that pollution is being controlled by humans.

2. Give an example for each of the following: preservation, conservation, restoration.

3. **Predict** What will happen to the biosphere during the next 20 years if humans do not change the way they live on the earth? Explain the reasons for your predictions.

4. **Communicate** Using words, drawings, and pictures cut out of magazines, describe five steps you plan to take to protect the environment.

Activity 22 *What things are in garbage?*

Skills Observe; Classify; Infer

Task 1 Prelab Prep
Collect the following items: plastic garbage bag, large sheet of plastic, paper towels, rubber gloves (optional).

Task 2 Data Record
On a separate sheet of paper, copy Table 22.2, leaving room for extra rows. Use the table to record your observations on the garbage that you collect.

Task 3 Procedure
1. Find a safe place to collect litter, such as your school yard or a park close to school.
2. Collect any litter that you find in your chosen area, and place it in the plastic bag.
    CAUTION! Avoid picking up any sharp objects.
3. Take the collected litter, or garbage, back to your classroom.
4. Pour the garbage you collected onto a large sheet of plastic. Put similar items, such as glass bottles and aluminum cans together so that you can count them.
5. In the data table, record the name and number for each type of item. Decide what should be done with each type of item, and record.
6. Classify the garbage that you collected into four or five different groups. Be sure that each group has at least one common characteristic.
7. Once the garbage is sorted into groups, share your method of classification with your classmates.
8. Dispose of the garbage properly. Recycle what can be recycled. Wash your hands.

Task 4 Analysis
1. What was the total number of items that you collected?
2. What was the most common item in your garbage?
3. How much of your garbage was recyclable? How much was reusable?
4. If you collected litter every school day for a week, how many items would you have?
5. **Classify** How did you classify your garbage? How was your method different from that of other groups?

Task 5 Conclusion
Write a short paragraph discussing the types of litter that can be found around your school. Explain how to keep the area litter-free.

Everyday Application
Take an inventory of all the garbage that your family throws out in a day. Then do the inventory list over a month. From your list, determine which items could be recycled or reused.

Table 22.2 Sorting Garbage

Type of Item Found	Number of Items	What Should Be Done with the Item?		
		Recycle	Reuse	Trash

Chapter 22 Review

Concept Summary

22.1 Human Ecology
▶ The culture of a society determines how its people interact with the environment. Cultures vary in their technology.
▶ The oldest way of living on the earth is practiced by people in hunting-and-gathering societies.
▶ Agricultural societies may form permanent settlements. They may grow large enough to support cities.
▶ Industrial societies have spread across the world. The amount of natural resources used per person is highest in industrial societies.
▶ The human population of the earth has increased greatly in the last 200 years and continues to increase.

22.2 Human Impact on the Environment
▶ Human use of natural resources modifies and destroys natural habitats, and changes natural cycles and ecosystems.
▶ The destruction of natural habitats, pollution, and the changing of ecosystems all reduce biodiversity.
▶ Pollution of the environment endangers human health.

22.3 Environmental Solutions
▶ People are taking steps to protect the biosphere by making more informed decisions about land use, conserving and preserving natural resources, restoring habitats, controlling pollution, and limiting resource use.
▶ People can help the environment by reducing, reusing, and recycling.

Chapter Vocabulary

endangered species (22.2)   toxins (22.2)   restoration (22.3)
biodiversity (22.2)   preservation (22.3)   recycling (22.3)
deforestation (22.2)   conservation (22.3)

Check Your Vocabulary

Use the vocabulary words above to complete the following sentences correctly.

1. Protecting the trees and wildlife of an area is an example of _____ .

2. Removing the trees of a forest is called _____ .

3. Animals and plants that are in immediate danger of becoming extinct are _____ .

4. Using the original material of an object over again is called _____ .

5. Poisonous substances that affect the health of organisms are called _____ .

6. When species become extinct, the biosphere's _____ is lowered.

7. The process by which a habitat is returned to its natural condition is called _____ .

8. Keeping wilderness in its natural condition is called _____ .

Write Your Vocabulary

Write a sentence using the vocabulary words above. Show that you know what each word means.

Chapter 22 Review

Check Your Knowledge

Answer the following in complete sentences.

1. Give three examples of how humans may destroy a habitat.

2. Why is recycling good for the environment? Give three reasons.

3. In what type of society were the first cities built?

4. Why do most hunting-and-gathering societies have a relatively small impact on the environment?

5. Give an example of how changing one part of an ecosystem may change other parts.

6. What are the causes of the lowering of the earth's biodiversity?

7. How may pollution endanger your health?

8. For what purposes is powered machinery used in industrial societies?

9. What is an environmental impact statement? What is its purpose?

Choose the answer that best completes each sentence.

10. Returning a habitat to its natural state is called (conservation, preservation, restoration, recycling).

11. When an area is kept in its natural condition, it is (preserved, conserved, deforested, damaged).

12. There are about (500,000; 5 million; 5 billion; 5 trillion) people living on the earth.

13. People in agricultural societies raise domesticated animals such as (deer, mice, lions, cows).

Check Your Understanding

Apply the concepts you have learned to answer each question.

1. Explain how the loss of one species may lead to the loss of others.

2. Describe three ways that automobiles affect the environment.

3. **Critical Thinking** Why is it difficult to restore a damaged habitat?

4. **Application** All the trees in a mountainous area of 200 km^2 are cut down for lumber. Describe the possible effects on the environment.

5. What is the difference between reusing and recycling? Give examples of both.

6. **Critical Thinking** Why did a rapid increase in the human population and the spread of industrial societies around the world occur at about the same time?

7. **Mystery Photo** The photograph on page 508 shows hilly grassland being prepared for the building of a housing development. Make a list of the ways that this piece of land will have changed from its natural condition when the houses are completed.

8. **Application** Think of three ways that a government could encourage its citizens to recycle.

9. Compare the environmental impact of an industrial society to that of a hunting-and-gathering society.

Develop Your Skills

Use the skills you have developed in this chapter to complete each activity.

1. **Interpret Data** The circle graph below shows the sources of air pollution in the United States.

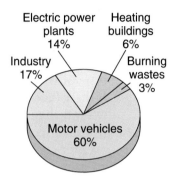

Electric power plants 14%
Heating buildings 6%
Industry 17%
Burning wastes 3%
Motor vehicles 60%

a. What creates the most air pollution?

b. How much of the total amount of air pollution is produced by electric power plants?

2. **Data Bank** Use information on page 613 to answer the following questions.

a. What percentage of the land in the United States is used to grow crops?

b. What type of land use in the United States takes up more land than any other type?

3. **Calculate** Use the information below to calculate the average population density, or number of people per km², of the earth's land surface.

Earth's population = 5.3 billion

Area of a sphere = $4\pi r^2$

Earth's radius (r) = 6,400 km

Earth's land surface = 30% of total

Make Connections

1. **Link the Concepts** Draw a concept map that shows how the following concepts from the chapter are connected. Add words to connect, or link, the concepts.

pollution   natural resources
biosphere   conservation
recycling   preservation
habitats   restoration

2. **Science and Society** Contact your local government to find out the estimated population of your city, town, or village every year for the past 10 years. Use this information to make a graph. Is the population of your town growing? How fast is the rate of increase?

3. **Science and Social Studies** Research to find out more about the Maya civilization. How did they live? What kind of technology did they use? Create a poster that shows some of the achievements of the Maya. Present your poster to the class.

4. **Science and You** Take charge of recycling at home. Find out what materials can be recycled in your area. Figure out ways to make it easier for people in your household to recycle. Encourage reusing and reducing. Set goals for reducing the amount of garbage your household produces.

5. **Science and Social Studies** Read about a group of people with a hunting-and-gathering culture. They may live in the present, such as certain groups in the South American or Indonesian rain forests, or in the past, such as some Native-American groups. How do the lives of these people differ from yours? How is their attitude toward nature different from yours?

It is toward the end of spring, and a woman and her daughter are hiking along the crest of some hills. The woman is in her late twenties, and the daughter is about twelve years old, although neither woman knows her age for sure since, like other Ohlones, they do not keep count of the years. Around their necks hang abalone necklaces, magic against rattlesnakes, which jingle and throw off glints of sunlight as they walk. Burden baskets, held in place by tumplines, bounce lightly against their backs. The women are wearing basketry caps to prevent the tumplines from chafing their foreheads. The artistry and weight of the abalone necklaces and the precise execution of the basketry caps are strong indications that these are women of a well-to-do family.

The two women now head away from the crest of the hills down the side of a ridge and follow

The Ohlone Way

The following excerpt is from the book The Ohlone Way *by Malcolm Margolin.*

the path alongside a tiny creek. . . .The women follow the path alongside the creek until they reach a broad, open meadow. Here they lay down their baskets and, removing their caps, they shake their long hair loose with a few nods of the head. They drink some of the water out of the creek and splash their faces and bodies.

The women now scan the meadow more closely. The mother touches the seed-heads of grass with experienced fingers. She shows her daughter that the brome grasses are ripe and ready to be collected. They remove scoop-like "beating baskets" from the larger burden baskets and hold them in their right hands. Then, cradling their burden baskets in their left arms, they wade out into the high sea of grass and flowers. They move slowly in an ancient, swaying motion. The beating basket sweeps through the seed heads, loosening the grass seeds and knocking many of them into the burden baskets. Soon the burden baskets are brimming with seed, and the women retrace their steps along the path toward the village.

Every day now the mother and daughter return to their meadow to collect seeds from the bromes and other grasses. Yet, as their hampers gradually fill, the women find themselves getting more and more annoyed with the task. The weather is hotter now, and the walk to the meadow is becoming more difficult. The creek has dried up so they can no longer bathe, splash, or even drink. The grasses, too, have become dry and they scratch unpleasantly as the women wade through them. Also, the baskets feel heavier now; the walk along the path seems longer. The mother grows impatient with her daughter, and they occasionally snap at each other and quarrel. "The harvest is over," declares the mother one day. "There is enough food. We deserve a rest."

But before they desert the meadow for the year, there is something else that has to be done.

The two women are holding torches made out of bundled grass. They touch the torches to the meadow. The grass crackles and sputters around them as the flames creep along the ground, heading toward the oak-bay forest. The heat becomes more intense. The women now drop their torches and hurry along the path, up alongside the creek bed, and over the ridge to the crest of hills to rejoin their people. They feel happy once again. The harvest is in, and it has been a good year.

As for the meadow, it will lie blackened and desolate throughout the summer. Then, when the first rains come in October, seeds in the ground will germinate again; by the following spring the meadow will once more be a rich source of flowers and grasses.

Skills in Science

Reading Skills in Science

1. **Find Context Clues** To what type of society do the women belong? Give reasons for your answer. Who are the Ohlones?

2. **Infer** In what ways do the women demonstrate knowledge about their environment and natural cycles? Explain.

3. **Classify** What are three natural resources used by the women? Are the resources renewable or nonrenewable? Explain.

Writing Skills in Science

1. **Identify** What are two things the women do that significantly affect the environment? What is the impact of their actions on their ecosystem? Write whether you think their way of life is or is not sustainable. Explain your reasoning.

Activities

Communicate Research the traditional lifestyle of Native Americans who lived near where you live. Write a short report describing (1) how their way of life was related to the earth's natural cycles and (2) how their way of life affected their ecosystem.

Science and Art Make a series of drawings showing the meadow at four different times from when the women begin gathering seeds to the following spring.

Where to Read More

The Talking Earth by Jean Craighead George. New York: Harper & Row, 1983. Billie Wind ventures into the Florida Everglades to test the legends of her Seminole ancestors and deepens her understanding of nature and her relationship with it.

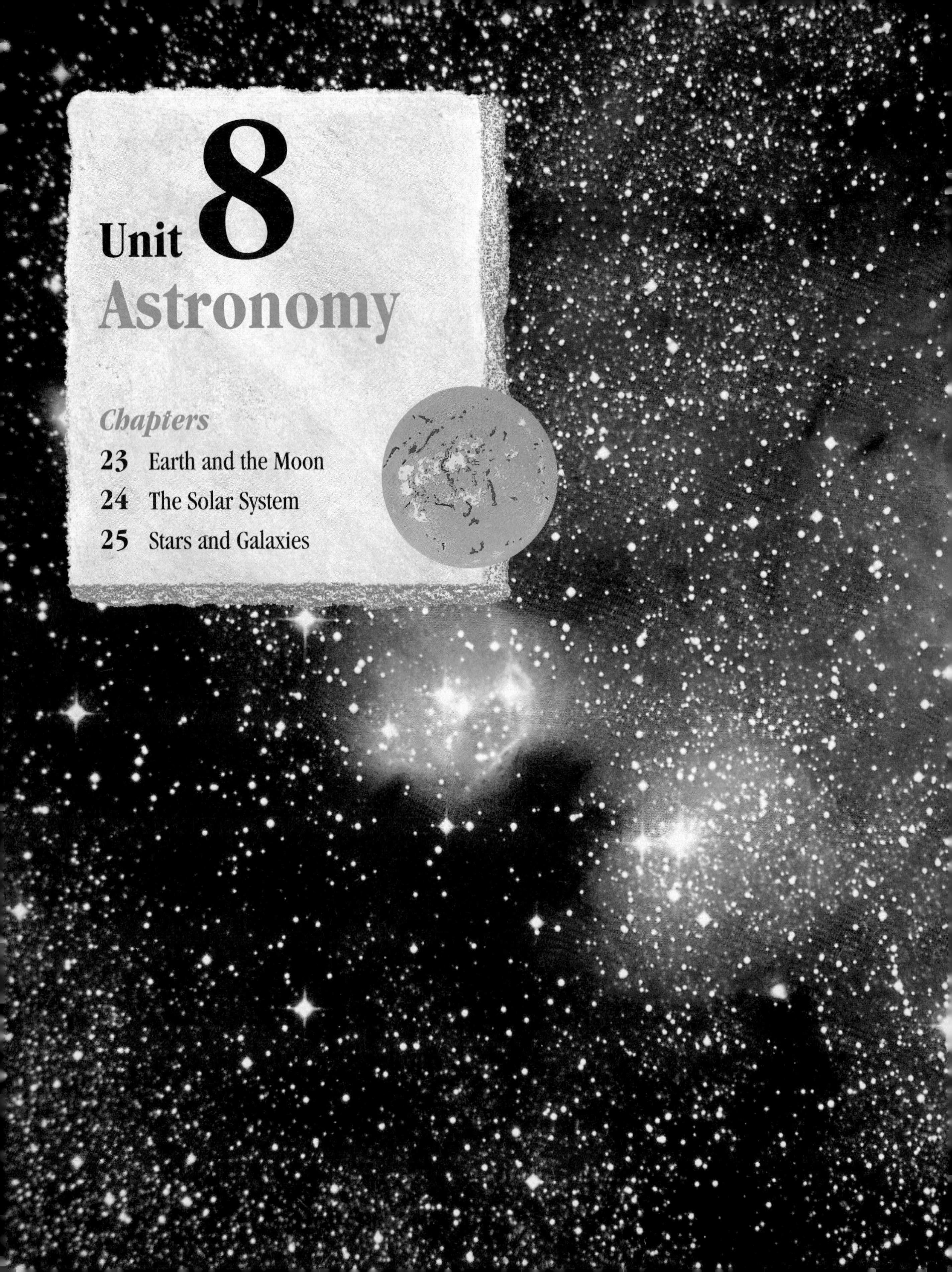

Unit 8
Astronomy

Chapters

Data Bank

Use the information on pages 612 to 625 to answer the following questions about topics explored in this unit.

Calculating

How much longer does it take Saturn to revolve around the sun than Mars?

Interpreting a Diagram

If you live in the Northern Hemisphere, where would you look in the night sky to see the Little Dipper in the spring?

Inferring

Why is Earth so much more dense than Saturn?

Collecting Data

Of the winter constellations shown, which ones contain bright stars? Make a list of these stars and their constellations.

The photograph to the left is of a group of stars in the constellation Sagittarius. Have you seen constellations in the night sky? If so, can you name any of them?

Chapter **23** Earth and the Moon

What do you see?

❝I see the Earth and it seems to be rising from another planet. It looks like the photograph was taken from another planet or maybe the moon. The photograph makes me curious about what other planets and the moon are like.❞

Eddie White
Mabelvale Junior High
   School
Mabelvale, Arkansas

To find out more about the photograph, look on page 556.
As you read this chapter, you will learn about Earth and its moon.

536

23.1 Earth in Space

Objectives

▶ **Describe** the rotation and revolution of planet Earth.

▶ **Explain** how time is measured on Earth.

▶ **Explain** how the tilt of Earth's axis affects life on the planet.

▶ **Make a model** of Earth's orbit.

You are a passenger on a gigantic spaceship called planet Earth. This spaceship spins like a top as it hurtles through space. But you don't sense the motion because everything on Earth moves and spins at the same speed.

Although you aren't directly aware of Earth's motions, you can probably point out some clues to its movements. For example, the sun appears to cross the sky every day. Summer changes to autumn. All these changes are caused by Earth's motions.

Earth's Rotation

Earth has a spherical, or ball-like, shape that is slightly more than 40 000 km in circumference, with a diameter of about 12 760 km. Look at Table 23.1. What is the surface area of Earth?

Earth moves in two ways. It travels, or revolves, around the sun. At the same time, it spins, or rotates, like a top. If you observe a spinning top, you can see that it turns around a line running through the center. This line is called an **axis**. Earth's axis is an imaginary line that extends from the North Pole through Earth to the South Pole. The spinning of Earth on its axis is called **rotation**. Earth makes one complete rotation in 23 hours and 56 minutes.

Have you ever observed a sunrise or a sunset? If so, you may know that the earth rotates from west to east. On Earth you see the sun come into view over the eastern horizon, move across the sky from east to west, and disappear below the western horizon. Earth's rotation is responsible for the changing of day and night.

Table 23.1 Facts about the Earth

Average distance from the sun	149 700 000 km
Surface area	512 175 090 km²
Circumference at equator	40 074 km
Circumference at poles	40 007 km
Diameter at equator	12 760 km
Diameter at poles	12 714 km
Period of rotation	23 h, 56 mn
Period of revolution around the sun	365.26 days

Earth is not a perfect sphere. Forces created by rotation displace some material, causing the planet to bulge slightly at the equator. So Earth's shape is actually a slightly flattened sphere. The distance around Earth at the equator is about 67 km greater than around the poles. However, this difference is so small in relation to the planet's size that the flattening isn't detected from space.

Earth as a Magnet

A compass can be used to find direction. One end of a compass needle always points north because Earth behaves like a giant bar magnet. Earth's magnetism is caused by the motion of materials in its molten outer core. Recall that the core is composed mainly of iron. Moving electric charges in the molten core material produce a magnetic field.

Look at the photograph in Figure 23.1. What happens when iron filings are sprinkled over a bar magnet? The filings form a pattern around the magnet. This pattern shows the lines of force surrounding the magnet. Earth is surrounded by similar lines of force. Notice in Figure 23.1 that the lines of force are most concentrated near the magnetic poles. The magnetic poles attract a compass needle. From the poles, the lines of force spread out to form a magnetic field, called the magnetosphere.

Figure 23.1

Compare the magnetic field around Earth to the forces around a bar magnet. ▼

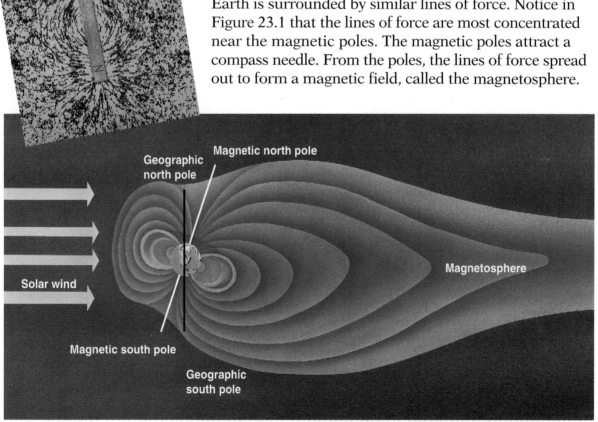

Geographic north pole

Magnetic north pole

Solar wind

Magnetosphere

Magnetic south pole

Geographic south pole

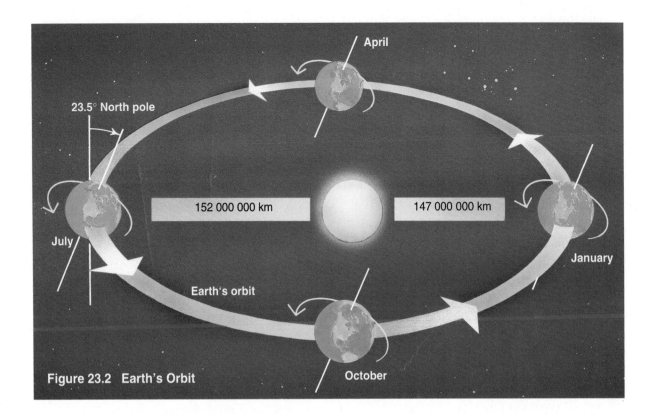

Figure 23.2   Earth's Orbit

Labels in figure: April, 23.5° North pole, 152 000 000 km, 147 000 000 km, January, July, Earth's orbit, October

Earth's Revolution

As Earth rotates on its axis, it also travels around the sun. The movement of a body in space around another body is called **revolution**. It takes Earth about 365 days, or one Earth year, to complete one revolution around the sun. During that time, Earth travels about 958 million km. To cover that distance, Earth and its passengers travel at a speed of about 107,275 km/hr!

The path a body follows as it revolves around another body is called its **orbit**. As shown in Figure 23.2, Earth's orbit is elliptical. So the distance between Earth and the sun changes throughout the year. The closest point of Earth's orbit to the sun is called *perihelion* (pur uh HEEL yuhn). Find the distance at perihelion in Figure 23.2. Earth reaches this point about January 3. Six months later, Earth reaches the farthest point from the sun, called *aphelion* (a FEEL yuhn).

Seasons

How do you know what season it is? How does winter compare with summer? Most people experience several seasons during a year. Notice in Figure 23.2 that Earth's axis is tilted at an angle of 23.5°. Also notice that as Earth revolves around the sun, its axis always points in the same direction. The tilt of the axis is important for the changing of seasons on Earth.

Because of the tilt of Earth's axis, the amount of sunlight falling on the different regions of the earth changes throughout the year. For example, when the Northern Hemisphere is tilted toward the sun, the sun's rays strike this area more directly. There are also more hours of sunlight. The combination of increased daylight and more direct rays cause higher temperatures. Look at Figure 23.2. Although Earth is at aphelion, the position of greatest distance, it is summer in the Northern Hemisphere.

When the Northern Hemisphere points toward the sun, the Southern Hemisphere tilts away from the sun. The sun's rays reach the Southern Hemisphere at a greater slant. Slanted rays spread out the heat. The number of daylight hours is short. It is winter.

Solstices and Equinoxes During the day, the most direct sunlight rays arrive when the sun reaches its highest elevation in the sky, at noon. The most slanted sunlight rays arrive when the sun is on the *horizon*, the line where the earth seems to meet the sky. The sun is on the horizon at sunrise and sunset.

The highest point of the sky is the **zenith.** When you stand outside, the zenith is directly overhead. Look at Figure 23.3. Due to the tilt of Earth, the noon sun appears directly overhead in various places between the latitudes 23°N and 23°S throughout the year. When the noon sun is directly overhead at either of these exact latitudes, it is called a **solstice.** The first day of summer is the summer solstice.

Between the two solstices are two equinoxes. An **equinox** (EE kwuh nahks) is when the noon sun is directly over the equator. During an equinox the hours of daylight and darkness are equal everywhere on Earth.

Figure 23.3 Solstices and Equinoxes on Earth ▼

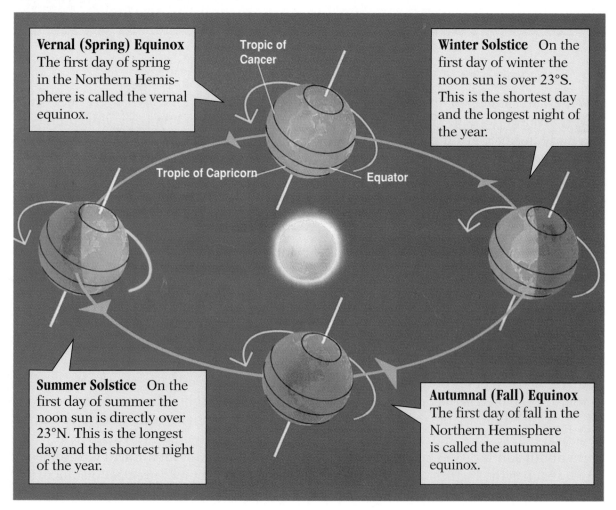

Vernal (Spring) Equinox The first day of spring in the Northern Hemisphere is called the vernal equinox.

Tropic of Cancer

Winter Solstice On the first day of winter the noon sun is over 23°S. This is the shortest day and the longest night of the year.

Tropic of Capricorn

Equator

Summer Solstice On the first day of summer the noon sun is directly over 23°N. This is the longest day and the shortest night of the year.

Autumnal (Fall) Equinox The first day of fall in the Northern Hemisphere is called the autumnal equinox.

Life Cycles and Seasons

How does your life and your daily routine change with the seasons? You probably dress differently at different times of the year. Your outdoor activities may be affected by the temperature and the number of hours of daylight. The activities of most living things change with the seasons. Animals and plants go through cycles of activity. These cycles are regulated by the availability of food and the number of daylight hours.

Some animals, especially birds, migrate with the changing seasons. Many birds follow the sun's movement in the sky north and south throughout the year. Migrating birds travel toward the equator in winter and away from the equator in summer. Other migrating animals include some types of fishes and whales.

Some plants always flower during summer, while other plants flower only in fall. Plants have a light-sensitive chemical that measures night length. Some plants need long nights to trigger blooming; others need short nights. ▼

▲ In areas with both mild and cold or dry seasons, deciduous trees grow. Sap flows freely through deciduous trees. In some trees, this sap is collected to make maple syrup. When fall arrives, leaves turn color and fall from deciduous trees. The plants enter a period of dormancy, ready to begin the cycle again the following spring.

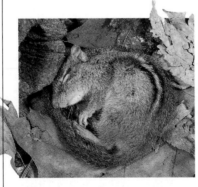

▲ In places where winter temperatures are low and food is scarce, some animals go through a period of dormancy. Chipmunks and bears hibernate. During dry seasons, amphibians may estivate (EHS tuh vayt), or burrow underground and remain dormant until wet weather arrives.

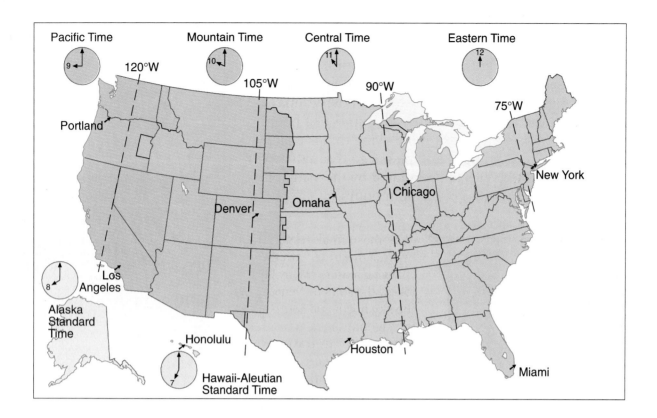

Pacific Time   Mountain Time   Central Time   Eastern Time

120°W   105°W   90°W   75°W

Portland

Los
Angeles

Alaska
Standard
Time

Denver   Omaha   Chicago   New York

Honolulu   Houston   Miami

Hawaii-Aleutian
Standard Time

Figure 23.4 ▲
How many time zones are
located in the United States?
Which time zone do you live in?

▼ ACTIVITY

Interpreting Data

Now Boarding . . .

Refer to Figure 23.4. If you
were to leave Anchorage,
Alaska, at 10:00 a.m., and it
took seven hours by plane to
reach Chicago, at what time
would you arrive in Chicago?
Use the time zone map.

SKILLS WORKOUT

Time Zones

People have always been interested in measuring time. About 2,500 years ago, shadow clocks, or sundials, kept track of time using the motion of the sun in the sky. Since the length of a day varies with Earth's revolution, these clocks weren't very accurate.

In 1884, an international system was established to standardize time measurement worldwide. This system divides Earth into 24 time zones. A time zone is the distance Earth rotates in one hour. Since Earth rotates 360° in 24 hours, each time zone is 15° wide. The map in Figure 23.4 shows the time zones in the United States.

The starting point of the world's time zones is at 0°, or the prime meridian. The prime meridian passes through Greenwich, England. Halfway around the world is the 180° meridian, or the international date line. At midnight, in Greenwich, it is noon at the international date line.

When you move across a time zone, the time changes by one hour. If you travel east, the time is one hour later; if you travel west, it is one hour earlier. When you cross the international date line, you change days! If you travel east across the meridian, you gain one day. If you travel west, you lose one day.

Every day, you are probably reminded of the date. You know the date of your birth and the dates of holidays. To keep track of these kinds of important events, calendars were developed hundreds of years ago.

Most ancient calendars were based on the changing shape and position of the moon. A lunar year has 354 days divided into 12 months. A month in the lunar calendar begins on the new moon and lasts 29 or 30 days. This type of dating system was used by the Babylonians and the Chinese. A type of lunar calendar is still used by the Moslems today.

About 4,000 B.C., the Egyptians developed a solar calendar. It was based on the apparent motion of the sun and the seasons. This calendar had 12 months. Each month had 30 days, with five days added at the end of the year.

The Jewish calendar is a combination of a lunar and solar calendar, or a lunisolar calendar. It is over 5,000 years old. In the Jewish calendar, each month is based on the orbit of the moon, as in the lunar calendar. However, a lunar year is 11 days shorter than a solar year. To correct this, a 19-year period was developed. Each 19-year period consists of 12 years of 12 months and 7 years of 13 months.

In the first century A.D., the Maya from Central America used several calendars. The calendar they used for agriculture had 365 days, with every fourth year containing an extra day.

Figure 23.5 ▲
The Aztecs, who lived in the central valley of Mexico, created this stone calendar during the 1480s. It weighs almost 20 tons and is called the Sun Stone.

Check and Explain

1. What are two important motions of Earth? Describe each motion.

2. If you take off from New York at noon in a jet plane, how is it possible to arrive in California at 11 a.m.? Explain.

3. **Infer** How would life on Earth be different if Earth's axis were not tilted?

4. **Make a Model** Using two thumbtacks, a piece of string, paper, cardboard, and a pencil, draw a figure that is similar in shape to that of Earth's orbit. Label the sun, perihelion, and aphelion.

Activity 23 *Why does Earth bulge at the equator?*

Skills Model; Infer; Measure

Task 1 Prelab Prep
Collect the following items: long, sharpened pencil, construction paper, metric ruler, scissors, tape, hole punch, sheet of paper.

Task 2 Data Record
On a sheet of paper, copy Table 23.2. Record your observations in the table.

Table 23.2 Earth Rotation Observations

Location on Earth	Observation 1	Observation 2
Equator		
Poles		

Task 3 Procedure
1. From the construction paper, cut 2 separate strips that each measure 3 cm by 40 cm.
2. Mark an X at the center of each strip.
3. Cross the strips at their centers, and tape them together.
4. Bring the four loose ends together. Overlap the ends, and secure together with tape.
5. Using a hole punch make a hole in the center of each end where the strips overlap.
6. Push the pencil through the holes in each end. The completed setup should look like Figure 23.6.
7. Hold each end of the pencil, and roll the pencil in your fingers. Observe what happens to the equator and the poles.
8. Record your observations of the equator and the poles in the data table under Observation 1.
9. Re-form a sphere with the strips of paper.
10. Place a sheet of paper on a flat surface.

11. Place the tip of the pencil on the paper. Twirl the pencil. Observe the equator and the poles. Record your observations in the data table under Observation 2.

Task 4 Analysis
1. What does the sphere represent?
2. What does rolling or twirling the pencil represent? Explain.
3. Describe what happens at the equator when the pencil is rolled or twirled.
4. Describe what happens at the poles when the pencil is rolled or twirled.
5. How is this model different from Earth? Explain.

Task 5 Conclusion
Write a short paragraph describing how your model is similar to what happens as Earth rotates.

Extension

How can you find out how much the sphere in your model flattened? Design an experiment to figure out how much your sphere flattens from its original shape when it is rotated.

Figure 23.6 ▼

23.2 Earth's Moon

Objectives

▶ **Identify** four features of the moon's surface.

▶ **List** some major events in the exploration of the moon.

▶ **Explain** how the motion of the moon affects the view of the moon from Earth.

▶ **Infer** which theory about the formation of the moon is the most logical.

▼ **ACTIVITY**

Inferring

Moonscapes

Based on your direct observations and on photographs of the moon, describe its shape, color, and composition in a paragraph.

SKILLS WARMUP

Imagine you are given a photograph of some object on Earth's surface taken from an altitude of 1,000 km. How would you try to identify the object? You would study the specimen and its surroundings very carefully. Then you would use your observations to compare the object with some familiar object. Finally, you would make inferences based on your observations.

For hundreds of years, scientists have used similar techniques to study an object about 384,400 km from Earth. That object is Earth's moon.

The Lunar Satellite

Dozens of artificial satellites circle the planet. But the moon is Earth's only natural satellite. The largest artificial satellite is dwarfed by the moon, which has a diameter of 3,476 km.

At its surface, the moon's gravity is about one-sixth that of Earth. Since weight measures the pull of gravity, a person's weight on the moon would be one-sixth of that on Earth. What is your moon weight?

During the 1970s, astronauts left many scientific instruments on the lunar surface. Data from these instruments reveals that the moon doesn't have a magnetic field, although some moon rocks show traces of magnetism from long ago. Seismic instruments record moonquakes and provide data about the moon's interior. This information shows that the moon's interior is layered like that of Earth, except with a smaller iron core and a thicker solid lithosphere.

Figure 23.7 ▲
You can see the moon's surface very clearly in this moonrise over New York City.

The Lunar Surface

Exploration of the moon's surface has shown it to be barren and lifeless. Temperatures may range from 130°C at lunar noon to −175°C at night. Evidence indicates there is no water on the lunar surface. There is almost no atmosphere. Consequently, there is no weather. The absence of water and an atmosphere means that no weathering of the lunar surface occurs. Therefore, the rocks and rock formations have remained almost unchanged for much of the moon's history.

◄ When Galileo first turned his telescope on the lunar surface almost 400 years ago, he clearly saw regions of bright and dark that are vaguely visible with the un-aided eye. Galileo thought the dark regions resembled seas here on Earth. So he called them *maria* (MAR ee uh), the Latin word for seas. Today, these dark regions are known to be broad, flat plains. Cutting across the maria are features called *rilles* (RIHLS). Rilles are long, narrow valleys.

The most obvious features on the moon's surface are circular indentations called **craters**. Most of the moon's craters were created by meteorites striking the lunar surface. But some of the smaller ones may be volcanic in origin. Copernicus, one of the largest craters, is more than 90 km in diameter. ▼

▲ The bright areas that Galileo saw on the moon are called *highlands*. Highlands consist of mountainous terrain on the surface of the moon.

Moon's Movements

The moon has an elliptical orbit around Earth. The moon remains in its orbit because the gravity of Earth and the gravity of the moon pull on each other. The moon's closest point to Earth is called *perigee*. (PEHR uh JEE) The farthest point in its orbit is called *apogee* (AP uh JEE).

The moon's period of revolution is the same as its period of rotation. The moon completes one revolution in 27.3 days. During this period, it also rotates once on its axis. Because these two periods are equal, the same side of the moon always faces Earth, as shown in Figure 23.8.

Origin of the Moon

For centuries, people have wondered about the origin of the moon. Although several theories have been developed, most have flaws.

▶ The *daughter theory* suggests that a piece of Earth split off to form the moon. However, the daughter theory doesn't explain why the moon is not solely composed of Earth's crust material. Also, there is no evidence that Earth ever spun fast enough to eject such a large mass.

▶ The *sister theory* states that Earth and the moon formed from gas and dust during the formation of the solar system. This theory can't account for the differences in the rock composition between the two bodies.

▶ The *capture theory* proposes that the moon formed elsewhere and was captured by Earth's gravity as it passed. It is argued that the moon couldn't have attained a stable orbit without assistance from a third body. No evidence of such a body has ever been found.

▶ The most accepted theory today is that an impact knocked a large quantity of material from Earth. Earth's gravity captured and collected material from the impacting body and Earth to form the moon.

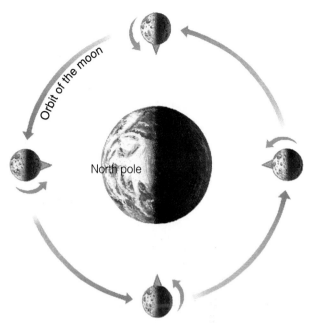

Figure 23.8 ▲
As the moon orbits Earth, the same side of the moon always faces toward Earth.

▼ **ACTIVITY**

Making a Model

A Fickle Moon

Draw an ellipse. Locate the center of the ellipse. Draw Earth in the center. Locate the point when the moon's position is farthest from (apogee) and closest to (perigee) Earth. Label these two points. What does your model represent?

SKILLS WORKOUT

Exploration of the Moon

In 1959, the Soviet spacecraft Luna 3 radioed back the first photographs of the moon's far side. Motivated by the Soviet's success, the United States began the Apollo project. The project's goal was to place an astronaut on the moon before 1970.

On July 16, 1969, Apollo 11 was launched. Neil Armstrong became the first person to set foot on the moon. He was followed by Edwin "Buzz" Aldrin, Jr. The two astronauts collected lunar materials and set up experiments before returning to Earth.

Over the next three years, five more lunar landings were accomplished. Astronauts explored large areas of the lunar surface. The last lunar mission, Apollo 17, was completed in December 1972. Since then, no people have returned to the moon. However, much information has been gained from instruments left on the moon by the astronauts.

Historical Notebook

Moon Landing

"One small step for man, one giant leap for mankind." These were the first words spoken by Neil Armstrong as he took the very first step on the moon. The results of this first step were uncertain. Would he sink into the dust? Would the ground be slippery? But when Armstrong stepped onto the moon's surface, he found it to be like walking on soot or flour.

Aldrin (shown at right) and Armstrong found that moving across the moon's surface was easiest when they floated across it with their feet in the air. They moved about 2 to 4 meters at a time.

These first astronauts discovered something strange about the lunar surface. When they planted the American flag into the ground, they had to press hard to force the flagstaff down. Once in the ground, the staff would easily fall over. The lunar soil resisted downward force, but shifted easily sideways.

1. Who were the first two people to walk on the moon?

2. What did the astronauts find out about the surface of the moon?

3. **Research** Find out how moon rocks helped scientists learn about the composition and history of the moon.

Science and Technology *Moon Machines*

Before 1969, the lunar surface was barren of any technology. Since then, machines have landed, traveled, and been left behind on the moon.

The machine that carried the astronauts to the lunar surface is called the lunar module, or LM. The lunar module is a small spacecraft that separates from the larger command module. The LM has a separate fuel system that allows it to land and take off. The LM serves as the headquarters for astronauts while they are on the moon. When the mission is completed, the lunar module leaves the moon to reconnect with the command module. The LM is later discarded into space.

Even though the LM doesn't remain on the moon, other machines brought to the moon are still on its surface. The Lunar Rover, or moon buggy, is a battery-powered vehicle similar to a dune buggy. It was first used during Apollo 15. The Lunar Rover allowed astronauts on Apollo missions 15, 16, and 17 to explore large areas of the lunar surface. It was left on the surface for possible use in the future.

Instruments were also left on the moon to conduct scientific experiments. The passive seismic experiment records moonquakes and meteorite impacts. The lunar surface gravimeter detects changes in the gravitational field. The lunar atmospheric composition instrument analyzes lunar gases. The solar wind spectrometer measures the number of electrons and protons streaming in solar wind. The data from these scientific devices is sent back to Earth for analysis.

Figure 23.9 ▲
Astronaut Eugene Cernan drives the Lunar Rover during the Apollo 17 mission.

Check and Explain

1. Describe four features of the moon's surface.

2. List two major events in the exploration of the moon. Explain why you chose these two events.

3. **Reason and Conclude** How would the view of the moon from Earth be different if the moon rotated around its axis more slowly than it now does?

4. **Infer** Decide which theory about the origin of the moon is the most logical. Explain why you chose this theory, and why you rejected the other theories.

The Phase is Familiar . . .

Using a calendar, list the dates of the new moon, quarter moon, and full moon for six months. Observe the rhythm of the moon cycles. Predict the date of the next full moon, new moon, and quarter moon. Check the calendar to see if your prediction was correct.

SKILLS WARMUP

23.3 Earth–Moon System

Objectives

▶ **Relate** the phases of the moon to its revolution.

▶ **Describe** a waxing moon and a waning moon.

▶ **Predict** how the distance of the moon affects tides.

▶ **Compare** and **contrast** a lunar eclipse and a solar eclipse.

I f you look at the sky at night, what do you see? You see stars, of course, and the moon. If you look at the sky during the day, what do you see? Do you ever see the moon? Sometimes you can see the moon even during the day.

**Figure 23.10
Phases of the Moon** ▼

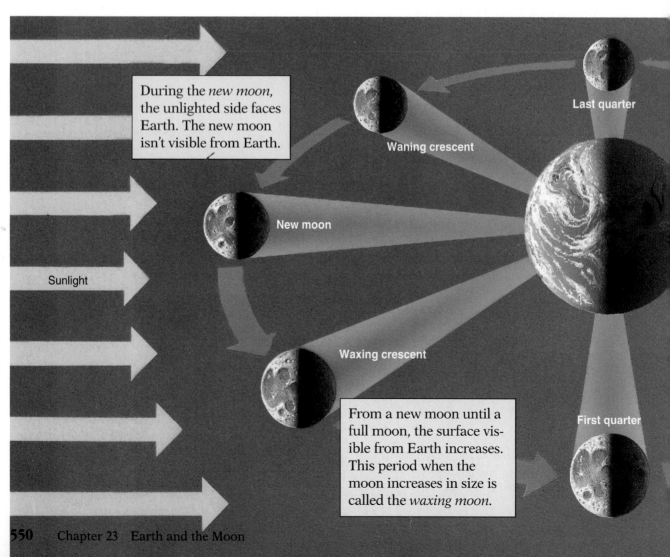

During the *new moon*, the unlighted side faces Earth. The new moon isn't visible from Earth.

Last quarter

Waning crescent

New moon

Sunlight

Waxing crescent

First quarter

From a new moon until a full moon, the surface visible from Earth increases. This period when the moon increases in size is called the *waxing moon*.

Phases of the Moon

The moon doesn't produce its own light. The moon is visible from Earth because sunlight reflects off its surface. Recall that the moon's period of rotation and revolution are both 27.3 days. Therefore, people on Earth can only view one side of the moon. And this view includes only the portion of the moon lighted by the sun each night.

Half of the moon's surface is always lighted by the sun. As the moon orbits Earth, the amount of the lighted surface that is visible from Earth changes. This causes the shape of the visible surface to change. Look at the various shapes of the moon as seen from Earth in the photographs on the right. The different shapes of the moon as seen from Earth are called phases. Locate the different phases of the moon in Figure 23.10. How many phases are shown?

Waxing crescent

First quarter

Full moon

Last quarter

Waning crescent

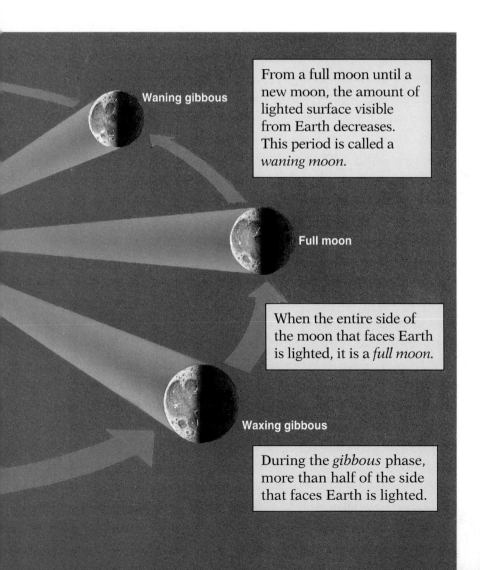

Waning gibbous

From a full moon until a new moon, the amount of lighted surface visible from Earth decreases. This period is called a *waning moon.*

Full moon

When the entire side of the moon that faces Earth is lighted, it is a *full moon.*

Waxing gibbous

During the *gibbous* phase, more than half of the side that faces Earth is lighted.

Eclipses

If you place your hand between a light and the wall, your hand blocks the light. You see a shadow on the wall. The same thing happens in space. When one planet passes between the sun and another body, it casts a shadow called an **eclipse** (ee KLIHPS).

Earth and the moon cast long shadows into space. In the shadow where light is completely blocked is a small, dark area called the **umbra** (UHM bruh). The **penumbra** (pee NUHM bruh) is a partial shadow where some light is blocked and other light fills it in.

When the moon moves into Earth's shadow, a *lunar eclipse* occurs. Earth's shadow blocks sunlight from the moon. All or part of the moon is darkened.

When the moon passes between the sun and Earth, a *solar eclipse* occurs. Look at Figure 23.12. The moon's shadow falls on Earth. Because the moon is smaller than Earth, its shadow covers only a small area.

Figure 23.11 Lunar Eclipse ▼

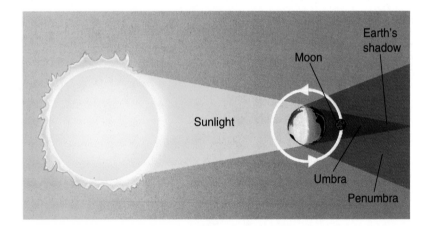

Figure 23.12 Solar Eclipse ▼

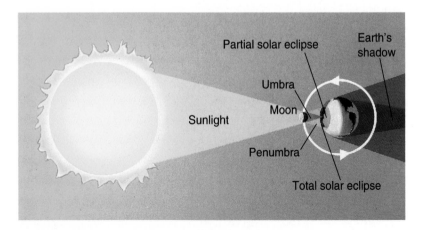

SkillBuilder *Making Models*

Eclipses

Just as your body creates a shadow on the sidewalk when you block the sun, bodies in space also create shadows. You will model how these shadows are created.

Obtain a flashlight, a softball, a table tennis ball, a ruler, and several sheets of paper. Lay the flashlight in the center of a table. Darken the room, and turn on the flashlight. Set the softball in the path of the light from the flashlight. Place the sheet of paper on the table so the shadow of the softball falls on the paper. Using the ruler, trace the shadow created by the softball on the sheet of paper. Remove the softball and paper from the table. Now place the table tennis ball in the path of the light from the flashlight. Trace the shadow created by the table tennis ball on a different sheet of paper.

Now use the balls to model a solar eclipse. Place the softball on the table in the path of the light from the flashlight. Holding the table tennis

ball in your fingers, circle it around the softball. When the shadow from the table tennis ball blocks the light that reaches the softball, an eclipse has occurred. Draw the position of the table tennis ball, the flashlight, and the softball at the time of the eclipse.

1. What was the shape of the shadow created by each of the balls?

2. What did the flashlight in your model represent? The softball? The table tennis ball?

3. What was the position of the balls and the flashlight at the time of the solar eclipse?

4. Model a lunar eclipse with the same materials you used for your solar eclipse model. In a short paragraph, compare your lunar eclipse and solar eclipse models.

Tides

The influence of the moon's gravitational pull causes the water of Earth's oceans to move. As a result, the local ocean level rises and falls as the moon revolves around Earth. Recall that these changes in ocean levels are called *tides*. Tides change about every six hours.

The sun's gravity also affects tides. However, because the sun is far away, its influence is less than that of the moon. The highest high tides and the lowest low tides occur when the sun, Earth, and moon align. These tides, called *spring tides*, occur during the full moon and the new moon.

Similarly, the lowest high tides and the highest low tides occur when the sun, moon, and Earth form a right angle. At these times, the sun's gravity offsets the effects of the moon's gravity on the oceans. These tides, called *neap tides*, occur during the quarter moon phases.

▼ ACTIVITY

Interpreting Data

Phase Facts

Refer to the monthly tide cycle shown in Figure 15.20 on page 358. Identify the new moon, full moon, first quarter moon, and last quarter moon in the diagram. Which type of tide corresponds with each moon phase?

SKILLS WORKOUT

It Was a Moonlit Night . . .

Work with a partner to create your own legend about the moon. Draw a picture that illustrates your legend. Share your legend and your picture with the class.

Science and Society *Moon Lore*

Have you ever heard that the moon is made of green cheese? Or that when you look at the full moon, you see the face of a man embedded in the moon? These and many other beliefs about the moon have been part of certain cultures' folklore for many centuries. Folklore is the traditional beliefs, legends, and customs of a people.

The surface of the moon has been a popular subject in legends from many cultures. Some legends decribed the moon as a mirror that reflected the seas and the continents of Earth. In other legends, various figures were observed in lunar surface markings. One legend tells of the man in the moon who was imprisoned for stealing. In some Asian cultures, people imagined seeing a long-eared rabbit or a monkey pounding rice. Other figures in legends included a beautiful woman, a cat, and a frog.

The moon has also been a source of much superstition among people. For example, people from the Middle Ages thought that sleeping in the light of the full moon would cause blindness or insanity. The word "lunatic" is derived from the Latin word that means "moonstruck." When the moon passed between Earth and the sun during an eclipse, it was believed to be an evil omen. People thought that an eclipse foretold of doom, such as famine, war, or other disasters.

The moon has also played a part in mythology. The word "lunar" comes from the Latin name for the full moon, Luna. According to Greek mythology, the moon was a goddess with three faces. At the new moon was the face of Hecate (HEHK uh tee). The waxing moon belonged to the face of Diana. The full moon showed the face of Luna.

Check and Explain

1. What causes the phases of the moon?

2. How can you tell if the moon is waxing or waning?

3. **Predict** How would tides be affected if the distance between Earth and the moon were halved?

4. **Compare and Contrast** How is a lunar eclipse similar to a solar eclipse? How is it different?

Chapter 23 Review

Concept Summary

23.1 Earth in Space
▶ Earth completes one rotation on its axis about every 24 hours.
▶ Earth completes one orbit, or revolution, around the sun each year.
▶ The tilt of Earth's axis causes seasons.
▶ Earth is surrounded by a magnetic field.
▶ Day length is affected by the tilt of Earth's axis and Earth's position in its yearly orbit around the sun.
▶ Earth is divided into time zones that begin at the prime meridian.

23.2 Earth's Moon
▶ The moon is Earth's natural satellite.
▶ Features on the surface of the moon include maria, craters, and highlands.

▶ The moon completes one revolution around Earth and one rotation in 27.3 days.
▶ There are many theories about the origin of the moon.
▶ Apollo 11 was the first spacecraft to land on the moon.

23.3 Earth–Moon System
▶ Sunlight reflects off the surface of the moon, creating the lunar phases.
▶ The phases of the moon include the new moon, full moon, quarter moon, and crescent moon.
▶ Bodies in space cast shadows.
▶ When one planet passes in between the sun and another body, an eclipse occurs.

Chapter Vocabulary

axis (23.1)	zenith (23.1)	eclipse (23.3)
rotation (23.1)	solstice (23.1)	umbra (23.3)
revolution (23.1)	equinox (23.1)	penumbra (23.3)
orbit (23.1)	crater (23.2)	

Check Your Vocabulary

Use the vocabulary words above to complete the following sentences correctly.

1. Circular indentations that are located on the surface of the moon are called _____.

2. The highest point the sun reaches in the sky is called the _____.

3. It takes about 365 days for Earth to complete one _____.

4. The partial shadow created by bodies in space is the _____.

5. Twice a year when the noon sun falls directly on Earth's surface between 23°N and 23°S, a(n) _____ occurs.

6. When a planet passes between the sun and another body and blocks light, it is called a(n) _____.

7. When the hours of daylight and darkness are equal, it is called a(n) _____.

8. The part of the shadow cast by bodies in space that blocks all light is the _____.

9. It takes about 24 hours for Earth to complete one _____ on its axis.

10. It takes Earth about 365 days to complete its _____ around the sun.

11. The imaginary line that extends through the Earth's poles is called the _____.

Chapter 23 *Review*

Check Your Knowledge

Answer the following in complete sentences.

1. What is a rille?

2. List the different phases of the moon.

3. How long is one revolution of Earth?

4. What is meant by a waxing moon? A waning moon?

5. Who was the first person to step on the surface of the moon?

6. What causes a neap tide?

7. What are the highlands that are found on the moon?

8. What probably creates Earth's magnetic field?

9. When do equinoxes occur?

10. Explain one way that organisms are affected by the seasons.

11. What is the international date line?

12. What is perigee?

Determine whether each statement is true or false. Write *true* if it is true. If it is false, change the underlined word(s) to make the statement true.

13. The path the moon follows around Earth is called its <u>revolution</u>.

14. The most slanted sun rays reach Earth when the sun is on the <u>horizon</u>.

15. The shortest day in the Northern Hemisphere is during the <u>winter</u> solstice.

16. When the entire side of the moon that faces Earth is light, it is a <u>new</u> moon.

17. The starting point for time zones passes through the <u>prime meridian</u>.

Check Your Understanding

Apply the concepts you have learned to answer each question.

1. Explain how the rotation of Earth affects its shape.

2. **Compare** How does the surface of the moon compare to the surface of Earth? How are they alike? How are they different?

3. Explain why only some people on Earth experience a complete solar eclipse.

4. Discuss what the moon would be like if it actually looked like Galileo's interpretations of the moon's surface from his telescope.

5. Explain what causes the different seasons on Earth.

6. Discuss why people on Earth view only one side of the moon.

7. **Predict** Discuss how the surface of the moon will change over time. Why?

8. Explain how you can be traveling about 107 000 km/hr right at this moment and not even notice it.

9. **Extension** Discuss how the changing tides affect organisms living on Earth.

10. **Application** When it is winter in the Northern Hemisphere, what is the season in the Southern Hemisphere? Why?

11. **Mystery Photo** The photograph on page 536 shows an Earth rise from the surface of the moon. Imagine you lived on the moon and had never visited Earth. Infer from the photograph the shape, composition, and color of Earth. Discuss how you reached these inferences.

Develop Your Skills

Use the skills you have developed in this chapter to complete each activity.

1. Interpret Data The diagram below shows the route of a ship traveling across the international date line.

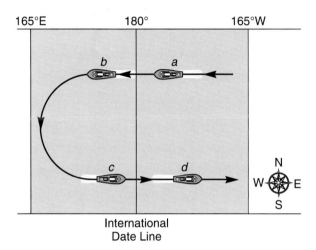

International
Date Line

a. If the ship is at point *a* on May 1 at 7:00 p.m., what are the date and time at point *b*?

b. What are the date and time at point *c*?

c. What are the date and time at point *d*?

d. If it takes one hour for the ship to travel from *a* to *d*, what will be the date and time when the ship reaches *d*?

2. Data Bank Use the information on page 618 to answer the following questions.

a. What is the diameter of Earth in km?

b. What is the distance in km from Earth to the moon?

c. How many Earths could fit into the distance between Earth and the moon?

Make Connections

1. Link the Concepts Below is a concept map showing how some of the main concepts in this chapter link together. Only part of the map is filled in. Copy the map and complete it using words and ideas from the chapter.

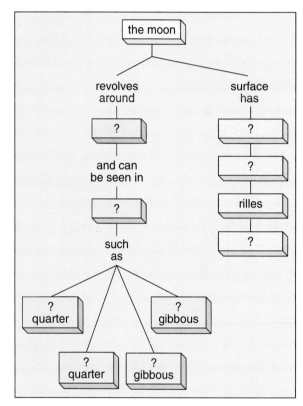

2. Science and Literature The moon is the subject of many songs and poems. Locate two poems or songs that focus on the moon. How is the moon portrayed in the writing? Is the information about the moon scientifically correct?

3. Science and Society Many people believe that the phases of the moon affect the behavior of organisms on Earth. Interview seven different people to discover how they think the full moon affects organisms on Earth.

Chapter 24   The Solar System

What do you see?

"In this picture I see many colors. These colors are swirling every which way. They look like smoky clouds. It looks like it's made of powerful gases mixed together. It seems to be very large. It probably covers a huge part of an extremely hot or cold planet."

YeVonne Simpson
Cimarron High School
Las Vegas, Nevada

To find out more about the photograph, look on page 582. As you read this chapter, you will learn about the solar system.

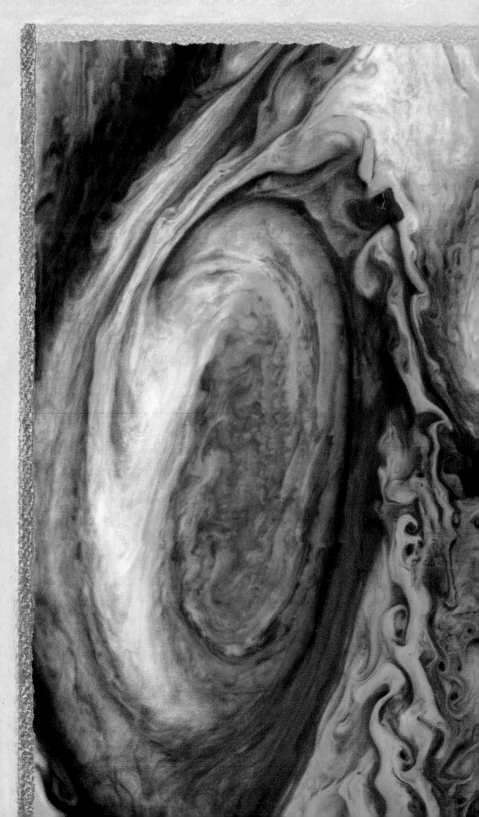

24.1 The Sun

Objectives

▶ **Explain** how energy is produced in the sun.

▶ **Describe** the three layers of the sun's atmosphere.

▶ **Explain** how sunspots, prominences, and solar flares are related.

▶ **Make a model** of the sun's interior.

You wake up and see the sun shining through the window. It perks you up to know what a nice day it is. Seeing the sun is reassuring. Fortunately, even on a cloudy day, the sun is always there, warming Earth and providing living things with energy. Almost all life depends directly on the sun.

The Sun as a Fusion Reactor

The sun is a star, average in size and brightness. It contains over 300,000 times more matter than Earth. It is the center of the **solar system.** The solar system includes Earth, eight other planets, and many smaller objects that orbit the sun. The sun holds the solar system together with a strong gravitational pull.

The sun, like all stars, produces huge amounts of energy in the form of heat, light, and radiation. You may think that the sun produces this energy by burning gases in the same way a stove burns gas to heat food. But the energy given off by the sun comes not from burning but from the conversion of matter into energy. This conversion takes place in a process called *nuclear fusion*. During nuclear fusion, the matter contained in four hydrogen nuclei rearranges to create a helium nucleus. As a result, some of the original matter becomes energy.

Nuclear fusion is very different from a chemical reaction such as burning. Chemical reactions change the chemical bonds between atoms, a change that involves only the atoms' electrons. Nuclear fusion, in contrast, involves changes in the nuclei of atoms. It is a process that creates new elements.

Figure 24.1 ▲
All human cultures have recognized the importance of the sun.

Energy Release Nuclear fusion releases far more energy than any chemical reaction. Very small amounts of matter release enormous amounts of energy during fusion. The fusion of just 0.00001 g of hydrogen produces more than enough energy to run everything in your home for a year.

The Sun's Fuel Nuclei of any of the lighter elements can undergo fusion. Most of the fusion reactions in the sun, however, involve only hydrogen nuclei. Hydrogen is the sun's major "fuel." Three-quarters of the sun's enormous mass consists of hydrogen. Nuclear fusion reactions in the sun change 3.6 million metric tons of hydrogen into helium every second.

Is the sun using up its supply of hydrogen? The answer is yes. But the sun contains so much hydrogen that it won't run out for about 4.5 billion years.

Figure 24.2 ▲
You can see how the sun appears through a telescope using special filters. Different colors show areas of different temperature.

Table 24.1   The Sun's Layers

Layer	Thickness (km)	Temperature (°C)
Core	139 200	15 000 000
Radiation zone	382 800	2 500 000
Convection zone	174 000	1 100 000
Photosphere	547	5,500
Chromosphere	2,000	27 800
Corona	Varies	2 200 000

Layers of the Sun

The sun is a huge sphere about 1.35 million km in diameter. It would take over 1 million Earths to equal the sun's volume. The sun's matter is mostly in the plasma phase. This matter forms layers. The layers don't have clear boundaries, but they vary greatly in temperature.

The innermost part of the sun is called the *core*. The core is where nuclear fusion occurs. Outside the core is the *radiation zone*. In this zone, heat energy produced by fusion radiates outward, spreading from atom to atom.

About 400 000 km from the core, the hot matter forms convection cells. Matter expands and rises, then cools, becomes denser, and sinks back. This zone is called the *convection zone*.

The layer of matter that is normally visible in the sun is the **photosphere** (FOHT uh sfeer). The photosphere is also the first layer of the sun's atmosphere. The second layer of the sun's atmosphere is the **chromosphere** (KROH muh sfeer). The third and outer layer of the sun's atmosphere is the **corona** (kuh ROH nuh). Find each of these layers in Figure 24.3.

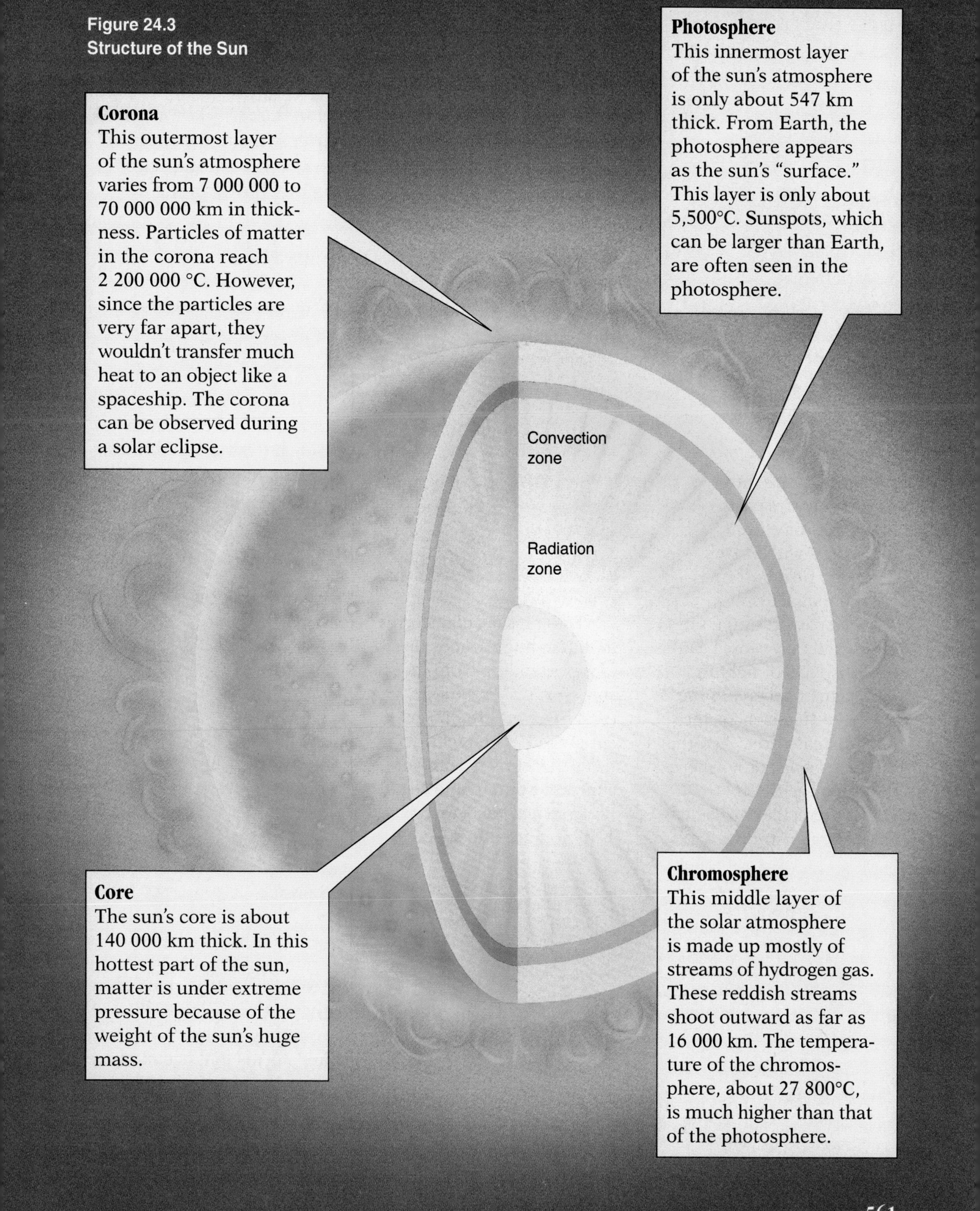

**Figure 24.3
Structure of the Sun**

Corona

This outermost layer of the sun's atmosphere varies from 7 000 000 to 70 000 000 km in thickness. Particles of matter in the corona reach 2 200 000 °C. However, since the particles are very far apart, they wouldn't transfer much heat to an object like a spaceship. The corona can be observed during a solar eclipse.

Photosphere

This innermost layer of the sun's atmosphere is only about 547 km thick. From Earth, the photosphere appears as the sun's "surface." This layer is only about 5,500°C. Sunspots, which can be larger than Earth, are often seen in the photosphere.

Convection zone

Radiation zone

Core

The sun's core is about 140 000 km thick. In this hottest part of the sun, matter is under extreme pressure because of the weight of the sun's huge mass.

Chromosphere

This middle layer of the solar atmosphere is made up mostly of streams of hydrogen gas. These reddish streams shoot outward as far as 16 000 km. The temperature of the chromosphere, about 27 800°C, is much higher than that of the photosphere.

Activity on the Sun

The surface of the sun is very active. In fact, three kinds of storms occur in the upper layers of the sun: sunspots, prominences, and solar flares. All of these solar storms are caused by changes in the magnetic field of the sun. Like Earth, the sun has a magnetic field that acts as if a huge bar magnet lies within it.

Solar Wind

The corona sends a steady stream of high-energy particles into space. This stream is called the *solar wind*. It interacts with Earth's magnetic field to form Earth's magnetosphere. Charged particles from the solar wind may cause beautiful displays of light in the magnetosphere. In the Northern Hemisphere, these light displays are called the *aurora borealis*, or northern lights. In the Southern Hemisphere, they are called the *aurora australis*.

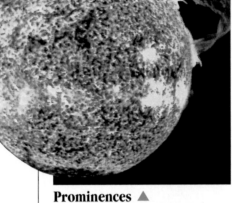

Prominences ▲

These spectacular storms look like huge arches or loops extending from the sun's surface. *Prominences* (prahm uh nuhn suhz) are supported by magnetic fields that stretch from one sunspot group to another. Prominences may extend 1 million km into space.

Solar Flares

Even more powerful than prominences are solar flares. A *solar flare* is a very intense spurt of radiation. In some flares, matter reaches a temperature of 20 million °C. A flare may last from 10 minutes to 1 hour. Cosmic rays produced by large solar flares interrupt radio communications on Earth. ▼

Sunspots

◄ Astronomers have observed spots like black blemishes on the sun for a long time. Sunspots look black because they are cooler than the surrounding matter. *Sunspots* are storms that occur where powerful magnetic fields break through the photosphere and prevent interior light and heat from escaping.

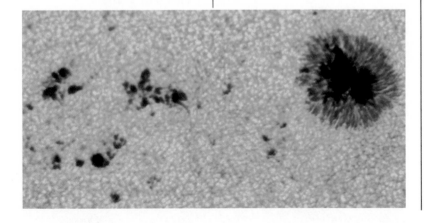

Energy Source for Life

All organisms need a constant supply of energy to fuel the chemical reactions in their cells. You get your energy from the food you eat. But where did the energy in the food come from? Its original source was the sun. Plants are the link in this flow of energy between the sun and you.

Plants use light energy from the sun to power a chemical reaction that produces glucose from water and carbon dioxide in the air. Recall that this process is called photosynthesis. Through photosynthesis, the sun's light energy is converted to chemical energy stored in the chemical bonds of glucose. Plants use the glucose and its stored energy to grow and produce new plant material.

When an animal eats a plant, the solar energy stored in the plant's cells transfers to the animal's body. The animal's body uses the energy to live and grow. When an animal eats another animal, solar energy originally captured by a plant enters its body, too.

Sunlight is also the source of the oil and coal that people burn for energy. Oil and coal formed millions of years ago from fossil plants. The energy in oil and coal, therefore, all came originally from the sun.

Figure 24.4 ▲
Photosynthesis occurs in the cells of leaves.

Figure 24.5
The sun is the original source of most energy used on Earth. ▼

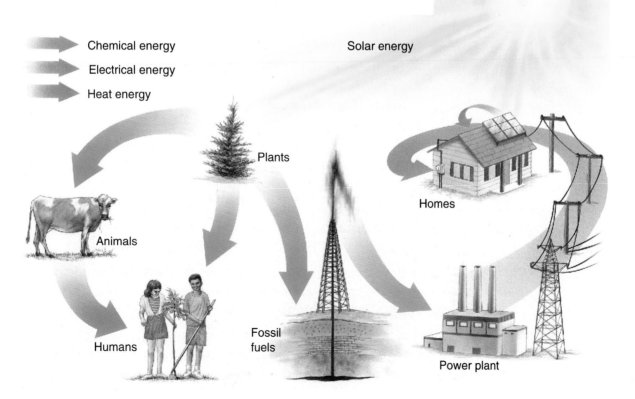

Chemical energy
Electrical energy
Heat energy

Solar energy

Plants

Homes

Animals

Humans

Fossil fuels

Power plant

▼ ACTIVITY

Inferring

Deep Sleep

What do you think would happen to your daily cycle if you lived for a week deep in a cave or under the ocean in a submarine? Would you be able to tell day from night? Would you want to go to bed at the same time as usual? Explain.

SKILLS WORKOUT

 Science and You
Sunlight and Body Rhythms

How does light affect the way plants grow? If you watch flowers, you may notice that some of them open when the sunlight has a certain brightness and close when the light begins to fade. Many animals also respond to light. They are active at dawn and rest at night. But did you know that sunlight also affects *your* body?

Your body has an internal clock that keeps your systems working according to a certain rhythm. Your body is used to a cycle of 8 hours of sleep and 16 hours of being awake. Sunlight helps your body set its clock to keep you in step with its cycle.

People who travel often experience jet lag if they cross time zones when flying. Jet lag causes them to feel tired, yet unable to sleep well. Jet lag especially affects people when they travel eastward. The reason is that the journey subtracts hours of daylight and upsets their biological clock.

Do you notice a difference between the way you usually feel in the winter and the way you usually feel in the summer? If so, it may be due to winter's shorter days. About 6 percent of the adults who live where winter days are very short are especially affected by shorter days. They suffer from an illness known as seasonal affective disorder, or SAD. In winter, these people are often depressed and tired because they receive too little daylight. Physicians treat the disorder by exposing their patients to bright lights. They quickly feel normal in spite of the shorter winter days.

Check and Explain

1. How does the sun produce energy?

2. Name the three layers of the sun's atmosphere and one distinguishing characteristic of each layer.

3. **Reason and Conclude** Why might astronomers find sunspots, solar flares, and prominences at the same time on the sun?

4. **Make a Model** Use different materials to make a model of the sun's interior and the processes occurring in the interior.

Activity 24   *How can you use the sun to tell time?*

Skills   Measure; Observe; Infer; Interpret Data

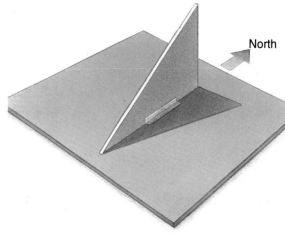

Task 1   Prelab Prep

1. Collect the following items: cardboard, tape, scissors, protractor, directional compass.
2. Look up the latitude of where you live.

Task 2   Data Record

1. Copy Table 24.2 on a separate sheet of paper, leaving more space than is shown.
2. Use the table to record the times you check your sundial and your observations.

Table 24.2   Sundial Observations

Date	Time	Observations

Task 3   Procedure

1. Cut out a square piece of cardboard about 30 cm on each side.
2. Make a cardboard triangle with a base 15.25 cm long. The angle at one end of the base should be 90°. The angle at the other end should be the same number of degrees as the latitude of the place where you live. The triangle is the *gnomon* (NOH mahn) of your sundial—the part that will cast a shadow.
3. Mount the gnomon on the cardboard with two strips of tape, as shown in Figure 24.6. Make sure the gnomon is vertical.
4. Take the sundial outdoors. Find a place where it won't be disturbed. Use a compass to find north. Position the sundial so the gnomon points north.

Figure 24.6 ▲

5. Check the shadow on the sundial at various times during the day. If possible, do it every hour on the hour. Each time you check the shadow, use a pencil to mark the leading edge of the shadow with a line, and label the line with the time.
6. Repeat this procedure for a few days.

Task 4   Analysis

1. **Observe**   Did the shadow fall at the same place at the same time each day?
2. Once you have labeled your sundial with all the hours, how accurate would it be for telling time?
3. Why do you have to make certain that the gnomon is always pointing north when you make your readings?
4. What does your sundial tell you about how Earth moves?

Task 5   Conclusion

Write a short paragraph explaining how your sundial works.

Everyday Application

If you take your sundial with you on vacation to another part of the country, will you have to make any adjustments? Explain.

24.2 Planets in the Solar System

Objectives

▶ **Describe** the theory of the formation of the solar system.

▶ **Explain** how the planets move around the sun.

▶ **Compare** and **contrast** the inner and the outer planets.

▶ **Hypothesize** which of the planets besides Earth could possibly have living things.

Imagine you are selected as part of the first team of astronauts to explore the entire solar system. How long will it take? How far will you go? You realize that the trip is not a pleasure cruise. For most of the trip, you will be stuck in your cramped spacecraft. But you will see things that no other human being has ever experienced directly.

Formation of the Solar System

Before you leave on your journey, you may want to learn more about how the solar system came into being. This knowledge will help you better understand your observations. According to the theory most widely accepted today, the solar system began as a large swirling sphere of gas and dust. This gas and dust cloud was similar to distant nebulae (NEHB yuh LEE) that can be observed from Earth today.

The particles making up the cloud slowly pulled themselves together because of gravitational attraction. The smaller and denser the cloud became, the faster it rotated. The matter gradually flattened out, forming a disk. Ninety-five percent of the matter accumulated at the center of the disk. This large mass of matter grew denser and became a primitive sun, or protosun. Some matter became concentrated in various parts of the disk, away from the protosun. Each of these clumps of matter grew by pulling neighboring matter into itself. In time, each spinning mass gave rise to a protoplanet.

Figure 24.7 ▲
This object may be the most recognizable planet in the solar system. Do you know its name?

The young sun continued to shrink and grow warmer. About 5 billion years ago, the sun became hot enough for nuclear fusion to begin inside it. It then started radiating great amounts of heat and light. This energy heated the protoplanets and swept away all the matter between them.

As each protoplanet rotated, it changed from a sphere to a disk. The center of each disk grew denser and then spherical. Just as the protosun became a star, each protoplanet became a planet. Matter circling the protoplanets became moons.

Astronomers recently observed how the stage may have been set for the collapse of the cloud of dust and gas that began the formation of the solar system. They observed a huge, faraway bubble of extremely hot gas, produced by the kind of explosion that occurs when a very large star dies. The shock wave from the explosion seems to have triggered the collapse of various clouds of dust and gas in the area. One star dies, and new ones are born. Astronomers hypothesize that the solar system began in this way. Think of it: The matter in your body may once have been part of a star.

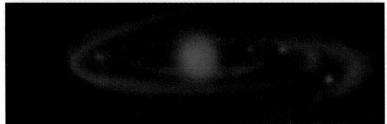

◀ **Figure 24.8**
The solar system began as a contracting cloud of dust and gas (top). As the cloud rotated, matter collected in the center and in outlying clumps (middle). The protosun gradually changed into the sun (bottom).

Planets

The solar system includes nine planets. On your journey, you will visit each one and observe its size, and unique features. Each planet in Figure 24.9 is drawn to scale. The relative sizes of the planets and sun are accurate, but the distances between them are not.

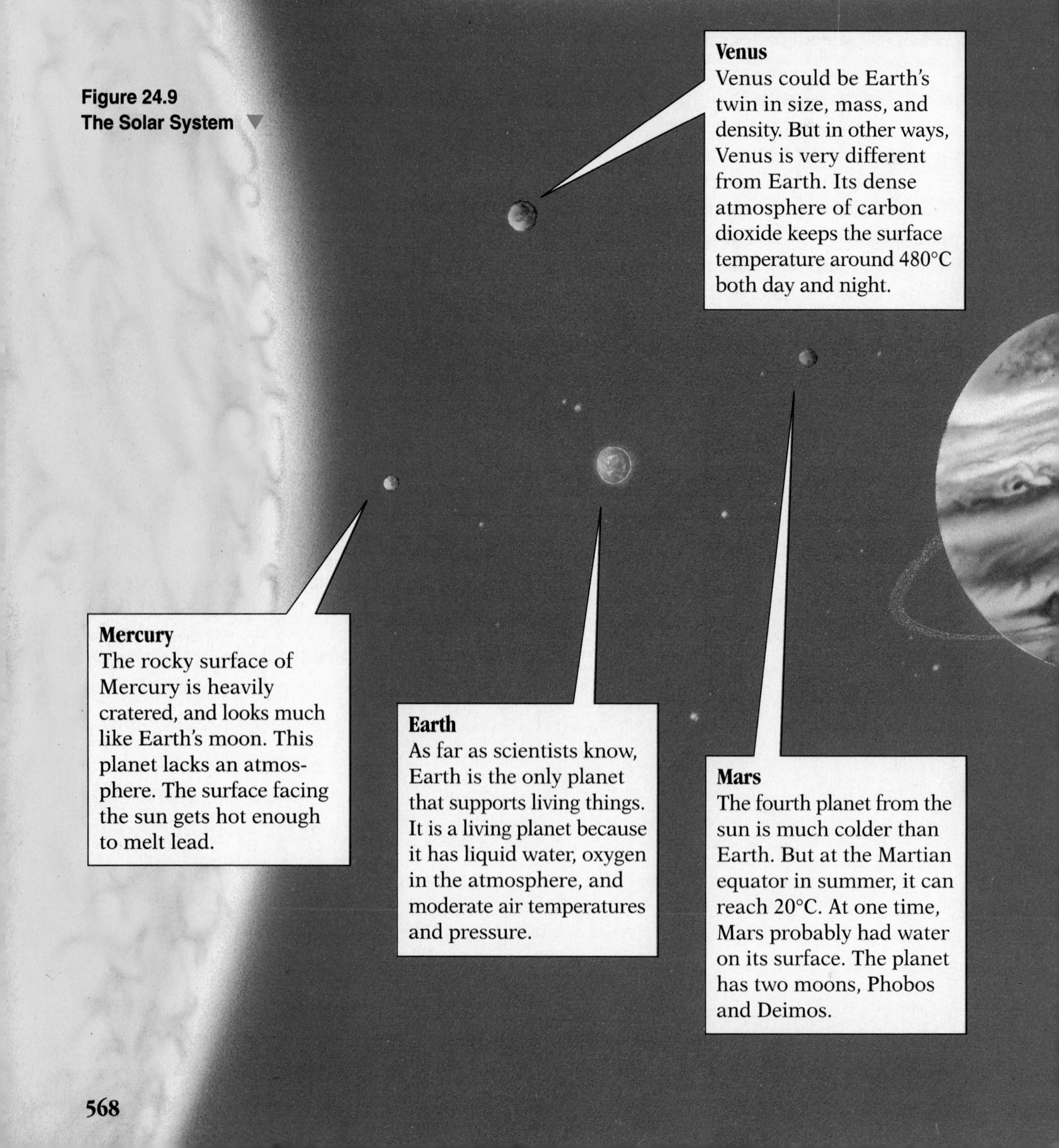

Venus
Venus could be Earth's twin in size, mass, and density. But in other ways, Venus is very different from Earth. Its dense atmosphere of carbon dioxide keeps the surface temperature around 480°C both day and night.
Mercury
The rocky surface of Mercury is heavily cratered, and looks much like Earth's moon. This planet lacks an atmosphere. The surface facing the sun gets hot enough to melt lead.
Earth
As far as scientists know, Earth is the only planet that supports living things. It is a living planet because it has liquid water, oxygen in the atmosphere, and moderate air temperatures and pressure.
Mars
The fourth planet from the sun is much colder than Earth. But at the Martian equator in summer, it can reach 20°C. At one time, Mars probably had water on its surface. The planet has two moons, Phobos and Deimos.

Figure 24.9
The Solar System

Saturn
Saturn is nearly as large as Jupiter but has only one third Jupiter's mass. Like Jupiter, it is made up mostly of hydrogen and helium gas. Saturn has a spectacular ring system and 23 or more moons.

Neptune
The eighth planet from the sun, Neptune, is similar to Uranus. It is a ball of water, ammonia, and molten rock, surrounded by hydrogen, helium, and methane. It has 8 moons and a number of rings.

Jupiter
Jupiter is a giant, with 300 times more mass than Earth. It is mostly a ball of hydrogen and helium gas. Clouds in Jupiter's atmosphere form colored bands around the planet. Jupiter has at least 16 moons.

Uranus
Beyond Saturn is Uranus, the third-largest planet. It appears greenish because of methane gas in its atmosphere. Uranus is unusual because its axis of rotation is nearly parallel to the plane of its orbit. Uranus has 15 moons and a system of rings.

Pluto
The ninth planet is not like the other outer planets. It is even smaller than Mercury in size. Its orbit is very elongated and tilted. Pluto has one moon, Charon, that is nearly half the size of the planet itself.

Inner Planets

As you have seen, the four inner-most planets have many common features and all are very different from the next four planets. For this reason, they are often grouped together and called the inner planets.

As the inner planets formed, the heat of the sun boiled off the lighter elements that surrounded them. Each inner planet was left with a liquid core made of nickel and iron and a rocky mantle and crust. Another common feature of these planets is that they have few or no moons.

But each inner planet is also unique. The surface of Mercury is extremely hot during the day and frozen at night. Venus rotates on its axis in the opposite direc-tion of the other planets. Earth is the only planet with oxygen in its atmosphere because many organisms, such as plants, produce oxygen as a waste product. Mars has the solar system's tallest mountain and its deepest canyon.

Figure 24.11 ▲
Gaseous Jupiter is a typical outer planet.

Outer Planets

The five planets farthest from the sun—Jupiter, Saturn, Uranus, Neptune, and Pluto—are called the outer planets. The first four are also known as Jovian planets because they share so many characteristics with Jupiter.

The Jovian planets are all mostly gas, with relatively small solid or liquid cen-ters. When these planets formed, they were too far from the sun for its heat to drive off lighter elements. As a result, they remain large and mostly gaseous.

All the Jovian planets have numerous moons. And, unlike the inner planets, the Jovian planets have rings. Scientists think the rings were created when aster-oids or meteors slammed into moons of these planets and smashed them to bits.

Pluto is very different from any of the Jovian planets. It is, however, sim-ilar to the large moons of these planets. Scientists hypothesize that Pluto may once have been a moon of Neptune. The gravity from a passing object may have pulled it far enough away from Neptune to form its own orbit around the sun.

Figure 24.10 ▲
How does Mars differ from Earth?

Moons of the Outer Planets

Orbiting the Jovian planets are more than 40 moons, or satellites. Unlike the planets they orbit, these moons are solid. Some are made of rock, some of ice, and others a combination of rock and ice. Six of these moons are about as large as, or larger than, Earth's moon. Each could be a planet on its own.

Jupiter has four large moons: Ganymede, Callisto, Io, and Europa. Ganymede is the largest moon in the solar system. It is even larger than Mercury. Io has active volcanoes. The large moons of Jupiter are good landing sites for your spacecraft, since Jupiter itself has no solid surface.

Saturn has the most moons of any planet, but only one—Titan—is larger than Earth's moon. Titan has its own atmosphere. The solar system's sixth large moon is Triton, in orbit around Neptune.

Figure 24.12 ▲
The colorful materials on Io's surface are sulfur-containing compounds spewed out by volcanoes.

SkillBuilder *Making a Model*

A Solar System Model

How big is the solar system? Figure 24.9 shows the relative sizes of the planets but not their relative distances from the sun.

Look at the table at the right. It shows the distance between each planet and the sun in astronomical units, or A.U. One A.U. is the average distance from Earth to the sun. Copy the table on a separate sheet of paper. Fill in the blank column of the table by simply rounding off the A.U. measurement for each planet.

Now draw a line 39.5 cm long. This line represents the distance between the sun and Pluto. Place the other planets on this line according to this scale. Draw each planet as a dot and label it.

1. Why do you think each planet is shown only as a dot?
2. What happens to the distance between planets as they get farther from the sun?

Write a paragraph on what you learned about the solar system by making this model.

Planet	Distance from Sun (AU)	Distance in Your Model (cm)
Mercury	0.39	
Venus	0.72	
Earth	1.0	
Mars	1.5	
Jupiter	5.2	
Saturn	9.5	
Uranus	19.2	
Neptune	30.0	
Pluto	39.5	

Planet Motions

Use two balls of different sizes to represent the sun and a planet. Demonstrate the rotation of the planet in combination with its revolution.

SKILLS WORKOUT

Figure 24.13

Each planet orbits the sun following an elliptical path. Except for Pluto and Mercury, the planets' orbits lie in roughly the same plane. ▼

Movement of the Planets

Like Earth, all the planets have two kinds of motion: revolution and rotation. Recall that a planet revolves in an orbit around the sun. A model of the solar system based on the planets orbiting the sun is called a *helio-centric*, or sun-centered, model.

Five-hundred years ago, scientists were convinced that Earth, not the sun, was the center of the solar system. Then, in 1543, Nicolaus Copernicus shocked the world by proposing that Earth and the other planets revolve around the sun.

When scientists finally accepted Copernicus's theory, they assumed the planets orbited in perfect circles around the sun. Then, in the early 1600s, Johannes Kepler discovered that the planets have *elliptical* orbits. Kepler also showed that the sun is not in the center of a planet's elliptical orbit, but off to one side at one of the focal points of the ellipse.

Gravity and Inertia Although Kepler described how the planets move, he did not explain why they move as they do. Isaac Newton showed that the planets do not fly off into space because of the gravitational attraction between the sun and each planet. This attracting force exists between objects because of their mass. The greater the mass, the greater the attraction of gravity.

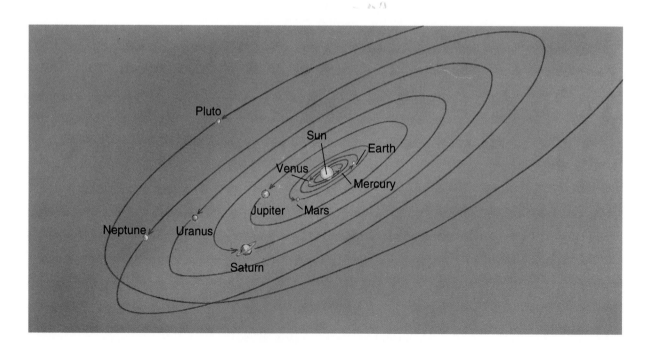

Newton also explained why planets keep moving in orbit around the sun. He found that an object's motion will not change in speed or direction unless it is acted on by an outside force. This law explains the property known as *inertia*. The dust cloud that became the solar system had inertia of motion because of its rotation. That inertia has kept the planets moving in orbit around the sun ever since. Look at Figure 24.14. You can see that a planet's orbit is the result of the combined forces of gravity and inertia.

The amount of time it takes for a planet to complete one revolution is called its *period of revolution*. A planet's period of revolution is equal to one year on that planet. Look at Table 24.3, which lists the periods of all the planets. You know that Earth has a period of revolution, or year, of just over 365 days. How long is a year on Pluto? Notice how the periods of revolution vary. What pattern do you detect in their variation?

Rotation The planets' speeds of rotation vary, too. One rotation around a planet's axis is equal to one day on that planet. Look again at Table 24.3. How long is a day on Venus? Which planet has a day about the same length as an Earth day? Notice that the planets' periods of rotation do not have any noticeable pattern.

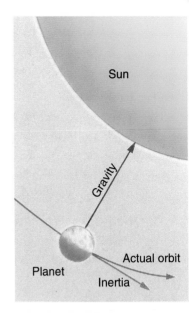

Figure 24.14 ▲
What would happen to the orbit of a planet without the force of the sun's gravitational attraction? What would happen to it without the force of inertia?

Table 24.3   Periods of Revolution and Rotation

Planet	Period of Rotation (Earth time)	Period of Revolution (Earth time)
Mercury	59 days	88 days
Venus	243 days	224.7 days
Earth	24 hours	365 days
Mars	24.6 hours	687 days
Jupiter	9.9 hours	11.9 years
Saturn	10.2 hours	29.5 years
Uranus	17.2 hours	84 years
Neptune	16 hours	164.8 years
Pluto	6.4 days	247.7 years

Science and Technology
Exploring Mars and Venus

Even though people have yet to set foot on Mars or Venus, scientists know a great deal about our nearest neighbors in the solar system. In 1962, the space probe Mariner 2 flew by Venus, sending back data to Earth. Mariner 4 completed a flyby of Mars in 1965. In 1971, the Soviet Union's Mars 3 landed on Mars, sending back the first images of the planet's surface. In 1976, two orbiter-landers from the United States—Viking 1 and 2—landed on Mars and carried out experiments.

Scientists are now designing rovers that will explore the surface of Mars. The rovers will be controlled by on-board computers. Rovers on the moon can be controlled by engineers on Earth because signals travel back and forth between the moon and Earth in only 2.6 seconds.

However, signals would take up to 40 minutes to make the round trip between Earth and Mars. Imagine what could happen if a Mars rover were left without guidance for 40 minutes!

The computer on the rover has to be programmed to keep the rover from driving off a cliff. And the rover itself must be able to move over boulders. One design for a rover is a wheelwalker that can step up and down, as well as roll forward and backward. The wheelwalker changes its shape and motion to adapt to the terrain.

A different method of exploration is already being used to study Venus. From September 1990 to October 1994, the Magellan space probe imaged the surface of our closest neighbor with radar. Global maps of Venus were created from these images. The maps show a rugged surface marked by volcanoes, some craters, and winding chan-

Figure 24.15 ▲

The terrain of Mars is rough and rocky, as shown in this photograph from Viking 1 (top). The experimental rover has six wheels and two camera "eyes."

Check and Explain

1. How did the solar system probably begin?

2. What forces control the movement of the planets around the sun?

3. **Compare and Contrast** Explain the main differences between the inner planets and the outer planets.

4. **Hypothesize** State a hypothesis that explains what planet besides Earth could best support life.

24.3 Asteroids, Meteoroids, and Comets

Objectives

▶ **Locate** the asteroid belt.

▶ **Compare** meteoroids, meteors, and meteorites.

▶ **Describe** the orbits of the comets.

▶ **Predict** how a comet will change over time.

▼ ACTIVITY

Communicating

Meteors

  With your classmates, share descriptions of shooting stars that you have seen. What do your observations have in common?

SKILLS WARMUP

The solar system is full of objects orbiting the sun that are neither planets nor moons. You couldn't travel through the solar system without observing some of them. In fact, you would have to be very careful not to let one of the larger ones crash into your spacecraft. These objects range in size from microscopic bits of ice to moon-sized masses of rock.

Asteroids

The larger objects you might see on a trip through the solar system are like small planets. As many as 100,000 of these small, irregularly shaped, solid bodies, called **asteroids** (AS tuh ROYDZ), revolve around the sun. All the asteroids move around the sun in the same direction as the planets do. The brightest asteroid, Vesta, is seen without a telescope.

Asteroid Belt Most asteroids exist between the orbits of Mars and Jupiter in an area known as the *asteroid belt*. Some scientists hypothesize that the asteroid belt formed when a planet was prevented from forming by the gravitational force of Jupiter. Scientists also think that some of the larger asteroids may have been ejected from the asteroid belt and are currently scattered throughout the solar system.

Other Asteroids Some asteroids have orbits that cross the orbit of Mars. Others, called the Apollo asteroids, cross Earth's orbit. The largest Apollo asteroid, called Icarus, has passed within 64 million km of Earth—about twice the distance to the moon.

Figure 24.16
Unlike planets, asteroids have irregular shapes. This is the asteroid Gaspra. ▼

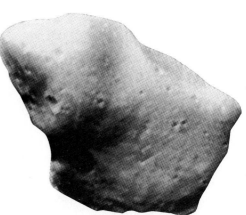

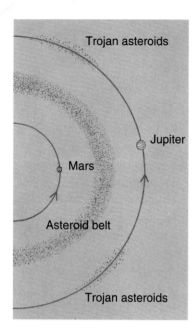

Figure 24.17 ▲

Where are most asteroids?

Two groups of asteroids follow the same orbit as Jupiter. They are called the Trojan asteroids. One group of Trojan asteroids travels ahead of Jupiter, the other trails behind. Still other asteroids are outside the orbit of Jupiter. Over time, the orbits of some asteroids change because of the gravitational pull of Jupiter and the other large planets.

Over 2,000 asteroids measuring at least 1 km in diameter, cross Earth's orbit at times. Every million years or so, an asteroid collides with Earth. Many scientists hypothesize that an asteroid collision 65 million years ago sent up a cloud of dust into the atmosphere that cut off sunlight for a long time. Many plant and animal species on the planet died at that time, including dinosaurs. A small asteroid coming close to Earth would just burn up in the atmosphere. A large asteroid more than 1 km in diameter, however, could have disastrous effects if it struck Earth.

Career Corner *Aerospace Worker*

Who Builds Spacecraft?

Space shuttles, satellites, and space probes gather valuable information about the solar system and the universe. Aerospace workers design, assemble, and repair these craft and the rocket boosters that launch them into space.

Aerospace employees may work on production lines, in machine shops, with engineering firms, or at space centers. Aerospace engineers design new spacecraft and the many machines that make them up. Inspectors check the quality of the crafts to make sure each machine is complete and safe. The aerospace industry also employs clerical workers, computer technicians, managers, and accountants.

The aerospace industry uses the latest technologies. Workers often specialize in a particular kind of machine. Most aerospace scientists and engineers have advanced college degrees in science or engineering. Aerospace machinists may train as apprentices or learn skills at trade schools. Mechanical drawing and blueprint reading are important skills for aerospace machinists. Almost every aerospace job requires some knowledge of computers.

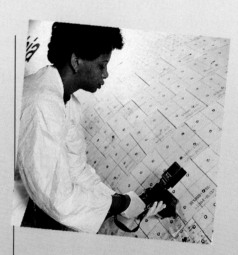

If you are interested in astronomy and space exploration, consider a career in the aerospace industry. Courses in science, mathematics, and shop will help you prepare for an aerospace career.

Meteoroids

Have you seen a shooting star? This streak of light in the night sky is caused by an object entering Earth's atmosphere and burning up. The object is called a meteoroid (MEE tee uh ROYD). A **meteoroid** is a chunk of rock or metal, smaller than an asteroid, in orbit around the sun.

Meteors The light that results from the entry of a large meteoroid into the atmosphere is called a **meteor**, or shooting star. Its glow may last for several seconds. The light is caused by friction between the fast-moving meteor and the atmosphere. A meteor is the luminous gas heated by the meteoroid passing through the atmosphere.

Most meteoroids are so small that they leave no visible trace when they burn up in the atmosphere. But each one leaves a small amount of dust that falls to Earth. So many tiny meteoroids burn up in the atmosphere that hundreds of tons of meteoroid dust fall to the ground each year.

As Earth moves in its orbit, it periodically crosses the orbit of a stream of meteoroids. The result is a meteor shower. The major meteor showers occur at regular times during the year. The most spectacular ones happen in August and October.

▲
Figure 24.18
This iron meteoroid survived its plunge through Earth's atmosphere to become a meteorite. It was sliced in two to show the inside.

Physical Science
L I N K

Review the section on meteors. What physical property causes the meteoroid and the area around it to heat up as it enters Earth's atmosphere?

Design an activity that demonstrates how this property produces heat. Can you connect this property to the presence of extensive cratering on the moon? Explain.

A C T I V I T Y

◀ **Figure 24.19**
These meteors were photographed during the Leonid meteor shower, which happens every year in November.

Meteorites When a meteoroid does not completely burn up in its passage through the atmosphere, it is called a **meteorite** (MEE tee uh RYT). Meteorites, like the one in Figure 24.18, have been found all over Earth's surface. The most common type of meteorite is made up of iron and nickel. Others are stone or a combination of stone and metal.

The huge crater in Figure 24.20 was caused by the impact of a large meteorite. The crater is 174 m deep and 1,219 m across. Like other craters, it is a bowl-shaped depression. At least 150 meteorite craters have been found on Earth. What do you think you would see and feel if you watched a large meteorite strike the ground?

Figure 24.20 ▲

The meteorite impact that made the Barringer crater in Arizona probably occurred within the last 50,000 years.

Comets

An icy object that travels around the sun, usually in a huge elliptical orbit, is called a **comet**. Scientists estimate that there are about 100,000 comets in the solar system. Most comets are far beyond the orbit of Pluto.

When a comet comes close to the sun, heat vaporizes some of its frozen matter. Solar radiation and solar wind force gases from the comet, causing a streaming tail to form. Notice the tail of the comet in Figure 24.21. With each pass close to the sun, a comet loses matter.

Comets may have formed in a ring close to the edge of the flattened disk of the early solar system. One by one, due to the gravitational force of the outer planets, comets changed their orbits. Their new orbits bring them close to the sun.

Figure 24.21

What causes the streaming tail of a comet? ▼

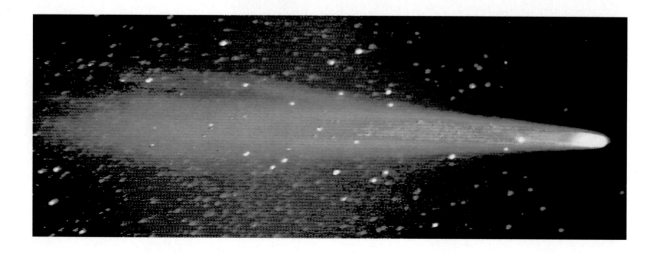

Orbits of Comets Edmond Halley, an English astronomer, was the first to recognize that comets travel in a fixed orbit around the sun. When he observed a comet in 1682, he found that a similar comet had been seen in 1531 and again in 1607. Halley hypothesized that these sightings were all of the same comet. The comet seemed to reappear every 76 years. This led him to theorize that comets orbit around the sun.

Look at Figure 24.22. It shows the orbits of several comets. Notice how their shapes differ from that of planets. Some comets have orbits that bring them close to the sun a few times in a decade. Others approach the sun only once in thousands of years. In 1973, Comet Kohoutek rounded the sun after a very long time away. Its period of revolution is 75,000 years. Comet West, seen in 1976, has a period of 500,000 years. Some comets are jolted out of orbit by a planet's gravity and sent out of the solar system, never to return.

Halley's Comet Halley predicted that the comet he observed in 1682 would reappear in 1758. Although Halley died before that happened, the comet was named after him because of his findings. Halley's Comet last approached the sun in 1986. If you missed that appearance, you'll have to wait until 2061 to see it.

▼ **ACTIVITY**

Inferring

Impact

Is it possible for a comet to collide with Earth? Explain your reasoning.

SKILLS WORKOUT

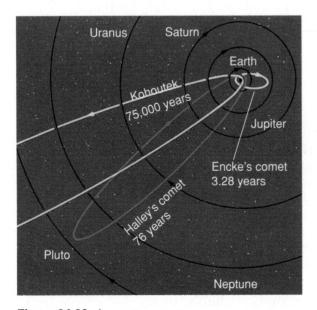

Figure 24.22 ▲
Comets have very elliptical orbits. Their periods of revolution vary greatly.

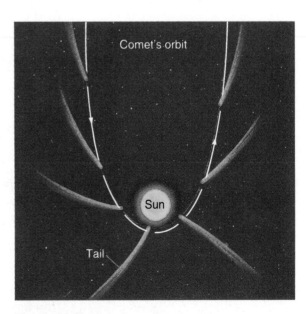

Figure 24.23 ▲
Why does a comet's tail always point away from the sun?

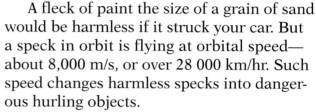

Science and Society *Dodging Space Junk*

Whoever said that space is empty? If you examined a spacecraft after it returned from space, you would find craterlike scars on the exterior. These pits are caused by collisions with objects in orbit around Earth, many of them left there by humans.

A fleck of paint the size of a grain of sand would be harmless if it struck your car. But a speck in orbit is flying at orbital speed— about 8,000 m/s, or over 28 000 km/hr. Such speed changes harmless specks into dangerous hurling objects.

More than just flecks of paint orbit Earth. Some of the items are slivers, bolts, screws, and clamps from exploded satellites and rocket bodies. There is even a lost camera from a Gemini flight still in orbit. The Long Duration Exposure Facility (LDEF), recovered by a space-shuttle mission after six years in orbit, was struck at least 5,000 times by small, high-speed objects. The hits caused craters, all of which were very small. However, if an instrument had been struck, it might have been put out of order.

To avoid damage to space shuttles, satellites, and, later, to a space station, experts work on ways to get rid of the debris in space. One plan is to have space garbage-collectors. They would collect the space junk and send it plunging into Earth's atmosphere, where it would burn up. In the meantime, designers plan to "harden" the planned space station against possible collisions.

Figure 24.24 ▲

This scanning electron micrograph shows a hole in a satellite that was returned to Earth. The hole was caused by impacts with paint flakes.

Check and Explain

1. Where is the asteroid belt? Where are other asteroids in the solar system located?

2. Explain how meteoroids, meteors, and meteorites are different.

3. **Uncover Assumptions**   The appearance of comets has been blamed for many kinds of events on Earth, such as hot weather and lost battles. Explain why this assumption is probably wrong.

4. **Predict**   What will eventually happen to a comet after it has made many trips around the sun? Explain.

Chapter 24 Review

Concept Summary

24.1 The Sun
▶ Nuclear fusion in the sun releases enormous amounts of energy.
▶ The sun is made up of many layers, including the core, the radiation zone, and the convection zone. Its atmosphere consists of three layers: the photosphere, chromosphere, and corona.
▶ Sunspots, prominences, and solar flares occur in the sun's outer layers.
▶ The sun is the original source of energy for nearly all living things on Earth.

24.2 Planets in the Solar System
▶ The solar system formed from a swirling cloud of dust and gas.
▶ The four inner planets are rocky planets with metal cores.

▶ Except for Pluto, the five outer planets are large balls of gas with solid or liquid cores and many moons.
▶ The planets revolve around the sun in elliptical orbits, the result of a balance between inertia and gravity.

24.3 Asteroids, Meteoroids, and Comets
▶ Asteroids are bodies of rock, too small to be planets, that orbit the sun.
▶ Meteoroids are chunks of rock or metal smaller than asteroids. They become meteors if they enter Earth's atmosphere, and meteorites if they reach the surface.
▶ Comets are icy objects with very huge elliptical orbits that periodically come close to the sun.

Chapter Vocabulary

solar system (24.1)	corona (24.1)	meteor (24.3)
photosphere (24.1)	asteroid (24.3)	meteorite (24.3)
chromosphere (24.1)	meteoroid (24.3)	comet (24.3)

Check Your Vocabulary

Use the vocabulary words above to complete the following sentences correctly.

1. During a solar eclipse, the sun's ____ is visible.
2. Meteor showers occur when Earth passes through the orbit of a swarm of ____.
3. The sun's coolest layer is the ____.
4. Another name for a ____ is a shooting star.
5. Streams of hydrogen gas make up the layer of the sun called the ____.
6. Bodies of rock resembling small planets are called ____.
7. An icy object that develops a tail when it nears the sun is a ____.

8. If a meteor doesn't completely burn up in the atmosphere, it becomes a ____
9. Earth, eight other planets and many smaller objects make up the ____

Explain the difference between the words in each pair.

10. asteroid, satellite
11. photosphere, sunspot
12. comet, meteor

Write Your Vocabulary

Write sentences using the vocabulary words above. Show that you know what each word means.

Chapter 24 Review

Check Your Knowledge

Answer the following in complete sentences.

1. List the four inner planets by increasing distance from the sun.

2. What is the shape of a planet's orbit around the sun?

3. Which of the outer planets is not like the others?

4. Name and describe the three kinds of storm activity that occur on the sun.

5. Which organisms on Earth can capture the sun's energy and convert it into chemical energy?

6. How are the moons of the Jovian planets different from the planets themselves?

7. How are sunspots and prominences related?

8. Name five different kinds of objects found in the solar system.

Choose the answer that best completes each sentence.

9. Nuclear fusion occurs in the sun's (core, radiation zone, convection zone, corona).

10. The time it takes a planet to complete a revolution around the sun is equal to a (day, month, season, year) on that planet.

11. Earth is the (first, third, fifth, seventh) planet from the sun.

12. The two planets most similar in size, mass, and density are Venus and (Mercury, Earth, Mars, Neptune).

13. The Trojan asteroids are in the same orbit as (Mars, Jupiter, Uranus, Saturn).

Check Your Understanding

Apply the concepts you have learned to answer each question.

1. How is the nuclear fusion that takes place in the sun different from a chemical reaction?

2. Why do all the planets revolve around the sun in the same direction?

3. **Infer**   From 1978 to 1999, Pluto was closer to the sun than Neptune. Explain how this is possible.

4. **Compare and Contrast**   How is the structure of the sun similar to the structure of Earth?

5. **Infer**   If Mars once had liquid water on its surface, where is that water now?

6. Which planet has a year closest in length to that of an Earth year? On which planet is a day about as long as an Earth day?

7. **Application**   Trace the path of energy from the sun's core to the light bulb in your room. How does the energy travel each step of the way? What different forms does the energy take on?

8. **Mystery Photo**   The photograph on page 558 shows the great red spot of Jupiter. The photograph was taken by Voyager 1. The great red spot can easily be seen from Earth with a powerful telescope. If you looked at Jupiter with such a telescope and couldn't find the great red spot, what would you conclude?

9. Is it possible for a comet to collide with Earth? Explain the reasons for your answer.

10. Why is it not possible for a spacecraft to land on Jupiter?

Develop Your Skills

Use the skills you have developed in this chapter to complete each activity.

1. **Interpret Data** The graph below shows the mass and volume of each inner planet as a proportion of Earth's mass and volume.

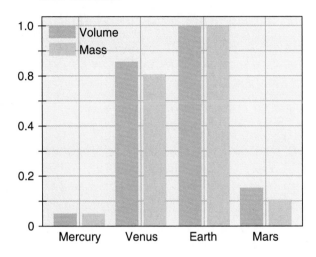

a. What is the mass of Venus compared to the mass of Earth? Express your answer as a percentage.

b. Which planet has the same mass-to-volume ratio as Earth?

c. Which of the four planets is the least dense?

2. **Data Bank** Use the information on page 612 to answer the following questions.

a. What is the diameter of Mars?

b. How far from the sun is Uranus?

3. **Estimate** The great red spot of Jupiter is about 29 000 km wide. Earth is about 12 760 km in diameter. About how many Earths could fit across the great red spot's width?

Make Connections

1. **Link the Concepts** Below is a concept map showing how some of the main concepts in this chapter link together. Only parts of the map are filled in. Complete the map, using words and ideas from the chapter.

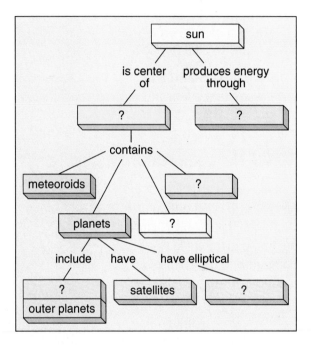

2. **Science and You** Record the number of hours you sleep each night for at least six months. Then analyze the data to determine if seasonal changes in day length might have had an effect on your sleep time.

3. **Science and Literature** The planets are all named after gods or goddesses from Roman and Greek mythology. Find out how each planet was named.

4. **Science and History** Learn more about the lives of important early astronomers such as Nicolaus Copernicus, Galileo Galilei, Tycho Brahe, and Johannes Kepler.

Chapter 25 Stars and Galaxies

What do you see?

"It looks like a picture of the Milky Way. This is our galaxy in space. The galaxy is large, but in the picture it is small compared to the space around it. The objects in it are vaguely roundish. There seems to be a spiral swirl of stars grouped together. The heat from the gases in the stars causes the blue-green color. Some of the other stars are red, pink, white, and orange, depending on how hot they are."

Annemarie Hanrahan
St. Mary of the
Annunciation School
Danvers, Massachusetts

To find out more about the photograph, look on page 608. As you read this chapter, you will learn about stars and galaxies.

25.1 The Study of Stars

Objectives

▶ **Describe** the electromagnetic spectrum.

▶ **Explain** how reflecting and refracting telescopes work.

▶ **Compare** and **contrast** optical telescopes and spectroscopes.

▶ **Infer** the relationship between the frequency of electromagnetic waves and their wavelength.

There are more than 200,000,000,000 billion stars in the universe. You may have looked up on a clear night and wished upon one of these stars. The star most important to Earth is the sun. The sun gives energy to all living things. Like all stars, it is a swirling, glowing ball of gas. In the past, the sun was so important to many cultures, such as the Zuni of New Mexico, that they looked upon it as a god and worshipped it.

And yet, in the universe, the sun is just an ordinary star. There are many stars much, much bigger and brighter than the sun. But these stars are so far away that they look like tiny dots of light from Earth.

Starlight Observation

What do you do when you're served a new kind of food? If you want to know more about the food before you eat it, you probably look at it and smell it. You might poke it with a fork to see what its texture is like. Finally, you might take a tiny bite and taste it. In other words, you use your five senses to make observations of the new food.

How do astronomers make observations of the stars? Stars can't be touched, smelled, or tasted, but they can be looked at in many ways. Stars send out many forms of energy. Light you see with your eyes is only one of these many forms of energy. The other forms of energy can be "seen," or detected, using a variety of special tools developed for space observation.

Figure 25.1 ▲
How do scientists observe the stars that fill the night sky?

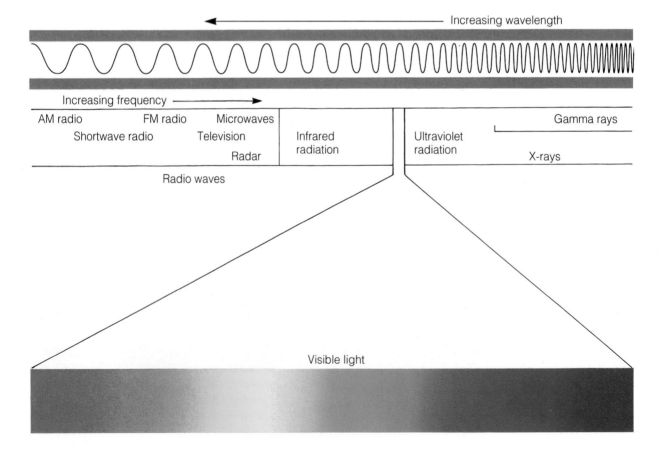
Figure 25.2

Stars and other objects in the universe produce many kinds of electromagnetic wave energy. All these forms of energy are part of the electromagnetic spectrum. ▼

Electromagnetic Spectrum

Stars produce visible light, radio waves, heat, X-rays, and other types of radiant energy. All these kinds of energy are in the form of *electromagnetic waves*. Each type of electromagnetic wave energy has a characteristic wavelength and frequency, or number of waves per second. All types of electromagnetic wave energy, from very low to very high frequency, make up the **electromagnetic spectrum**. You can see the different parts of the electromagnetic spectrum in Figure 25.2.

Visible light occupies only a small part of the middle of the electromagnetic spectrum. This part of the spectrum's visible light is made up of red, orange, yellow, green, blue, indigo, and violet light. These colors combine to make "white" light.

The first astronomers had to observe the sky with only their eyes, observing pinpoints of visible light. Astronomers today have many important tools to help them observe stars. These tools not only let them see much more with the visible light that reaches Earth, but also much more of the electromagnetic spectrum.

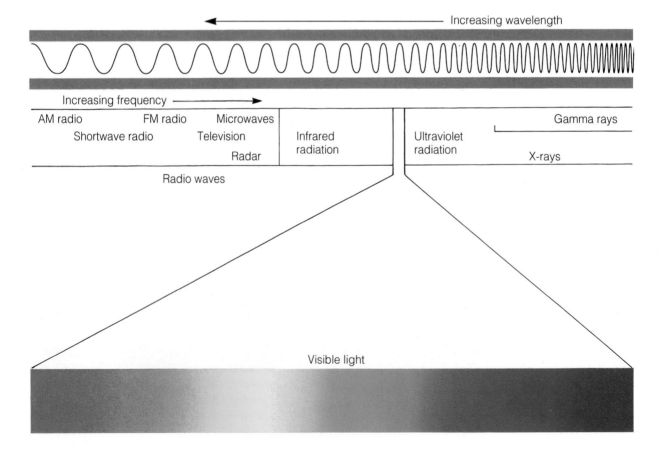

Increasing wavelength

Increasing frequency

| AM radio | FM radio | Microwaves | | | | Gamma rays |

Shortwave radio — Television

Radar — Infrared radiation — Ultraviolet radiation — X-rays

Radio waves

Visible light

Optical Telescopes

How do you see more detail in a very small object? You may use a hand lens or a microscope. In these tools, lenses collect visible light from the object and produce an image that appears much larger than the object. An optical telescope works in much the same way. It also uses lenses to collect visible light. The main difference is that the light comes from a very large but distant object instead of a very small one. An optical telescope makes the distant object, such as a star, look larger and closer to the viewer.

A Dutch eyeglass maker named Hans Lippershey is thought to have made the first simple telescope in 1608. Just one year later, Galileo used a telescope to observe craters on the moon and to discover moons orbiting Jupiter. Modern telescopes are much more powerful than the one Galileo used.

A refracting telescope uses lenses to collect and focus visible light. A reflecting telescope, in contrast, uses mirrors. The way each of the telescopes works is shown in Figure 25.3.

The larger a telescope's mirror or lenses, the brighter the image it can produce. Both mirrors and lenses, however, are limited in size. If they get too big, they bend from their own weight. A telescope with one of the largest single mirrors, 5 m in diameter, is at the Hale Observatory in California.

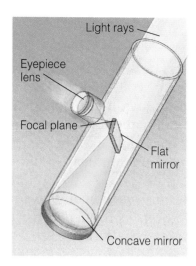

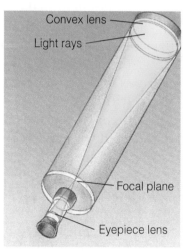

Figure 25.3 ▲

Which of these is a reflecting telescope? Which is a refracting telescope? How do you know?

◀ **Figure 25.4**

This building at Lick Observatory in California houses a large reflecting telescope.

Spectroscopes

The visible light given off by a star can be collected to make a larger image of the star. It also contains valuable information about the star's composition. A star's visible light has characteristic spectrum, or array of light with different wavelengths. A star produces a spectrum because each chemical element in the star blocks particular wavelengths of light given off by the star. By observing a star's spectrum, scientists can determine the star's chemical makeup.

Scientists use certain tools to break up a star's visible light into its spectrum. A *spectroscope* contains a prism that separates the light. The spectrum is then viewed with a small optical telescope. A *spectrograph* separates light through a prism or a device called a diffraction grating. The spectrum is recorded with a camera or electronic detector.

With data from these tools, scientists have determined that most stars contain about 70 percent hydrogen and 28 percent helium. There are also smaller amounts of other elements.

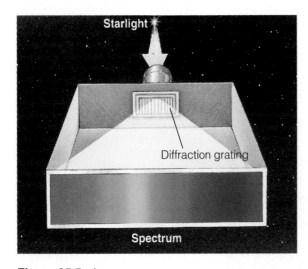

Figure 25.5 ▲
What does a star's spectrum tell you?

Figure 25.6 ▲
This radio telescope at Arecibo, Puerto Rico, has a dish 300 m wide.

Radio Telescopes

Optical telescopes and spectroscopes have some limits in their usefulness. Gas and dust may block the faint visible light from very distant objects. But many distant objects produce radiant energy in other parts of the electromagnetic spectrum that isn't as easily blocked.

Radio waves are especially valuable to space scientists. As you saw in Figure 25.2, radio waves have wavelengths much longer than those of visible light. Radio waves from distant objects in space are not affected by visible light, Earth's atmosphere, or space dust.

Scientists collect radio waves from space with radio telescopes like the one in Figure 25.6. The reflecting dish collects weak radio waves that are reflected to the antenna, and then amplified. Computers record and interpret the data.

Radio telescopes are important tools for studying quasars and pulsars, objects in space that emit radio waves as well as visible light. Radio telescopes have also helped scientists learn about the materials in the center of our own galaxy.

Science and Technology
The Keck Telescope

For many years, the reflecting telescope at the Hale Observatory was thought to be the biggest telescope that could be built. A telescope with a mirror larger than the Hale's 5-m mirror could not be built because it would bend from its own weight. Then scientists thought of making telescopes with many separate mirrors, called multiple-mirror telescopes.

The largest multiple-mirror telescope now in use is the Keck telescope. It is located on top of Mauna Kea, an extinct volcano in Hawaii. Together, its 36 six-sided mirrors equal a single mirror 10 m across.

The small mirrors of the Keck telescope adjust to changing temperatures more quickly than a big mirror. And the lightness of the mirrors makes them easy to support. If one massive mirror was used, it would crush the mount holding it up.

The use of so many small mirrors does have some drawbacks. It is difficult to keep each one aligned so that all the mirrors work together. To solve this problem, the mirrors on the Keck telescope have computer-controlled pistons that adjust twice a second. This adjustment keeps the mirrors perfectly aligned.

With the Keck telescope, astronomers see more objects in the universe. They form clearer images of distant objects. Scientists using the telescope hope to learn more about how the first stars formed. Other powerful multiple-mirror telescopes are now being built.

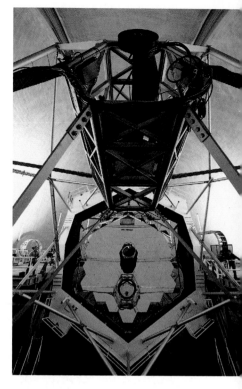

Figure 25.7 ▲

If you look closely you can see the separate six-sided mirrors of the Keck telescope.

Check and Explain

1. What types of radiant energy make up the electromagnetic spectrum?

2. Trace the path of light from a star through the parts of a reflecting telescope to the eye of an observer. What happens to the light at each part?

3. **Compare and Contrast** How are optical telescopes and spectroscopes similar? How do they differ?

4. **Infer** Study Figure 25.2. What can you infer about the relationship between the frequency and wavelength of electromagnetic wave energy?

Stars in the Sky

Make a list of the sun's characteristics. Which of these characteristics do you think are shared by all other stars? Which characteristics of the sun are different from other stars?

25.2 Characteristics of Stars

Objectives

▶ **Relate** the temperature of a star to its color.

▶ **Explain** how measurements of parallax are used to measure a star's distance from Earth.

▶ **Contrast** absolute magnitude and apparent magnitude.

▶ **Interpret data** from the H-R diagram.

How do stars vary? When you look at the night sky, you can tell some stars are brighter than others. You may also notice that stars have slightly different colors. Some are bluish, and others are reddish or yellowish. Besides these visible characteristics, scientists know that stars vary greatly in size and mass. All these characteristics are used to describe and classify stars.

Color and Temperature

The color of a star is related to its temperature. The coolest stars are 2,800°C and appear red. The hottest stars are 29,727°C or higher and look blue. The sun, a yellowish star, has a temperature of 5,500°C at its surface. Stars a little cooler than the sun appear orange. Stars a little hotter than the sun are white. Look at Table 25.1. What is the color and temperature of Polaris?

Table 25.1
Color and Temperature of Some Stars

Name	Color	Temperature (°C)	Name	Color	Temperature (°C)
Betelgeuse	Red	2,800	Polaris	Yellow	5,800
Antares	Red	2,900	Altair	White	7,800
Castor C	Red	3,300	Vega	White	9,700
Aldebaran	Orange	3,600	Algol	Blue	11,700
Arcturus	Orange	4,100	Spica	Blue	22,700
Sun	Yellow	5,500	Beta	Blue	28,000

Distance of Stars

Hold a finger in front of your face. Look at it with your left eye closed. Then look at it with your right eye closed. What do you observe? Your finger seems to move, or change position, relative to the background. This apparent change in the position of an object caused by a change in the position of the observer is called **parallax** (PAIR uh laks).

Scientist use parallax to determine how far away a star is from Earth. Look at Figure 25.8. Because of Earth's movement around the sun, nearer stars appear to change position relative to the more distant stars behind them. The closer a star is to Earth, the greater its apparent change of position. Measurements of this change in position can be converted into measurements of distance. Very distant stars don't seem to shift position at all. Scientists must use other methods to determine their distance from Earth.

Distances between stars are so great that scientists cannot use any of the units of measurement for distances on Earth for measuring distances in the universe. For this reason, scientists express distances to the stars in light-years. A **light-year** is the distance that light, traveling at a speed of 299,792 km per second, will cover in one year. Since light travels fast enough to circle Earth seven times each second, it can travel very far in a year. A light-year is about 9.5 *trillion* km.

Only a few stars are within 10 light-years. The closest star, Proxima Centauri, is 4.3 light-years from Earth. Many of the stars you see in the sky are hundreds of light-years away.

Figure 25.8 Parallax ▼

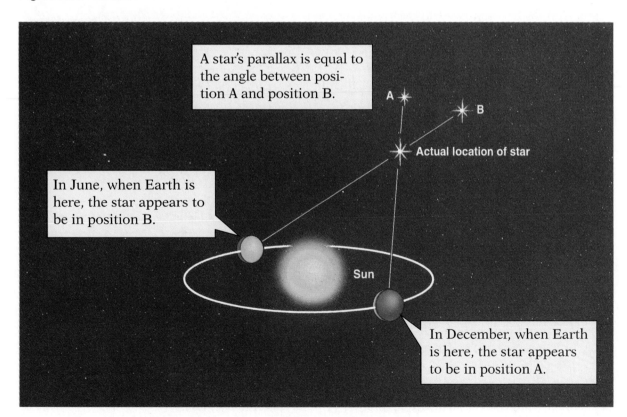

A star's parallax is equal to the angle between position A and position B.

A

B

Actual location of star

In June, when Earth is here, the star appears to be in position B.

Sun

In December, when Earth is here, the star appears to be in position A.

Magnitude of Stars

When you look at the night sky, some stars appear brighter than others. Astronomers compare the brightness of stars by using a number called the star's **magnitude** (MAG nih tood). The brighter the star is, the smaller the number that describes its magnitude. The brightest stars have negative magnitudes. A star with a magnitude of –2 is brighter than one with a magnitude of 2.

A star's brightness, as it appears from Earth, is called its *apparent magnitude*. However, the way stars appear to you does not tell you how much light they actually give off. There are very bright stars so far away that they don't look very bright from Earth. To describe the actual brightness of a star, scientists use *absolute magnitude*. A star's absolute magnitude is the brightness a star would appear to have if it were a standard distance, or 32.6 light-years, from Earth.

SkillBuilder *Interpreting Data*

Factors Affecting Magnitude

Why are some stars brighter than others? By studying data on the mass and size of stars, you can infer relationships between these characteristics and a star's magnitude. Study the table at the right, then answer the following questions.

1. How much larger than the sun is Polaris?

2. Explain how mass and absolute magnitude are related.

3. Explain how diameter and absolute magnitude are related.

4. Which is most closely related to magnitude, mass or diameter?

5. Which stars in the table have a *density* much greater than that of the sun? How do you know? Which stars are much less dense than the sun?

6. Is there a relationship between density and magnitude? Explain.

Write a paragraph about the relationships you see between a star's magnitude and its mass, diameter, and density.

Star	Absolute Magnitude	Mass*	Diameter*
Sun	5	1	1
Sirius	1	3	2
Arcturus	0	4	18
Spica	–3	14	7
Polaris	–5	14	90
Rigel	–7	43	22
Deneb	–7	42	44

*In relation to the sun.

The Hertzsprung-Russell Diagram

In your study of planet Earth, you have learned how to classify many things. These include rocks, elements, faults, volcanoes, clouds, and soils. Stars can also be classified according to their characteristics.

In the early 1900s, Ejnar Hertzsprung and Henry Norris Russell found an interesting pattern in the characteristics of stars. Each of them graphed a large number of stars according to magnitude and temperature. The resulting diagram is shown in Figure 25.9. It is called the Hertzsprung-Russell diagram, or H-R diagram, for short.

Look closely at Figure 25.9. A star's position on the graph is determined by its temperature and absolute magnitude. Most stars are grouped in a diagonal band from the hot, bright area to the dim, cool corner. These are the main-sequence stars. As you can see in Figure 25.9, other stars are classified in one of three other types depending on their location in the H-R diagram. What kind of star is the sun?

Figure 25.9
The H-R Diagram ▼

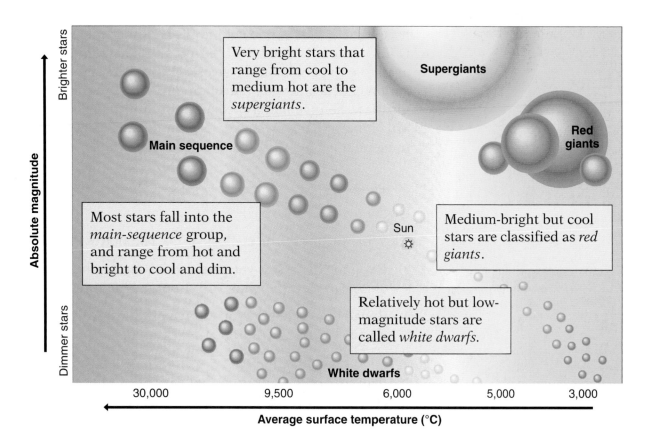

Very bright stars that range from cool to medium hot are the *supergiants*.

Supergiants

Red giants

Main sequence

Most stars fall into the *main-sequence* group, and range from hot and bright to cool and dim.

Sun ☆

Medium-bright but cool stars are classified as *red giants*.

Relatively hot but low-magnitude stars are called *white dwarfs*.

White dwarfs

Brighter stars

Dimmer stars

Absolute magnitude

30,000   9,500   6,000   5,000   3,000

Average surface temperature (°C)

Science and You *Discoveries by Amateurs*

Astronomy is one of the only branches of science in which amateurs play a serious part. Thousands of devoted star-gazers spend hours every year observing the night sky and collecting important data. Sometimes they make new discoveries.

In 1885, there was a giant explosion in the Andromeda galaxy. This bright spot in the sky was discovered by several amateur observers. One such observer was a Hungarian baroness who had dinner guests at the time. For fun, she set up a telescope on the lawn in front of her castle. She and her party were among the first to view this extraordinary event.

There are certain kinds of astronomical studies that professionals rarely take on, but amateurs do. For example, amateurs often make a serious study of variable stars. They spend many hours recording the changing brightness of these stars. Amateurs also monitor the surfaces of planets and search for comets. They produce data that professionals often find valuable.

One amateur astronomer, John Dobson, did much to make astronomy a popular pastime. At first, he lived in a monastery as a monk. But he was asked to leave because he spent too much time behind his handmade telescopes. Dobson then devoted his life to making astronomy available to people on the street. He created an organization called Sidewalk Astronomers. While in the organization, he invented a special mount for his telescope. This mount is now widely used among amateur astronomers. It is both stable and easily transportable.

Figure 25.10 ▲
Have you looked at objects in the sky through a telescope?

Check and Explain

1. What color are the coolest stars? The hottest?

2. Explain why a star you observe in January has changed position when you observe it again in July.

3. **Generalize** What do you know about a star that appears from Earth to be very bright?

4. **Interpret Data** Choose one star, other than the sun, from the H-R diagram in Figure 25.9. Compare this star's absolute magnitude, temperature, and color to that of the sun.

Activity 25 *How are star observations affected by location?*

Skills Observe; Measure; Predict; Calculate; Interpret Data

Task 1 Prelab Prep

1. Collect the following items: metric ruler or tape measure, chalk, paper, masking tape, long pencil.
2. At eye level, draw 11 parallel, vertical lines, 10 cm apart, on the chalkboard. Label the line on the left 0, the next line 10, and so on, until you have a metric ruler on the chalkboard labeled in cm.
3. Measure 4 m straight out from the 50-cm line on the chalkboard, and put a piece of tape on the floor to mark this spot.
4. Also mark with tape the places on the floor that are 3, 2, and 1 m from the chalkboard.

Task 2 Data Record

On a separate sheet of paper, copy Table 25.2.

Task 3 Procedure

1. Stand at the 4-m mark, facing the chalkboard.
2. Have a classmate hold the pencil vertically exactly over the 3-m mark, so that the pencil is 1 m away from your face. The pencil should remain as still as possible.
3. Use your left eye to observe the pencil's position against the lines on the chalkboard. Estimate this apparent position in cm. Record this observation in your data table.

4. Without moving your head or the pencil, repeat step 2, this time observing with your right eye. Record the result.

Task 4 Analysis

1. The apparent change in the position of the pencil, in relation to the lines on the chalkboard, is called parallax. Calculate the parallax for your two observations in cm. Record your answer in your data table.
2. Predict how your data will change when you move the pencil farther away from your face. Discuss and compare your predictions with your classmates.
3. Repeat steps 2 and 3 in Task 3, having your partner hold the pencil 2 m̄ and then 3 m away from your face. Record your data, and calculate the parallax for each pair of left-eye and right-eye observations.

Task 5 Conclusion

How does the position of an object appear to change when you look at it with only one eye and then with only the other?

What is the relationship between the amount of parallax and your distance from the pencil?

Everyday Application

Most of the time you look at objects using both of your eyes. Why do you think people have two eyes rather than just one?

Table 25.2 Density Comparisons

Distance from pencil (m)	Position viewed with left eye (cm)	Position viewed with right eye (cm)	Difference between positions (cm)
1.			
2.			
3.			

Comparing

The Life of Stars

List and describe each stage of the human life cycle. How do you think the human life cycle is different from that of a star?

SKILLS WARMUP

25.3 Life Cycles of Stars

Objectives

▶ **Explain** how stars come into being.

▶ **Describe** the stages of a star's life cycle.

▶ **Contrast** the different ways in which high-mass and low-mass stars end their life cycles.

▶ **Predict** what will happen for the rest of the sun's life cycle.

Think of some of the ways you have changed since you were born. You've grown taller and gained weight. Your voice may have changed. Your muscles have gotten stronger. Eventually, your skin will wrinkle, and your hair may turn gray. These events are a part of the human life cycle. The human life cycle lasts about 75 years.

Stars have life cycles, too. In fact, a star is born, changes, and then dies. In contrast to the human life cycle, the life cycle of a typical star is measured in billions of years.

Every star in the sky is at a different stage in its life cycle. Some stars are relatively young, while others are near the end of their existence. The sun, as you may recall, is about halfway through its 10-billion-year-long life cycle.

Figure 25.11
The Horsehead nebula is one of many nebulae visible from Earth. ▼

Birth of a Star

If you could travel among the stars, you would notice that the space between them is not entirely empty. In some places, there are great clouds of gas and dust. Each of these clouds is a **nebula** (NEHB yoo luh). A nebula is where stars are born.

The element hydrogen makes up most of a nebula. Helium and a sprinkling of dust are also present. The particles in a nebula are spread very thin. In fact, the particles are a million times less dense than the particles in the air you breathe. However, since nebulae are very large, they contain enormous amounts of matter.

◄ **Figure 25.12**
Scientists observe protostars and young stars within the Orion nebula.

Gravity causes matter to be attracted to other matter. Therefore, as a nebula travels through space, it collects more dust and gas. The cloud becomes packed tighter and tighter, as gravity pulls it all together.

Whenever matter is packed in this way, it heats up. An specially dense part of the nebula may form a hot, spinning ball of matter. Such a ball of hot matter is called a *protostar*.

A protostar doesn't yet shine by ordinary light, but it does give off infrared energy. Scientists identify protostars within nebulae using infrared telescopes. A protostar eventually becomes hot enough for nuclear fusion to take place in its core. When nuclear fusion produces great amounts of energy, a star comes to life.

Look at Figure 25.12. It shows the Orion nebula, which is 1,500 light-years away from Earth. It contains several "newborn" stars, less than a million years old.

Life of a Low-Mass Star

Stars begin their life cycles with different masses. A star's mass determines how long its life cycle will last and how it will die. Stars with a mass less than five times that of the sun are called low-mass stars. Most stars are in this group.

A low-mass star begins its life cycle as a main-sequence star. Over a period of billions of years, its supply of hydrogen is slowly changed by nuclear fusion into helium. During this time, the star undergoes few major changes.

▼ **ACTIVITY**

Communicating

Fred the Star

Make up a name for a star. Write its life story, from birth until death. Describe each stage of its life cycle.

SKILLS WORKOUT

Red Giant Stage As the hydrogen in the core of a low-mass star is used up, the core starts to collapse. The core of the star becomes denser and hotter. The increased temperature causes another kind of nuclear reaction. Helium is converted to carbon. This nuclear reaction gives off great amounts of energy, causing the star to expand. It becomes a red giant.

The red giant stage in a star's life is relatively short. The sun will be a main-sequence star for a total of 10 billion years. But the sun will be a red giant for only about 500 million years.

Dwarf Stage Eventually, most of the helium in a red giant's core is changed into carbon. Nuclear fusion slows. The star cools, and gravity makes it collapse inward. The matter making up the star is squeezed together very tightly, and the star becomes a white dwarf, as shown in Figure 25.13.

A typical white dwarf is about the size of Earth. But its matter is far denser than any matter on Earth. Eventually, the star becomes a burned-out black chunk of very dense matter that gives off no visible light. Then it is called a black dwarf.

Figure 25.13
Stellar Evolution ▼

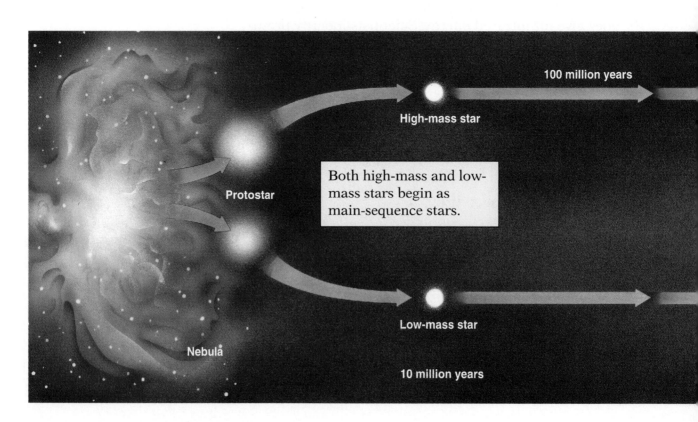

Both high-mass and low-mass stars begin as main-sequence stars.

100 million years

High-mass star

Protostar

Low-mass star

10 million years

Nebula

Life of a High-Mass Star

Stars more than six times as massive as the sun have a very different life cycle than low-mass stars. A high-mass star uses up its hydrogen at a much faster rate. After only about 50 to 100 million years, a high-mass star has no hydrogen left. At this time, the core collapses, and the outer layers expand greatly. The star becomes a supergiant, as shown in Figure 25.13.

Eventually, the core of the supergiant can no longer stand the pressure of the outside layers of the star. The outside layers crash inward very suddenly, causing a tremendous explosion that gives off an extraordinary amount of light. Great shells of gases fly off the star. The star becomes a **supernova**. A supernova explosion is the most violent event known to happen in the universe.

After a supernova explodes, only the tiny core of the star remains. This core, made up of neutrons, is called a *neutron star*. Neutron stars are extremely dense. Astronomers hypothesize that after a very massive star undergoes a supernova explosion, it may also become a *black hole*. A black hole is so dense, and its gravity so strong, that nothing can escape from it, not even light.

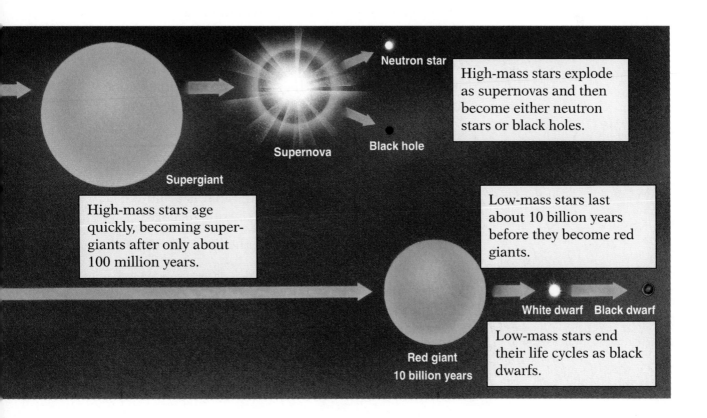

Neutron star

High-mass stars explode as supernovas and then become either neutron stars or black holes.

Supernova

Black hole

Supergiant

High-mass stars age quickly, becoming supergiants after only about 100 million years.

Low-mass stars last about 10 billion years before they become red giants.

White dwarf   Black dwarf

Red giant
10 billion years

Low-mass stars end their life cycles as black dwarfs.

Science and Technology
New Evidence for Black Holes

Do black holes really exist? So far, scientists have no real proof. Black holes do not release light, so they can't be observed directly. However, the Hubble Space Telescope enables scientists to collect new evidence for black holes. The light that comes to the telescope from distant objects doesn't have to pass through Earth's atmosphere. The telescope can, therefore, "see" faraway objects more clearly than a telescope based on Earth.

One strong piece of evidence for a black hole has come from Hubble's observations of M87, a galaxy over 50 million light-years away. You can see Galaxy M87 in Figure 25.14. Using Hubble's technology, scientists peered into this galaxy. They made the clearest photograph yet of a bright but fuzzy blob at the galaxy's center.

The photograph shows that the blob is an extremely dense cluster of stars. Scientists hypothesize that a very massive black hole at the center of the blob holds the stars together. The black hole would require a mass about 2.6 billion times that of the sun in order to have the necessary gravitational attraction.

Similar observations of other galaxies provide more good evidence of other black holes. In the center of the Andromeda galaxy, for example, stars orbit rapidly around some object with great mass. Scientists hope to have more direct evidence of a black hole soon.

Figure 25.14 ▲

Galaxy M87 may contain a black hole at its center.

Check and Explain

1. From what does a star form? What is a star called before nuclear fusion begins inside its core?

2. List, in order, four stages in the life cycle of a low-mass star.

3. **Infer** Does a red giant star contain any more mass than the main-sequence star from which it formed? Explain.

4. **Predict** Based on what you know about the lives of stars, predict what will happen to Earth as the sun goes through the rest of its life cycle.

25.4 Galaxies and Star Groups

Objectives

▶ **Describe** the four types of galaxies.

▶ **Explain** what a constellation is and how it differs from a galaxy or a star cluster.

▶ **Explain** how scientists know the universe is expanding.

▶ **Predict** how the constellations will look in the distant future.

H ave you looked at the sky on a clear, moonless night and seen the Milky Way? It is a broad band of murky, faint light. If you look at the Milky Way with a telescope or even binoculars, you see incredible numbers of stars. And behind those stars is still more murky light coming from millions of stars so far away you can't see them as separate points of light.

Galaxies

The stars of the Milky Way make up a very large group of stars called a galaxy. A **galaxy** is a collection of stars, nebulae, gases, dust, and planets. The objects in a galaxy move through space as a unit, held together by gravity. There are at least ten billion galaxies in the universe.

Look at Figure 25.15. The Milky Way galaxy is shaped like a disk. Notice where the sun is. When you see the Milky Way in the sky, you are looking through the diameter of the disk.

Almost every point of light you see in the sky is also in the Milky Way galaxy, except for a few other nearby galaxies. People in the Northern Hemisphere, for example, can see the Andromeda galaxy. It is 2 million light-years away. The light coming from this galaxy has been traveling through space for over 2 million years. People in the Southern Hemisphere can see two other galaxies, the Large and the Small Magellanic Clouds. These galaxies are about 160,000 and 180,000 light-years away. They appear as small smudges of light even though they are close neighbors to the Milky Way.

Earth's solar system

Figure 25.15 ▲
Earth is located in one of the spiral arms of the Milky Way galaxy.

Types of Galaxies

Through powerful telescopes, scientists observe many different galaxies outside the Milky Way. They classify these galaxies into four types, based on shape. Within each group, galaxies vary in their size. The average galaxy contains billions of stars.

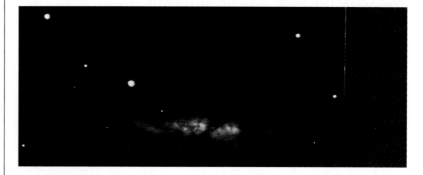

Elliptical Galaxies ▲

Some galaxies are shaped something like a football or a slightly flattened sphere. Most of these *elliptical galaxies* do not rotate as spiral galaxies do. Those that rotate do so more slowly than spirals. Elliptical galaxies also contain less dust and gas than spiral galaxies. The largest elliptical galaxies are made up of trillions of stars.

Irregular Galaxies ▲

Many galaxies don't have regular shapes. They are called *irregular galaxies*. Irregular galaxies vary greatly in size. The Small Magellanic Cloud, a very small galaxy near the Milky Way, is an irregular galaxy. Irregular galaxies are the least common type of galaxy.

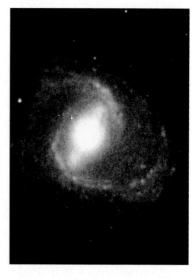

Spiral Galaxies ▶

Many galaxies are shaped like a flat disk with a bulge in the center. They have long, spiral arms that swing out from the center of the galaxy and rotate around it like a pinwheel. These *spiral galaxies* usually contain large amounts of gas and dust. The Milky Way is classified as a spiral galaxy. The sun rotates around the center of the galaxy about every 220 million years.

Barred Spiral Galaxies ▲

Some galaxies have a spiral shape but differ from spiral galaxies because their arms are attached to a straight bar shape. Usually, the bar is much brighter and denser than the arms. These galaxies are called *barred spiral galaxies*. They are less common than spiral galaxies.

Other Star Groups

Galaxies are not the only groupings of stars in the universe. Galaxies form even larger clusters of galaxies. The Milky Way is part of a cluster of over 20 galaxies called the *local group*.

Other star groups are much smaller than galaxies. Within the Milky Way are large numbers of *star clusters*. Star clusters are areas where many stars are grouped especially close together. If you live in the Northern Hemisphere, you can see a star cluster of seven stars called the Pleiades (PLEE uh deez). If you look at the Pleiades with a telescope, you can see that among the seven bright stars are many, many more stars.

The smallest and most common type of star groups are simple pairs of stars called *binary stars*. They are even more numerous than single stars. Many of the stars you see in the sky are binary stars that appear as one point of light.

Constellations

For thousands of years, people have looked at the stars and seen patterns shaped like people and animals. These star patterns are called **constellations**. If you've found the Big Dipper in the sky, then you've seen part of the constellation Ursa Major. Astronomers officially recognize a total of 88 constellations.

Constellations are unlike other star groups because the stars that make them up are usually not close together at all. They appear close as viewed from Earth, but they may actually be far apart. Rigel and Betelgeuse (BEET uhl JOOZ), for example, are both in the constellation of Orion. And yet they are separated by the huge distance of 600 light-years.

Constellations are important in the study of space because they help form a map of the sky. Any location in the sky is described in relation to a constellation. Stars are also named according to the constellation in which they are located.

Figure 25.16

You can see these constellations during autumn in the Northern Hemisphere. ▼

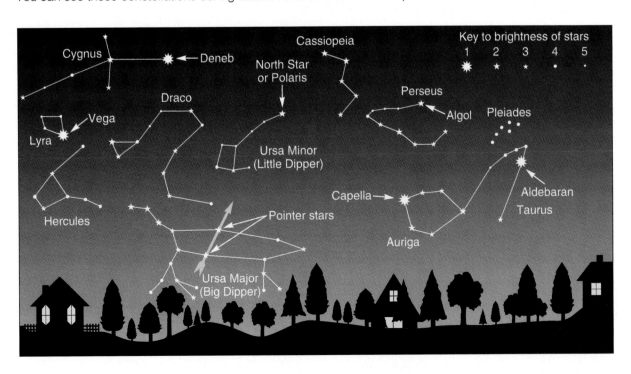

Expansion

1. Obtain a thick rubber band. Draw four dots on one side.

2. Carefully stretch the rubber band. Be sure not to let go of it.

What happens to the spacing between the dots? What are you modeling with the rubber band?

SKILLS WORKOUT

Expansion of the Universe

About 15 to 20 billion years ago, all the matter in the universe was packed into one giant fireball. The fireball exploded, spreading matter and energy outward in every direction. As the matter cooled, the force of gravity pulled together the particles of matter to form stars and galaxies. The universe was born. The theory for the origin of the universe is called the *big bang theory*.

There are several other ideas about how the universe began, but the big bang theory is accepted by most scientists. The main piece of evidence supporting the big bang theory is the observation that the universe is expanding. This observation is expected if the universe began in a huge explosion.

How do scientists know the universe is expanding? Look at Figure 25.17. The light waves from an object moving away from Earth are spaced more widely apart than they would be if the object were standing still. The waves appear to have a longer wavelength than they really have. The waves shifted to the red end of the visible-light spectrum. This apparent change in wavelength due to an object's motion is called the **Doppler effect**. Spectroscopic study of other galaxies shows that all galaxies have a red shift in their spectrums. Therefore, all the other galaxies are moving away from Earth.

Figure 25.17

Because of the Doppler effect, an object moving away from the earth shows a red shift in its spectrum. ▼

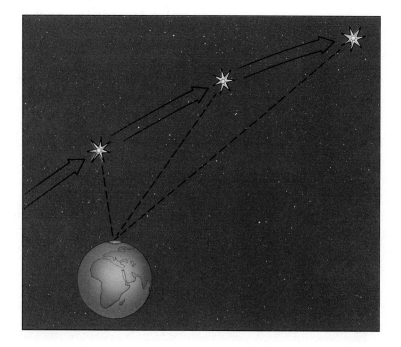

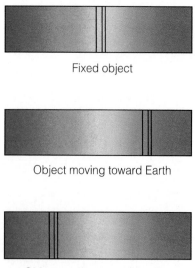

Fixed object

Object moving toward Earth

Object moving away from Earth

Science and Technology *Exploring Space*

Will people ever explore beyond the solar system? Some scientists think that reaching other stars may some day be possible. But many obstacles stand in the way. The greatest problem is distance. The closest star is 4.2 light-years away. So a spaceship traveling at the speed of light would take over 8 years to make the round-trip journey to this neighboring star. Another major obstacle is providing for the needs of astronauts for this long trip. Imagine the room needed to store 8 years worth of food and other supplies! In addition, no technology exists for making a spaceship travel anywhere near as fast as the speed of light.

Because it will be so difficult for people to journey beyond the solar system, scientists are focusing on other ways of exploring space. Space probes, for example, can be sent out of the solar system. They can collect data and relay the information back to Earth.

Consider This

Is Space Exploration Worth the Cost?

Exploring space is one of the challenges of this age. However, space exploration is costly and sometimes dangerous. People debate whether the cost is worth the results obtained.

Space exploration has many benefits. It helps you better understand your planet. It lets different countries work together peacefully. New discoveries in space give young people an interest in the study of science. In addition, the technologies developed for space exploration often have many uses on Earth. The heat and fire resistant suits worn by the firefighters in the photograph are one such "spinoff" that can help solve world problems.

However, it costs billions of dollars to fund space research. Many people argue that the money would be better spent helping people on Earth.

Think About It How valuable is more knowledge about the universe? What could be done with the money that is currently being used for space exploration?

Debate It Write a paper stating your position for or against

funding space exploration. Include your reasons for your position. Then, have a class debate in which two teams debate their opposing views.

The space probe Voyager II is now on its way into deep space. It was launched from Earth in 1979 to explore the outer planets. It flew by Jupiter, Saturn, Uranus, and Neptune, returning detailed photographs of these planets. Voyager II will continue sending information from deep space until the year 2020. However, a space probe such as Voyager won't get close to another star within your lifetime.

Another way of learning more about what lies beyond the solar system is to build better tools of observation. More powerful telescopes are built on Earth, but there is a limit to what they see because of Earth's atmosphere. The atmosphere causes distortion of the light waves from distant objects. This distortion is what makes stars appear to twinkle.

To overcome the problems caused by the atmosphere, scientists built the Hubble Space Telescope. Recall that the Hubble Telescope has been used to collect evidence of black holes. It was launched in 1990.

The Hubble Telescope is the largest astronomical instrument ever place in orbit. Hubble's main telescope has a mirror 2.4 m in diameter. This telescope is smaller than the largest Earth-based telescopes, but it can form clearer images because it is above the atmosphere. Unfortunately, a flaw in the mirror kept the telescope from working as well as it could until 1993. In December of 1993, a team of astronauts aboard the space shuttle *Endeavour* successfully repaired the telescope.

Figure 25.18 ▲
The Voyager II space probe has been sending data back to Earth since 1979.

Check and Explain

1. Name the four types of galaxies, and draw a simple model of each type.

2. How do constellations differ from galaxies and star clusters?

3. **Reason and Conclude** Why are different constellations visible in the summer and winter? Explain your reasoning.

4. **Predict** A million years from now, will the constellations look the same as they do today? Explain the reasons for your answer.

Chapter 25 Review

Concept Summary

25.1 The Study of Stars
▶ Stars produce many different types of electromagnetic wave energy, including visible light, radio waves, and X-rays.
▶ Optical telescopes use visible light to form images of distant objects.
▶ Spectroscopes reveal a star's composition by analyzing the makeup of its visible light.
▶ Radio telescopes detect the radio waves from distant objects.

25.2 Characteristics of Stars
▶ The color of a star is related to its temperature.
▶ By measuring a star's apparent change of position, or parallax, its distance from Earth can be calculated.
▶ A star's absolute magnitude and distance from Earth determine its apparent magnitude.

▶ Stars are classified into four groups depending on their location on the H-R diagram.

25.3 Life Cycles of Stars
▶ Stars come into being in nebulae.
▶ A low-mass star goes through the stages of main-sequence star, red giant, white dwarf, and black dwarf.
▶ A high-mass star goes through the stages of main-sequence star, supergiant, supernova, and neutron star or black hole.

25.4 Galaxies and Star Groups
▶ Galaxies are classified into four types based on shape.
▶ Within galaxies, stars form star clusters and exist as binary stars.
▶ To an observer on Earth, stars form patterns called constellations.

Chapter Vocabulary

electromagnetic spectrum (25.1)   magnitude (25.2)   galaxy (25.4)
parallax (25.2)   nebula (25.3)   constellation (25.4)
light-year (25.2)   supernova (25.3)   Doppler effect (25.4)

Check Your Vocabulary

Use the vocabulary words above to complete the following sentences correctly.

1. Outside of the Milky Way, there are many other ____ .

2. The brighter the star is, the smaller the number that describes its ____ .

3. All types of electromagnetic wave energy together make up the ____ .

4. A star begins to form when matter in a(n) ____ is drawn together by gravity.

5. Light from other galaxies shows a red shift because of the ____ .

6. A supergiant star will eventually become a(n) ____ .

7. Scientists map the sky using the ____ .

8. Because of ____ , some stars appear to shift position from winter to summer.

9. The star nearest the solar system is 4.2 ____ away.

Write Your Vocabulary

Write sentences using the vocabulary words above. Show that you know what each word means.

Chapter 25 Review

Check Your Knowledge

Answer the following in complete sentences.

1. What characteristic of a star determines whether it will explode as a supernova at some time in its life cycle?

2. What is the difference between a star's apparent magnitude and its absolute magnitude?

3. How do scientists think the universe began?

4. What type of galaxy is the Milky Way?

5. What is a constellation? Give an example of a constellation.

6. What type of star ends its life cycle as a black hole?

Determine whether each statement is true or false. Write *true* if it is true. If it is false, change the underlined word(s) to make the statement true.

7. A low-mass star will end its life cycle as a black dwarf.

8. An optical telescope is used to determine the composition of a star.

9. A binary star is made up of three stars together.

10. The higher the frequency of electromagnetic wave energy, the higher the wavelength.

11. A star with a low magnitude and high surface temperature is a white dwarf.

12. A light-year is the distance light travels in a month.

13. Stars come into being in star clusters.

Check Your Understanding

Apply the concepts you have learned to answer each question.

1. Compared to the three other types of stars in the H-R diagram, how old are main-sequence stars?

2. Draw a diagram showing how two stars may appear close together from Earth even though they are far apart.

3. **Infer** Arrange the following in order of increasing density.

   a. Red giant.

   b. White dwarf.

   c. Black hole.

   d. Main-sequence star.

4. **Application** Suppose two stars have the same absolute magnitude, but one is ten times farther away. Which star will appear brighter from Earth? If both stars were moved to the same distance from Earth, how would their brightness compare? Explain your answers.

5. **Critical Thinking** What type of star would you expect to contain the largest amount of the element iron?

6. To predict the entire life cycle of a "newborn" star, what do scientists need to know about it?

7. **Critical Thinking** Why do you think spiral and barred spiral galaxies are disk-shaped?

8. **Mystery Photo** The photograph on page 584 shows the galaxy M33, which is over 2 million light-years away.

   a. Which type of galaxy is M33?

   b. What was happening on Earth when the light that made this photograph left M33?

Develop Your Skills

Use the skills you have developed in this chapter to complete each activity.

1. Interpret Data Each sequence of colored points on the H-R diagram below represents stages in the life cycle of a star.

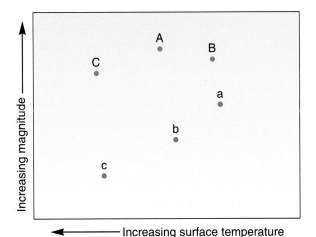

a. What type of star is A?

b. What type of star is C?

c. What is the correct order of stages for the star shown with red dots? Describe each stage.

d. What is the correct order of stages for the star shown with blue dots? Describe each stage.

2. Data Bank Use the information on pages 614–615 to answer the following questions.

a. What constellation is nearly overhead in the spring sky, as viewed from the middle latitudes of the Northern Hemisphere?

b. In which constellation is the bright star Sirius?

c. If you live in the Northern Hemisphere, where would look in the night sky to see the Big Dipper in autumn?

Make Connections

1. Link the Concepts Draw a concept map showing how the concepts below link together. Add terms to connect, or link the concepts: stars, optical telescope, constellations, elliptical galaxy, nebulae, high-mass star, black dwarf, spiral galaxy, black hole, low-mass star, spectroscope, barred spiral galaxy, irregular galaxy.

2. Science and Society Do research on how stars, star maps, and constellations have been used by sailors throughout history for navigation on the oceans.

3. Science and You What is your astrological sign? Most signs are named after constellations. Find out where your constellation is located, and try to see it at night. What are the names of the stars that make it up? What stories are connected with this constellation?

4. Science and Art Choose a constellation. Draw the pattern of stars in the constellation as they appear in the sky. Then, around these stars, draw the animal or mythological figure for which the constellation is named.

5. Science and Technology Do research on plans for large, multiple-mirror telescopes, such as the Very Large telescope in Europe, the Columbus telescope, and the Magellan telescope. How do these telescopes differ from the Keck telescope?

6. Science and You Read about amateur astronomy. Obtain a telescope that you can use, and begin observing the stars at night. If you find you enjoy astronomy, you may want to build your own telescope or form an astronomy club.

The best part of being in space is being weightless. It feels wonderful to be able to float without effort; to slither up, down, and around the inside of the shuttle just like a seal; to be upside down as often as I'm right side up and have it make no difference. On Earth being upside down feels different because gravity is pulling the blood toward my head. In space I feel exactly the same whether my head is toward the floor or toward the ceiling.

When I'm weightless, some things don't change. My heart beats at about the same rate as it does on Earth. I can still swallow and digest food. My eyes, ears, nose, and taste buds work fine; I see, hear, smell, and taste things just as I do at home.

Astronauts can't always resist the fun of playing with weightless food. On one of my flights, we set a cookie floating in the middle of the room and then "flew" an astronaut, with

To Space and Back

The following excerpt is from the book To Space and Back *by Sally Ride with Susan Okie.*

his mouth wide open, across the cabin to capture it. We often share bags of peanuts because it gives an excuse to play catch, floating peanuts back and forth into each other's mouths. We race to capture spinning carrots and bananas, and practice catching spoonfuls of food in our mouths while they twirl in mid-air. These tricks are easy in space, but I don't recommend trying them on Earth.

After meals we clean up. We simply wipe off whatever utensils have been used and stow them in our pockets. Since each serving of food comes in its own carton, can, or pouch, "washing the dishes" really means disposing of the trash. We pack our empty food containers into garbage bags and bring all our trash back to Earth with us.

The first time I tried to sleep while weightless, I discovered that my arms and legs moved automatically into a "sleep position." Instead of hanging at my sides, as they would on Earth, my arms drifted out in front of me, motionless, at about shoulder height. It was strange to open my eyes and see my arms dangling in front of my face.

I also found that I couldn't turn over in space. There was no such thing as lying on my back, on my side, or on my stomach—it was all the same. No matter how much I twisted and turned, my body would go back to exactly the same natural sleep position as soon as I relaxed.

I don't use my pillow because I have discovered that my head will not stay on it unless I strap it there. I don't use the stiff pad, either—just the light bag. When it's time to sleep, I gather my bag, my sleep mask, and my tape player with earphones and float up to the flight deck. Then I crawl into the bag, zip it around me, and float in a sort of sitting position just above a seat, right next to a window. Before I pull the mask down over my eyes, I relax for a while, listening to music and watching the Earth go by beneath me.

When I'm in orbit it seems as though I don't need quite as much sleep as I do on Earth. Maybe that's because when I am weightless I don't use my muscles as much, so I don't feel as tired. Or maybe it's because I'm excited to be in space and don't want to waste time sleeping.

Skills in Science

Reading Skills in Science

1. **Detect the Writer's Mood** How does the author seem to feel about her experiences in space? Give evidence to support your answer. What do you think the author wants to convey to the reader?

2. **Infer** The author states that before falling asleep she pulls the sleep mask down over her eyes. Why is this necessary?

Writing Skills in Science

1. **Generalize** In the selection, the author describes the effect weightlessness had on her actions. Think about how weightlessness might affect your daily actions. Write a limerick or other poem that describes life in a weightless state. Share your poem with the class.

2. **Communicate** Imagine you are flying in the space shuttle with Sally Ride. Write three or four entries in your daily journal describing the experiences. What was it like to sleep and eat in the shuttle? What views of space did you have from the shuttle?

Activities

Make a Model Visit the school or local library to find out more about the structure of a space shuttle like the one Sally Ride lived in while in space. Use the information to draw a model of the shuttle. Present your model to the class.

Make a Model Identify an everyday task that would be difficult to do in a weightless state. Design an invention that members of the space shuttle crew could use to complete the task. You may wish to draw the model or make a "prototype" from materials such as cardboard. Examples of tasks to consider may include brushing one's teeth, combing one's hair, writing a letter, and sleeping.

Where to Read More

Flying to the Moon and Other Strange Places by Michael Collins. New York: Farrar, 1976. The space program before the advent of the space shuttle is described through the eyes of Michael Collins, the command pilot of the spacecraft Columbia.

Data Bank

Silt Loads of Major Rivers

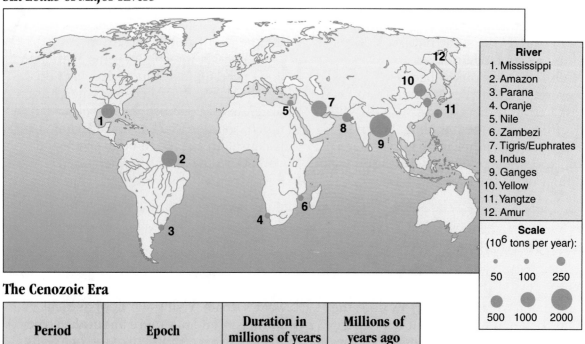

River
1. Mississippi
2. Amazon
3. Parana
4. Oranje
5. Nile
6. Zambezi
7. Tigris/Euphrates
8. Indus
9. Ganges
10. Yellow
11. Yangtze
12. Amur

Scale
(10^6 tons per year):

50   100   250

500   1000   2000

The Cenozoic Era

Period		Epoch	Duration in millions of years	Millions of years ago
Quaternary		Pleistocene	1.6	1.6
Tertiary	Neo-gene	Pliocene	3.7	5
		Miocene	18.4	24
	Paleogene	Oligocene	12.9	37
		Eocene	21.2	58
		Paleocene	8.6	66

Planetary Statistics

Planet	Density (g/cm^3)	Diameter (km)	Rotation (Earth time)	Revolution (Earth time)	Average Orbital Speed (km/s)	Average Distance to Sun (AU)
Mercury	5.42	4 878	59 days	88 days	47.89	0.387
Venus	5.24	12 104	243 days	224.7 days	35.03	0.723
Earth	5.50	12 756	24 hours	365 days	29.79	1.000
Mars	3.94	6 794	24.5 hours	687 days	24.13	1.524
Jupiter	1.31	142 796	9.9 hours	11.9 years	13.06	5.203
Saturn	0.70	120 660	10.2 hours	29.5 years	9.64	9.529
Uranus	1.30	51 118	17 hours	84 years	6.81	19.191
Neptune	1.66	49 528	16 hours	164.8 years	5.43	30.061
Pluto	2.03	2 290	6.4 days	247.7 years	4.74	39.529

Climate and Weathering

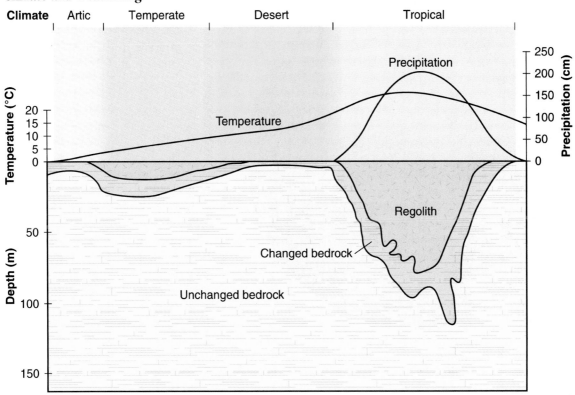

Climate   Artic   Temperate   Desert   Tropical

Temperature (°C)

Depth (m)

Precipitation (cm)

Precipitation

Temperature

Regolith

Changed bedrock

Unchanged bedrock

Earth Depths

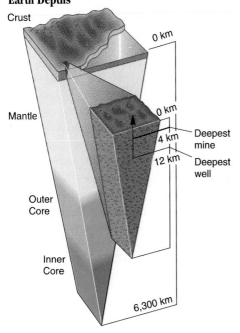

Crust

Mantle

Outer Core

Inner Core

0 km

0 km

4 km — Deepest mine

12 km — Deepest well

6,300 km

Land Use in the United States

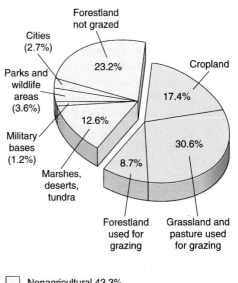

Forestland not grazed
23.2%

Cities (2.7%)

Parks and wildlife areas (3.6%)

Military bases (1.2%)

Marshes, deserts, tundra
12.6%

Cropland
17.4%

Grassland and pasture used for grazing
30.6%

Forestland used for grazing
8.7%

☐ Nonagricultural 43.3%

▨ Agricultural 56.7%

Star Charts for the Northern Hemisphere

SPRING

When using a star chart, hold it up toward the sky in the direction you are looking. Rotate it until the star pattern on the map matches the pattern that you see in the sky.

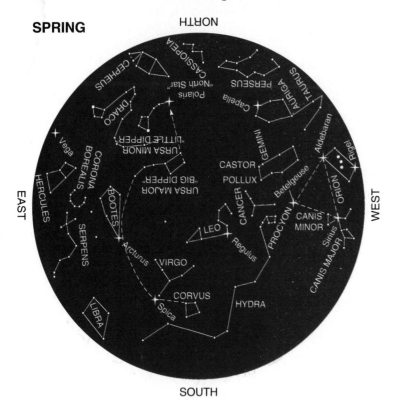

SUMMER

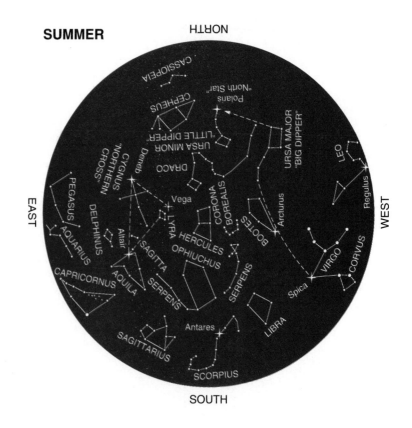

AUTUMN

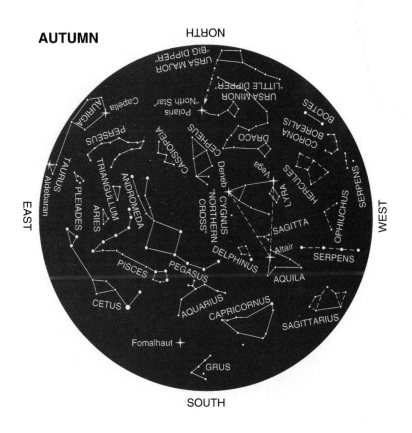

WINTER

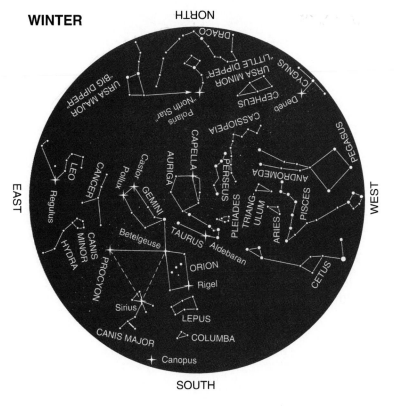

Synoptic Chart

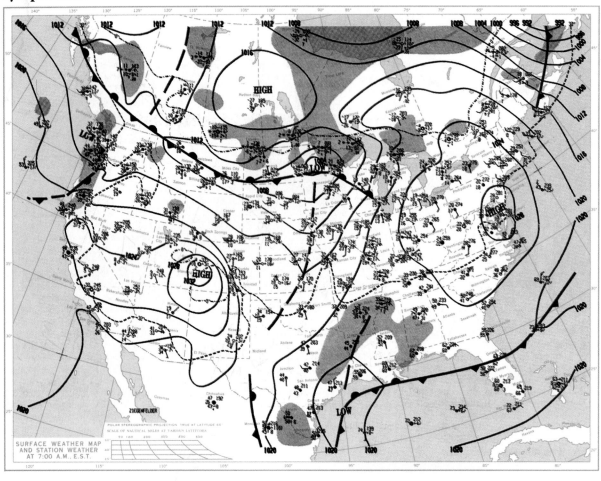

Tide Table — Week of January 24–30

Date/Day	A.M.				P.M.			
	Time	Meters	Time	Meters	Time	Meters	Time	Meters
24 Sunday	1:06	1.5	6:00	0.7	NOON	1.7	6:25	0.0
25 Monday	1:31	1.5	6:39	0.7	12:35	1.6	6:54	0.1
26 Tuesday	1:58	1.6	7:21	0.7	1:14	1.5	7:23	0.2
27 Wednesday	2:25	1.6	8:09	0.6	1:57	1.4	7:54	0.4
28 Thursday	2:56	1.6	8:58	0.6	2:51	1.2	8:27	0.6
29 Friday	3:31	1.7	10:01	0.6	4:03	1.1	9:08	0.7
30 Saturday	4:12	1.7	11:07	0.5	5:45	1.1	10:01	0.9

Average Temperatures and Precipitation for Selected World Cities

City	Average Daily Temperature (°C)				Average Annual Precipitation
	Jan. Max.	Jan. Min.	July Max.	July Min.	(cm)
Athens, Greece	12	6	32	22	40
Bangkok, Thailand	31	19	32	24	147
Bogotá, Colombia	19	9	17	10	106
Capetown, South Africa	25	15	17	7	51
Denver, Colorado, USA	6	−17	31	15	39
Geneva, Switzerland	4	−2	25	14	39
Istanbul, Turkey	7	2	26	18	80
Lagos, Nigeria	30	23	28	23	184
Lima, Peru	28	19	19	13	4
Manila, Philippines	30	20	31	23	208
Moscow, Russia	−6	−13	24	12	63
Reykjavik, Iceland	2	−2	14	9	86
Shanghai, China	8	0	32	23	114
Sydney, Australia	25	18	15	8	118

Rocks in North America

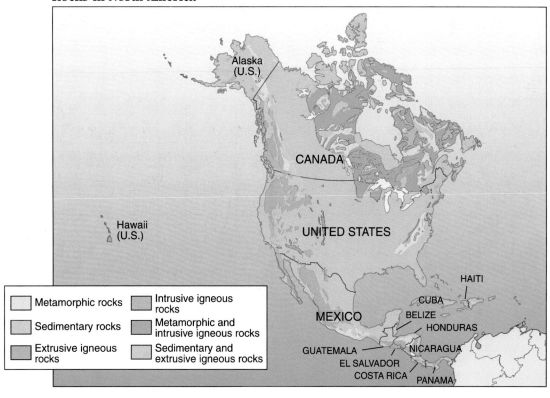

Distance Between the Earth and Moon

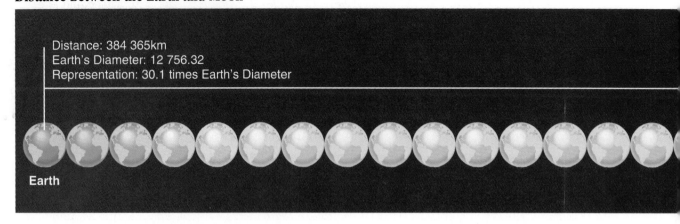

Distance: 384 365km
Earth's Diameter: 12 756.32
Representation: 30.1 times Earth's Diameter

Earth

The Tallest Mountain on Each Continent

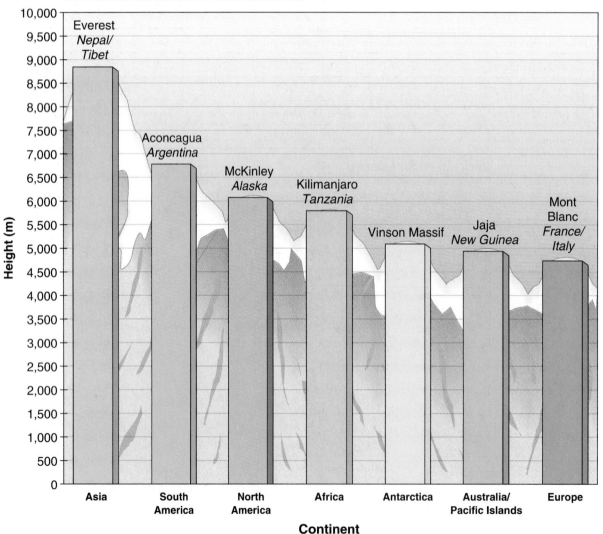

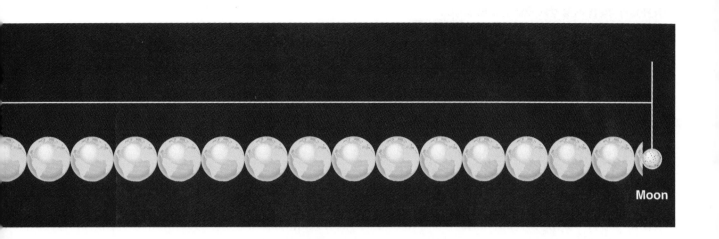

Moon

Some Major Earthquakes in the Twentieth Century

Location	Date	Magnitude	Deaths
Japan	Mar. 2, 1933	8.9	2,990
India, Assam	Aug. 15, 1950	8.7	1,530
China, Gansu	Dec. 16, 1920	8.6	100,000
Alaska	Mar. 27, 1964	8.4	131
Chile, Chillan	Jan. 24, 1939	8.3	28,000
China, Tangshan	July 28, 1976	8.2	242,000
NW. Argentina	Nov. 23, 1977	8.2	100
Mexico City	Sept. 19 & 21, 1985	8.1	9,500
Indonesia	Sept. 12, 1979	8.1	100
Indonesia	Aug. 19, 1977	8.0	200
Colombia, Ecuador	Dec. 12, 1979	7.9	800
N. Afghanistan	June 17–19, 1956	7.7	2,000
N. Peru	May 31, 1970	7.7	66,794
NW. Iran	June 21, 1990	7.7	40,000+
Luzon, Philippines	July 16, 1990	7.7	1,621
Italy, Messina	Dec. 28, 1908	7.5	83,000
Guatemala	Feb. 4, 1976	7.5	22,778
Romania	Mar. 4, 1977	7.5	1,541
New Guinea, Irian Jaya	June 26, 1976	7.1	433
San Francisco Bay Area	Oct. 17, 1989	7.1	62
Morocco, Agadir	Feb. 29, 1960	5.8	12,000

Physical Map of the United States

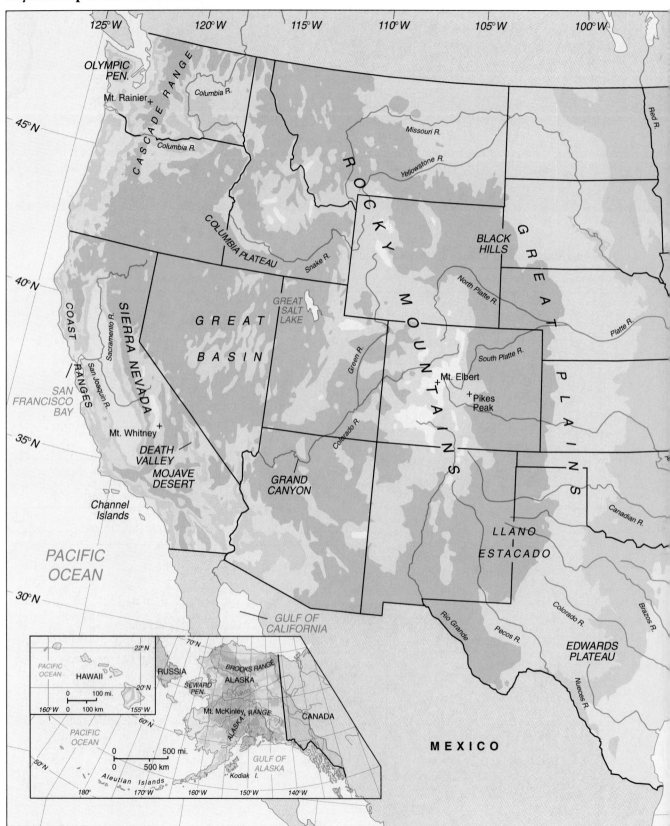

OLYMPIC PEN.

Mt. Rainier

CASCADE RANGE

Columbia R.

Columbia R.

ROCKY

Missouri R.

Yellowstone R.

COLUMBIA PLATEAU

Snake R.

45° N

40° N

BLACK HILLS

GREAT

North Platte R.

GREAT SALT LAKE

GREAT BASIN

SIERRA NEVADA

COAST RANGES

Sacramento R.

San Joaquin R.

SAN FRANCISCO BAY

35° N

Mt. Whitney

DEATH VALLEY

MOJAVE DESERT

Channel Islands

Green R.

Colorado R.

GRAND CANYON

MOUNTAINS

Mt. Elbert

Pikes Peak

South Platte R.

Platte R.

PLAINS

LLANO ESTACADO

Canadian R.

PACIFIC OCEAN

30° N

GULF OF CALIFORNIA

Rio Grande

Pecos R.

Colorado R.

Brazos R.

EDWARDS PLATEAU

Nueces R.

MEXICO

125° W   120° W   115° W   110° W   105° W   100° W

Red R.

PACIFIC OCEAN

HAWAII

22° N

20° N

0   100 mi.
0   100 km

160° W   155° W

RUSSIA

BROOKS RANGE

ALASKA

SEWARD PEN.

Yukon

70° N

60° N

Mt. McKinley

ALASKA RANGE

RANGE

CANADA

PACIFIC OCEAN

50° N

0   500 mi.
0   500 km

180°   170° W   160° W   150° W   140° W

Aleutian Islands

Kodiak I.

GULF OF ALASKA

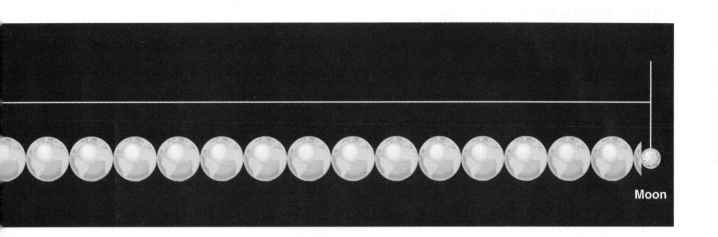

Moon

Some Major Earthquakes in the Twentieth Century

Location	Date	Magnitude	Deaths
Japan	Mar. 2, 1933	8.9	2,990
India, Assam	Aug. 15, 1950	8.7	1,530
China, Gansu	Dec. 16, 1920	8.6	100,000
Alaska	Mar. 27, 1964	8.4	131
Chile, Chillan	Jan. 24, 1939	8.3	28,000
China, Tangshan	July 28, 1976	8.2	242,000
NW. Argentina	Nov. 23, 1977	8.2	100
Mexico City	Sept. 19 & 21, 1985	8.1	9,500
Indonesia	Sept. 12, 1979	8.1	100
Indonesia	Aug. 19, 1977	8.0	200
Colombia, Ecuador	Dec. 12, 1979	7.9	800
N. Afghanistan	June 17–19, 1956	7.7	2,000
N. Peru	May 31, 1970	7.7	66,794
NW. Iran	June 21, 1990	7.7	40,000+
Luzon, Philippines	July 16, 1990	7.7	1,621
Italy, Messina	Dec. 28, 1908	7.5	83,000
Guatemala	Feb. 4, 1976	7.5	22,778
Romania	Mar. 4, 1977	7.5	1,541
New Guinea, Irian Jaya	June 26, 1976	7.1	433
San Francisco Bay Area	Oct. 17, 1989	7.1	62
Morocco, Agadir	Feb. 29, 1960	5.8	12,000

Physical Map of the United States

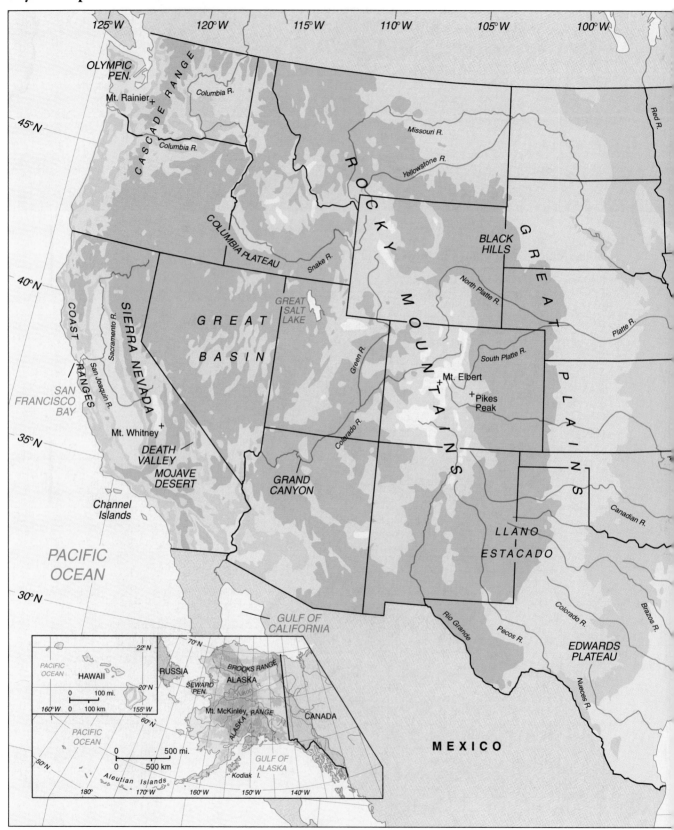

OLYMPIC PEN.

Mt. Rainier

Columbia R.

Columbia R.

CASCADE RANGE

COLUMBIA PLATEAU

Snake R.

Missouri R.

Yellowstone R.

R O C K Y

BLACK HILLS

North Platte R.

Platte R.

G R E A T

45° N

40° N

35° N

30° N

125° W 120° W 115° W 110° W 105° W 100° W

Red R.

COAST RANGES

SIERRA NEVADA

Sacramento R.

San Joaquin R.

SAN FRANCISCO BAY

Mt. Whitney

DEATH VALLEY

MOJAVE DESERT

Channel Islands

GREAT BASIN

GREAT SALT LAKE

Green R.

Colorado R.

GRAND CANYON

M O U N T A I N S

South Platte R.

Mt. Elbert

Pikes Peak

P L A I N S

LLANO ESTACADO

Canadian R.

Colorado R.

Brazos R.

PACIFIC OCEAN

GULF OF CALIFORNIA

Rio Grande

Pecos R.

EDWARDS PLATEAU

Nueces R.

MEXICO

HAWAII

PACIFIC OCEAN

22° N

20° N

160° W

155° W

0 100 mi.
0 100 km

RUSSIA

BROOKS RANGE

SEWARD PEN.

ALASKA

Yukon R.

Mt. McKinley

ALASKA RANGE

CANADA

PACIFIC OCEAN

50° N

60° N

70° N

180°

170° W

160° W

150° W

140° W

Aleutian Islands

Kodiak I.

GULF OF ALASKA

0 500 mi.
0 500 km

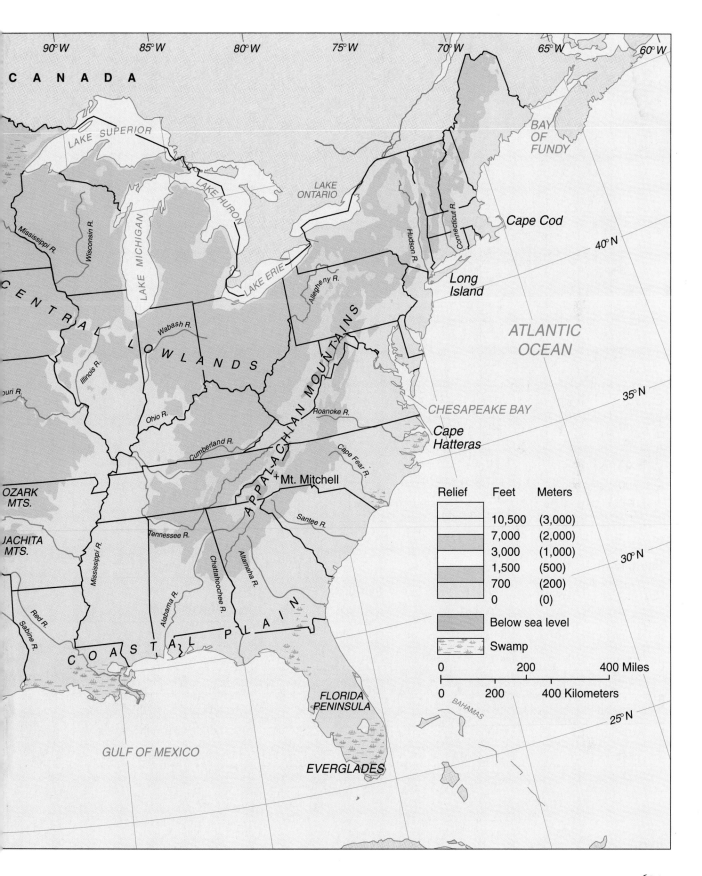

90° W   85° W   80° W   75° W   70° W   65° W   60° W

C A N A D A

LAKE SUPERIOR

BAY
OF
FUNDY

LAKE HURON

LAKE MICHIGAN

LAKE
ONTARIO

LAKE ERIE

Cape Cod

Mississippi R.

Wisconsin R.

Hudson R.

Connecticut R.

40° N

Allegheny R.

Long
Island

C E N T R A L

Wabash R.

ATLANTIC
OCEAN

Illinois R.

L O W L A N D S

Missouri R.

Ohio R.

35° N

Roanoke R.

CHESAPEAKE BAY

Cumberland R.

Cape
Hatteras

OZARK
MTS.

Cape Fear R.

+ Mt. Mitchell

A P P A L A C H I A N   M O U N T A I N S

Relief   Feet   Meters

OUACHITA
MTS.

Tennessee R.

Santee R.

10,500 (3,000)

7,000   (2,000)

Mississippi R.

30° N

3,000   (1,000)

Chattahoochee R.

Altamaha R.

1,500   (500)

Alabama R.

700   (200)

Red R.

0   (0)

Sabine R.

C O A S T A L   P L A I N

Below sea level

Swamp

0   200   400 Miles

0   200   400 Kilometers

FLORIDA
PENINSULA

BAHAMAS

25° N

GULF OF MEXICO

EVERGLADES

World's Largest Oceans and Seas

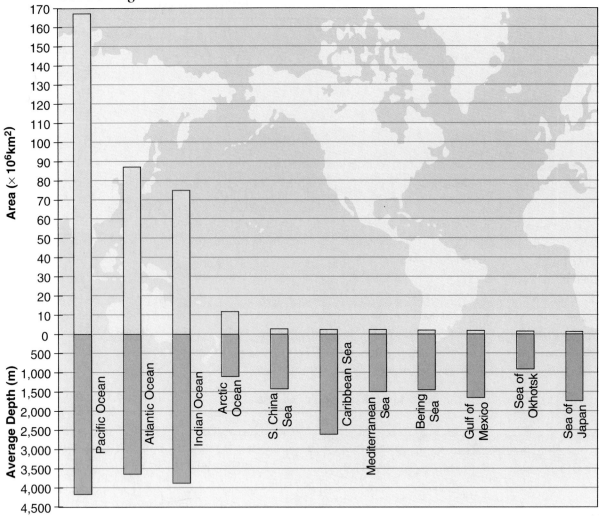

Area ($\times 10^6 km^2$)

Average Depth (m)

170
160
150
140
130
120
110
100
90
80
70
60
50
40
30
20
10
0
500
1,000
1,500
2,000
2,500
3,000
3,500
4,000
4,500

Pacific Ocean
Atlantic Ocean
Indian Ocean
Arctic Ocean
S. China Sea
Caribbean Sea
Mediterranean Sea
Bering Sea
Gulf of Mexico
Sea of Okhotsk
Sea of Japan

Radioactive Isotopes

Isotope	Decay Product	Half-life (years)	Is Used to Date
Rubidium-87	Strontium-87	50 billion	Very old rocks
Thorium-232	Lead-208	14 billion	Very old rocks
Uranium-238	Lead-206	4.5 billion	Old rocks and fossils in the rocks
Potassium-40	Argon-40	1.3 billion	Old rocks and fossils in the rocks
Uranium-235	Lead-207	713 million	Old rocks and fossils in the rocks
Carbon-14	Nitrogen-14	5,730	Fossils less than 50,000 years old

World Crude Oil Reserves, 1990 (in billion barrels)

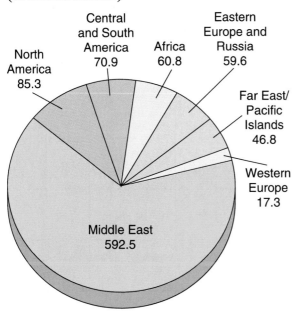

North America 85.3
Central and South America 70.9
Africa 60.8
Eastern Europe and Russia 59.6
Far East/Pacific Islands 46.8
Western Europe 17.3
Middle East 592.5

World Natural Gas Reserves, 1990 (in trillion cubic meters)

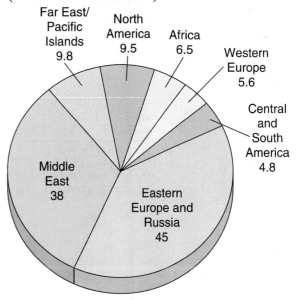

Far East/Pacific Islands 9.8
North America 9.5
Africa 6.5
Western Europe 5.6
Central and South America 4.8
Middle East 38
Eastern Europe and Russia 45

Human Causes and Health Effects of Major Air Pollutants

Pollutant	Human Causes	Health Effects
Carbon monoxide	Transportation; Industry	*Short-term intense exposure:* headache, dizziness, decreased energy, death *Long-term exposure:* stress on cardiovascular system, decreased tolerance to exercise, heart attack
Sulfur oxides	Home, business and power plant energy use; Industry	*Short-term intense exposure:* inflammation of respiratory tract, aggravation of asthma *Long-term exposure:* emphysema, bronchitis
Nitrogen oxides	Transportation; Home, business and power plant energy use	*Short-term intense exposure:* irritation of lungs *Long-term exposure:* bronchitis
Particulates	Home, business, and power plant energy use; Industry	*Long-term exposure:* Irritation of respiratory system, cancer
Hydrocarbons	Transportation	Unknown
Photochemical oxidants	Transportation; Home, business, and power plant energy use (indirectly, through hydrocarbons and nitrogen oxides)	*Short-term intense exposure:* respiratory irritation, eye irration *Long-term exposure:* emphysema

Properties of Selected Common Minerals

Mineral	Color	Streak	Type of Cleavage	Hardness	Specific Gravity	Symbol
Metals/Non-metals						
gold	rich yellow	yellow	none (fracture)	2.5–3	19.3	Au
silver	white	white	none (fracture)	2.5–3	10–12	Ag
iron	steel-gray	gray	3 directions	2.5–3	10–12	Fe
graphite	silver-gray to black	grayish-to black	1 direction	1–2	2.3	C
sulfur	light yellow	white to yellow	indistinct	1.5–2.5	2	S
Sulfides						
galena	bluish lead gray	lead gray	3 directions	2.5–2.7	7.5	PbS
sphalerite	colorless to yellowish-black	yellowish	6 directions	3.5–4	4	ZnS
pyrite	rich yellow	greenish-black	none (fracture)	6–6.5	5	FeS_2
Oxides						
bauxite	white to red-brown	white to red-brown	poor	1–3	2.0–2.5	$Al(OH)_2$
magnetite	black	black	none (fracture)	6	5.2	Fe_3O_4
Halides						
halite	colorless and various colors	colorless	3 directions	2.5	2.1	NaCl
fluorite	variety of colors	colorless	4 directions	4	3–3.2	CaF_2

Mineral	Color	Streak	Type of Cleavage	Hardness	Specific Gravity	Symbol
Carbonates						
calcite	variety of colors	colorless	3 directions; not 90°	3	2.7	$CaCO_3$
Sulfates						
gypsum	yellowish, reddish	colorless	2 directions	2	2.3	$CaSO_4 \cdot 2H_2O$
Phosphates						
apatite	variety of colors	white	indistinct	5	3.2	$Ca_5(PO_4)_3$ (Cl,F)
Silicates						
quartz	variety of colors	colorless	none (fracture)	7	2.6	SiO_2
talc	white, greenish-gray	colorless	1 direction	1	2.8	$Mg_3Si_4O_{10}$ $(OH)_2$
olivine	yellowish, greenish	white to light green	none (fracture)	6.5	3.5	$(MgFe)_2$ SiO_4
serpentine	greenish	colorless	none (fracture)	2–5	2.2-2.6	$Mg_3Si_2O_5$ $(OH)_4$
hornblende	green to black	gray to white	2 directions	5–6	3.4	complex structure
muscovite (mica)	white to dark	colorless	1 direction	2–2.5	2.8	complex structure
topaz	variety of colors	colorless	3 directions	8	3.5	complex structure

Glossary

A simple, phonetic spelling is given for words in this book that may be unfamiliar or hard to pronounce.

Stressed syllables are printed in capital letters. Sometimes a word has two stressed syllables. The syllable with the primary stress is printed in full capitals. The syllable with the secondary stress is printed in small capitals.

Example: *Asteroid* is pronounced AS tuh ROYD.

Most of the time, the phonetic spelling can be interpreted without referring to the key. The key to the right gives the pronunciations for letters that are commonly used for more than one sound.

Pronunciation Key

a	cat	ih	pin
ah	hot	oh	grow
ai	care	oo	rule, music
ah	all	ow	now
ay	say, age	oy	voice
ee	meet	u	put
eh	let	uh	sun, about
eye	ice or by	ur	term

A **abrasion** Mechanical weathering process that is the result of gravity, wind, or moving water, causing rocks to rub against each other, wear each other down, or break into smaller pieces. (pp. 241, 282)

absolute age The approximate age in years of particular rocks, determined through radiometric dating. (p. 83)

absolute magnitude The brightness a star would appear if it were a standard distance (32.6 light-years) from Earth. (p. 592)

abyssal plain (uh BIHS uhl) Flat areas, covered with layers of sediment, deep on the ocean floor. (p. 374)

adapted Characteristic of a species that makes it able to survive in its environment. (p. 290)

air mass One of six different types of weather conditions in a given area: continental polar, continental tropical, maritime polar, maritime tropical, equatorial, and arctic. (p. 440)

air pressure The pressure exerted by air in a particular area. (p. 397)

alluvial fan (uh LOO vee uhl) Fan-shaped type of sediment deposit formed when a river flows down a steep mountain slope onto a broad, flat, desert area. (p. 268)

altitude A location's distance above sea level. (p. 464)

anthracite (AN thruh syt) The fourth stage of coal formation, anthracite is about 90 percent carbon, generating a great amount of heat while releasing few pollutants. (p. 493)

anticline (ANT ee klyn) A fold that produces an upward bulge. (p. 115)

anticyclonic wind pattern Air, rushing away from a high-pressure center, creates a clockwise wind pattern, resulting in warm, sunny weather. (p. 445)

aphelion (uh FEEL yuhn) The place in the Earth's orbit where Earth is farthest away from the sun. (p. 539)

apogee (AP uh JEE) Point in the moon's orbit where it is farthest away from the Earth. (p. 547)

apparent magnitude The measure of a star's brightness as it appears from Earth. (p. 592)

aquifer (AH kwih fur) A groundwater-containing layer of rock or sediment. (p. 331)

archipelago A chain or cluster of islands. (p. 35)

asteroid (AS tuh ROYD) A small, irregularly-shaped body that revolves around the sun in the same direction as the planets do. (p. 575)

asteroid belt In the gap between Mars and Jupiter, a large group of asteroids makes up this belt. (p. 575)

asthenosphere (as THEHN uhs FEER) The hot, semi-liquid layer of the earth's mantle below the lithosphere. (p. 57)

atmosphere An envelope of gases surrounding the earth that extends about 1,000 km above the earth's surface. (p. 402)

atoll (A tohl) The ring of coral left behind when a volcanic island has sunk below the surface of the water. (p. 375)

atom The smallest particle of an element, with all the properties of this element, that can combine with other atoms to form a molecule. (p. 161)

atomic number The number of protons in an element's nucleus that identifies the element. (p. 162)

aurora australis In the Southern Hemisphere, the beautiful display of lights in the sky, caused by charged particles carried by solar wind. (p. 562)

aurora borealis In the Northern Hemisphere, the display of beautiful lights in the sky that is caused by a steady stream of solar wind from the sun's corona, which carries charged particles. (p. 562)

axis An imaginary line extending through the Earth from the North Pole to the South Pole, around which the Earth rotates. (p. 537)

B **barometer** (buh RAHM uh tur) Instrument used to measure air pressure. (p. 443)

barred spiral galaxy A galaxy with a spiral shape, with the arms attached to a straight bar shape. (p. 602)

batholith A large pluton that has been exposed at the earth's surface by erosion. (p. 124)

bathymetric map (BATH uh MEH trihk) Topographic map of the ocean floor. (p. 368)

bathyscaph (BATH ih skaf) A small, submarinelike submersible that scientists use to explore the ocean depths. (p. 370)

beach Shoreline formed when sand, gravel, or other sediments accumulate over a long period of time. (p. 272)

bedrock Layer of solid rock that underlies soil, sand, clay, and gravel layers on the earth's surface. (p. 230)

benthos (BEHN thohs) Organisms, such as clams, crabs, seaweeds, and tube worms, that live on the ocean floor. (p. 380)

big bang theory Theory stating that the universe was at one time one giant fireball that exploded; as the matter cooled, the force of gravity pulled particles together to form stars and galaxies. (p. 604)

binary stars The most common type of star group, this is two stars close to each other, that sometimes appear as one bright star. (p. 603)

biodiversity (BY oh dih VURS uh tee) The wide variety of different species in an ecosystem. (p. 517)

biome A large community of plants and animals whose makeup is determined by soil and climate. (p. 36)

biosphere (BY uhs feer) A life-supporting zone extending from the earth's crust into the atmosphere. (p. 24)

bituminous coal (by TOO mihn uhs) Most common type of coal mined and used in the United States; about 85% carbon, it burns cleaner and releases fewer pollutants than lignite. (p. 493)

black hole The remains of a supernova explosion, it is a dense object with very strong gravity from which nothing can escape, including light. (p. 599)

C **capture theory** Idea proposing that the moon formed elsewhere and was trapped by the Earth's gravity. (p. 547)

carbonation Chemical weathering process produced by carbonic acid, where the rock develops small pits or holes; common in rocks like limestone and marble. (p. 243)

cast Fossil formed by minerals in water that build up in a mold. (p. 295)

cementation Sedimentary process where sediment spaces fill and bind together with minerals. (p. 221)

Cenozoic Era (SEE nuh ZOH ihk) The time from the end of the Mesozoic Era (66 million years ago) up to the present. (p. 85)

chemical bond The force of attraction that holds atoms or ions together. (p. 163)

chemical change Change in the chemical identity of a substance. (p. 168)

chemical formula A combination of chemical symbols used to represent compounds. (p. 166)

chemical rock Rock formed when minerals come out of solution and crystallize. (p. 223)

chemical symbol A one- or two-letter abbreviation for every element, used by scientists worldwide. (p. 166)

chemical weathering Type of weathering that changes the chemical composition of rock. (p. 242)

chromosphere (KROH muh sfeer) The middle layer of the sun's atmosphere, made up mostly of streams of hydrogen gas. (p. 561)

cinder cone volcano A volcano formed from ash, cinder, and other volcanic debris. (p. 147)

cirque (SURK) Large, bowl-shaped hole in the side of a mountain where a glacier began. (p. 276)

clastic rock Rock that is formed when particles of country rock and mineral grains compact together. (p. 222)

cleavage Property of a mineral when it breaks along a flat plane or surface. (p. 194)

climate Characteristic weather for a region over a long period of time, determined by latitude, altitude, distance from the ocean, topography, and prevailing winds. (p. 463)

climate zone A region with a particular range of temperatures, based on latitude. (p. 469)

cold front Weather boundary characterized by strong gusts of wind and rain where cold, dry air displaces warm, moist air. (p. 441)

comet An object made of ice that travels in an orbit around the sun. (p. 578)

compaction Sedimentary rock process where the water is squeezed out of the spaces, and the particles of sediment pack tightly together. (p. 221)

composite volcano A volcano that contains alternating layers of volcanic debris and lava. (p. 147)

composting Creating a garden area where organic material can break down to be reused in the soil as fertilizer. (p. 527)

compound A substance made of two or more chemically combined elements. (p. 165)

compression Type of stress in the earth's crust where rocks are squeezed together. (p.114)

conchoidal Property of a mineral when it breaks and forms a curving surface. (p. 194)

condensation Phase change that occurs when water vapor rises in the air, then cools, forming liquid droplets which make clouds. (p. 320)

condensation nuclei In the atmosphere, small particles of salt, dust, or smoke around which water condenses when the relative humidity reaches 100 percent. (p. 423)

conduction The transfer of heat energy or electrons between objects in direct contact. (p. 398)

conservation The careful use of our natural resources. (p. 523)

constellation Star pattern seen in the sky in the shape of a person, animal, or object. (p. 603)

continent One of the seven major landmasses of the earth. (p. 32)

continental drift The theory that all the world's landmasses were at one time joined together in a supercontinent called Pangaea. (p. 91)

continental glacier A glacier that covers a large area in a polar region. (p. 274)

continental margin The downward-sloping part of a continent that extends out into the ocean. (p. 372)

continental rise Part of the continental margin; the area from the continental slope to the deep ocean floor. (p. 373)

continental shelf The gently-sloping surface of the continental margin, extending underwater from the shoreline. (p. 373)

continental slope Part of the continental margin, at the edge of the continental shelf, that drops off steeply to the ocean floor, where the boundary between the continental crust and ocean crust occurs. (p. 373)

contour line Line on a topographic map connecting points that have the same elevation. (p. 45)

control A test where all variables are identical to the experiment being performed except the independent variable. (p. 7)

convection (kuhn VEHKT shuhn) Circular flow of matter in currents in a heated material. (p. 59)

convection zone About 400 000 km from the core of the sun, the area where matter expands and rises, then cools, becomes denser, and sinks back. (p. 560)

convergent boundary Boundary where two plates collide. (p. 100)

core The innermost layer of the earth, composed primarily of iron and nickel. Also, the innermost layer of the sun where nuclear fusion occurs. (pp. 56, 560)

Coriolis effect (KOR ee OH lihs) Caused by the earth's rotation, this effect makes the earth's winds and ocean currents bend and curve. (p. 345)

corona (kuh ROH nuh) The outermost layer of the sun. (p. 560)

crater A hollowed-out area at the top of a volcano; or, a circular indentation on the surface of the moon. (pp. 145, 546)

creep Slow, steady movement along an active fault. Also, the gradual downslope movement of soil. (pp. 140, 264)

crest The highest point of a wave. (p. 352)

crust Outermost layer of the earth that covers the mantle. (p. 56)

cumulonimbus cloud (KYOO myuh low NIM buhs) A tall, dark, puffy rain cloud. (p. 425)

cumulus cloud (KYOO myuh luhs) Large, puffy cloud common on a warm summer day. (p. 424)

current The flow and movement of water in the ocean. (p. 345)

cyclone A hurricane that forms over the Indian Ocean. (p. 450)

cyclonic wind pattern (sy CLAH nihk) Counter-clockwise wind pattern that surrounds a low-pressure area, creating hurricanes and major winter storms. (p.445)

 data Information from which analyses and conclusions can be made. (p. 3)

database A large collection of organized material in a computer. (p. 520)

daughter theory Idea that suggests that the moon was formed from a piece of the Earth that split off at some time. (p. 547)

decay Process where an atom of a radioactive isotope breaks down and releases matter and energy from its nucleus. (p. 300)

deflation Process of wind carrying away loose sediment. (p. 282)

deforestation The systematic cutting down of forests. (p. 518)

deformation A change in the shape or structure of the earth's crustal material resulting from bending, folding, breaking, sliding, or tilting. (p. 113)

delta Triangular-shaped sediment deposit formed at the mouth of a river. (p. 268)

density Measure of how much matter exists in a given volume; density = mass/volume. (p. 16)

dependent variable The observed variable in an experiment that changes in response to the independent variable. (p. 7)

deposition (DEHP uh ZIH shuhn) The buildup of sediments on the bottoms of lakes, valleys, and the ocean floor. (pp. 78, 263)

desert pavement Hard, pebbly surface that is left behind after the wind carries away any loose sediment. (p. 282)

dew point Certain temperature at which the air becomes saturated with water vapor. (p. 416)

diatomaceous earth (DY uh tuh MAY shuhs) Powdery material, made of glasslike skeletons of diatoms. (p. 384)

diurnal tides Pattern of tides with one high tide and one low tide per day. (p. 357)

divergent boundary Any boundary where plates move away from each other, and where new crust is being created. (p. 100)

divide A ridge separating different drainage systems. (p. 325)

domesticated Characteristic of plants and animals that are cared for by agricultural societies. (p. 511)

Doppler effect A change in wave frequency, and therefore in the pitch of sound, caused by movement of either the source or the receiver of the sound. (p. 604)

drainage system A pattern of streams and rivers that flows into the ocean. (p. 325)

dry climate Located on both sides of the equator between 15° and 30° north and south latitudes, this climate includes some of the earth's driest deserts. Dry climates also occur in the middle latitudes between 35° and 50° north latitudes in western North America and the Asian interior, and are characterized by little rainfall, cold winters, and warm to very hot summers. (p. 470)

ductile Able to change shape without breaking. (p. 113)

dune A deposit formed from windblown sand. (p. 283)

E **earthquake** Movement of the earth's crust that occurs when rocks suddenly break and release stored energy. (p. 133)

eclipse (ee KLIHPS) The shadow caused when one astronomical body passes between the sun and another body. (p. 552)

ecosystem (EEK oh SIHS tuhm) Area in which living things interact with each other and the environment. (p. 381)

elastic limit The amount of stress a material can absorb without breaking apart. (p. 134)

electromagnetic spectrum The entire range of visible and invisible electromagnetic waves, from radio waves to gamma rays. (p. 586)

electromagnetic wave Wave of energy that makes up the electromagnetic spectrum. (p. 586)

electron (ee LEHK trahn) A subatomic particle with a negative charge located outside an atom's nucleus. (p. 161)

elevation Distance measured above sea level. (p. 34)

elliptical Referring to an object's orbit in space, which is not in a perfect circle, but rather in the shape of an ellipse. (p. 572)

elliptical galaxy A galaxy shaped like a slightly flattened circle. (p. 602)

El Niño A disturbance of ocean winds and currents off the western coast of South America, occurring every three to eight years, that warms coastal waters, killing many organisms and starving many fishes. (pp. 350, 478)

endangered species Particular species of plant or animal that is in immediate danger of becoming extinct. (p. 517)

epicenter The point on the earth's surface directly above the focus of an earthquake. (p. 134)

epoch Subdivision of a geological period on the geologic timescale. (p. 85)

equator The imaginary line around the earth's center, equidistant from the poles, and perpendicular to the earth's axis of rotation. (p. 38)

equinox (EE kwuh nahks) The first day of spring or fall, when the sun is directly over the equator, called the vernal equinox (spring) or autumnal equinox (fall). (p. 540)

era The largest division of the earth's history; the Precambrian, Paleozoic, Mesozoic, and Cenozoic Eras are measured in millions of years. (p. 84)

erosion (ee ROH zhuhn) Process by which smaller particles of rock are displaced by moving water, wind, or ice. (pp. 77, 263)

estivate (EHS tuh vayt) What amphibians, such as frogs, do when they burrow in the mud and remain dormant for the winter. (p. 541)

estuary (EHS choo AIR ee) A bay or inlet of low salinity, where river water mixes with ocean water. (p. 340)

evaporation Phase change when liquid water turns to vapor by the heat energy of the sun. (p. 320)

evaporite Sedimentary rock formed from the evaporation of ocean or lake waters. (p. 223)

evolution A change in a living population over time. (p. 290)

exfoliation (EHKS foh lee AY shun) Process where outer layers of granite expand, crack, and flake off; caused by extreme changes in temperature. (p. 239)

exosphere Outermost layer of the atmosphere that extends several thousand kilometers above the earth. (p. 403)

exponential growth (EHKS poh NEHN shuhl) Growth of a population that doubles its numbers at regular, predictable intervals. (p. 513)

extinction The dying out of a species that is unable to adapt to its environment. (p. 290)

extrusive rock Igneous rock formed from lava that solidifies on or near the earth's surface. (p. 215)

F

fault A fracture in the earth's crust where movement has occurred. (p. 117)

fault plane The fracture line of a fault. (p. 117)

fissure Long crack in soil or rock resulting from an earthquake. (p. 141)

floodplain Valley area surrounding the banks of a river that has been built up from sediment left by repeated flooding. (pp. 267, 269)

fluorescence (flor EHS uhns) Property of a mineral that glows when exposed to ultraviolet light. (p. 196)

focus The point along a fault where rocks first break and move, causing an earthquake. (p.134)

fog A cloud that forms on the earth's surface. (p. 426)

folding The bending of rock layers resulting from compressional stress. (p. 115)

foliated rock Striped-looking, metamorphic rock with grains arranged in parallel bands. (p. 228)

food chain Sequence of organisms through which food energy passes. (381)

footwall Formed from the rocks below the fault plane. (p. 117)

fossil Remains or traces of an organism that lived in the past. (p. 79)

fossil fuel An energy source made from the buried remains of decayed plants and animals that lived hundreds of millions of years ago: coal, oil, and natural gas. (p. 492)

fossil record Record of life on the earth provided by fossils. (p. 294)

fracture Property of a mineral that breaks, leaving an uneven or splintered surface. (p. 194)

front The boundary where two different air masses meet, causing sudden weather changes. (p. 441)

G

galaxy A very large collection of stars, nebulae, gases, dust, and planets, that travels through space bound together by gravity. (p. 601)

gem Rare, beautiful mineral that is cut and polished; used for jewelry and ornamentation. (p. 203)

geode Mineral rock formed when hot, mineral-containing liquid inside the rock evaporates, leaving the rock's interior lined with mineral crystals. (p. 187)

geologic time The time scale of the history of the earth and its life. (p. 76)

geothermal energy Alternative energy source that comes from heat energy within the earth, such as water that has been heated near igneous rocks by magma. (p. 499)

geyser Vent in the ground where superheated water builds up pressure and finally blows out of the small surface opening. (p. 332)

gibbous moon Phase of the moon when more than half of the side that faces Earth is lighted. (p. 551)

glacier Formed when the amount of snow is so great that all of the snow is unable to melt. (p. 274)

Gondwanaland (gahnd WAH nuh LAND) The large southern continent formed when the supercontinent of Pangaea broke apart. (p. 92)

gravity The attracting force between the sun and each planet that exists because of their mass, keeping the planets in their orbits. (p. 572)

greenhouse effect A process that traps energy from the sun by allowing radiant energy to enter a given space, but preventing heat energy from escaping. (p. 408)

groundwater Water beneath the earth's surface that soaked into the ground from rain or melted snow. (p. 329)

gully Channel formed from stream erosion when rainwater produces rills, and the rills join together, flowing downhill and removing topsoil. (p. 266)

guyot (GEE oh) Volcanic island that has stopped growing and been flattened by wave action. (p. 375)

gyre (JY ur) Surface current that flows in a circular pattern: clockwise in the Northern Hemisphere, and counterclockwise in the Southern Hemisphere. (p. 347)

H **habitat** (HAB uh tat) The area where an organism naturally lives in an ecosystem. (p. 379)

hachures (HASH oorz) Short lines used on a map to indicate slopes, their degree, and direction. (p. 46)

hail Type of precipitation that forms when small snow pellets or frozen raindrops collide with supercooled water droplets in a cloud, are caught in upward-rising air, and returned to the thundercloud. (p. 431)

half-life Measurement scientists use to describe how long it takes for half of the atoms in a sample to decay. (p. 300)

hanging wall Formed from the rocks above the fault plane. (p. 117)

heft Property of a mineral that is measured by picking the mineral up and comparing its mass to an equal volume of another mineral. (p. 194)

heliocentric Descriptive of something that is centered around the sun, as a model of the solar system. (p. 572)

hemispheres The halves of the earth north and south of the equator; also the halves of the earth east and west of the prime meridian. (p. 38)

highland Bright, mountainous terrain on the surface of the moon. (p. 546)

high tide Highest level the ocean water reaches on the shore. (p. 356)

hominid (HAHM uh nihd) First humanlike organism that appeared between 4 and 8 million years ago. (p. 307)

Homo erectus First upright-walking ancestor of modern man, whose fossils date back about 1.6 million years. (p. 307)

Homo sapiens Species of human that evolved from Homo erectus, and appeared between 500,000 and 130,000 years ago. (p. 307)

horizon One of the three boundary layers of mature soils. Also, the line where the Earth seems to meet the sky. (pp. 248, 540)

horn Sharp peak formed when several cirques are close together. (p. 276)

hot spot An area of frequent volcanic activity on the earth's surface, which develops from an especially hot area of the mantle. (p. 148)

humid cold climate Found in the northern temperate zone, climate characterized by short, warm, wet summers, and long, very cold winters. (p. 471)

humidity Amount of water vapor that is contained in the air. (p. 415)

humus (HYOO muhs) The uppermost, nutrient-rich layer of soil. (p. 248)

hurricane A violent, tropical storm with sustained winds of at least 120 km/h that forms over warm oceans near the equator. (p. 450)

hydroelectric energy Alternative energy resource that produces electricity from water moving through dams; also uses tidal energy to make electricity, but this process has limited use. (p. 499)

hygrometer A device that measures humidity using human hair. (p. 418)

hypothesis (hy PAHTH uh sihs) A possible answer or solution to a particular problem, based on current information. (p. 5)

I **igneous rock** (IHG nee uhs) Rocks produced by the cooling and solidifying of magma. (p. 215)

impermeable Describes a rock with spaces that do not easily conduct water. (p. 329)

independent variable A manipulated variable in an experiment that causes the change in the dependent variable. (p. 7)

inertia The tendency of an object to remain at rest or in motion until acted upon by an external force. (p. 573)

infer To make a conclusion based on available data. (p. 4)

inner planets Mercury, Venus, Earth, and Mars, all of which have a liquid core made of nickel and iron, and a rocky mantle and crust. (p. 570)

interglacial Period of warming that separated the ice ages, when glaciers melted and retreated. (p. 477)

international date line The imaginary line of longitude where the date changes, directly opposite the prime meridian. (p. 39)

intrusive rock Igneous rock formed when magma cools and solidifies beneath the earth's surface. (p. 215)

invertebrate Animal without a backbone common during the early Paleozoic Era. (p. 304)

ion (EYE ahn) An atom or group of atoms having an electric charge as a result of losing or gaining one or more electrons. (p. 161)

ionic bond (eye AHN ihk) A chemical bond between a metal and a nonmetal in which electrons are transferred from one atom to another. (p. 163)

ionosphere (eye AHN oh sfihr) An indistinct layer of air within the upper mesosphere and the thermosphere where solar radiation strips atoms and molecules of their electrons, which then become ions. These ions reflect light and radio signals, and bounce them back to earth. (p. 404)

irregular galaxy The least common type of galaxy, without a regular shape or form. (p. 602)

isobar Line on a weather map that connects points of equal atmospheric pressure. (p. 443)

isobath (EYE soh bath) Contour line on a bathymetric map. (p. 368)

isostasy (eye SAHS teh see) The balance of gravity and buoyancy in the earth's crust. (p. 127)

isotherm (EYE soh thurm) Curving line on a weather map that connects points with the same temperature. (p. 457)

isotope (EYE soh tohp) Atoms of the same element having different numbers of neutrons, with resultant different atomic masses. (p. 162)

J **jet stream** A narrow ribbon of winds located 8 000 to 12 000 m above the earth's surface. (p. 445)

K **kettle lake** Lake formed when a block of ice breaks off from a glacier, is buried, and melts. (p. 277)

kilogram Basic SI unit of mass; abbreviated kg. (p. 15)

kingdom One of the five major divisions into which all living things can be classified. (p. 291)

L **laccolith** A bulge or dome-shaped formation resulting from magma intruding into layers of existing rocks. (p. 217)

landform Main feature of the earth's surface. (p. 34)

landslide Type of mass movement where large amounts of rock and soil move rapidly downhill. (p. 264)

lateral fault A fault characterized by side-to-side movement, caused by shear stress, with little or no up-and-down movement. (p. 117)

laterite (LAYT er YT) Rusty, red tropical soil, heavily leached by frequent rains, with a high content of iron oxide. (p. 257)

latitude Distance measured in degrees north and south of the equator. (pp. 39, 463)

Laurasia (lawr AY zhuh) The large northern continent that was formed when the supercontinent of Pangaea broke apart. (p. 92)

lava Hot liquid rock (magma) which reaches the earth's surface. (p. 144)

layer A single thickness of a material covering a surface, usually horizontally. (p. 55)

leaching Chemical weathering process where rainwater carries dissolved minerals from the surface soil deeper into the ground, resulting in mineral-poor surface soil with a mineral-rich layer below it. (p. 243)

levee Sediment that is deposited in a long ridge along a mature or old riverbank during floods. (p. 269)

light-year The distance light travels in one year at a speed of 310 000 km per second, about 9.5 trillion km. (p. 591)

lignite The second stage of coal development, lignite is a soft brown coal that contains about 40% carbon, and releases harmful pollutants when burned; used in some European countries. (p. 493)

liter Metric unit of volume; abbreviated L. (p. 15)

lithification Process where sediment is hardened into rock. (p. 221)

lithosphere (LITH uhs FEER) The cool, solid, outer layer of the earth extending to a depth of about 100 km. (p. 57)

littoral zone (LIHT uh ruhl) Ocean life zone in the shallow water area between the low-tide line and the high-tide line. (p. 380)

local group A large cluster of galaxies including the Milky Way galaxy. (p. 603)

loess Fine-grained angular particles, formed from rocks during the last ice age, that are deposited by wind erosion to make up prairie soil. (pp. 255, 283)

longitude (LAHN jih tood) Imaginary lines, measured in degrees, running from pole to pole; also called meridians. (p. 39)

longitudinal wave A wave consisting of a series of compressions and rarefactions, that moves through a medium in the same direction as the wave is traveling. (p. 135)

longshore current A continuous back-and-forth motion of wave action that forms a zig-zag current parallel to the shore. (p. 349)

low tide Lowest level that the ocean water reaches on the shore. (p. 356)

lunar eclipse When the moon is darkened by the Earth's shadow blocking sunlight from reaching the moon. (p. 552)

luster The way a mineral reflects light from its surface. (p. 193)

M **magnetism** Property of a mineral containing iron or nickel that makes the mineral attracted to magnets. (p. 196)

magnetosphere An area in the thermosphere where solar particles are trapped; contains a belt of charged particles called the Van Allen radiation belt. (p. 404)

magnitude (MAG nih tood) A number that indicates the brightness of a star; the smaller the number, the brighter the star. (p. 592)

main-sequence A star that ranges from hot and bright to cool and dim. (p. 593)

mantle The layer of rock in the earth that extends to a depth of about 3,000 km. (p. 56)

maria (MAR ee uh) Dark, broad, flat plains on the surface of the moon. (p. 546)

mass The scientific measurement of the amount of matter that an object contains. (p. 15)

mass number A number used to identify different isotopes, containing the total number of protons and neutrons in an atom's nucleus. (p. 162)

mass movement The action of gravity moving rocks or soil down a slope. (p. 264)

matter Any object or substance that has mass and takes up space. (p. 159)

meander Series of curves formed when a mature river erodes and shifts the sides of its banks. (p. 267)

mechanical weathering Process of weathering resulting from ice wedging, temperature changes, wind and water abrasion, and the abrasions of animals and plants. (pp. 240, 241)

meniscus (meh NIHS kuhs) The curved surface of a liquid in a graduated cylinder. (p. 15)

mesosphere A layer of the atmosphere that extends from the edge of the stratosphere to about 65 km. (p. 403)

Mesozoic Era (MEHZ uh ZOH ihk) The era in the earth's history when dinosaurs were the dominant life form, from about 245 million years ago to 66 million years ago. (p. 85)

metamorphic rock Rock that has undergone a change in structure, appearance, and composition from its original state, as a result of heat, pressure, and chemical action. (p. 226)

metamorphism Changes in the structure, appearance, and composition of rock that occur beneath the earth's surface. (p. 226)

meteor The light in the night sky that results from a meteoroid entering the earth's atmosphere. (p. 577)

meteorite (MEE tee uh RYT) A meteoroid that does not completely burn up in the atmosphere, and lands on the earth's surface. (p. 578)

meteoroid (MEE tee uh ROYD) An object entering the Earth's atmosphere, made from a chunk of rock or metal smaller than an asteroid, which causes a meteor (shooting star). (p. 577)

meter Basic SI unit of length; abbreviated m. (p. 14)

microclimate Climate that exists in a very small, limited area. (p. 474)

mineral Naturally-occurring inorganic solid with a definite chemical composition and a particular crystalline structure. (p. 185)

model A small-scale representation of a larger object. (p. 10)

Moho (Mohorovičić discontinuity) The boundary between the earth's crust and mantle, about 30 km below the surface. (p. 62)

Mohs' scale Scale of hardness of ten minerals that is used to measure the relative hardness of minerals. (p. 195)

mold Fossil impression left in rock by the hard parts of an organism. (p. 295)

molecule (MAHL ih KYOOL) Two or more chemically bonded atoms; the smallest part of a compound with all the properties of that compound. (p. 164)

monocline (MAHN oh klyn) Type of folding where rock layers on one side of a bend are higher than on the other side. (p. 115)

monsoon A heavy, seasonal rainstorm, particularly in southern Asia. (p. 451)

moraine Sediment that is left when a glacier retreats. (p. 277)

mudflow Mass movement caused when heavy rains mix with sediment and wash down a slope. (p. 264)

N **natural gas** A fossil fuel that is a gaseous mixture of hydrocarbons, often found above petroleum deposits. (p. 494)

natural resource Material from the environment that people use to carry on their daily lives. (p. 489)

natural selection Darwin's theory which states that the traits of a species as a whole change over time. (p. 290)

neap tide Daily tide cycle with the least difference between high and low tides. (pp. 358, 553)

nebula (NEHB yoo luh) A great cloud of dust and gas where stars are born. (p. 596)

nekton Freely-swimming organisms such as fishes, dolphins, squids, and whales. (p. 380)

neritic zone Ocean life zone extending from the low-tide line to the edge of the continental shelf, with plenty of sunlight, fairly constant water temperature, and abundant ocean life. (p. 380)

neutron (NOO trahn) A subatomic particle located in an atom's nucleus, having no electric charge, with a mass similar to that of a proton. (p. 161)

neutron star The tiny core of star that remains after a supernova explosion. (p. 599)

nitrogen cycle Closed cycle in which the total amount of nitrogen on the earth is kept constant. Nitrogen is removed from the air to combine with other elements to form nitrogen compounds, which are used by organisms and then returned to the soil or released into the air. (p. 395)

nitrogen fixation Part of the nitrogen cycle where nitrogen is removed from the air to combine with other elements, forming useful nitrogen compounds. (p. 395)

nonrenewable resource A natural resource, such as petroleum, that cannot be replaced by natural processes. (p. 489)

normal fault A fault where the hanging wall moves downward in relation to the footwall, as a result of tension. (p. 117)

nuclear fission (FIHSH uhn) Controversial alternative energy resource where the nucleus of an atom of uranium is split, producing a great amount of energy. (p. 500)

nuclear fusion The energy process that takes place in the sun where two or more atoms' nuclei join together, releasing an enormous amount of energy. (p. 559)

nucleus (NOO klee uhs) The central region of an atom where neutrons and protons are located. (p. 161)

O **occluded front** (uh KLOOD uhd) Boundary where a cold front overtakes a warm front, producing showers. (p. 442)

optical telescope A telescope that uses a large lens or mirror to gather light rays and focus them, with smaller lenses to magnify the image. (pp. 25, 587)

orbit The path that one body takes as it revolves around another body in space. (p. 539)

ore Mineral-rich rock deposit containing usable amounts of metal; the metal is removed from the ore by the process of smelting. (pp. 200, 489)

organic matter A substance in the soil made from living or dead organisms containing carbon. (p. 178)

organic rock Sedimentary rock, like limestone or coal, that is formed from the remains of living things. (p. 223)

organism The highest level of cell organization. All organisms carry out life processes. (p. 23)

outer planets Jupiter, Saturn, Uranus, Neptune, and Pluto. (p. 570)

outwash The sorted and layered glacial deposit formed when the heaviest sediments drop out first. (p. 277)

outwash plain Deltalike area at the front of a glacier, formed when the melting water deposits sediments. (p. 277)

oxbow lake Type of lake formed when an old river cuts across a meander, and sediments build up at both ends of the meander, cutting it off from the rest of the river. (p. 267)

oxidation Chemical weathering process where oxygen in the air combines with iron in a rock to form rust (iron oxide). (p. 242)

oxygen-carbon dioxide cycle Closed cycle where the amount of carbon and oxygen is kept constant. Carbon moves through the atmosphere and into the earth as fossil fuels, in soil, and the oceans; oxygen is released into the air by plants and green algae. (p. 394)

ozone (OH zohn) Gas that forms a layer in the stratosphere, protecting the earth from excessive ultraviolet radiation. (p. 403)

ozone depletion Chlorofluorocarbons, released into the air in aerosols and air conditioners, break down the layer of ozone that protects the earth from ultraviolet radiation. (p. 409)

P **Paleozoic Era** (PAY lee UH ZOH ihk) Second era in the earth's history, from about 640 million years ago to about 245 million years ago, when plants and animals began to live on land. (p. 84)

Pangaea (pan JEE uh) The giant supercontinent where all the world's landmasses were once joined. (p. 91)

parallax (PAIR uh laks) An apparent change in the position of an object caused by a change in position of the observer. (p. 591)

parent rock The rock that weathers and breaks down into smaller fragments to produce soil. (p. 246)

peat The first stage in the formation of coal, composed of partially decayed plant fibers, and burned for heat in parts of Europe. (p. 493)

penumbra (pee NUHM bruh) In an eclipse, an area of partial shadow caused by the Earth, moon, or other body. (p. 552)

perigee (PEHR uh JEE) Point in the moon's orbit where it is closest to the Earth. (p. 547)

perihelion (pur uh HEEL yuhn) The point in the Earth's orbit where it comes closest to the sun. (p. 539)

period The subdivision of a geologic era. (p. 85)

periodic table A tabular arrangement of the elements according to their atomic numbers; elements with similar properties are in the same column. (p. 176)

period of revolution The time it takes a planet to complete one revolution. (p. 573)

permafrost Permanently frozen, deep layer of subsoil found in the polar regions. (p. 257)

permeability Characteristic that measures how easily water flows through a rock. (p. 329)

petrified (PEHT ruh fyd) Characteristic of bone, wood, or other living material where the matter making up the parts of the once-living thing becomes replaced by mineralized deposits, which eventually turn to stone. (p. 295)

petrochemicals Useful chemical compounds produced from petroleum or natural gas. (p. 495)

petroleum Also known as crude oil, a liquid mixture of hydrocarbons, a fossil fuel made from the decayed remains of once-living plants and animals. (p. 494)

phase change When a substance in a solid, liquid, or gas phase changes from one phase to another (i.e., from gas to liquid), without altering its chemical composition. (p.169)

photosphere (FOHT uh sfeer) The normally visible layer of the sun's atmosphere, on which sunspots are sometimes seen from Earth. (p. 561)

photosynthesis Process by which plants use energy from sunlight and raw materials from air and water to make glucose to obtain energy. (p. 322)

physical change A change in a substance's physical properties but not in its chemical identity. (p.168)

plankton A collection of small or microscopic plant organisms that floats on or near the surface of salt or fresh water, producing much of the available oxygen in the atmosphere. (pp. 37, 380)

plasma The fourth phase of matter having some properties of a gas and some unique properties. Formed at very high temperatures. (p. 170)

plasticity Condition of some of the earth's material which is soft and flowing, but not completely liquid. (p. 57)

plateau Flat, elevated area of the earth's crust. (p. 126)

plate tectonics (tehk TAHN ihks) Theory of the formation and movement of the rigid crustal pieces covering the earth's surface. (p. 98)

pluton A raised body of rock formed from magma below the surface of the earth. (p. 124)

podsol Type of forest soil formed as a result of acidic leaching. (p. 254)

polar molecule A molecule whose atoms have a slight negative and positive electric charge. (p. 318)

polar zone Coldest of the three climate zones, located between 60° north and south latitude and the poles. (p. 469)

porosity Percentage of a material's volume that is pore space. (p. 329)

Precambrian Era (pree KAYM bree uhn) First and longest era of the earth's history, from the time of the earth's formation to about 640 million years ago, when many new and different life forms began to appear. (p. 84)

precipitation All forms of water that fall from the atmosphere. Also, the process where liquid in a mineral-containing solution evaporates, leaving the minerals. (pp. 187, 320, 428)

preservation Creating parks, preserves, and reserves to keep the wilderness areas in their natural condition. (p. 522)

prevailing winds Winds that blow from one general direction, frequently carrying rain. (p. 466)

primary wave (or P wave) A seismic wave that travels by back–and–forth movement of rock particles. (pp. 62, 134–135)

prime meridian Zero meridian, passing through Greenwich, England, from which longitude is measured. (p. 39)

principle of superposition Principle stating that younger rock layers are formed on top of older rock layers. (p. 298)

product New substances formed in a chemical reaction. (p. 171)

projection The image of a geometric figure reproduced on a flat surface. (p. 40)

prominence (PRAHM uh nuhnts) Spectacular storms on the sun's surface that may extend 1 million km into space. (p. 562)

proton (PROH tahn) A subatomic particle with a positive charge located in the nucleus of an atom. (p. 161)

protostar A hot, spinning ball of matter that forms in a nebula. (p. 597)

psychrometer (sy KRAHM ih tur) A device that measures humidity by calculating the difference between dry-bulb and wet-bulb temperatures. (pp. 418–419)

 radiation fog Fog that forms when warm air cools. (p. 426)

radiation zone Just outside the sun's core, where heat energy produced in the core radiates outward, spreading from atom to atom. (p. 560)

radio telescope A telescope that picks up radio waves emitted by bodies in space. (pp. 26, 588)

rain shadow The dry region on the leeward side of the mountain, the side facing away from the wind. (p. 467)

reactant The starting materials in a chemical reaction. (p. 171)

reclamation Returning the environment of a mining site to its former natural condition. (p. 491)

recycling Reusing already-used materials, such as aluminum cans. (p. 524)

red giant A cool, medium-bright star. (p. 593)

reflecting telescope A telescope that uses one concave mirror as its objective. (pp. 25, 587)

refraction Bending of a wave caused by the change of speed that occurs when the wave moves from one medium to another. (p. 62)

refracting telescope A telescope that uses a convex lens as its objective. (p. 26)

regolith All of the loose, weathered material, including the soil layer, that covers the earth's surface. (p. 245)

relative age Determining the age of a layer of sedimentary rock, or a fossil in such a layer, by comparing its position to other rock layers around it. (pp. 83, 298)

relative humidity The concentration of water vapor in the air compared to the total amount of water vapor that is possible at a particular temperature. (p. 415)

renewable resource A natural resource, such as trees or soil, that can be replaced by natural cycles or processes. (p. 489)

reservoir Artificial lake formed when a dam is constructed on a river. (p. 326)

restoration Returning a habitat to its natural condition. (p. 523)

reverse fault A fault where the hanging wall moves upward in relation to the footwall, as a result of compression. (p. 117)

revolution In space, the movement of one body around another. (p. 539)

rip current Powerful, narrow stream of water that flows away at a right angle to the shore. (p. 349)

Richter magnitude A number on the Richter scale which reflects the amount of ground motion caused by an earthquake. (p. 136)

rift valley A long, narrow fracture in the earth's crust. (p. 123)

rill (RIHL) A very small channel formed when rainwater flows downhill. (p. 266)

rille A long, narrow valley cutting across a maria on the surface of the moon. (p. 546)

rock cycle Series of processes involving heat, pressure, melting, cooling, and sedimentaion, whereby rocks change from one type to another. (p. 210)

rogue wave The high crest of an enormous wave formed when the crests of two ordinary waves collide and match up, creating a wave with the combined energy of both waves. (p. 355)

rotation The spinning of a body on its axis. (p. 537)

runoff Rainwater that is unable to soak into hard-packed, frozen, or saturated ground. (p. 321)

 salinity (suh LIHN uh tee) A measure of the amount of salt in water (g/kg). (p. 340)

sand bar A spit that extends completely across to the other shore. (p. 272)

scale A proportion used to determine the distance between two points on a map. (p. 43)

scarp Cliff created by sudden earth movements along a fault. (p. 141)

schist Coarse-grained metamorphic rock formed from shale or slate. (p. 226)

scientific method Involves the systemized testing of hypotheses, predictions, and inferences about the scientific world, where scientists constantly exchange ideas and information. (p. 8)

sea-floor spreading The theory claiming that the mid-ocean ridge is a huge crack in the earth's crust where the hot mantle pushes through and spreads the ocean floor apart. (p. 97)

seamount Formed near mid-ocean ridges, a volcanic mountain that rises more than 1,000 meters above the ocean floor. (p. 375)

secondary wave (or S wave) A seismic wave that travels by up–and–down movement of rock. (pp. 62, 134–135)

sediment Particles carried away by erosion. (p. 77)

sedimentary rock Rock formed from layered sediments that pile up and squeeze together, providing clues to the earth's past. (pp. 78, 220)

seismic array (SYZ mihk) Cluster of interconnected seismographs. (p. 65)

seismic wave Shock wave in the earth caused by an earthquake. (pp. 61, 134)

seismograph Instrument used to detect earthquake (seismic) waves. (p. 65)

semidiurnal tides Pattern of tides where there are two high tides and two low tides each day. (p. 357)

shadow zone An area around the earth directly opposite the focus of an earthquake, where no seismic waves can be detected. (p. 63)

shear Type of stress where rocks in the earth's crust are pushing in different horizontal directions. (p. 114)

shield volcano A volcano with a flat, shieldlike top that produces runny, easily-flowing lava. (p. 147)

SI (Système internationale d'unités) The metric system, the most commonly used system of measurement based on the meter. (p. 13)

silicates Rocky materials in the crust and mantle, composed of silicon, oxygen, and other elements, such as aluminum, iron, and magnesium. (p. 56)

sister theory Theory that proposes that the Earth and moon formed at the same time and from the same material. (p. 547)

sleet Type of precipitation formed when raindrops or snowflakes fall through air layers of different temperatures. (p. 430)

slide Rapid downslope movement of soil, debris, and rock. (p. 141)

slope Steepness of a landform. (p. 47)

slump Mass movement caused by weak layers of underlying material moving downslope as a single unit. (p. 264)

smog Air pollution caused by using fossil fuels, which results in air that is unhealthy to breathe. (p. 408)

soil profile A cross section of the layers of soil, such as a hole that is dug in the ground. (p. 248)

solar eclipse When the moon passes between the sun and the Earth, causing the moon's shadow to fall on Earth. (p. 552)

solar energy Energy from the sun used to heat buildings and homes. (p. 502)

solar flare On the sun's surface, a very intense spurt of radiation, lasting from 10 minutes to 1 hour, which interrupts radio communications on Earth. (p. 562)

solar system The Earth and the eight other planets, along with various other bodies that orbit the sun. (p. 559)

solar winds A steady stream of charged particles from the corona of the sun that are responsible for the displays of light in the sky called the aurora borealis and the aurora australis. (p. 562)

solstice In the northern hemisphere, the first day of summer when the noon sun is directly over 23°N; or, the first day of winter when the noon sun is directly over 23°S. (p. 540)

sonar Devices that bounce sound waves off the ocean floor, providing scientists with an accurate image of the ocean-floor topography. (pp. 96, 366)

species (SPEE sheez) The basic unit of classification, the division of a genus, made of very similar organisms that are able to mate and reproduce offspring of the same type. (p. 290)

specific gravity Ratio of a mineral's density compared to the density of water. (p. 194)

spectrograph Tool used to separate light through a prism or diffraction grating. The spectrum is recorded with a camera or electronic detector. (p. 588)

spectroscope An instrument used by scientists that disperses a beam of light into a spectrum of its component wavelengths. (p. 588)

spiral galaxy A pinwheel-shaped galaxy like the Milky Way. (p. 602)

spit A deposit of sediment, extending out from a beach across a bay or inlet. (p. 272)

stalactite An icicle-like mineral form that hangs from cavern ceilings. (p. 331)

stalagmite A pillar of minerals that forms on a cavern floor. (p. 331)

star cluster A group of stars close together, but smaller in number than a galaxy. (p. 603)

stationary front Boundary between two nonmoving air masses, generally causing light rain. (p. 442)

steam fog Fog that forms when cold air moves over warm water. (p. 426)

stratosphere Layer of the atmosphere, between the troposphere and the mesosphere, that contains the ozone layer. (p. 403)

stratus cloud (STRA tuhs) Widespread flat, dull gray clouds that frequently produce rain or drizzle. (p. 424)

streak Colored powder that a mineral leaves on a streak plate. (p. 193)

stress Forces that act on the rocks of the earth's crust, causing movement of the crust, or a change in shape or volume. (p. 114)

stromatolite (stroh MAT uh lyt) Oldest known fossil of moneran that lived about 3,500 million years ago. (p. 303)

subduction (suhb DUHK shuhn) The process of one plate moving under another plate. (p.101)

submarine canyon Canyons made from currents, and cut by rivers that carried great amounts of water and sediments to the ocean during the ice ages. (p. 373)

submersible (suhb MUR suh buhl) Underwater research vessels that enable scientists to explore deep in the ocean. (p. 367)

sunspot Cool, black looking storm areas that occur on the sun's surface. (p. 562)

supergiant A very bright star, ranging from cool to medium hot. (p. 593)

supernova The most violent event known to occur in the universe, it is the explosion of a supergiant. (p. 599)

surface tension Property of liquids that makes their molecules tend to stick together in a stretched, cohesive manner like a membrane. (p. 318)

swell Wave energy that forms a series of smooth, rolling hills of water. (p. 352)

syncline (SIHN klyn) Type of folding where a middle area has sunk below the level of its two sides. (p. 115)

synoptic chart A weather map that shows current weather data from many different locations, using symbols for air temperature, type of storm or cloud cover, wind direction and speed, and atmospheric pressure. (p. 457)

T **temperate zone** Mildest of the three climate zones, lying on both sides of the tropical zone and extending to 60° north and south latitude. (p. 469)

tension Type of stress in the earth's crust where rocks are stretched or pulled apart. (p. 114)

theory A set of facts, based on separate but related hypotheses, explaining the behavior of a particular phenomenon. (p. 9)

thermocline (THUR moh KLYN) Zone of rapid temperature change in ocean water beneath the surface zone. (p. 341)

thermosphere Layer of the atmosphere right below the exosphere. (p. 403)

thrust fault Fault where the hanging wall rides up and over the footwall as a result of compression. (p. 117)

thunderstorm Caused when a cumulonimbus cloud, filled with positive and negative ions, has a great enough difference in charges to cause lightning and thunder. (p. 449)

tide Daily ebb and flow of water levels in the oceans and other large bodies of water. (pp. 356, 553)

till Mixture of different sediment sizes in a moraine. (p. 277)

topography A precise description of the surface features of a particular area, including elevation. (pp. 45, 467)

tornado (tor NAY doh) A whirling, funnel-shaped windstorm, with rotating winds of more than 500 km/h, that moves or skips on a narrow path along the ground. (p. 451)

toxin A chemical with the capacity to damage the health of organisms. (p. 519)

trace fossils Footprints, tracks, trails, and burrows left by animals or early humans. (p. 295)

transducer Device that changes energy from one form to another. (p. 202)

transform boundary Boundary where two plates slide in opposite directions beside each other. (p. 100)

transpiration (TRAN spuh RAY shun) Process where water moves up through a plant, eventually exiting through tiny holes in the leaves. (p. 322)

transverse wave A wave in which matter moves at a right angle to the direction of the wave. (p. 135)

trench A deep valley on the ocean floor. (p. 101)

tributary (TRIHB yoo TAIR ee) A small stream that flows into a larger one. (p. 325)

tropical zone Warmest of the three climate zones, located between latitudes 30°N and 30°S, characterized by high temperatures and heavy amounts of rain. (p. 469)

troposphere (TROH puh sfihr) Life-containing layer of the atmosphere that is closest to the surface of the earth. (pp. 403, 439)

trough (TROF) The lowest point of a wave. (p. 352)

tsunami (soo NAHM ee) A giant ocean wave that travels at speeds over 700 km/h, caused by underwater earthquakes, landslides, or volcanic eruptions. (pp. 142, 354)

typhoon A hurricane that forms over the western Pacific Ocean. (p. 450)

U **umbra** In an eclipse, the blackest part of a shadow cast by the Earth, moon, or other body. (p. 552)

unconformity (UHN kuhn FORM uh tee) A definitive line between two rock layers indicating a break in geologic time. (p. 83)

undertow Type of current formed when water, carried to the shore in waves, pulls back toward the ocean. (p. 349)

universal solvent Another name for water, so-named because it can dissolve more substances than any other liquid. (p. 319)

uplift Process by which parts of the earth's crust are raised up higher than other parts, forming mountains and plateaus. (p. 78)

upwelling In the ocean, the upward movement of cold, deep water. (p. 348)

V **valley glacier** Glacier that forms in a high mountain valley. (p. 274)

Van Allen radiation belt A belt of charged particles that surrounds the earth; a part of the magnetosphere, which is part of the thermosphere. (p. 404)

vent An opening in the earth's surface where volcanic material, gas, or steam emerges. (p. 145)

vertebrate Animal with a backbone that appeared during the Ordovician period. (p. 304)

volcano An opening in the earth's crust that has released molten rock. (p. 144)

volume The amount of space that something occupies. (p. 15)

W **watershed** Surrounding land area that supplies runoff to streams in a drainage system. (p. 325)

warm front Boundary where a warm, less dense air mass overtakes a cold, dense air mass, producing cloudy skies, rain, or snow. (p. 442)

water table The boundary between the zone of aeration and the zone of saturation. (p. 330)

wave The periodic up-and-down motion of a body of water. (p. 351)

wave height The vertical distance measured between a wave's crest and its trough. (p. 352)

wavelength The distance measured from the crest of one wave to the crest of another wave. (p. 352)

weathering The process during which rocks are broken up into smaller particles by the action of water, the atmosphere, and organisms. (pp. 77, 239)

white dwarf A low-magnitude, relatively hot star. (p. 593)

X **x-axis** The horizontal line on a graph. (p. 20)

Y **y-axis** The vertical line on a graph. (p. 20)

Z **zenith** The highest point in the sky, directly overhead. (p. 540)

Index

Acknowledgments

Photographs

Title page iTL Dan McCoy/Rainbow; iTLC NASA; iTR Robert Caputo/Stock, Boston; iTRC Joyce Photographics/Photo Researchers; iB Geoffrey Nilsen*

Contents iiiB Bjorn Bolstad/Photo Researchers; iiiT Ken Karp*; ivC Kevin Schafer/AllStock; ivLB NASA; ivLT Kevin Schafer & Martha Hill/Tom Stack & Associates; ivR Roger Ressmeyer/Starlight; vBC Geoffrey Nilsen*; vBL Geoffrey Nilsen*; vRC M. Long/Visuals Unlimited; vTL Geoff Tompkinson/SPL/Photo Researchers; vTR Larry Lefever/Grant Heilman Photography; viBL Adam Hart-Davis/SPL/Photo Researchers; viBR Douglas Mazonowicz/Gallery of Prehistoric Art; viC Andrew Leitch/Discover Magazine; viTL David M. Dennis/Tom Stack & Associates; viTR Gregory G. Dimijian/Photo Researchers; viiBC Dave Fleetham/Tom Stack & Associates; viiBR Jeff Simon/Bruce Coleman Inc.; viiCR Jan Hinsch/SPL/Photo Researchers; viiL Jeff Foott/DRK Photo; viiTR F. Stuart Westmorland/AllStock; viiiBL Runk-Schoenberger/Grant Heilman Photography; viiiBR Mike Price/Bruce Coleman Inc.; viiiTL Joel W. Rogers/AllStock; viiiTR Gary Withey/Bruce Coleman Inc.; ixBR William McCoy/Rainbow; ixCR Paul Silverman/Fundamental Photographs; ixL Will & Deni McIntyre/AllStock; ixTR K. H. Switak/Photo Researchers; xBL NASA; xR NASA/Jet Propulsion Lab; xTL Jim Ballard/AllStock; xiBCL Ernst Jahn/Bruce Coleman Inc.; xiBL Tom McHugh/Photo Researchers; xiBR Renee Purse/Photo Researchers; xiBRC George Whiteley/Photo Researchers; xiTR NASA; xiiiL Craig Walker/Rainbow; xiiiR Wetmore/Photo Researchers; xivBR Eric Simmons/Stock, Boston; xivL Michael Fogden/Bruce Coleman Inc.; xivTR John Elk/Bruce Coleman Inc.; xvBC Randy Brandon/Peter Arnold, Inc.; xvBL Bill Gallery/Stock, Boston; xvT Geoffrey Nilsen*; xviBC NASA/Peter Arnold, Inc.; xviBL Breck P. Kent/Animals, Animals; xviBR Runk-Schoenberger/Grant Heilman Photography; xviTR Runk-Schoenberger/Grant Heilman Photography.

Unit 1 xii Stocktrek Photo Agency; 1 Galen Rowell

Chapter 1 2 National Center for Atmospheric Research; 3 Runk-Schoenberger/Grant Heilman Photography; 4B Peter B. Kaplan/Photo Researchers; 4T Tom Bean/DRK Photo; 5 Tom Bean/AllStock; 7 Ken Karp*; 10 Ken Karp*; 14 Ken Karp*; 15 Ken Karp*; 16 Ken Karp*; 17 Ken Karp*; 18 National Institute of Standards & Technology; 25 Ken Karp*; 26L Tom Tracy/The Stock Shop; 26R Greg Hadel/Tony Stone Images

Chapter 2 30 George Hall/Woodfin Camp & Associates; 31 NASA; 37 Richard Kolar/Earth Scenes; 42 NASA; 44 Ken Karp*; 45 Tom Bean/AllStock; 47 Peeter Vilms*; 49 Andy Sacks/Tony Stone Images

Chapter 3 54 Dieter Blum/Peter Arnold, Inc.; 55 Bjorn Bolstad/Photo Researchers; 60 Randall Hyman/Stock, Boston; 61 Will & Deni McIntyre/Photo Researchers; 64 Ocean Drilling Program, Texas A&M University; 65 Vince Streano/The Stock Market; 70-71 Cesar Rubio Photography;

Unit 2 72 Krafft/Photo Researchers; 72-73 Alberto Garcia/Saba

Chapter 4 74 Kim Heacox/AllStock; 75 Chip Carroon/AllStock; 76T David Cannon/Allsport; 77L K. & M. Krafft/Explorer/Photo Researchers; 77R Keith Gunnar/Bruce Coleman Inc; 78L Darrell Gulin/AllStock; 78R Laura Dwight/Peter Arnold, Inc.; 79B SPL/Photo Researchers; 79T Kevin Schafer & Martha Hill/Tom Stack & Associates; 82 Spencer Swanger/Tom Stack & Associates; 83 Albert J. Copley/Visuals Unlimited

Chapter 5 90 William Waterfall/The Stock Market; 91 NASA; 102BL George Hall/Woodfin Camp & Associates; 102BR F. Gohier/Photo Researchers; 102TL David Falconer; 103L David Madison/ Bruce Coleman Inc.; 103R Keren Su/Stock, Boston; 104 Dan McCoy/Rainbow; 107 Simon Fraser/SPL/Photo Researchers

Chapter 6 112 Michael Collier/Stock, Boston; 113 Joyce Photographics/Photo Researchers; 116 Collier-Condit/Stock, Boston; 117 Tom Bean/DRK Photo; 118 Fletcher & Bayles/Photo Researchers; 121 Tom Bean/DRK Photo; 122B J. Couffer/Bruce Coleman Inc.; 122T NASA/Grant Heilman Photography; 123 Peter French Photography/DRK Photo; 124 Roy Bishop/Stock, Boston; 125 Steve Vidler/Leo de Wys Inc.; 125B Peeter Vilms*; 126B Tibor Bognar/The Stock Market; 126T David Muench; 128 Keren Su/Stock, Boston

Chapter 7 132 Dan McCoy/Rainbow; 133 Ted Mahieu/The Stock Market; 135 Tim Davis*; 140 Kevin Schafer/AllStock; 141BR Mike Andrews/Earth Scenes; 141L Yoav Levy/Phototake; 141TR Francois Gohier/Photo Researchers; 142B Steve McCutcheon/AllStock; 142T Hank Morgan /Rainbow; 144 Galen Rowell; 146C Dieter & Mary Plage /Bruce Coleman Inc.; 146L Dan McCoy/Rainbow; 146R Keith Murakami/Tom Stack & Associates; 147B Darrell Gulin /AllStock; 147L Lindsay Hebberd/Woodfin Camp & Associates; 147T Breck P. Kent/Earth Scenes; 149B Stella Snead/Bruce Coleman Inc.; 149T Oddo & Sinibaldi/The Stock Market; 150 Roger Ressmeyer/Starlight; 154-155 J. Lotter/Tom Stack & Associates

Unit 3 156 Karl Hartmann/ Sachs/Phototake; 156-157 David Muench

Chapter 8 158 Dan McCoy/Rainbow; 159 Art Wolfe/AllStock; 160BC Dennis Purse/Photo Researchers; 160BL M. Long/Visuals Unlimited; 160BR Ron Watts/Westlight; 160T Kip Peticolas/Fundamental Photographs; 162CL Michael Dalton/Fundamental Photographs; 162CR Geoffrey Nilsen*; 162T Larry Lefever/Grant Heilman Photography; 163 Omikron/Science Source/Photo Researchers; 164 Geoffrey Nilsen*; 165BL Paul von Stroheim; 165BR Breck P. Kent; 165CL Michael Dalton/Fundamental Photographs; 165CR Paul Silverman/Fundamental Photographs; 168B Geoffrey Nilsen*; 169 Geoffrey Nilsen*; 170BC Kent Wood/Peter Arnold, Inc.; 170T Chlaus Lotscher/Peter Arnold, Inc.; 171 Erwin & Peggy Bauer/Bruce Coleman Inc.; 172 Geoffrey Nilsen*; 173 Geoff Tompkinson/SPL/Photo Researchers; 175 Geoffrey Nilsen*; 178B John Gerlach/Visuals Unlimited; 178T Kevin Schafer/ Peter Arnold, Inc.; 179 F. Stuart Westmorland/Tom Stack & Associates

Chapter 9   184 Martin Land/SPL/Photo Researchers; 185 Geoffrey Nilsen*; 186 Geoffrey Nilsen*; 187 Geoffrey Nilsen*; 188 Geoffrey Nilsen*; 190 Breck P. Kent; 192 Geoffrey Nilsen*; 193 Geoffrey Nilsen*; 194 Geoffrey Nilsen*; 195 M. Courtney-Clarke/Photo Researchers; 196 E. R. Degginger; 198 Geoffrey Nilsen*; 199 E. R. Degginger; 200 Gene Stein/Westlight; 201 Richard Hutchings/Photo Researchers; 202 Geoffrey Nilsen*; 203B George Holton/Photo Researchers; 203T Geoffrey Nilsen*; 204 Jim Larsen/West Stock

Chapter 10   208 Richard Steedman/The Stock Market; 209 Geoffrey Nilsen*; 210 Geoffrey Nilsen*; 211 Geoffrey Nilsen*; 212 Geoffrey Nilsen*; 214 Joseph Nettis/Stock, Boston; 215 Geoffrey Nilsen*; 216 Geoffrey Nilsen*; 218 Geoffrey Nilsen*; 219 C. J. Allen/Stock, Boston; 220 S. J. Krasemann/Peter Arnold, Inc.; 221B Breck P. Kent; 221T J. C. Leacock/West Stock; 222B Grant Heilman/Grant Heilman Photography; 222C John Cancalosi/Peter Arnold, Inc.; 222T Runk-Schoenberger/Grant Heilman Photography; 223B Kevin Schafer/Tom Stack & Associates; 223T Barbara Filet/Tony Stone Images; 224 Frank Fisher/West Stock; 226 Geoffrey Nilsen*; 228 Geoffrey Nilsen*; 229B Ernst Jahn/Bruce Coleman Inc.; 229BL Geoffrey Nilsen*; 229BR Geoffrey Nilsen*; 229CL Geoffrey Nilsen*; 229CR Geoffrey Nilsen*; 229TL Geoffrey Nilsen*; 229TR Geoffrey Nilsen*; 230 Steve Leonard/Tony Stone Images; 234-235 Ric Ergenbright/AllStock; 234BL George Whiteley/Photo Researchers; 234BR Renee Purse/Photo Researchers; 234T Geoffrey Nilsen*; 235 Ed Cooper Photo

Unit 4   236 Breck P. Kent/Earth Scenes; 236-237 John Shaw/Tom Stack & Associates

Chapter 11   238 Richard Weymouth Brooks/Photo Researchers; 239 Craig Walker/Rainbow; 240C Tom Bean/DRK Photo; 240L Copr. Jim Cummins/AllStock; 240R Len Rue Jr./Stock, Boston; 241C Stan Osolinski/The Stock Market; 241L David M. Dennis/Tom Stack & Associates; 241R Andy Levin/Photo Researchers; 242BL GHP Studio*; 242BR GHP Studio*; 242L Charlie Ott/Photo Researchers; 242TR Robert Harding Picture Library; 243C Adam Hart-Davis/SPL/Photo Researchers; 243L Gerald Davis/Phototake; 243R Gregory G. Dimijian/ Photo Researchers; 244B Runk-Schoenberger/Grant Heilman Photography; 244T Carlos V. Causo/Bruce Coleman Inc.; 245 John Coletti/Stock, Boston; 248 Kenneth W. Fink/Photo Researchers; 249C Runk-Schoenberger/Grant Heilman Photography; 249L Jeff Foott /Bruce Coleman Inc.; 249R Kim Taylor/Bruce Coleman Inc.; 251 J. C. Carton/Bruce Coleman Inc.; 254B James B. Sanderson/The Stock Market; 254TL Michael P. Gadomski/Earth Scenes; 255BL David Muench; 255BRC Tom Bean/AllStock; 256BL Manfred Gottschalk/ Westlight; 256TL K. Gunar/Bruce Coleman Inc.; 257L Charlie Ott/Photo Researchers; 257R Randall Hyman/Stock, Boston; 258 Gary R. Zahm/DRK Photo

Chapter 12   262 Don Mason/The Stock Market; 263 Robert Caputo/Stock, Boston; 264BL Brian Parker/Tom Stack & Associates; 264BR Owen Franken/Stock, Boston; 264C Dick Canby/Positive Images; 264T Barbara Alper/Stock, Boston; 265 Smolan/Stock, Boston; 267B Steve McCutcheon/Visuals Unlimited; 267C Kim Heacox/DRK Photo; 267T Breck P. Kent; 268B Keith Gunnar/Bruce Coleman Inc.; 268T Bill Ross/AllStock; 269B Thomas G. Rampton/Grant Heilman Photography; 269T Jack

Couffer/Bruce Coleman Inc.; 271B Michael Ventura/Bruce Coleman Inc.; 271C Randy Brandon/ Peter Arnold, Inc.; 271TL Brian Parker/Tom Stack & Associates; 271TR W. Cody/Westlight; 272L Keith Gunnar/ Bruce Coleman Inc.; 272T T. Kitchin/Tom Stack & Associates; 273 Fred Whitehead/Earth Scenes; 274L Breck P. Kent; 274R Dr. E. R. Degginger; 275 Douglas Mazonowicz; 278 Ann Hawthorne/Black Star; 280 Jerry Howard/Stock, Boston; 281 Peter Pickford/DRK Photo; 282B David Epperson/AllStock; 282T Tom Bean/DRK Photo; 283B Stanley Breeden/DRK Photo; 283C Dr. E. R. Degginger; 283T Francois Gohier/Photo Researchers

Chapter 13   288 John Cancalosi/Tom Stack & Associates; 289B Ken Lucas/Biological Photo Service; 289T Francois Gohier; 294 Jack Helle/AllStock; 295L Jeff Gnass/West Stock, Inc.; 295R Breck P. Kent; 296 Breck P. Kent; 297 Breck P. Kent; 298 Richard Kolar/Earth Scenes; 301 Andrew Leitch/Discover Magazine; 307B Tom McHugh/Photo Researchers; 307T John Reader/SPL/Photo Researchers; 312-313 Dallas & Jim Heaton/Westlight

Unit 5   314 Johnny Johnson/DRK Photo; 314-315 Ed Cooper

Chapter 14   316 Stephen Frisch/Photo 20-20; 319 Steve Solum/Bruce Coleman Inc.; 322 Runk-Schoenberger/Grant Heilman Photography; 324 Bill Horsman/Stock, Boston; 325L USGS EROS Data Center; 326B Doug Wilson/Westlight; 326C Milton Rand/Tom Stack & Associates; 326T Rich Buzzelli/Tom Stack & Associates; 328 C. C. Lockwood/Cactus Clyde Productions; 329B Geoffrey Nilsen*; 329T Runk-Schoenberger/Grant Heilman Photography; 332B Holt Confer/Grant Heilman Photography; 332T Prisma/Westlight; 333 Jeff Amberg/Gamma-Liaison

Chapter 15   338 Steve Lissau/Rainbow; 339 Tom Van Sant/Geosphere Project, Santa Monica/SPL/Photo Researchers; 342B Jan Hinsch/SPL/Photo Researchers; 342TL F. Stuart Westmorland/AllStock; 342TR Zig Leszczynski/ Animals, Animals; 343 Grant Heilman/Grant Heilman Photography; 357L Breck P. Kent; 357R Breck P. Kent/Earth Scenes; 359B George Post/CA Maritime Academy; 359T Jeff Foott/DRK Photo; 360 Jean Pierre Ducatez

Chapter 16   364 Runk-Schoenberger/Grant Heilman Photography; 365 Jeff Simon/Bruce Coleman Inc.; 366C Rona/Bruce Coleman Inc.; 366L Barry L. Runk/Grant Heilman Photography; 366R Dr. Ken C. MacDonald et. al./UCSB; 367B NASA; 367C NASA; 367T Richard Pasley/Stock, Boston; 370 Rona/Bruce Coleman Inc.; 372 Charles Preitner/Visuals Unlimited; 376 Dr. Peter W. Sloss/NOAA/ NGDC; 378 C. C. Lockwood/Animals, Animals; 379 Dave B. Fleetham/Tom Stack & Associates; 382R Dr. E. R. Degginger; 382L Scott Blackman/Tom Stack & Associates; 383L Helen Elizabeth Carr/Biological Photo Service; 383R Tom McHugh/Photo Researchers; 384 Runk-Schoenberger/Grant Heilman Photography; 388-389 David Muench

Unit 6   Runk-Schoenberger/Grant Heilman Photography; 390-391 Richard Kaylin/AllStock

Chapter 17   392 Brett Baunton/AllStock; 402 Joyce Photographics/ Photo Researchers; 405 Will McIntyre/Photo Researchers; 408 Owen Franken/Stock, Boston; 409B Philippe Plailly/SPL/Photo Researchers; 409T NASA/Jet Propulsion Lab

Chapter 18 414 John Gerlach/Tom Stack & Associates; 416B Gary Withey/Bruce Coleman Inc.; 416T Don Kelly/Grant Heilman Photography; 417CB M. & R. Borland/Bruce Coleman Inc.; 417CL Michael Fogden/Bruce Coleman Inc.; 417CT Jerry Howard/Positive Images; 417L Bill Everitt/Tom Stack & Associates; 417TL Harry Haralambou/Positive Images; 419 Runk-Schoenberger/Grant Heilman Photography; 422L W. Cody/Westlight; 423L Manfred Gottschalk/Westlight; 424B Milton Rand/Tom Stack & Associates; 424C Larry Lefever/Grant Heilman Photography; 424T Joseph Schuyler/Stock, Boston; 425C E. R. Degginger; 425L Joel W. Rogers/AllStock; 425R Copr. Thomas L. Dietrich/ AllStock; 426 Owen Franken/Stock, Boston; 427 A. Glauberman/ Photo Researchers; 430BR E. R. Degginger; 430CB Charles Feil/Stock, Boston; 430TL David C. Hauston/ Bruce Coleman Inc.; 430TR Mike Price/Bruce Coleman Inc.; 431 Nuridsany & Perennou/Photo Researchers; 432B Link/ Visuals Unlimited; 432T Stephen Frisch*; 434 Judy Canty/ Stock, Boston

Chapter 19 438 European Space Agency/SPL/Photo Researchers; 443B Richard Palsey/Stock, Boston; 443T Runk-Schoenberger/Grant Heilman Photography; 445 Peeter Vilms*; 446 USDA/Grant Heilman Photography; 448 Wetmore/Photo Researchers; 450T Dr. Fred Espenak/ SPL/Photo Researchers; 451B E. R. Degginger/Bruce Coleman Inc.; 451T E. R. Degginger; 452 Chris Brown/Stock, Boston; 453 E. R. Degginger; 454B Mark C. Burnett/Photo Researchers; 454L Phil Degginger; 454R David Parker/SPL/Photo Researchers; 454T Bill Gallery/Stock, Boston; 458 NASA

Chapter 20 462 Brian Parker/Tom Stack & Associates; 463B David Madison/Bruce Coleman Inc.; 463T Carl Purcell/Photo Researchers; 464L Patti Murray/Earth Scenes; 464R Rob Crandall/Stock, Boston; 468B N. Pecnik/Visuals Unlimited; 468T Ben Blankenburg/Stock, Boston; 469 Manfred Gottschalk/Tom Stack & Associates; 472B Leonard Lee Rue III/Stock, Boston; 472BR K. H. Switak/Photo Researchers; 472C Stephen J. Krasemann/DRK Photo; 472TL Chip & Jill Isenhart/Tom Stack & Associates; 472TLC Michael Fogden/ DRK Photo; 472TR Bruce Forster/AllStock; 473BL John Mitchell/Photo Researchers; 473BR Craig Aurness/ Westlight; 473C Jim Zipp/Photo Researchers; 473CR Johnny Johnson/ Earth Scenes; 473TL E. R. Degginger/Bruce Coleman Inc.; 474 Jon Bertsch/Visuals Unlimited; 477L Tom Bean/DRK Photo; 477R Phil Degginger; 478 Tom Nebbia; 479 T. Kitchin/Tom Stack & Associates; 480 Ray Hoffman/USGS; 484-485 Jim Corwin/AllStock; 484B Christopher Arnesen/ AllStock; 484T Brian Parker/Tom Stack & Associates; 485 W. Bertsch/Bruce Coleman Inc.

Unit 7 486 Jim Zuckerman/Westlight; 486-487 Kathleen Campbell/AllStock

Chapter 21 488 Robert Winslow/Tom Stack & Associates; 489B John Cancalosa/Tom Stack & Associates; 489T Paul Silverman/Fundamental Photographs; 490B George Hunter/ Tony Stone Images; 490L Lester Lefkowitz/Tony Stone Images; 490T Larry Lefever/Grant Heilman Photography; 492 Nicholas Devore/Bruce Coleman Inc.; 494L Grant Heilman/ Grant Heilman Photography; 494R Ken Graham/ AllStock; 496 Anne Dowie*; 497B Larry Lefever/ Grant Heilman Photography; 497T Kristin Finnegan/ AllStock; 498 Jerry Howard/Positive Images; 499B E. R. Degginger/Bruce

Coleman Inc.; 499T Kevin Schafer/Tom Stack & Associates; 500 Dr. Jeremy Burgess/SPL/Photo Researchers; 501 Will McIntyre/Photo Researchers; 502T Andrew Rakoczy/Bruce Coleman Inc.; 503 William McCoy/Rainbow

Chapter 22 508 Barrie Rokeach; 510C John Eastcott-Yva Momatiuk/DRK Photo; 510L David R. Austen/Stock, Boston; 510R Bruce Davidson/Earth Scenes; 511BR Craig Aurness/ Westlight; 511L Nigel Smith/Animals, Animals; 511TR Tom Nebbia; 512B Peter French/Bruce Coleman Inc.; 512R Andy Sacks/Tony Stone Images; 512TL Anne Dowie*; 513 Tom Nebbia; 514T Waugh/Peter Arnold, Inc.; 515 Bob Daemmrich/ Stock, Boston; 517C George H. Harrison/Grant Heilman Photography; 517L Tom Walker/Stock, Boston; 517R Tom McHugh/Photo Researchers; 518R Bernard Wolff/Photo Researchers; 518L Tom Bean/AllStock; 519 Kevin Morris/ AllStock; 520 Alan D. Carey/Photo Researchers; 521 Chip & Jill Isenhart/Tom Stack & Associates; 522 Runk-Schoenberger/ Grant Heilman Photography; 523B Larry Lefever/Grant Heilman Photography; 523T Greg Vaughn/Tom Stack & Associates; 524B Will & Deni McIntyre/AllStock; 524R Anne Dowie*; 524L GHP Studio*; 524TC J. Cancalosi/DRK Photo; 525BR Jerry Howard/Positive Images; 525C Dewitt Jones/ Woodfin Camp & Associates; 525TR Joe Sohm/Chromosohm/ AllStock; 526L Robert E. Daemmrich/Tony Stone Images; 526R Robert E. Daemmrich/Stock, Boston; 532-533 Greg Ryan-Sally Beyer/AllStock

Unit 8 534 SPL/Photo Researchers; 534-535 Royal Observatory, Edinburgh

Chapter 23 536R NASA/Rainbow; 538T Richard Megna/ Fundamental Photographs; 541BL James P. Rowan/ Tony Stone Images; 541C Breck P. Kent/Animals, Animals; 541CL David Carriere/Tony Stone Images; 541L Carson Baldwin, Jr./Earth Scenes; 541TL Jeff Lepore/ AllStock; 543T George Holton/Photo Researchers; 545 Ed Degginger/Bruce Coleman Inc.; 546BL NASA/Peter Arnold, Inc.; 546R NASA; 548 NASA/Finley Holiday Film; 549 NASA; 551 Lick Observatory; 552B NASA; 552T S. Nielsen/Bruce Coleman Inc.

Chapter 24 558 NASA JPL/Starlight; 559B Eric Simmons/ Stock, Boston; 559T John Elk/Bruce Coleman Inc.; 560 National Optical Astronomy Observatories; 562BL National Optical Astronomy Observatories; 562CT NASA; 562R NASA/Science Source/Photo Researchers; 562TL Johnny Johnson/AllStock; 563 Del Mulkey/Photo Researchers; 566 NASA; 570B F. Rossotto/Stocktrek; 570T NASA; 571 NASA/ Jet Propulsion Lab; 574B Bruce H. Frisch/Photo Researchers; 574T NASA/Grant Heilman Photography; 575 NASA; 576 Lockheed; 577B National Optical Astronomy Observatories; 577T Richard Megna/ Fundamental Photographs; 578B Lowell Observatory/ NOAO; 578T Breck P. Kent/Earth Scenes; 580 NASA

Chapter 25 584 Dr. Jean Lorre/SPL/Photo Researchers; 585 Jim Ballard/AllStock; 587 John Lawlor/Tony Stone Images; 588T Roger Ressmeyer/Starlight; 589 Roger Ressmeyer/ Starlight; 594 Robert E. Daemmrich/Tony Stone Images; 596 Royal Observatory, Edinburgh; 597 Royal Observatory, Edinburgh; 600 Lick Observatory; 602BC Regents, Univ. Hawaii; 602CR National Optical Astronomy Observatories; 602TL National Optical Astronomy Observatories; 602TR U.S. Naval Observatory; 605 G. Robert Bishop/AllStock; 606 NASA/Jet Propulsion Lab;

610-611 National Optical Astronomy Observatories; 610BL NASA; 610BR NASA; 610T NASA

*Photographed expressly for Addison-Wesley Longman, Inc. All rock and mineral specimens photographed expressly for Addison-Wesley Publishing Company, Inc. were provided by The California Academy of Sciences.

Illustrations

Margo Stahl-Pronk
pgs. 14-15, 16, 18, 70, 71, 154, 155, 210-211, 216-217, 221

Precision Graphics
pgs. 19, 20, 29, 53, 62, 66, 69, 85, 89, 111, 131, 135, 153, 178, 179, 183, 189, 205, 213, 233, 247, 261, 270, 289, 293, 300, 302, 311, 317, 337, 355, 357, 363, 371, 387, 393, 407, 413, 416, 456, 461, 483, 495, 507, 513, 518, 525, 531, 557, 583, 593, 603, 609, 612, 613, 614, 615, 616, 617, 618-619, 622, 623, 624-625

Rolin Graphics
pgs. 76, 83, 92, 93, 94, 96, 97, 102-103, 105, 108, 228, 266, 268-269, 275, 276-277, 281, 284, 292, 312325, 341, 344, 345, 349, 351, 352-353, 354, 358, 396, 397, 398, 401, 403, 404, 415, 419, 421, 422, 423, 429, 437, 544, 565, 567, 572, 573, 576, 586, 587, 601

Sarah Woodward
pgs. 22-23, 34-35, 50, 58, 99, 101, 134, 197, 227, 318, 319, 320-321, 394-395, 493, 494, 500, 502, 516, 598-599

Michael Maydak
pgs. 145, 147, 290, 306, 552, 388, 389

Marlene May-Howerton
pgs. 303, 304, 305, 532, 533

John Foerster
pgs. 297, 380, 381, 399, 547, 550-551

Carla Simmons
pgs. 114, 115, 116, 117, 118, 123, 124, 291, 299

Carlyn Iverson
pgs. 162, 163, 165, 170, 246, 247, 248, 250, 252, 254, 255, 256, 257, 439, 441, 441, 442

Warren Budd & Associates
pgs. 38, 39, 41, 56-57, 59, 63, 100, 106, 120, 127, 373, 374-375, 406, 466, 561, 579, 590, 603

Charles Thomas
pgs. 444, 450, 563, 568-569

Larry Hughston
pgs. 538, 539, 540

Mapping Specialists
pgs. 40, 43, 46, 47, 48, 124, 136, 137, 148, 253, 327, 340, 346, 347, 348, 350, 356, 433, 440, 444, 445, 464, 465, 470, 470-471, 477, 542, 612, 616, 617, 620-621

Science and Literature Credits

Unit 1 From *Farewell to Manzanar* by James D. Houston and Jeanne Wakatsuki Houston, pp. 69-71. Copyright © 1973 by James D. Houston. Reprinted by permission of Houghton Mifflin Co. All rights reserved.

Unit 2 From *Legend Days* by Jamake Highwater, pp. 42-44. Copyright ©1984 by Jamake Highwater. Reprinted by permission of HarperCollins Publishers.

Unit 3 From *A Journey to the Centre of the Earth* by Jules Verne, 1864. (NY: Dodd, Mead, 1959, pp. 73, 74, 82.)

Unit 4 From *Tales Of A Dead King* by Walter Dean Myers, pp. 66-69. Copyright ©1983 by Walter Dean Myers. By permission of William Morrow & Co., Inc., Publishers.

Unit 5 From *The Land I Lost* by Huynh Quang Nhuong, pp. 41-45. Copyright ©1982 by Huynh Quang Nhuong. Reprinted by permission of HarperCollins Publishers.

Unit 6 From *Going Home* by Nicholasa Mohr, pp. 3-10. Copyright ©1986 by Nicholasa Mohr. Used by permission of Dial Books for Young Readers, a division of Penguin Books USA, Inc.

Unit 7 From *The Ohlone Way: Indian Life in the San Francisco-Monterey Bay Area* by Malcolm Margolin, pp. 46-49. Copyright ©1978 by Malcolm Margolin. Reprinted by permission of Heyday Books.

Unit 8 From *To Space and Back* by Sally Ride and Susan Okie, pp. 29, 42, 46. Copyright ©1986 by Sally Ride and Susan Okie. By permission of William Morrow & Co., Inc. Publishers.

Mauro
Mosca